THE FAMILIES OF
FLOWERING PLANTS

VOLUME I

DICOTYLEDONS

Oxford University Press, Amen House, London E.C.4

GLASGOW NEW YORK TORONTO MELBOURNE WELLINGTON
BOMBAY CALCUTTA MADRAS KARACHI KUALA LUMPUR
CAPE TOWN IBADAN NAIROBI ACCRA

THE FAMILIES OF FLOWERING PLANTS

VOLUME I

DICOTYLEDONS

arranged according to a new system
based on their probable

PHYLOGENY

BY

J. HUTCHINSON

LL.D. (St. Andrews), F.R.S., V.M.H.
LATE KEEPER OF MUSEUMS OF BOTANY
ROYAL BOTANIC GARDENS, KEW

SECOND EDITION

21079

OXFORD
AT THE CLARENDON PRESS

Second Edition 1959
Reprinted 1960

First edition 1926
published by Macmillan & Co., Ltd.
St. Martin's St., London

© *Oxford University Press 1959*

21079

DEDICATED
TO THE MEMORY OF
GEORGE BENTHAM
AND
JOSEPH DALTON HOOKER
AUTHORS OF THE
'GENERA PLANTARUM'

PREFACE TO SECOND EDITION

THIRTY-THREE years have elapsed since the first edition of the first volume of this book was published in 1926. Though it has been long out of print, there is still a demand for it. During the interval I have naturally added considerably to my store of knowledge of the phylogeny and classification of flowering plants, broadened by further valuable field experience in Africa,[1] and, largely due to the Second World War, renewed acquaintance with many of our less spectacular, but no less interesting, native wild flowers.[2]

As the work in its original form does not now adequately show the results of these further studies, I am glad, even at this late date, to have the opportunity to rearrange and revise it in a second edition.

Botanical systems can never remain static for long, because new facts and methods of approach are liable at any time to modify them. Like other things in this changing world, that which seems to be a probability or even a certainty one day may quite well prove to be a fallacy the next.

It should be emphasized at the outset, however, that the *principles* on which the system is based are precisely the same as in the original scheme (see p. 20). All that has been done in this new version is to apply them with added conviction, the result being that the *fundamentally woody* subphylum, the LIGNOSAE, and the *fundamentally herbaceous* subphylum, the HERBACEAE, are now completely separated in the linear sequence.

In the system here shown (see diagram, p. 24) it will be seen that no longer are *Magnoliaceae* and *Ranunculaceae*—*Rosaceae* and *Saxifragaceae*—*Araliaceae* and *Umbelliferae*—*Myrsinaceae* and *Primulaceae*—or even *Verbenaceae* and *Labiatae*, ranged next to or even near each other, but are placed far apart, in the belief, rightly or wrongly, that the supposed relationship between these pairs of families is considered to be due to parallel development.

An equally great change, also foreshadowed in the first edition, is the distribution of the *sympetalous* (*gamopetalous*) families amongst their presumed nearest relations, either with or without petals. Perhaps few present-day botanists will quarrel with me over this except in minor details, for it is long overdue. Systematic botany has endured too long those artificial groups such as *Polypetalae, Gamopetalae, Monochlamydeae, Thalamiflorae, Disciflorae* and *Calyciflorae, Inferae, Tetracyclicae, Bicarpellatae, Parietales*, and such like, nearly all depending on a single character and often resulting, to some extent at any rate, in a more or less artificial classification and not a few taxonomic absurdities.

Some may consider that in making a primary division of the Dicotyledons into two separate and parallel lines of evolution, the relatively more ancient

---

[1] J. Hutchinson, *A Botanist in Southern Africa* (Gawthorn, London, 1946).

[2] J. Hutchinson, *Common Wild Flowers, More Common Wild Flowers*, and *Uncommon Wild Flowers* (Penguin Books, 1945, 1948, 1950), recently republished in two volumes entitled *British Wild Flowers* (Penguin Books, 1955). *British Flowering Plants*, Evolution and Classification of Families and Genera, with notes on their distribution (Gawthorn, 1948).

LIGNOSAE, and the generally more advanced HERBACEAE, I have merely returned to the ancient classification into *trees*, *shrubs*, and *herbs* of the early herbalists.

I feel very strongly, however, that it is only by means of this hypothesis that the tangle of families which exists in some of the groups in both the Bentham and Hooker and the Englerian systems may be sorted out into smaller and more natural (homogeneous) groups held together by a combination of characters rather than by single ones.

I commend a study by my more widely experienced botanical contemporaries of the arrangement of the orders on p. 19, and feel that they will have some difficulty in tracing actual close relationship between any of the groups belonging to the two divisions, not even excepting the families *Araliaceae* and *Umbelliferae*!

In putting forward this little less than revolutionary system, I am well aware that I may be regarded as a 'crank'. According to the *Century Dictionary* a 'crank' is 'a person whose mind is ill-balanced or awry . . . who takes up some impracticable notion or project and wages it in and out of season, in short a monomaniac'. I willingly run this risk trusting that botanists who know me personally will not all share this view, and hoping that future generations at any rate will find that this new classification, like the curate's egg, is at least *good in parts*.

Though this is the first appearance of the complete new scheme, it has been used in some of my books already published and noted at the foot of the previous page. If I live long enough I hope to be able to further elaborate it in more detail in a larger work, dealing with all the known genera of flowering plants.

In addition to those to whom I was indebted when preparing the first edition, alas several of them no longer with us, I am grateful to Mr. J. E. Dandy, Keeper of Botany at the British Museum (Natural History) for the account of the *Magnoliaceae* in vol. 1 and the *Hydrocharitaceae* in vol. 2; to Dr. C. C. J. van Steenis, of the Rijksherbarium, Leiden, Holland, for generously sending me advance information of his researches; to Dr. C. R. Metcalfe for advice on anatomical matters; to Mr. A. A. Bullock, B.Sc., for scrutinizing the proofs and for assistance with nomenclature and to Miss Lesley Elliott-Fletcher for arranging the index.

From the Herbarium, Royal Botanic Gardens, Kew, 1959

PREFACE TO FIRST EDITION

VOLUME I

THE book here presented is partly the outcome of a larger task the author has set himself in his leisure hours, towards which contributions have already been published in the *Kew Bulletin* during the last few years. The need for a small *Handbook of the Families of Flowering Plants* has long been felt by teachers, students, gardeners, travellers, and lovers of plants in general. The difference in the concept of plant families shown in the *Genera Plantarum* of Bentham and Hooker and in the latest edition of Engler and Gilg's *Syllabus* is very considerable, and students are apt to be confused by this divergence of treatment. The families of DICOTYLEDONS are therefore described according to more modern practice, i.e. they are smaller and in better defined groups, which are more easily fitted into the new phylogenetic scheme of classification here presented in complete form for the first time. In compiling these descriptions the fullest use has been made of the *Genera Plantarum*. A second volume will be devoted to the *Monocotyledons*, which the author intends to study specially before venturing to propose a new arrangement.

An *artificial analytical key* to these families, based on easily observed characters, would be useful it is thought to teacher and student alike, and by the use of this key and a pocket lens it should not be impossible for an intelligent person with only a slight knowledge of botany to allocate to their families most of the plants which he may meet with in any part of the world. A key based on the families as defined in Bentham and Hooker's *Genera Plantarum* was published by F. Thonner[1] in 1895, but has for a long time been out of print and unobtainable. The key here presented has been made entirely independently of that by Thonner and on somewhat different lines.

It is regrettable that the classical *Genera Plantarum* of Bentham and Hooker, perhaps the greatest pioneer botanical work of modern times, has never been made available to English readers in a popular form. The general sequence, however, appeared in a translation from the French work of Le Maout and Decaisne, edited by Hooker, and now long out of print. Had those distinguished authors seen fit to issue an English translation illustrated by their gifted botanical artist, Walter Fitch, it is probable that their work would still have held the field. As it is, it has largely been superseded by the great German work by Engler and Prantl, *Die natürlichen Pflanzenfamilien*, published in German and copiously illustrated. Whilst the *Genera Plantarum* was based on the De Candolle system, which did not claim to be a phylogenetic system, the German work did make this claim. It is interesting to know what Hooker thought of the new system, and we may learn this from his *Life and Letters* by L. Huxley, vol. ii, p. 22. Writing to Arber he says: 'With regard to your queries respecting the primitive type of Angiospermous plants, that subject has never been far from my mind for upwards of half a century, during which period I have failed to grasp a feature in the morphology, physiology, or

[1] F. Thonner, *Analytical Key to the Natural Orders of Flowering Plants*, London, 1895.

geographical distribution of Angiosperms that gave much colour to whatever speculations I may have indulged in respecting it. I do not share Engler's views as expressed in his classification and writings. The classification is neither better nor worse in the abstract than De Candolle's (so called), and is far more troublesome to apply for practical purposes. I hold to Robert Brown's view of the orders being reticulately not lineally related.'

The supposition that the unisexual flower of the *Amentiferae*, or catkin group of plants, is primitive has been too readily accepted, and during recent years this theory has been frequently questioned. There is now a considerable body of opinion[1] in favour of the view that the whole of the *Dicotyledons* and *Monocotyledons* have been evolved from one common stock, and that that stock has at the present day its most primitive living representatives exhibited in the *Magnoliaceae* and *Ranunculaceae* and allied families, and that from such primitive types as these all other flowers have been derived by specialization or reduction. In these early families we find the following characters associated:

(1) free sepals and petals, (2) free and numerous hypogynous stamens, (3) free and numerous carpels, (4) small straight embryo in abundant uniform endosperm.

Furthermore, we believe that in flowering plants the arboreal or *woody* habit is generally more ancient than the herbaceous; that only in some cases herbs have been derived from shrubs and trees. There are some very obvious examples. For instance, the *Papilionaceae*, largely herbaceous, are clearly derived from the more woody *Caesalpiniaceae*; but *Clematis* (softly woody) is derived from *Anemone* (herbaceous). Perhaps it may be contended that in the present arrangement of families I have laid too much stress on the difference between the *woody* and the *herbaceous* habit. By separating these two types on very broad lines as a beginning, however, it becomes possible to establish more natural groups of closely allied families. Thus families such as the *Flacourtiaceae* (woody) and the *Violaceae* (mostly herbaceous), which have been closely associated on account of a single character, the *parietal placentation*, are now more widely separated. It is, too, significant that many of the primitive families are either *entirely woody* or *entirely herbaceous*. Examples that are wholly woody are *Magnoliaceae*, *Annonaceae*, &c.; herbaceous, *Ranunculaceae*, *Papaveraceae*, *Crassulaceae*, *Saxifragaceae* (*sensu stricto*), *Caryophyllaceae*; and often this habit character has persisted right to the end of a phylum, such as in *Lauraceae* (woody) and *Cruciferae* (herbaceous). In the primitive groups this difference in habit is often closely associated with a marked difference in the structure of the stomata of the leaves. In the woody group the guard cells are usually accompanied by special subsidiary cells parallel to the pore, whilst in the early herbaceous groups the guard cells have no special subsidiary cells.[2] Of course, in the case of more advanced families which show a mixed habit and which may have recruited their members from

---

[1] The student who wishes to read up the literature which deals with this subject should consult the following papers: C. E. Bessey in *Bot. Gaz.* **24**, 145–78 (1897); Arber and Parkin in *J. Linn. Soc. Bot.* **38**, 29–80 (1907); C. E. Bessey, 'The Phylogenetic Taxonomy of Flowering Plants', in *Ann. Missouri Bot. Gard.* **2**, 109–64 (1915); Hutchinson in *Kew Bull.* 1924, 114.

[2] Parkin has independently been impressed with this stomatal difference. See his note in *Ann. Bot.* **38**, 795 (1924).

both groups on account of convergence and parallel development, one would expect to find both types of stomata. This is well shown in the *Rosaceae*, amongst which the remarkably distinct woody tribe *Chrysobalaneae* is distinguished from the remainder of the family by having special subsidiary cells to the stomata.[1]

A phylogenetic classification is not necessarily one by which all plants may be readily determined; rather the reverse. In the past too little regard to general affinity and too much notice of *Key* characters and *Floral Diagrams* has apparently been taken in working out systems of classification. For key characters are not always the characters of greatest phylogenetic importance. Very often a key is of necessity considerably artificial. It depends on the group; the more natural the group, the more artificial the key. *A key mostly emphasizes the differences amongst plants.* A truly natural and phylogenetic classification, however, should rather emphasize their *resemblances*, by which alone their true affinities may be ascertained. This I have attempted to do in the pages of this book.

I am particularly indebted to Mr. W. E. Trevithick, Temporary Assistant in the Herbarium, Kew, who has devoted much of his leisure time to the execution of many of the drawings in the following pages. The remainder are my own work, and our respective initials are inserted merely to distinguish them. A few only of these drawings are original, the remainder being adapted from other works (and they have lost nothing under his skilful pen). Their origin is always indicated. They are intended to give the student some idea of the general structure of each family, and they will probably be welcomed as a change from the continued repetition of the same drawings found in most textbooks.

I am also very much indebted to my colleague, Mr. C. H. Wright, F.R.M.S., for reading the proofs; to Dr. J. Burtt Davy for helpful suggestions and for testing the key with his *Flora of the Transvaal*; to various other colleagues who have from time to time tested the key and assisted in other ways, including Dr. J. M. Dalziel, Mr. V. S. Summerhayes, Mr. P. G. Greenway; and to Mr. H. A. G. Alston and Dr. W. Robyns (Brussels), who have also worked out a few of the maps.

I should also here make grateful acknowledgement of the kind help and encouragement extended by Dr. A. W. Hill, F.R.S., Director of the Royal Botanic Gardens, Kew, and to Mr. A. D. Cotton, F.L.S., Keeper of the Herbarium and Library, for facilities in the use of the unrivalled collections of specimens and drawings.

I shall welcome suggestions which will help to improve the system; these will be gratefully acknowledged in the final work.

[1] See Solereder, *Systematic Anatomy of the Dicotyledons*, Engl. edn., **1**, 301 (1908).

Kew
May 1925

CONTENTS

VOLUME I

SIGNS AND ABBREVIATIONS   XV

INTRODUCTION TO THE FIRST EDITION   1
  Systems of classification   2
  Bentham and Hooker's *Genera Plantarum*   2
  The system of Engler and Prantl   3
  Considerations for the delimitation of orders   4
  Considerations for the delimitation of families   6

SHORT HISTORY OF THE CLASSIFICATION OF FLOWERING PLANTS   7
  I. Before Linnaeus   7
  II. Linnaeus and after   10

LINEAR SEQUENCE OF ORDERS   18

GENERAL PRINCIPLES ADOPTED FOR THE CLASSIFICATION OF FLOWERING PLANTS IN THE PRESENT SYSTEM   20

CONSPECTUS OF PRINCIPAL LIVING GROUPS OF FLOWERING PLANTS   22

GYMNOSPERMAE   22

ANGIOSPERMAE   22
  DICOTYLEDONES   23
    Lignosae   23
    Herbaceae   27
  MONOCOTYLEDONES (for classification see vol. II).   29

BIBLIOGRAPHY FOR STUDENTS   35

LIST OF FAMILIES WITH CERTAIN MORE OR LESS CONSTANT CHARACTERS   36

KEY TO THE FAMILIES OF DICOTYLEDONES   39

INDEX TO FAMILIES OF DICOTYLEDONES FOR READY REFERENCE (also included in general index)   101

SEQUENCE OF ORDERS AND FAMILIES IN THE NEW SYSTEM   104

DESCRIPTIONS OF ORDERS AND FAMILIES, WITH KEYS TO GENERA OF SMALLER FAMILIES   122

GLOSSARY   509

CONTENTS

VOLUME II

SIGNS AND ABBREVIATIONS x

INTRODUCTION
Classification of Monocotyledons 511
Bentham and Hooker's *Genera Plantarum* 511
The system of Engler and Prantl 512
The New Phylogenetic System here proposed 513
Monocotyledons monophyletic or polyphyletic? 513
Lotsy's classification of Monocotyledons 514
Bessy's classification of Monocotyledons 515
Separate calyx and corolla 515
Phylogenetic diagram for Monocotyledons 517

INDEX TO FAMILIES OF MONOCOTYLEDONES FOR READY REFERENCE (also included in General Index) 519

SEQUENCE OF ORDERS AND FAMILIES IN THE NEW SYSTEM 520

KEY TO ARTIFICIAL GROUPS AND TO FAMILIES OF MONOCOTYLEDONES 527

DESCRIPTIONS OF ORDERS AND FAMILIES, WITH KEYS TO GENERA OF SMALLER FAMILIES 536

GLOSSARY 742

INDEX 743

SIGNS AND ABBREVIATIONS

♂   = male flower.
♀   = female flower.
☿   = hermaphrodite (bisexual) flower.
B.H.   = Bentham and Hooker, *Genera Plantarum*.
E.P.   = Engler and Prantl, *Die natürlichen Pflanzenfamilien*.
E.P.N. = Engler and Prantl, *Nachträge*.

INTRODUCTION

(TO FIRST EDITION, VOL. I)

PERHAPS no subject is of more general interest to the younger generation of botanists of the present decade than the problem of the early race-history or *phylogeny* of plant life, and especially during recent years of flowering or seed-plants. The study of phylogeny, combined with that of the past and present distribution of plants, tends to awaken a new interest in Taxonomic Botany, and it should furnish important evidence in regard to the question of former land connexions between areas now separated by wide oceans, a subject which has repeatedly attracted the attention of biologists. Especially is this the case where marked similarity in the floras of far-distant regions is clearly evident, such, for example, as those of (1) the Eastern United States and Eastern Asia, (2) the flora of the West African rain forest with that of the Eastern coast of Brazil, (3) the Mascarene flora and that of Southern India, (4) the South African and West Australian floras, (5) the New Zealand and South-west American floras, and nearer home (6) the Southwest British and Lusitanian floras.

Whether these areas were at one time connected by intervening land bridges, where now are deep oceans, or whether they were actually once contiguous areas which have now become separated, will for long remain a debatable question.[1] Certainly the comparatively new theory of the origin of continents,[2] i.e. by displacement and gradual divergence one from another, would easily explain many of the problems of plant distribution. Though this subject cannot be dealt with here, it seems significant that with few exceptions these floral affinities of distant areas are entirely in an east-and-west direction and hardly ever north-and-south. I disregard for the moment the supposed affinity between the Mediterranean and South African floras, which may be due to parallel evolution in the two hemispheres and to similarity of climate and environment in these areas.

The distribution of the filmy fern, *Hymenophyllum ferrugineum*, of Juan Fernandez, Chile, and New Zealand, cannot easily be explained otherwise than by a former land connexion, especially when we consider also the distribution of *Galaxias attenuata*,[3] a freshwater fish, which occurs in Southeast Australia, Tasmania, New Zealand, and subantarctic South America. A further parallel is the distinct genus *Eucryphia*. I merely quote these examples from among several others to show that the phylogeny of plants is intimately connected with many interesting biological problems and should not be neglected, and that a phylogenetic system of classification should be the ultimate aim of taxonomy. In fact the description of every new genus,

---

[1] See A. Wegener, 'The Origin of Continents and Oceans', in *Discovery*, **3**, 114–18, figs. 1–3 (1922), and his book with the same title (Methuen & Co. 1924).

[2] The theory of Continental Drift has received much support in recent years.

[3] See Cockayne, 'The Vegetation of New Zealand', in Engl. and Drude, *Die Veg. der Erde* **14**, 326 (1921).

B

every new species or form of plant, may be regarded as a contribution towards this end.

SYSTEMS OF CLASSIFICATION[1]

The number of systems of classification is now very considerable. There is not space here to consider them, but for an excellent account of the earlier systems the reader is referred to Lindley's *Vegetable Kingdom* (1846), and for later schemes to Rendle's *Classification of Flowering Plants* (vol. i, *Monocotyledons* (1904)). Since Lindley's time, however, only two great treatises have appeared which have commanded universal attention—(1) the *Genera Plantarum* of Bentham and Hooker, published in 1862–83, which elaborated the de Candolle System, and (2) *Die natürliche Pflanzenfamilien* of Engler and Prantl (1887–1909). From a phylogenetic standpoint both these works have been subjected to a considerable amount of criticism, especially that of Bentham and Hooker. And in recent years the Englerian System has been assailed by certain North American[2] and British[3] botanists who have devoted special attention to the subject. Opinion in America in particular seems to have changed from an almost universal acceptance of the German system in favour of a modification of the arrangement of Bentham and Hooker. This criticism referred especially to the question of the relative primitiveness of the various groups from which a start should be made, such, for example, as the position of the 'Amentiferae' and other apetalous groups, and of the Monocotyledons.

BENTHAM AND HOOKER'S *GENERA PLANTARUM*

The system of Bentham and Hooker was never intended to express a complete phylogenetic scheme of classification, for it is but a more extended arrangement of Jussieu's work elaborated as long ago as 1779, and further expounded by de Candolle in 1818, when botanists were still imbued with the idea of the fixity of species, and long before they had the aid of the Darwinian theory of descent as their guide. Perhaps Jussieu should be reckoned second only to Linnaeus in that he was the first botanist to co-ordinate the genera of plants into families more or less as we now know them. Although a few of the names of his groups are unfamiliar to present-day botanists, nearly all are still in use in a slightly modified form. Bentham and Hooker's work was primarily concerned with a practical handbook to the genera of plants arranged in such a manner as best to facilitate their determination. For the moment, however, we may assume that Bentham and Hooker's *Genera Plantarum* was intended to express a more or less natural system, and proceed to examine the arrangement of their main groups. They began with the *Polypetalae*, their first order (cohort) being the *Ranales*, composed of the well-known *Ranunculaceae* and allied families, characterized by apocarpy and hypogyny of the flower. From these they proceeded to a discifloral series and

---

[1] A short historical account of them is added at the end of this introduction.

[2] See especially C. E. Bessey, 'The Phylogeny and Taxonomy of Angiosperms', *Bot. Gaz.* **24**, 145–78 (1897); and *Ann. Missouri Bot. Gard.* **2**, 109–64 (1915).

[3] E. A. N. Arber and J. Parkin, 'The Origin of Angiosperms', *J. Linn. Soc. Bot.* **38**, 29 (1907). See also H. F. Wernham's suggestive papers on 'Floral Evolution' in *New Phytol.* **10**, 73 et seq. (1911).

finally (in the *Polypetalae*) to the calycifloral perigynous and epigynous types of flower. After these the *Gamopetalae* were enumerated, then the *Monochlamydeae* (*Apetalae*) and Gymnosperms, and finally the Monocotyledons. In elaborating their system, the *Monochlamydeae* were unfortunately retained as a group apart from the *Polypetalae*, and it is to this point and also to the anomalous position of the Gymnosperms that most criticism has been directed in the past. I use the word 'retained', for these distinguished authors were well aware of the true affinities of the families which are included in these two unnatural groups. This is clearly seen by reference to the notes on relationships at the end of each family description, wherein they point out quite clearly their affinities with families in the *Polypetalae*.

THE SYSTEM OF ENGLER AND PRANTL

The chief difference between this system and that of Bentham and Hooker is the amalgamation of Jussieu's groups *Polypetalae* and *Monochlamydeae* under the single group *Archichlamydeae*, and in the Monocotyledons taking precedence of the Dicotyledons. But in Engler's *Archichlamydeae* those apetalous families composing the so-called group *Amentiferae* or catkin bearers (*Betulaceae*, &c.) are regarded as being the most primitive and precede such petaliferous families as *Ranunculaceae* and *Magnoliaceae*. Bessey[1] contended, however, and many botanists have agreed with him, that polypetaly was earlier and that one of the first modifications of it was probably in the direction of apetaly, a condition reached by many plants in the earlier geological periods, but by relatively smaller numbers at the present day.

C. Robertson[2] ably discussed the question of the primitive or non-primitive character of the 'Amentiferae' group of *Apetalae*, on which the acceptance of Engler's views so much depends. He offered the theory that primitive Angiosperms were already entomophilous and that anemophilous types are metamorphosed entomophilous flowers resulting from reduction and degradation, and are not at all primitive. Probably too much importance has been attributed to the anemophily of the *Amentiferae*, on the false analogy of the Gymnosperms. It seems very probable that extreme reduction of the perianth and consequent loss of attractiveness to insects would result in the adoption of another mode of pollen transference, by the wind, *which in this case would not be a primitive condition* as it undoubtedly is in Gymnosperms. In my opinion the universally accepted theory[3] of the foliar origin of the carpel *is fatal to the assumption that the 'Amentiferae' are primitive*. Many of the *Amentiferae* have an ovary composed of the *union of two or more carpels*, which must be the result of cohesion and reduction from older groups *which originally had free carpels*.

Regarding the origin of *Ranunculaceae* and allied families, after a careful examination of these groups, I find myself unable to accept Hallier's view[4]

[1] Bessey, *Bot. Gaz.* **24**, 151 (1897).

[2] C. Robertson, 'The Structure of the Flowers and the Mode of Pollination of the Primitive Angiosperms', *Bot. Gaz.* **37**, 294–8 (1904).

[3] See Arber and Parkin in *J. Linn. Soc. Bot.* **38**, 47 (1907).

[4] H. Hallier, 'Provisional Scheme of the Natural (Phylogenetic) System of Flowering Plants', in *New Phytol.* **4**, 151–62 (1905); see especially p. 157.

that the *Ranunculaceae* and *Nymphaeaceae* have descended from the *Magnoliaceae* through the *Schizandraceae*, *Lardizabalaceae*, and *Berberidaceae*. It is a far cry indeed from a buttercup to a magnolia. To my mind the floral structure of *Berberidaceae* and *Lardizabalaceae* suggests evolution in entirely the opposite direction, i.e. from the *Ranunculaceae*. There are many connecting links between the *Ranunculaceae* and the *Berberidaceae*, and the latter appear to be the reduced and more recent forms. The relative antiquity of woody and herbaceous plants has been the subject of most interesting and instructive papers by Sinnott and Bailey,[1] whose researches go to show that in the flowering plants herbs, as a rule, have been derived from woody plants. However probable this may be, I do not think it can account for the origin of *Ranunculaceae* from any existing woody group. That herbs have been derived from ligneous types in certain families seems clear from some of the examples they quote, but it seems to me that the theory should be applied with considerable caution, for it is reasonable to suppose that the reverse may have frequently occurred, and that a herbaceous group may have evolved woody or semi-woody types. The study of this subject from both standpoints might be productive of interesting results. The type of wood peculiar to *Clematis*, *Berberis*, and the *Menispermaceae* generally, may owe its peculiarity to derivation from *herbaceous* ancestors. From a consideration of floral structure and wide distribution the genus *Clematis* with its woody habit, opposite leaves, its induplicate-valvate sepals and apetalous condition, in conjunction with this view regarding the origin of woody structure, may be traced back through the intermediate genus *Clematopsis* (*Kew Bull.*, 1920, 12–22) to the herbaceous and more primitive genus *Anemone*, by way of *Anemone*, § *Pulsatilla*. There are wide gaps in the relationships of the genera of *Berberidaceae*,[2] but the genus *Berberis* may be similarly traced through *Mahonia*, and some lost type of plant related to *Epimedium*, which is itself a highly evolved member of the family. And similar reasoning may be put forward regarding the origin of the *Menispermaceae* and *Aristolochiaceae*, where in the case of the latter family complete suppression of the inner perianth has been carried out, as in *Clematis*. It is significant that the production of peculiar woody structure in these groups should be accompanied by reduction and degradation of the flowers. For instance all the New Zealand species of *Clematis* are dioecious.

The table opposite summarizes the fundamental differences between the systems of (1) Bentham and Hooker, (2) Engler and Prantl, and (3) the system proposed in these pages.

CONSIDERATIONS FOR THE DELIMITATION OF GROUPS OF FAMILIES

With the exception of the primary division into DICOTYLEDONS and MONO-COTYLEDONS, large groups are usually artificial, especially if the characteristic fixed upon to distinguish them is a *general tendency* and founded on a *single* character. Examples are the de Candollean artificial groups *Thalamiflorae*, *Disciflorae*, *Calyciflorae*, *Inferae*, and to a less extent the *Parietales*, *Centrospermae*, and *Amentiferae*. The special characteristics indicated by the names

[1] E. W. Sinnott and J. W. Bailey, 'The Origin and Dispersal of Herbaceous Angiosperms', in *Ann. Bot.* **28**, 547–600 (1914).

[2] In this new edition the *Berberidaceae* are restricted to *Mahonia* and *Berberis*.

Bentham and Hooker, *Genera Plantarum*	Engler and Prantl, *Die natürlichen Pflanzenfamilien*	System here proposed[1]
Flowering plants divided into a few large groups based mainly on single and mostly artificial characters. Closely allied families often widely separated in consequence. This was never claimed to be a phylogenetic system, but for practical purposes has served a very useful term. Based on the earlier de Candolle System (1818), itself an elaboration and slight modification of Jussieu's arrangement proposed as early as 1779. This system was therefore conceived under the influence of the old dogma of the fixity of species, and long before the theory of descent was propounded. As a *Genera Plantarum*, will ever remain a classic.	A phylogenetic system proposed subsequent to the acceptance of the theory of descent. Based on Eichler's System, and on the assumption that in flowering plants the *absence of a perianth* is a *primitive* feature. Thus families such as *Casuarinaceae, Piperaceae, Salicaceae, Betulaceae, Fagaceae, Urticaceae*, &c., are regarded as primitive and are placed before families such as *Magnoliaceae* and *Ranunculaceae*. Disregards the fact that many of these families without a perianth are characterized by having a gynaecium composed of the union of two or more carpels, a condition at variance with the universally accepted theory that the carpel is a modified leaf. With such an accepted view as to the origin of the carpel a *syncarpous* ovary could hardly have preceded an *apocarpous* one. Moreover a syncarpous ovary is characteristic of nearly all the *highly placed* of Engler's *Archichlamydeae* and of *Metachlamydeae* (*Gamopetalae*),the latter group accepted by all authors as being the most highly evolved of the Dicotyledons. Monocotyledons precede the Dicotyledons. Recent work on the fossil records gives little support to this system.	A phylogenetic system based on the assumption that plants *with sepals and petals*, associated with other floral and anatomical characters regarded as also primitive, are *more ancient phylogenetically* than plants without sepals or petals. This seems a logical interpretation of the theory that the parts of an angiospermous flower are modified leaves. *Free parts* are regarded as *primitive*, and *connate* or *adnate* parts as *more recent*. The *spiral* arrangement of parts is more primitive than the *cyclic* (whorled), and *numerous free* stamens are earlier than the *few* or connate. Also the bisexual precedes the unisexual flower. In this system the groups (orders or cohorts) are smaller, and families are associated which show close general relationship. *Resemblances* emphasized rather than *differences*. The *Monochlamydeae* and *Gamopetalae* of Bentham and Hooker are distributed amongst the *Polypetalae* according to their relationships. The Monocotyledons are placed after the Dicotyledons, from which they were derived at an early stage, the point of origin being the *Ranales*.

of some of these groups are *general tendencies* in many families of flowering plants. Although it may be very convenient to recognize two main groups of Dicotyledons as *Archichlamydeae* (Polypetalae+Monochlamydeae) and *Metachlamydeae* (Gamopetalae, Sympetalae, &c.),[2] a phylogenetic classification is better attained if the gamopetalous character be regarded in its true light, i.e. as a *general tendency*, for gamopetaly is quite a common feature in many

[1] This column is revised slightly to coincide with the phylogenetic sequence in this new edition.

[2] In this new edition these two groups are not recognized (see Preface to second edition).

so-called polypetalous families. The result is the closer approximation of such clearly related families as the *Caryophyllaceae, Primulaceae*, and *Gentianaceae*; the *Rhamnaceae* and *Myrsinaceae*, &c. In this new classification, therefore, smaller groups are recognized, which are bound together by a *combination of characters*, and which allow the association of the general tendencies of floral development such, at any rate, as *perigyny, epigyny*, and *apetaly*. For this reason I proposed (*Kew Bull.*, 1921, 185–91) the establishment of the order *Magnoliales* as distinct from *Ranales*, because I considered that they may have been evolved from separate primitive stocks and have been developed on parallel lines, i.e. with strobilus-like, hypogynous, polycarpellary flowers. The ultimate development of the more primitive families of these two groups, the *Magnoliaceae* and *Ranunculaceae* respectively, is entirely dissimilar, the one remaining arboreal, the other mainly herbaceous. Of course portions of these two main phyla may have often converged on similar lines and may be represented in some of the higher families such as *Euphorbiaceae, Compositae, Scrophulariaceae*, &c.

CONSIDERATIONS FOR THE DELIMITATION OF FAMILIES

A great divergence of opinion is evident in the two principal systems of classification in regard to the delimitation of families. Thus the number of families of flowering plants, including the Gymnosperms, in the *Genera Plantarum* is 200, in the *Pflanzenfamilien* 280, whilst the number is further increased in the various editions of Engler and Gilg's *Syllabus*. There is much to be said in favour of reducing the size of families wherever reasonably possible, and I am in favour of going slightly further even than Engler. For instance, to include in the *Magnoliaceae* such distinct families as the *Winteraceae, Schisandraceae, Trochodendraceae, Himantandraceae*, and *Cercidiphyllaceae* is decidedly incrongruous. If these latter families are excluded, the *Magnoliaceae* proper is a homogeneous group, the characters of which are easily grasped. A similar argument may be advanced for the segregation of *Papaveraceae* and *Fumariaceae*, the *Clusiaceae (Guttiferae)* and *Quiinaceae*, the *Theaceae (Ternstroemiaceae), Marcgraviaceae*, and *Caryocaraceae*, and many other families, even the *Leguminosae* into the *Caesalpiniaceae, Mimosaceae*, and *Papilionaceae (Fabaceae)*. On the other hand, I should consider it going too far to divide the *Compositae* into the *Asteraceae, Vernoniaceae, Eupatoriaceae*, &c., whilst the wisdom of separating the *Rosaceae* into several families is rather doubtful. If more than one family be recognized in *Rosaceae*, then at least ten will have to be segregated. I am not in favour of this undue multiplication. All this goes to prove that the delimitation of families, of genera, and of species is sometimes very much a matter of taste and personal idiosyncrasy, but I would also add of judgement and experience! And it is on this account that the work of Bentham and Hooker carries perhaps more weight, from being the production of a single pair of minds, than that of Engler and Prantl, who enlisted the services of a large number of botanists, including some little experienced pupils, to carry out the work, resulting in a great diversity of treatment, especially as regards the genera.

SHORT HISTORY OF THE
CLASSIFICATION OF FLOWERING PLANTS

(NOT INCLUDED IN THE FIRST EDITION)

I. BEFORE LINNAEUS

The history of the development of plant classification is of considerable interest. Like the plants themselves, it has gradually evolved from a small beginning.

THEOPHRASTUS (370 B.C.), a pupil of Plato and friend of Aristotle, PLINY, and DIOSCORIDES, knew a considerable number of plants, to which they referred as herbs, shrubs, trees, fruits, cereals, or in terms indicating their general growth-habit or use to man. They had no system of classification, of course, but gave a short description of each plant, and an account of its medicinal uses and supposed virtues.

According to Greene the different types of insertion of floral members characteristic of *hypogynous, perigynous*, and *epigynous* plants were clearly recognized by Theophrastus. Greene translates Theophrastus as follows:

Some produce the flower around the (base of the) fruit, as do the grape-vine and olive tree. In the greater portion of plants the fruit thus occupies the centre of the flower. But there are not wanting such as support the flower on the summit of the fruit, as do the pomegranate, apple, and rose, all of which have their seed (ovules) underneath the flower. A few bear the flower on the summit of the seed itself, such as thistles, and all that have their flowers in that manner crowded together.

Greene states further that Theophrastus

learned this springing of the 'flower' from the top of the 'seed' to be characteristic of the whole family of umbellifers, and a few of the rubiaceous plants that he knew, as well as of the thistles and their kindred. . . . At this juncture the sublime old Greek will appear to have lived before his time by more than two thousand years.[1]

Theophrastus wrote a *Historia Plantarum*, in which he indicated the essential differences between Dicotyledons and Monocotyledons, and he gave accounts of woodland, marsh, lake, river, and other plant associations. Thereby he has the greatest claim to be called the 'father of botany'.

DIOSCORIDES, A.D. 64, a physician of Asia Minor, compiled a book concerned mainly with medicinal plants which remained the supreme authority for over sixteen centuries. PLINY, a contemporary, also wrote a *Historia Naturalis* (A.D. 77), largely compiled from Greek authors. Then for over fourteen centuries there is no botanical history.

In the city of Mainz there was published in 1475 a book on general natural history entitled *Ortus Sanitatis*. It contains crude descriptions and woodcuts of plants which sometimes show little or no knowledge of the objects treated.

[1] Quotation from Gertrude E. Douglas, 'The Inferior Ovary', *Bot. Rev.* **10**, 133 (1944).

No definite arrangement is evident. Many editions of this work were published in various languages.

In the sixteenth century several herbals appeared, those of BRUNFELS (1530),[1] BOCK (1539), FUCHS (1542),[2] and LOBELIUS (1581), illustrated by wood engravings. In these it was recognized that some plants had much in common with others, such as the species of a genus, and larger groups like the daisy family (*Compositae*), carrot family (*Umbelliferae*), grasses (*Gramineae*), &c.

OTTO BRUNFELS published *Herbarium* at Strassburg from 1530 to 1536, and from this date it may be said that the scientific study of plants really commenced. These herbals contain figures and descriptions from actual specimens, a botanical terminology gradually appeared, and plants such as orchids, having a general likeness, were grouped together. The woodcuts are excellent examples of their kind.

Brunfels was the son of a cooper at Castle Brunfels, near Mainz, and was born there about the year 1488. He was at first a Carthusian monk, but became a convert to Protestantism, and went to Strassburg, where he started a school. Later he took up medicine and moved to Berne, where he died in 1534.

WILLIAM TURNER is the acknowledged 'father of English botany' and was the author of several botanical works. He wrote the first *English Herbal*. The first part was published in London in 1551, and the second and third parts in Cologne in 1562 and 1568 respectively. The arrangement is alphabetical and the woodcuts are inferior to those of Brunfels.

Turner was born in 1512 at Morpeth, a small town a few miles north of Newcastle, Northumberland.

The herbal of VALERIUS CORDUS (1561)[3] of Wittenberg showed a great advance and is a landmark in descriptive botany.

The most important of the British herbals was written by JOHN GERARD, entitled *Herbal or General Historie of Plantes*. This was published in London in 1597. Gerard was born at Nantwich, Cheshire, in 1545, and was educated locally. He became a barber-surgeon in London and had a garden near Holborn. In 1596 he published a catalogue of the plants cultivated by him, and this is probably the first complete published catalogue of any single garden. His *Herbal*, however, was modelled on Dodoens's *Stirpium Historiae Pemptades* published in 1583 at Antwerp, and he borrowed the blocks used by Tabernaemontanus in his *Icones* of 1590, with a few original additions. He died in London in 1612. Gerard adopted the arrangement of L'Obel, whose *Plantarum seu Stirpium Historia* was published at Antwerp in 1576. The groups of plants recognized are based on well-marked characters of general form, manner of growth, and economic uses. They started with supposed simpler forms, grasslike plants with narrow leaves, and advanced through the broader-leaved bulbous and rhizomatous Monocotyledons to dicotyledonous herbs, culminating in shrubs and trees, the latter being

---

[1] 'The Herbal of Otto Brunfels'—T. A. Sprague, *J. Linn. Soc. Bot.* 48: 79–124 (1928).
[2] 'The Herbal of Leonhart Fuchs'—T. A. Sprague & E. Nelmes, *J. Linn. Soc. Bot.* 48: 545–642 (1931).
[3] 'The Herbal of Valerius Cordus'—T. A. & M. S. Sprague, *J. Linn. Soc. Bot.* 52: 1–113 (1939).

regarded as the most perfect. Already the germs of a more natural grouping are evident.

ANDREA CAESALPINO published his *De Plantis* in Florence in 1583. He considered that a natural classification should be based on the characters of the fruit, seed, and embryo, but still recognized the two main divisions into woody and herbaceous plants. Caesalpino was born at Arezzo, in Italy, in 1519, and studied under Ghini, director of the public garden at Pisa, in the University of which he became Professor of Medicine and Anatomy. He was eventually chief physician to Pope Clement VIII, and died in Rome in 1603. He also wrote numerous anatomical works, and is said to some extent to have anticipated Harvey's discovery of the circulation of the blood.

CASPAR BAUHIN's *Prodromus Theatri Botanici* was published in Frankfort in 1620, and reached quite a high state of precision. The general arrangement is still on the primitive lines to be observed in L'Obel and Gerard, but the descriptions are more scientific, and much of the medical details of early works is omitted.

Bauhin was born at Basle in 1550 and was a pupil of Leonhart Fuchs (after whom was named the genus *Fuchsia*), and he collected plants in Italy, France, and Switzerland. He became Professor at Basle and died in 1624.

ROBERT MORISON published his *Plantarum Historia Universalis* at Oxford in 1680. His system much resembles that of Caesalpino. Woody plants are kept distinct from herbaceous, and the latter are divided into fifteen sections based partly on habit and partly on characters derived from the fruit and seed. Copperplates take the place of the woodcuts of the older herbals.

Morison had the distinction of publishing the first systematic monograph of a limited group. This was his *Plantarum Umbelliferarum Distributio Nova*, issued in Oxford in 1672. The arrangement is based on the form of the fruit, which is still employed for the classification of *Umbelliferae*.

Morison was born in Aberdeen in 1620 and studied at that University, and afterwards in Paris, taking the degree of Doctor of Physic at Angers in 1648. From 1650 to 1660 he was in charge of the Duke of Orleans's garden at Blois, on the Loire. He returned to England at the Restoration of King Charles II, and was appointed King's Physician and Regius Professor of Botany, and in 1669 Keeper of the Physic Garden at Oxford. He died as the result of an accident in a London street in 1683.

The classification of JOHN RAY (1682) was a great improvement on that of his predecessors, for he was the first to recognize the importance of the character of the embryo and the presence of one or two cotyledons. The old division into *herbs* and *trees* is retained. His primary groups of these are as follows:

```
        ⎧ Imperfectae (flowerless)
Herbs  ⎨                              ⎧ Dicotyledones
        ⎩ Perfectae (flowering)——⎨
          ⎧ Monocotyledones        ⎩ Monocotyledones
Arbores ⎨
          ⎩ Dicotyledones
```

Some of the modern groups and families are recognized in his thirty-three classes, such as *Fungi, Umbelliferae, Stellatae (Rubiaceae), Verticillatae (Labiatae), Leguminosae, Stamineae* (Grasses). Ray also made use of the characters afforded by the flower and fruit as well as of other parts of the plant.

Ray was born at Black Notley in Essex in 1627, and was educated at Braintree and Cambridge University. He became a Fellow of Trinity College in 1649, and subsequently held various appointments at his college. In 1660 he issued his *Catalogue of Cambridge Plants.* Together with his friend and pupil Francis Willughby, he made several journeys in Britain for the study of natural history. In 1662 he was deprived of his fellowship because he refused to subscribe to the new Act of Uniformity, and from 1663 to 1666 he travelled on the continent of Europe. In 1670 he published his *Catalogue of English Plants,* and in 1682 his *Methodus Plantarum Nova,* in which he proposed the system of plant classification, which, with some improvements, he adopted for his *Historia Plantarum.* The first volume of this great work appeared in 1686, the second in 1687, and the third (a supplement) in 1704. Ray returned to his birthplace in 1679 and died there in 1705.

JOSEPH PITTON DE TOURNEFORT was born at Aix, in Provence, in 1656. He studied anatomy and medicine at Montpellier and made botanical journeys in southern France and Spain. In 1683 he was appointed Professor of Botany at the Jardin des Plantes, Paris. In 1694 he published his *Elemens de botanique,* of which the *Institutiones* is an enlarged Latin edition.

Tournefort's system was based solely on the corolla, and was thus artificial, comparing unfavourably with that of Ray, though many of the classes are identical. Tournefort was one of the first botanists accurately to define *genera.*

Generic names had been used before his time, but he was the first to provide them with descriptions and to give them a status distinct from the species.

In 1700 he was sent on a voyage of scientific exploration to Greece and Asia Minor, and returned in 1702 with large natural history collections, including 1,356 new species of plants. The work of describing these collections, together with the strain of his professional and medical duties, proved too arduous, and he died in 1708.

CAMERARIUS was the first to show that plants had sex, and he proved in his work entitled *De Sexu Plantarum Epistola* (1694) that pollen is necessary for fertilization and the formation of seeds.

II. LINNAEUS AND AFTER

CARL LINNAEUS, the 'father of modern botany', the most lauded naturalist of all time, was born at Rashult, a small village in Smäland, Sweden, on 23 May 1707. His father was rector of a neighbouring parish. In 1727 he entered Lund University for the study of medicine, but removed the next year to Uppsala. There he was put in charge of the botanic garden as assistant to Professor Rudbeck, whose name he commemorated later in *Rudbeckia (Compositae).*

In 1732 Linnaeus made a tour through Lapland. In 1735 he went to Holland and obtained a doctor's degree and made the acquaintance of George Clifford, a well-to-do Englishman, who engaged him to study and superintend the large collection of plants in his garden at Hartecamp. These are described in his famous *Hortus Cliffortianus*, published in 1737. The herbarium of plants on which this was based was eventually acquired by Sir Joseph Banks, who bequeathed it to the British Museum (Natural History), London.

In Holland, also, his *Systema Naturae* appeared in 1735, his *Genera Plantarum* in 1737, and his *Classes Plantarum* in 1738. He visited England in 1736. In 1738 he returned to Stockholm, and practised medicine until 1741, when he was appointed Professor at Uppsala, where he spent the remainder of his life.

In 1753 his famous *Species Plantarum* appeared, since then celebrated not only for its great merits, but because it was subsequently selected as the starting point of the binomial system of nomenclature, which is credited to him. Previous to his time a plant name usually consisted of a short descriptive phrase. For example, instead of calling the bulbous buttercup 'Ranunculus foliis ovatis serratis, scapo nudo unifloro', he named it *Ranunculus bulbosus* L.

Linnaeus was the originator of the sexual system, in which he recognized twenty-four classes, determined mainly by the number, or some obvious character, of the stamens. The classes are subdivided into orders according to the number of the styles. The simplicity and convenience of this novel system led to its universal adoption, and it held the field until superseded by the more natural arrangement of Jussieu, and later of de Candolle.

In 1751 Linnaeus's *Philosophia Botanica* appeared. It consists of a revised account of the system previously published in his *Classes Plantarum* of 1738. The genera of flowering plants then known are arranged in sixty-eight orders, based, not on one character, but on his idea of their relationships, depending, as he expressed it, on the simple symmetry of all parts. No diagnoses of the orders are given, many of which had been already recognized by Ray and others. A few are still recognized, such as *Palmae, Coniferae, Compositae, Umbellatae* (*Umbelliferae*), *Multisiliquae* (*Ranunculaceae*), and *Papilionaceae*, several of which had been proposed by earlier botanists. But many of his other groups, compared with modern standards, were very artificial.

So far, the classification of flowering plants had been artificial. Linnaeus, in his *Sexual System* (1753), brought closely together many plants which were obviously related, as well as many that were not. He was the first to recognize the full significance of floral and fruit structure. As already stated, he divided plants into twenty-four *classes*, determined mainly by the number, or some obvious character, of the stamens. The classes were again divided into *orders* according to the number of the styles. Those plants with one stamen were placed in *Monandria*, those with two in *Diandria*, with three in *Triandria*, and so on up to *Dodecandria*, with twelve stamens. This simple and for a time convenient system became deservedly very popular and held the field for three-quarters of a century or more.

MICHEL ADANSON published his *Familles des plantes* in Paris in 1763. This contains an exhaustive account of previous systems, and an arrangement of genera in fifty-eight families, which are named and characterized. Like Tournefort, Adanson was born at Aix, in Provence, in 1727, and studied medicine, botany, and astronomy in Paris, where he was a pupil of Réaumur. In 1748 he went to Senegal, West Africa, and spent six years studying the geography, climate, and natural history of that part of tropical Africa. The results were published in his *Histoire naturelle du Senegal.* He died in 1806, and his name is commemorated by the Baobab tree, *Adansonia,* belonging to the *Bombacaceae.*

From Sweden the centre of botanical activity was switched over to France, and another Frenchman became distinguished because of the great advances he made in systematic botany. This was ANTOINE LAURENT DE JUSSIEU, whose *Genera Plantarum* was published in Paris in 1789. His uncle, Bernard de Jussieu, had made full use of Linnaeus's works in his arrangement of the living plants in the Trianon, and Antoine further improved it. Little by little the system of Linnaeus became the system of Jussieu. The latter defined 100 *natural orders,* and arranged them in a system of fifteen *classes* under the great groups suggested by Ray—*Acotyledones, Monocotyledones,* and *Dicotyledones.* The *Dicotyledones* were subdivided into *Apetalae, Monopetalae, Polypetalae,* and *Diclines Irregulares.*

His *Genera Plantarum secundum Ordines* (1789) was the first system which could claim to be more or less natural. Artificial grouping still persisted, however, because of the reliance on single characters. Dicotyledons and Monocotyledons were maintained and large subdivisions of these were distinguished by the presence, absence, or union of petals, and on the relative position of the floral parts, especially the stamens in relation to the ovary. It was in that system that the terms *hypogynous, perigynous,* and *epigynous* (hinted at by Theophrastus) became so prominent and persisted until the advent of Engler's system (1887–98).

The younger Jussieu was born at Lyons in 1748. In 1765 he went to Paris to finish his medical and scientific studies under the direction of his uncle, Bernard, who was in charge of the Royal garden. From 1770 to 1785 he continued the work of rearrangement begun by his uncle, and on the establishment of the Museum d'Histoire Naturelle in 1793 became Professor of Botany, and later Director and Treasurer of the Museum. Jussieu published numerous carefully elaborated accounts of some genera and families of Dicotyledons. He died in 1836.

The name of ROBERT BROWN looms fairly large in the chronicles of systematic botany, because he has often been referred to as *botanicorum facile princeps.* The present writer has often wondered why, because there were several other distinguished botanists at about that time, notably Augustin P. de Candolle, Sir William Jackson Hooker, John Lindley, &c. The appellation was bestowed by Alexander von Humboldt, and Humboldt, though a very distinguished traveller and physicist, was not botanically best qualified to judge the relative merits of the botanists of his period. Brown was the first Keeper of the Botanical Department of the British Museum.

Born at Montrose, Scotland, in 1773, Brown was educated at Aberdeen and Edinburgh universities. In 1801 he went as naturalist on the expedition under Captain Flinders to Australia, and returned in 1805 with a large collection of plants, representing nearly 4,000 species. In 1810 he became librarian to Sir Joseph Banks, who on his death in 1820 bequeathed to Brown for life the use of his library and collections. In 1827 these were transferred to the British Museum, and Brown went with them as Keeper, a post he held until his death in 1858.

In 1810 Brown published his *Prodromus Florae Novae Hollandiae*, containing descriptions of Australian plants collected by Banks and Solander on Captain Cook's first voyage around the world in 1768–71, and by Brown himself on Flinders's voyage in 1801–5. He wrote valuable notes on the relationships of some plant families, some of which, such as *Santalaceae* and *Stylidiaceae*, were established for the first time.

In 1827 Brown published a paper entitled 'The Female Flower in Cycadaceae and Coniferae', and in this he announced the important discovery of the distinction between Angiosperms and Gymnosperms. There is no doubt that by his investigation of difficult points in the morphology of the flower and seed and his critical work on relationships, Brown ranks high.

The family name of DE CANDOLLE occupies a large place in the history of taxonomic botany. AUGUSTIN PYRAMUS DE CANDOLLE was born in Geneva in 1778, where his boyhood was spent. From 1798 to 1808 he was in Paris, where he associated with prominent French naturalists. He published various botanical works, including a new edition of Lamarck's *Flore française*. In 1808 he became Professor of Botany at Montpellier, where he remained until 1816. During this period he made botanical journeys in France and neighbouring countries and wrote many botanical works. In 1816 he visited England, whence he returned to Geneva, and he remained there until his death in 1841.

A. P. de Candolle's classic work, *Théorie élémentaire de la botanique*, was published in Paris in 1813. He showed that the relationships of plants were best ascertained by the comparative study of the structure and development of their organs (morphology) and not by their functions (physiology), and he defined the principles of a natural system. His arrangement was as follows:

I. Vascular plants or plants with cotyledons

  1. Exogens or Dicotyledons

    (a) With distinct calyx and corolla
        { *Thalamiflorae* (petals free and hypogynous)
          Calyciflorae (petals perigynous and epigynous)
          Corolliflorae (petals united and hypogynous)

    (b) *Monochlamydeae*, with a single perianth whorl (including *Coniferae*)

  2. Endogens or Monocotyledons

    (a) Phanerogams (including *Cycadaceae*)
    (b) Cryptogams

II. Cellular plants or plants without cotyledons

> (a) Foliaceous and of known sexuality (Mosses and Liverworts)
> (b) Without leaves and of unknown sexuality (Lichens, *Fungi*, *Algae*).

In this system there was a great improvement in the arrangement of the Dicotyledons, but the inclusion of Vascular Cryptogams among Monocotyledons was a backward step.

de Candolle's famous *Prodromus Systematis Naturalis Regni Vegetabilis* was published in Paris from 1824 to 1873. Most of the families were the work of A. P. de Candolle and his son ALPHONSE, who continued the work after his father's death. It is comparatively rarely that a son carries on the work of his father in natural science. The de Candolles and Hookers were notable exceptions. The *Prodromus* contained descriptions of all the known species of Dicotyledons and Gymnosperms, and was a monumental work which has been indispensable to taxonomists ever since.

JOHN LINDLEY, as a botanist, has always ranked high in the mind of the present writer. He was born in 1799 at Catton, near Norwich, and was educated at the Grammar School in that town. In 1819 he became associated with the then great patron of the sciences, Sir Joseph Banks, and was secretary of the Royal Horticultural Society from 1822 to 1858. From 1829 till 1861 he also occupied the Chair of Botany at University College, London, being the first Quain Professor of Botany. In 1841 he founded the *Gardeners' Chronicle* and edited that journal until his death in 1865.

Lindley was the son of a gardener, and in his twentieth year began his career as a writer by translating Richard's *Analyse du fruit*. Then he came to London and was for some time engaged in the heavy task of writing the descriptive portion of Loudon's *Encyclopaedia of Plants*, which appeared in 1829. Besides his professorship at London University, Lindley was also lecturer in botany at the Royal Institution and at the Chelsea Botanic Garden.

Lindley earned a very high reputation as an advocate for a more natural system than that proposed by Linnaeus, and his ideas were far advanced for the period. As early as 1830 he announced his views of its importance and advantages in an essay accompanying his *Introduction to the Natural System of Botany*, and to establish and illustrate it was the chief aim of his life. The more important of his works are *The Vegetable Kingdom* (1846), *Flora Medica* (1838), *Fossil Flora of Great Britain* (1831–7), *The Genera and Species of Orchidaceous Plants* (1830–40), *Folia Orchidacea* (1852–5), *Theory of Horticulture* (1840), and that delightful little book, with Thomas Moore, *The Treasury of Botany* (1866). Lindley died at Acton, west of London, in 1865.

STEPHAN ENDLICHER is celebrated for his *Genera Plantarum* (1838–41), which for a period was widely used on the continent of Europe, but was followed by Bentham and Hooker's *Genera Plantarum*, and finally by Engler and Prantl's *Natürliche Pflanzenfamilien*. Endlicher was born at Pressburg, Czechoslovakia, in 1804. After a theological education he devoted himself to natural history, and in 1836 became Keeper of the Herbarium in the Imperial Collections of Natural History in Vienna, where in 1840 he succeeded Jacquin as Professor of Botany and Director of the Botanic Garden. He died at an early age in 1849.

Instead of commencing with families in which both sepals and petals are present, as in the Jussieu–de Candolle systems, he began with a group without petals. Thus commenced the great divergence of the two main systems still in use, for Bentham and Hooker in their *Genera Plantarum* followed that of Jussieu–de Candolle, whilst Engler in the *Natürliche Pflanzenfamilien* followed Endlicher, later modified by Eichler.

Endlicher's system showed an advance in the treatment of the Cryptogams, which are placed first and arranged in a fairly natural sequence. The chief defects are the rank assigned to Gymnosperms and the inclusion of the Cycads and some parasitic flowering plants with the Cryptogams.

WILHELM HOFMEISTER's brilliant embryological researches threw more light on the relationship of the groups of Cryptogams to each other and to the Phanerogams, and indicated the position of the Gymnosperms between the higher Cryptogams and the Angiosperms. He supplied the basis for the distinction of the later generally recognized great plant groups: *Thallophyta, Bryophyta, Pteridophyta, Gymnospermae,* and *Angiospermae.*

Hofmeister was born at Leipzig in 1824, and was at first engaged in business. In 1863 he occupied the Chair of Botany at Heidelberg, and in 1872 succeeded Hugo von Mohl at Tübingen University. He died in 1877.

AUGUST WILHELM EICHLER, in his *Syllabus,* published in Berlin in 1883, united the apetalous and polypetalous groups of Dicotyledons, the families of which he attempted to arrange in a series advancing from the (supposed) primitive to the more highly advanced. But Eichler's chief original work was the well-known *Blüthendiagramme* (1875–8), which was perhaps responsible more than any other book for maintaining much artificial classification.

Eichler was born at Neunkirchen, Germany, in 1839, and studied mathematics and natural history at Marburg. In 1861 he went to Munich to assist Martius in the preparation of the great *Flora Brasiliensis,* of which he became sole editor after Martius's death in 1868. In turn this great man occupied the Chair of Botany at Munich, Graz, Kiel, and Berlin. He died in 1887.

HENRI BAILLON's *Histoire des plantes* (1867–95), a work of thirteen volumes, contains useful descriptions of the families and genera of flowering plants. Its chief merits, however, are the splendid illustrations with accurate dissections. He also published monographs on *Euphorbiaceae* and *Buxaceae,* &c. accompanied by beautifully reproduced plates. Baillon was born at Calais in 1827. In 1874 he was president of the newly founded Linnean Society of Paris, and remained so until his death in 1895.

BENTHAM and HOOKER's system (1862–83) was written before the evolutionary views propounded by Darwin had taken root, and whilst the dogma of the constancy of species still dominated biology. Hence their system laid no particular claim to being a phylogenetic one. On the other hand, that of Engler and Prantl was written when the Darwinian theory had become generally accepted. The principal difference between the two systems is that Bentham and

Hooker began with families having petaliferous flowers such as *Magnoliaceae* and *Ranunculaceae*, whilst Engler and Prantl placed first those families without petals, which are wind-pollinated, popularly called 'Amentiferae' (*Apetalae, Monochlamydeae*), such as the birches, sweet chestnuts, and oaks, inferring that these were more primitive than those with petals.

Before the publication of Bentham and Hooker's monumental undertaking, apart from the pioneer work of Linnaeus (1754), there were but two complete 'Genera Plantarums', the first by Jussieu in 1789, and the second by Endlicher, with its supplements ranging over the five years from 1836 to 1840. When the latter became out of date, Bentham and Hooker jointly undertook the great task of preparing a work to replace it. They wished that their work should be a joint production of both of them, though each was responsible for separate families.[1]

In the first volume the families were fairly equally divided between them. Of the larger families Hooker did the *Cruciferae*, whilst Bentham elaborated the remainder of the *Thalamiflorae*. Hooker described most of the *Disciflorae*. Of the *Calyciflorae* Bentham did all the *Leguminosae*, and Hooker the *Myrtaceae*, *Umbelliferae*, and *Araliaceae*.

In volume two Hooker classified the *Rubiaceae*, whilst Bentham 'endeavoured to reduce to some order the intricate almost endless details of the innumerable closely allied and often distinct genera of *Compositae*'. He carried out this task in a masterly manner and continued with *Campanulaceae*, whilst Hooker wrestled with the *Ericales* in spite of increasing official duties as Director of Kew.

Volume three contained the *Monochlamydeae* ('Apetalae'), of which Hooker described the *Curvembryeae*, but the largest two families, *Euphorbiaceae* and *Urticaceae* fell to Bentham, as also did all the Gymnosperms.

In this concluding volume Hooker described the Palms and Bentham the *Orchidaceae* and *Gramineae*, whilst the remaining families were shared, though most of them fell to Bentham.

Their classic work at once established a reputation for Kew which has been maintained to the present day, and has ever since been an inspiration to generations of Kew botanists.

ENGLER and PRANTL, *Die natürlichen Pflanzenfamilien* (1887–98). A great step forward was made in this monumental work by the amalgamation of the *Polypetalae* and *Apetalae* of the Jussieu–de Candolle–Bentham and Hooker system. But the placing of apetalous families as being most primitive was challenged especially by Bessey (1897), Hallier (1905), Arber and Parkin (1907), and by the present author (1926, 1934), and the following account is based on the system of the last mentioned and modified here in full for the first time.

In my system Dicotyledons and Monocotyledons are maintained, and the families in these two groups are linked together into orders and arranged in an ascending series, showing generally an increasing specialization of the flower associated with other characters. Dicotyledons are regarded as being generally more primitive than Monocotyledons. The large groups of previous

[1] See *J. Linn. Soc. Bot.* **20**, 304–8 (1883).

systems such as *Polypetalae, Calyciflorae, Archichlamydeae, Gamopetalae* (*Sympetalae* or *Metachlamydeae*), and *Apetalae*, are considered to be largely artificial, depending as they do mainly on single characters, and are not retained as separate groups in this system. Instead they are primarily divided into two main divisions, **Lignosae** and **Herbaceae**, the former embracing families which are primitively and predominantly woody, the latter those that are primitively and predominantly herbaceous. By this arrangement certain families previously associated in the same group or even in the same family are now far apart. Examples are *Magnoliaceae* and *Ranunculaceae, Rosaceae* and *Saxifragaceae, Araliaceae* and *Umbelliferae*, &c. It is considered that the apparent relationships between each of these pairs of families is due to parallel development from separate stocks.

LINEAR SEQUENCE OF ORDERS

ON the opposite page is a 'bird's-eye view' of the linear sequence of the orders of Angiosperms in the present system.

On the left are the LIGNOSAE, beginning with the most primitive order *Magnoliales* and ending with the *Verbenales*. The more important basic orders are printed in bold-face type (black), and their connexions with groups higher up the scale are shown by arrows.

Such herbs as occur in these orders are clearly derived from *woody* ancestors and are not related to the herbs in the middle column, HERBACEAE. Conversely the few woody members found in the orders of the *Herbaceae* are in turn not related to any in the *Lignosae* column.

In the middle column, HERBACEAE, it is suggested that the *Ranales* are a parallel development of the *Magnoliales*, perhaps evolved from common but relatively remote ancestors, and that the climax group at the top, the *Lamiales*, are a parallel development equivalent to but not phylogenetically related to the *Verbenales* at the head of the *Lignosae* column. The more important basic orders are also shown in bold-face type.

In the right-hand column are the MONOCOTYLEDONS, the more primitive orders of which appear to be closely related to the *Ranales* and derived from less remote common *herbaceous* ancestors.

The groups at the foot of each column are characterized by having free carpels, free stamens, free sepals, and free petals.

Monocotyledons are dealt with in volume II.

Dicotyledones

Lɪɢɴᴏsᴀᴇ

VERBENALES
BIGNONIALES
RUBIALES
APOCYNALES
LOGANIALES
SAPINDALES
MELIALES
RUTALES
EBENALES
MYRSINALES
RHAMNALES
SANTALALES
OLACALES
CELASTRALES
MYRTALES
GUTTIFERALES
ERICALES
OCHNALES
THEALES
EUPHORBIALES
MALPIGHIALES
MALVALES
TILIALES
CACTALES
CUCURBITALES
PASSIFLORALES
LOASALES
POLYGALALES
VIOLALES
TAMARICALES
CAPPARIDALES
PITTOSPORALES
PROTEALES
THYMELAEALES
BIXALES
URTICALES
CASUARINALES
JUGLANDALES
FAGALES
BALANOPSIDALES
MYRICALES
LEITNERIALES
SALICALES
HAMAMELIDALES
ARALIALES
STYRACALES
CUNONIALES
LEGUMINALES
ROSALES
CORIARIALES
DILLENIALES
LAURALES
ANNONALES
MAGNOLIALES

Dicotyledones

Hᴇʀʙᴀᴄᴇᴀᴇ

LAMIALES
BORAGINALES
POLEMONIALES
GERANIALES
PERSONALES
SOLANALES
ASTERALES
GOODENIALES
CAMPANALES
VALERIANALES
UMBELLALES
PODOSTEMALES
SARRACENIALES
SAXIFRAGALES
PLANTAGINALES
PRIMULALES
GENTIANALES
LYTHRALES
CHENOPODIALES
POLYGONALES
CARYOPHYLLALES
RESEDALES
CRUCIALES
RHOEADALES
PIPERALES
ARISTOLOCHIALES
BERBERIDALES
RANALES

Monocotyledones

GRAMINALES
CYPERALES
JUNCALES
ORCHIDALES
BURMANNIALES
HAEMODORALES
CYCLANTHALES
PANDANALES
PALMALES
AGAVALES
IRIDALES
AMARYLLIDALES
TYPHALES
ARALES
DIOSCOREALES
ALSTROEMERIALES
LILIALES
ZINGIBERALES
BROMELIALES
ERIOCAULALES
XYRIDALES
COMMELINALES
NAJADALES
POTAMOGETONALES
APONOGETONALES
JUNCAGINALES
TRIURIDALES
ALISMATALES
BUTOMALES

HYPOTHETICAL PROANGIOSPERMS

GENERAL PRINCIPLES ADOPTED HERE FOR THE CLASSIFICATION OF FLOWERING PLANTS[1]

Other things being equal, it may be stated that:

1. Evolution is both (1) upwards and (2) downwards, the latter involving degradation and degeneration; examples: (1) towards the sympetalous condition; epigyny; (2) towards the apetalous state of many flowers; unisexuality in flowering plants.

2. Evolution does not necessarily involve all organs of the plant at the same time; and one organ or set of organs may be advancing whilst another set is stationary or retrograding.

3. Evolution has generally been consistent, and when a particular progression or retrogression has set in, it is persisted in to the end of the phylum; examples: the strong tendency to zygomorphy of the corolla coupled with the reduction in the number of stamens in Engler's hypogynous *Metachlamydeae*; the great tendency to perigyny and epigyny in the *Archichlamydeae* and *Metachlamydeae* as exhibited in the families *Umbelliferae* and *Rubiaceae* respectively.

Relating to the General Habit of Plants

4. In certain groups, trees and shrubs are probably more primitive than herbs; examples: *Mimosaceae* and *Caesalpiniaceae* (trees and shrubs) as compared with the derived family *Papilionaceae* (*Fabaceae*) (often herbaceous).

5. Trees and shrubs are older than climbers, the latter habit having been acquired through particular environment.

6. Perennials are older than biennials, and from them annuals have been derived; note the extraordinarily few annuals in the primitive family *Ranunculaceae*; the great number in the more advanced and natural family *Cruciferae*.

7. Aquatic Phanerogams are as a rule more recent than terrestrial (at any rate in the members of the same family or genus), and the same may be said of epiphytes, saprophytes, and parasites.

Relating to the General Structure of Flowering Plants

8. Plants with collateral vascular bundles arranged in a cylinder (Dicotyledons) are more primitive in origin than those with scattered bundles

[1] The reader is referred here to an essay by Bessey, 'Phylogenetic Taxonomy', published in the *Ann. Missouri Bot. Gard.* 2, 112.

(Monocotyledons), though it does not necessarily follow that the latter have been directly derived from the former.

9. The spiral arrangement of leaves on the stem and of the floral leaves precedes that of the opposite and whorled type.

10. As a rule simple leaves precede compound leaves.

Relating to the Flowers and Fruits of Plants

11. Bisexual (hermaphrodite) precede unisexual flowers, and the dioecious is probably more recent than the monoecious condition.

12. The solitary flower is more primitive than the inflorescence, the highest forms of the latter being the umbel and capitulum; examples of the latter: *Umbelliferae* and *Compositae* respectively.

13. Spirally imbricate floral parts are more primitive than whorled and valvate; examples: *Magnolia* and *Clematis*.

14. Many-parted flowers (polymerous) precede, and the type with few parts (oligomerous) follows from it, being accompanied by a progressive sterilization of reproductive parts (sporophylls); examples: *Magnolia* and *Cheiranthus*.

15. Petaliferous flowers precede apetalous ones, the latter being the result of reduction.

16. Free petals (polypetaly) are more primitive than connate petals (sympetaly).

17. Actinomorphy (regularity) of the flower is an earlier type than zygomorphy (irregularity); examples: *Caltha* and *Delphinium*.

18. Hypogyny is the primitive structure, and from it perigyny and epigyny were derived later.

19. Free carpels (apocarpy) are more primitive and from them connate carpels resulted; sometimes, however, when the carpels have remained loosely united during evolution they may again become quite free; example: *Asclepiadaceae*.

20. Many carpels (polycarpy) precede few carpels (oligocarpy); examples: *Ranunculus* and *Nigella*.

21. The endospermic seed with small embryo is primitive and the non-endospermic seed more recent; examples: *Ranunculaceae* and *Rosaceae*.

22. In primitive flowers there are many stamens, in more advanced flowers few stamens; examples: *Ranunculus* and *Cheiranthus*. This condition may, however, be reversed within the confines of a single family like *Papaveraceae*, where bees feed on the pollen.

23. Separate stamens precede connate stamens; examples: *Tiliaceae* and *Malvaceae*; *Campanulaceae* and *Lobeliaceae*.

24. Aggregate[1] fruits are more recent than single fruits, and as a rule the capsule precedes the drupe or berry.

[1] i.e. fruits formed from several separate flowers, as in *Morinda* (*Rubiaceae*).

CONSPECTUS OF
PRINCIPAL LIVING GROUPS
OF FLOWERING PLANTS

PHYLUM I. GYMNOSPERMAE.[1]—Ovules naked, not enclosed by an ovary, receiving the pollen-grains (microspores), mainly borne by the wind, directly on the micropyle; embryo-sac enclosed in the nucellus and filled with tissue (rudimentary prothallus) before fertilization and containing two or more egg-cells (archegonia), the latter usually consisting of a large egg-cell and a short neck; pollen-grains (microspores) spherical or oval, often with a bladder-like extension of the outer coat (extine), containing a prothallus of two or more cells, one of which produces two non-motile or rarely motile male cells. Cotyledons two or several, very rarely one by suppression. Wood (except in *Gnetaceae*) with no true vessels. Trees and shrubs with usually evergreen xerophilous, needle-like or fern-like foliage and unisexual 'flowers', mainly found in the mountainous and cool temperate regions of the world, extending to the limits of phanerogamic ligneous vegetation on high mountains and towards the poles. A comparatively small but very ancient phylum of plants, abundant in past ages, but now represented only by the cycads, yews, pine trees, &c., very numerous in individuals and yielding many valuable timber trees, but no food plants of any importance.

PHYLUM II. ANGIOSPERMAE.—Ovules enclosed in an ovary usually crowned by a style and stigma, the latter receiving the pollen-grains (microspores) mainly through the agency of insects, becoming wind-pollinated when much reduced. Wood when present consisting of true vessels.[2] A more recently evolved phylum than the *Gymnospermae*, and constituting the bulk of the present world vegetation, yielding valuable timbers and practically all food, forage, and medicinal plants.

SUBPHYLUM I. DICOTYLEDONES.—Embryonic plant with 2 seed-leaves (cotyledons). Vascular bundles of the stem usually arranged in a circle (except in a few genera of the lower herbaceous families which have scattered bundles). Leaves typically net-veined, opposite or alternate. Flowers usually pentamerous or tetramerous.

DIVISION I. **Lignosae.** Trees and shrubs, and some herbs clearly derived from and related to other woody plants—a *fundamentally woody* group.

DIVISION II. **Herbaceae.** Herbs, or rarely shrubby plants clearly related to and derived from herbaceous stocks—a *fundamentally herbaceous* group.

SUBPHYLUM II. MONOCOTYLEDONES. Embryonic plant with only 1 seed-leaf; vascular bundles of the stem closed and scattered. Leaves typically parallel-nerved, alternate. Flowers usually trimerous. (This group is dealt

[1] For convenience I include in this conspectus the Gymnosperms, though they are not, strictly speaking, true flowering plants.
[2] Except in some *Winteraceae* (*Drimys*, &c.).

with in the second volume, but a brief sketch of its main families and their linear sequence are given on p. 29.)

ANGIOSPERMAE[1]

Angiosperms are flowering plants in which the ovules are enclosed in a carpel or in several carpels united into an ovary. Mainly by this character they are distinguished from Gymnosperms, with ovules not enclosed in carpels. The ovules of Angiosperms are fertilized by transference, mainly by insects, of pollen from the stamens of the same or a different flower to the stigma or stigmas, these being usually supported on a style or styles.

The angiospermous flower may be regarded as consisting of modified leaves, a typical example, such as that of a *Magnolia* or buttercup, is made up of an outer whorl of sepals (collectively forming the calyx), an inner whorl of petals (corolla), then stamens (androecium), and in the middle carpels (gynoecium). Only the stamens and carpels are absolutely essential, the calyx being largely protective and usually green, the corolla usually serving to attract insects, by which the more advantageous cross-pollination is effected, failing which self-pollination is often possible.

Up to the present the classification of flowering plants has been largely based on the structure of the flower, fruits, and seeds, combined with certain major anatomical characters. Thus all modern systems recognize a primary division into Dicotyledons and Monocotyledons, the former with 2 seed-leaves (cotyledons), usually net-veined leaves, the vascular bundles of the stem arranged in a ring or rings, and the parts of the flower usually in fives or fours or multiples of these numbers, and the latter with only 1 seed-leaf (cotyledon), usually parallel-veined leaves, scattered vascular bundles, and the parts of the flower usually in threes.

DICOTYLEDONES. Lignosae

The woody group, LIGNOSAE, begins with **Magnoliaceae**, which is regarded as the most primitive living family of Angiosperms, whilst the most generally advanced is *Verbenaceae*.

The HERBACEAE start with **Ranunculaceae**, regarded as a parallelism of the *Magnoliaceae*, and end finally in *Labiatae*, in turn considered to be more or less equivalent to the *Verbenaceae* at the top of the woody group.

Magnoliaceae is the basic family for the order MAGNOLIALES, with free sepals, free petals, numerous free stamens, and numerous free carpels, all arranged on an elongated or conical floral axis; example *Magnolia*. To the closely related **Illiciaceae** the star anise, *Illicium verum*, belongs.

Annonaceae is the principal family of ANNONALES, with a short floral axis, and with ruminate endosperm in the seed. The tropical fruits, cherimoyer, *Annona cherimolia*, and custard apple, *Annona reticulata*, belong here.

Lauraceae are typical of LAURALES; they have no petals, and the anthers open by valves; sweet bay, *Laurus nobilis*, avocado pear, *Persea americana*

---

[1] These notes are additional to the first edition and have been included to explain the present system mainly for less advanced students.

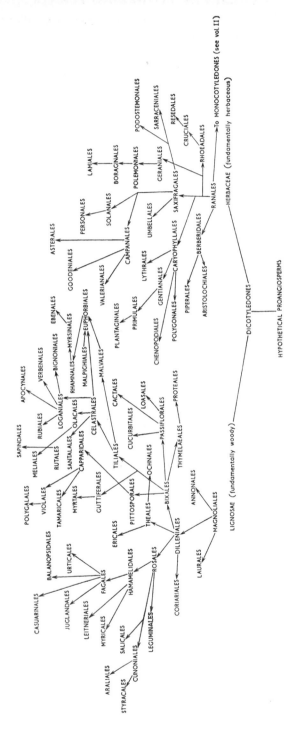

Diagram showing the probable phylogeny and relationships of the Orders of Angiosperms

(The families belonging to these orders are shown in the linear sequence on p. 19)

(a tropical American fruit), cinnamon, *Cinnamomum zeylanicum*, and sassafras, *Sassafras variifolium*, are well-known economic plants of this family. The nutmeg family, **Myristicaceae**, is closely related; nutmeg, *Myristica fragrans*.

Dilleniaceae (DILLENIALES) are of little economic importance; they are also related to *Magnoliaceae* but are more tropical; leaves simple, usually large with strong parallel nerves; carpels still free, seed mostly with a crested or laciniate aril. **Connaraceae** are related, also with free carpels, arillate seeds, but leaves compound.

Rosaceae (ROSALES) are a large natural group, mostly with free carpels, but flowers perigynous or epigynous; many lovely garden plants and edible fruits such as apple, plum, apricot, prune, almond, strawberry, blackberry, loquat, and others; a mostly woody family, but some herbs, such as meadowsweet, *Filipendula ulmaria*, and species of *Potentilla*. Hawthorn, *Crataegus*, rowan, *Sorbus aucuparia*, and wild roses, *Rosa*, are typical of the family in Europe.

Related to *Rosaceae* is the order LEGUMINALES, often divided into three families, **Caesalpiniaceae**, **Mimosaceae**, and **Papilionaceae**; the last mentioned most advanced and becoming partly herbaceous; the first two families mostly important for valuable timbers. **Papilionaceae** for its food and forage plants, including garden pea, *Pisum sativum*, broad bean, *Vicia faba*, ground nut, *Arachis hypogaea*, soy bean, *Glycine max*, and clovers, *Trifolium* spp. The common broom, *Cytisus scoparius*, and gorse or whin, *Ulex europaeus*, are typical European examples. Dyes from indigo, and insecticides from *Derris* and *Lonchocarpus* spp.

Philadelphaceae, **Grossulariaceae** (gooseberry and currant) (CUNONIALES), and **Cornaceae** and **Araliaceae** (ARALIALES) follow on, and are succeeded by **Styracaceae** (STYRACALES), and by a most interesting group, the HAMAMELIDALES, to which the witch hazel, *Hamamelis*, the box, *Buxus*, and London plane, *Platanus*, belong. These form the link between the *Rosaceae* and the largely wind-pollinated catkin-bearing families such as poplars, **Salicaceae**, birches and alders, **Betulaceae**, beeches, oaks, and sweet chestnut, **Fagaceae**, **Juglandaceae**, walnut, *Juglans regia*, hickory, *Carya alba*, **Corylaceae** (hornbeam, hazel, and filbert), the fig family, **Moraceae**, elm family, **Ulmaceae**, the nettle family, **Urticaceae**, and the hops and hemp, **Cannabiaceae**.

Related back to the **Dilleniaceae** are the **Flacourtiaceae** (BIXALES), to which *Hydnocarpus kurzii* belongs, from which the chaulmoogra oil, used in the treatment of leprosy, is obtained. Related families are **Thymelaeaceae** and **Proteaceae**, characteristic of South Africa and Australia. From *Flacourtiaceae* other related families are derived, such as **Capparidaceae**, **Tamaricaceae**, **Violaceae**, **Polygalaceae**, and **Loasaceae**, mostly of lesser economic importance. And finally in this line of relationship a climax in floral development is reached in the passion-flower family, **Passifloraceae**, and the family **Cucurbitaceae**, and cactus, **Cactaceae**, the last-mentioned characteristic of desert regions of the new world.

The lime-tree family, **Tiliaceae**, is also closely related to *Flacourtiaceae*; jute is obtained from *Corchorus* spp., and to this TILIALES group belongs **Sterculiaceae**, with cocoa, *Theobroma cacao*, and kola, *Cola* spp., and

Bombacaceae, with kapok, *Ceiba pentandra*, and the giant baobab of Africa, *Adansonia digitata*. **Malvaceae,** a climax family of this alliance, are partly herbaceous but very fibrous; the stamens are united into a column, and the anthers unilocular through division of the filament; cotton from seeds of *Gossypium* spp. Related groups embrace **Linaceae** (flax, *Linum usitatissimum*) and **Zygophyllaceae** (creosote bush, *Larrea mexicana*, and lignum vitae, *Guaiacum officinale*). **Euphorbiaceae,** a vast family found mainly in the tropics, show a very mixed relationship with several other groups; they are often without petals; para rubber, from *Hevea brasiliensis*, castor oil, *Ricinus communis*, tung oil, *Aleurites fordii*, and cassava meal, *Manihot utilissima*, are the most important economic products. The spurges (*Euphorbia*) represent a large genus, and also *Croton*; cascarilla bark, *Croton eluteria*.

Associated in the THEALES are several small families, the tea family, **Theaceae,** being the largest and most important; tea is *Camellia chinensis*. **Dipterocarpaceae** provide valuable timbers in Malaya; they are distinguished by their remarkably winged fruits.

The heath family, **Ericaceae,** with sympetalous corollas, anthers opening by terminal pores, and superior ovary, is connected with *Theaceae* through the small family **Clethraceae,** with free petals. **Vacciniaceae** have an inferior ovary; whortleberry, *Vaccinium myrtillus*, cranberry, *Oxycoccus palustris*.

Clusiaceae (*Guttiferae*) form the principal family of GUTTIFERALES, which also includes **Hypericaceae**; mangosteen is *Garcinia mangostana*. Related are **Myrtales,** with perigynous or epigynous flowers and usually gland-dotted opposite leaves; to **Myrtaceae** belong eucalyptus, clove, *Eugenia caryophyllus*, guava, *Psidium guajava*, and myrtles, *Myrtus* spp.; CELASTRALES embrace the holly family, **Aquifoliaceae** (maté tea, *Ilex paraguensis*) and **Empetraceae** (crowberry, *Empetrum nigrum*). Following these are OLACALES, mainly tropical and SANTALALES, the latter embracing **Loranthaceae**; mistletoe, *Viscum album*. To RHAMNALES belong **Rhamnaceae** with stamens equal in number and opposite to the petals; cascara sagrada, *Frangula purshiana*; **Ampelidaceae** (*Vitaceae*) give the grape vine, *Vitis vinifera*, and the ornamental Virginia creeper, *Parthenocissus tricuspidata*. Related to these are **Myrsinaceae,** with united petals, the stamens opposite the corolla-lobes, and a free basal placenta.

Sapotaceae (SAPOTALES) are mostly tropical, with sympetalous corolla, and are probably most nearly related to *Myrsinaceae*; sapodilla, *Achras zapota*, is a delicious fruit, and the best gutta percha is obtained from the latex of *Palaquium gutta*, a native of Malaya. Related are **Ebenaceae,** the chief source of ebony wood being *Diospyros ebenum*; an edible fruit is kaki or date plum, *Diospyros kaki*.

Large and mainly tropical groups follow on, mostly with compound leaves; these are RUTALES (**Rutaceae**), MELIALES (**Meliaceae**), and SAPINDALES (**Sapindaceae**). To **Rutaceae** belong the orange, lemon, grapefruit, lime, and rue; to **Meliaceae,** mahogany, *Swietenia mahagoni*, and other valuable timbers; to **Sapindaceae** the guarana, *Paullinia cupana*, and to **Hippocastanaceae** the horse-chestnut, *Aesculus hippocastanum*; to **Aceraceae,** with winged fruits, the maple and sycamore; and to **Anacardiaceae** the mango, *Mangifera indica*, cashew nut, *Anacardium occidentale*, pistachio nut, *Pistacia vera*, and the sumach, *Rhus coriaria*.

The remainder of the families in this woody group, LIGNOSAE, have sympetalous corollas, all actinomorphic except the more highly advanced **Bignoniaceae** and **Verbenaceae**; the bulk are found in the tropics. In **Loganiaceae** and allied families the ovary is superior, and the leaves usually have no stipules; a related family is **Strychnaceae**; nux vomica is *Strychnos nux vomica*. Related also are **Oleaceae**, with two stamens and usually opposite compound leaves; ash, *Fraxinus excelsior*, and olive, *Olea europaea*. Becoming more specialized in their flowers with secondary apocarpous gynoecium are **Apocynaceae**, often with milky juice producing latex (rubber from *Landolphia* spp. and *Funtumia*), and **Asclepiadaceae**, with waxy pollen-masses and a corona, a completely climax group very abundant in southern Africa.

Rubiaceae (RUBIALES) is a large and very important tropical family; leaves always opposite and entire with inter- or intra-petiolar stipules; ovary inferior. Important economic plants are coffee, *Coffea arabica*, quinine, *Cinchona* spp., ipecacuanha, *Psychotria ipecacuanha*, and madder dye, *Rubia tinctorum*; woodruff is *Asperula odorata*.

Bignoniaceae (BIGNONIALES) are more ornamental than economic; *Catalpa bignonioides*, a handsome hardy flowering tree; leaves in the family opposite, usually compound, with no true stipules; many handsome climbers by means of leaf-tendrils.

Finally, the climax of the woody group is considered to be **Verbenaceae**; flowers usually zygomorphic, with four or two stamens and habit becoming partly herbaceous; teak wood is *Tectona grandis*, the most important hardwooded tree of India and Malaya.

DICOTYLEDONES. Herbaceae

In this system it is necessary to start again with the most primitive family of the herbaceous group, i.e. the **Paeoniaceae**, and with the **Helleboraceae** and its closely related family **Ranunculaceae**. In other systems these were usually placed next to *Magnoliaceae*, but here they are regarded as parallel families and not really closely related. As in *Magnoliaceae* the sepals and petals are free and the stamens and carpels are free and numerous, and arranged on a more or less conical axis; seeds rich in reserve food material, endosperm, with a small embryo; herbs with radical or alternate leaves, except *Clematis*. *Paeonia* is mostly of ornamental value. To **Helleboraceae** belong the aconite, *Aconitum napellus*, and baneberry, *Actaea spicata*; and to **Ranunculaceae** the buttercups, *Ranunculus* spp., *Anemone*, and the lesser celandine, *Ficaria verna*. The water-lily family, **Nymphaeaceae**, is also closely related, with the carpels often sunk in the torus.

BERBERIDALES are next; in **Berberidaceae** and a few related small families the ovary is usually reduced to one carpel. Related are ARISTOLOCHIALES, without petals; **Aristolochiaceae**, with broad medullary rays, and the very specialized **Nepenthaceae**, pitcher plants (*Nepenthes*). PIPERALES are also without petals, but with scattered vascular bundles as in Monocotyledons, a character perhaps retained from the Ranalean ancestors; pepper, *Piper nigrum*.

RHOEADALES contain the poppy family, **Papaveraceae**, with numerous stamens, but no nectar, and ovules on the walls of the ovary; common poppy, *Papaver rhoeas*, opium poppy, *Papaver somniferum*; **Cruciferae** is a climax family of this alliance, with 4 petals, 6 stamens, 4 long and 2 short, and ovary with two placentas on the walls; no endosperm in the seeds, and folded embryo; cabbage, *Brassica oleracea*, turnip, *Brassica rapa*, radish, *Raphanus sativus*, horse-radish, *Armoracia lapathifolia*, watercress, *Nasturtium officinale*, honesty, *Lunaria rediviva*, wallflower, *Cheiranthus cheiri*.

RESEDALES and CARYOPHYLLALES are more advanced, **Caryophyllaceae** with opposite entire leaves, a definite number of stamens, and syncarpous ovary with free central placentation of the ovules; embryo curved in abundant endosperm; mainly of not more than decorative value. **Ficoidaceae** are mostly in semi-desert areas. Derived from the preceding are the apetalous families, **Polygonaceae** (rhubarb, buckwheat, and sorrel) and **Chenopodiaceae** (beet and spinach), whilst perigynous relatives are **Lythraceae** and **Onagraceae**.

Sympetalous related groups are GENTIANALES (**Gentianaceae**), gentian root, *Gentiana lutea*, and many beautiful rock-garden plants in *Gentianaceae*; PRIMULALES (**Primulaceae**), primrose, *Primula vulgaris*, and pimpernel, *Anagallis arvensis*, in *Primulaceae*; and PLANTAGINALES (**Plantaginaceae**).

SAXIFRAGALES form another basic group related to *Ranunculaceae*; in **Crassulaceae** the carpels are still free, sometimes with the rare combination of a sympetalous corolla, such as in the navel-wort, *Umbilicus pendulinus*. **Saxifragaceae**, in this system, is *sensu stricto*, i.e. excluding *Hydrangea*, *Cunonia*, *Escallonia*, gooseberry, and others; the flowers are perigynous, the ovary syncarpous and usually bilocular with axile placentation; seeds with endosperm and minute embryo. Related are **Sarraceniaceae** and **Droseraceae**, the former pitcher plants (*Sarracenia*), the latter sometimes insectivorous (*Drosera*).

More distantly related are **Valerianaceae**, with inferior ovary and sympetalous corolla; valerian, *Valeriana officinalis*; and **Dipsacaceae**, with some similar characters but flowers in heads; fuller's teasel, *Dipsacus fullonum*.

Umbelliferae (UMBELLALES) are considered to be derived from the saxifragaceous stock and regarded as a parallel family with *Araliaceae* in the woody group; the umbel is a climax type of inflorescence, combined with the inferior ovary and specialized type of fruit with resin canals (vittae); useful plants are celery, *Apium graveolens*, carrot, *Daucus carota*, parsnip, *Peucedanum sativum*, caraway, *Carum carvi*, dill, *Peucedanum graveolens*, coriander, *Coriandrum sativum*, fennel, *Foeniculum capillaceum*, and parsley, *Petroselinum crispum*.

CAMPANALES (**Campanulaceae**, &c.) are sympetalous derivatives from *Saxifragales* and point to the origin of the vast and climax family *Compositae*; the ovary has become inferior, the corolla sympetalous, but the stamens remain free from the corolla; harebell (bluebell of Scotland) *Campanula rotundifolia*.

Compositae is one of the most successful families of flowering plants; only a few are of economic use; Jerusalem artichoke, *Helianthus tuberosus*, globe artichoke, *Cynara scolymus*, santonin, *Artemisia cina*, chicory, *Cichorium intybus*, lettuce, *Lactuca scariola*, sunflower, *Helianthus annuus*, chamomile, *Anthemis nobilis*, coltsfoot, *Tussilago farfara*; many decorative plants;

leaves are without stipules; flowers collected into heads, surrounded by an involucre of bracts; ovary inferior, unilocular with one ovule; anthers united into a tube through which the style pushes out the pollen; seeds without endosperm.

SOLANALES (**Nolanaceae, Solanaceae,** and **Convolvulaceae**) also show links with the saxifragaceous stock; **Solanaceae** have no stipules, corolla sympetalous, lobes the same number as the stamens, and a bilocular superior ovary; useful plants, potato, *Solanum tuberosum*, tomato, *Lycopersicum esculentum*, deadly nightshade, *Atropa belladonna*, henbane, *Hyoscyamus niger*, thorn-apple, *Datura stramonium*, tobacco, *Nicotiana tabacum*. **Convolvulaceae** are mostly twiners, with plaited aestivation of corolla, and one or two ovules; sweet potato, *Ipomoea batatas*, scammony, *Convolvulus scammonia*.

PERSONALES embrace more advanced families, including **Scrophulariaceae** and **Acanthaceae,** with increasing zygomorphy of the corolla, a progressive reduction in the number of stamens, with alternate to opposite leaves, indicating a climax type of flower comparable with that of the family *Labiatae*; some have become parasitic or semiparasitic; foxglove, *Digitalis purpurea* (*Scrophulariaceae*).

GERANIALES (**Geraniaceae, Oxalidaceae, Tropaeolaceae,** and **Balsaminaceae**), rather remotely related to the *Ranunculaceae*, are, in this system, regarded as the basic group for **Boraginaceae** (BORAGINALES), leading finally to **Labiatae,** noted for their secretion of oil used in perfumery; lavender oil, *Lavandula officinalis* (*vera*), patchouli, *Pogostemon heyneanus*, peppermint, *Mentha piperita*, thyme, *Thymus vulgaris*, marjoram, *Origanum marjorana*, sage, *Salvia officinalis*. *Labiatae* is regarded as the highest family in the Dicotyledons, and as showing more or less parallel floral structure with *Verbenaceae, Scrophulariaceae,* and *Acanthaceae.*

MONOCOTYLEDONES

(FOR CLASSIFICATION SEE VOL. II)

A few families of Monocotyledons show a close relationship with Dicotyledons, especially the flowering rush family, **Butomaceae,** and the Alisma family, **Alismataceae.** These are very similar in the general structure of their flowers and fruit to the buttercup family, *Ranunculaceae,* the carpels being completely free in both groups.

This system for the Monocotyledons begins, therefore, with these families in which in addition, as in most Dicotyledons, there is a *distinct calyx and corolla.* The grasses, *Gramineae,* are placed last, as they are in the Bentham and Hooker system, though not in the German system of Engler and Prantl, which begins with them.

Three main groups are recognized: (1) CALYCIFERAE (calyx-bearers), with a distinct (usually green) calyx and corolla; (2) COROLLIFERAE, in which these are more or less similar; and (3) GLUMIFLORAE, in which the perianth is much reduced or represented by lodicules, as in the grasses. The first group begins with **Butomaceae** and ends with bromeliads (**Bromeliaceae**), in some of which the stamens are reduced to *one* as in orchids. The second group starts with **Liliaceae** and ends with orchids, and the third begins with **Juncaceae** and the climax family is **Gramineae**. The grasses are wind-pollinated, a condition correlated with extreme reduction in the flowers, which are arranged in very specialized inflorescences.

The flowering rush family, **Butomaceae** (BUTOMALES), has several characters considered to be primitive. The sepals and petals are in two distinct whorls, and the free carpels have several ovules which are scattered over the inner surface, and not confined to special placentas. They thus resemble the family *Cabombaceae* in the Dicotyledons. Related is the frogbit family, **Hydrocharitaceae**, with an inferior ovary.

Alismataceae (ALISMATALES) have numerous free carpels, usually with only one ovule and much resembling the carpels of *Ranunculaceae*. One member, *Ranalisma*, as may be inferred from the name, combines the characteristics and appearances of *Ranunculus* and *Alisma*.

Most of these early or apparently primitive families favour wet or aquatic habitats, and derivatives, such as **Juncaginaceae** and **Posidoniaceae**, are still more aquatic, and even marine, whilst a few are saprophytic, like **Triuridaceae**.

Another family probably derived from the same stock is **Aponogetonaceae**, represented by one genus, *Aponogeton*, nearly confined to the Southern Hemisphere. The water uintje of South Africa, *Aponogeton distachyon*, is cultivated in ponds in Europe and N. America. A related marine family is **Zosteraceae**, which includes the grass wrack or eel grass, *Zostera marina*, the dried leaves of which are used for packing and for stuffing mattresses. The flowers are unisexual, and represent a complete climax in reduction, the male to a single anther, the female to one carpel. The pondweeds, **Potamogetonaceae**, belong to the same group of related aquatic families. In *Potamogeton* pollination is effected by the wind when the flower-spikes are pushed above the water. It is clear that the last-mentioned families represent climax types in evolution, like the wind-pollinated trees in the Dicotyledons already mentioned.

Commelinaceae (COMMELINALES) is a large family with very distinct calyx and corolla, and most of them have retained 6 stamens. A common garden example is the Virginian spiderwort, *Tradescantia virginiana*. This family is most abundant in the tropics and is moisture-loving. The leaves are rather grasslike, and have always a basal membranous closed sheath, which sometimes embraces the flower-cluster so closely that the latter bursts a hole through it.

Related to but more advanced than the *Commelinaceae* are three small families which may be regarded as the 'Compositae' of the Monocotyledons. One of them is the pipewort family, **Eriocaulaceae**, in which the inner perianth segments are united, and the flowers are unisexual. The single British example, *Eriocaulon septangulare*, is of exceptional interest because it is found only on the coasts of the islands to the west of Scotland and on the west coast of Ireland, and also in N. America. **Xyridaceae** and **Rapateaceae** are tropical families of the same affinity, some of the latter greatly resembling certain *Cyperaceae*.

In all the families of Monocotyledons mentioned so far the ovary is *superior*, i.e. above the sepals, petals, and stamens. In the next group, however, the ovary is often *inferior*, a more advanced feature. This group includes the large pine-apple family, **Bromeliaceae**, and many are epiphytic and a few of economic importance, such as the pine-apple, *Ananas sativus*; silk grass or pita fibre is *Bromelia magdalenae*. This family is found only in Tropical and Subtropical America, with the exception of one species, *Pitcairnia feliciana*, discovered in recent years in French Guinea, West Africa.

The climax development in this line of descent, in which the flowers have retained a separate calyx and corolla, is reached in ZINGIBERALES, to which belong the ginger family, **Zingiberaceae**, the banana family, **Musaceae**, the canna family, **Cannaceae**, and the arrowroot family, **Marantaceae**. This group has been regarded as the prototype of, or at any rate related to, the orchids, but in this system it is considered to be a parallel group, in most advanced members the stamens being reduced to one, as in many orchids. As in grasses the leaf-sheath is usually provided with a ligule, a feature absent from orchids. In many the abortive stamens are transformed into petaloid staminodes; the ovary is always inferior. The remarkable flower, *Strelitzia*, a native of South Africa, and the striking travellers' tree of Madagascar, *Ravenala*, belong to the family **Strelitziaceae**, a member of this group. The banana and plantain are the fruits of *Musa* spp. (**Musaceae**), and manila hemp is prepared from *Musa textilis*.

The basic and principal family of the second group of Monocotyledons, in which the two whorls of perianth-leaves are more or less alike, petaloid, and often merged into one whorl, is **Liliaceae**. Some of these have an underground rootstock (rhizome) but many have developed a newer form of root system, the bulb. Those with the ordinary rootstock include the Aloe and Asparagus; lily of the valley, *Convallaria majalis*; and solomon's seal, *Polygonatum multiflorum*. In this group the *Aspidistra* tribe is of great interest, as it shows a close relationship with the arum family, **Araceae**, *Liliaceae* with a corm or bulbous rootstock are better adapted for life in drier regions such as the Mediterranean and certain parts of South Africa, where they are very abundant. The lily, *Lilium*, tulip, *Tulipa*, bluebell, *Scilla*, and the meadow saffron, *Colchicum*, are familiar genera of this group.

All *Liliaceae* have a superior ovary and the flowers are never arranged in umbels as they are in the more advanced amaryllis family, **Amaryllidaceae**, in which the ovary is mostly inferior (below the perianth and stamens). On account of its umbellate inflorescence, the onion tribe, *Allieae*, is moved from *Liliaceae* and placed, in this system, in the *Amaryllidaceae*.

The aroid family, **Araceae**, represents a remarkable development among Monocotyledons, and there is scarcely a parallel amongst the Dicotyledons with the exception of *Piperaceae*. In the whole family the minute flowers are arranged on a fleshy axis, the spadix, more or less enclosed in a large bract, the spathe. That the latter is nothing more than a modified leaf is shown clearly in the skunk cabbage, *Lysichitum*, a favourite bog plant in British gardens. In this the stalk of the spathe is only loosely wrapped around the stalk of the spadix, and the spathe is clearly just a leaf very slightly modified.

A well-known greenhouse plant of this family is the lily of the Nile, *Zantedeschia aethiopica*. A common example is *Arum maculatum*. Another remarkable plant is the water soldier *Pistia stratiotes*, which floats on the top of waters in the tropics, and forms the 'sudd' which clogs up the waterways in the Nile region. A giant species, *Amorphophallus titanum*, is found in Sumatra, with a spadix up to 6 ft. high, encircled by a spathe beautifully mottled with green and lined with purple. Related are **Sparganiaceae** and the reedmace family, **Typhaceae**.

The amaryllis family, **Amaryllidaceae**, is clearly derived from the same stock as *Liliaceae*, and the writer has transferred to it the onion tribe, *Allieae*, from *Liliaceae*. The rootstock is a bulb, and the inflorescence an umbel subtended by a spathe-like bract or bracts; except in tribes *Allieae* and *Agapantheae*, the ovary is *inferior*. Few are of any economic use except the onion and leek, but most are very ornamental, such as the lovely belladonna lily, *Amaryllis belladonna*, a native of South Africa, and the numerous species and hybrids of *Hippeastrum* in Tropical America.

In both the lily and amaryllis families there are always 6 stamens, but in the iris family, **Iridaceae**, the number is reduced to 3. The rootstock is usually a corm, and the ovary is inferior. Again there are many lovely garden plants, such as *Iris*, *Gladiolus*, *Freesia*, and *Crocus*, and saffron dye is obtained from the stigmas of *Crocus sativus*. Orris root, *Iris* spp., is used as a perfume and dentifrice.

The yam family, **Dioscoreaceae**, is a climbing relative of *Liliaceae*. The leaves are mostly broad with net-veins as in Dicotyledons. The black bryony, *Tamus communis*, belongs here, and a remarkable example is the elephant's foot, *Testudinaria elephantipes*, which has a large woody base, slender annual climbing stems, and it grows in dry regions in southeast Africa.

Next come one or two families which are intermediate in growth-form and lead up to the palms. These are the **Xanthorrhoeaceae** and the agave family, **Agavaceae**, formerly placed in the *Amaryllidaceae*. To the latter belong the dragon tree of the Canary Islands, *Dracaena draco*, and several valuable fibre plants such as New Zealand hemp, *Phormium tenax*, and sisal hemp, *Agave sisalana* and *A. amaniensis*, the last being cultivated in East Africa.

The palms, **Palmae**, represent a complete climax development and are widely distributed in the tropics. It is mainly due to them that the vegetation of warmer regions looks so different from that of cooler zones, and they include the only monocotyledonous trees, which are often branched. The flowers are very small and inconspicuous and are bunched into large inflorescences. The family is of considerable economic importance, especially for its fibres. To this family belong the coco-nut, *Cocos nucifera*, the date palm, *Phoenix dactylifera*, and the oil palm, *Elaeis guineensis*.

Following the palms is the screw pine family, **Pandanaceae**, which in Engler's system occupies a very lowly place, but is here regarded as being very highly advanced. The stems often have aerial stilt roots, and the small unisexual flowers are crowded into dense inflorescences enclosed by large spathe-like bracts. They grow mainly in oceanic islands in the tropics and subtropics.

Related to the amaryllis family, and forming something of a connecting link with the orchids is the haemodorum family, **Haemodoraceae**. They grow mostly in the Southern Hemisphere, where Monocotyledons are especially numerous; the ovary is inferior. In one interesting family, **Apostasiaceae**, the stamens are reduced to 3 or even 2 as they are in the more primitive members of the orchid family.

The peak or climax of floral structure in the petaloid Monocotyledons is reached in the orchid family, **Orchidaceae.** Some of these grow in the ground, but many are epiphytic and there are a few saprophytes. The perianth-segments are in two whorls, and are usually petal-like, often very much modified and forming a zygomorphic flower with a great range of form and colour. The stamens are reduced to 2 or 1, and the pollen, from granular in the more primitive group, becomes waxy and in masses in the more advanced. The ovary is inferior, often twisted, and the seeds are very numerous and minute.

There remain now only a few families of Monocotyledons, which together comprise the third group, the GLUMIFLORAE. These are the rush family, **Juncaceae,** the restio family, **Restiaceae,** and the sedge, **Cyperaceae,** and grass, **Gramineae,** families. All except the *Restiaceae*, found mainly in the Southern Hemisphere, are of world-wide distribution. The *Gramineae*, especially, are the most highly evolved as they are the most successful of Monocotyledons, and their much-reduced flowers have reverted to wind-pollination, as those people who suffer from hay fever know to their embarrassment.

Juncaceae seem to be reduced forms derived directly from the liliaceous stock. In this family there is still retained a small perianth of 6 parts, though it is dry and calyx-like. Common examples are the rushes, *Juncus* spp., and the field woodrush, *Luzula campestris.* A striking sub-arborescent kind is *Prionium serratum*, a native of South Africa.

Closely related to *Juncaceae* are the **Restiaceae**, a family which shows a close relationship between the floras of South Africa, Madagascar, Australasia, and Chile, though there is only one species in Madagascar.

The sedge family, **Cyperaceae,** includes grasslike plants with three-sided (triquetrous), solid stems (culms), a closed leaf-sheath, and without a ligule such as is characteristic of grasses. They grow mostly in marshy places, often in soils too acid for grasses, especially in arctic regions where they form about one-tenth of the flora. The family is classified into two groups, one more primitive than the other, with bisexual flowers, the second with unisexual flowers. These are arranged in heads or small spikes and are solitary within glume-like bracts, the latter spirally arranged or in 2 rows. The perianth is reduced to scales or bristles or is absent, though in one apparently very primitive genus, *Oreobolus*, found in the Antarctic and the Andes, there are retained 6 distinct perianth-segments, thus linking up the family with *Juncaceae.* The tubers of *Cyperus esculentus* are edible, and the stems and leaves of many kinds are used for making mats. In ancient times the papyrus, *Cyperus papyrus*, served as paper. Cotton-grass is *Eriophorum vaginatum.*

The grass family, **Gramineae,** rivals the orchids for second place in size after *Compositae.* They are here regarded as the most highly evolved and successful of all plant families, for they grow where other vegetation is almost non-existent. The much-reduced flowers are pollinated by the wind, and grass pollen is the chief cause of hay fever in many countries. Grasses are easily distinguished from sedges by their cylindrical jointed stems (culms), closed at the nodes but hollow between them; and at the junction of the leaf-sheath and blade there is usually a membranous or hairy outgrowth, the ligule.

Probably the most primitive tribe is that to which the bamboo belongs, the *Bambuseae*, some of which are woody. In one sub-tribe of this group there are still retained 6 stamens as in most other Monocotyledons. In most other grasses the stamens are reduced to 3.

Besides being of great importance as food and fodder, grasses are very useful in other ways. The genus *Spartina* has been instrumental in reclaiming salt marshes in southern England and elsewhere, and others are planted as sand-binders, such as the marram-grass, *Ammophila arenaria*. The most important food grasses are wheat, *Triticum*, barley, *Hordeum*, oats, *Avena*, rice, *Oryza*, and maize or Indian corn, *Zea mays*. The canary grass, *Phalaris canariensis*, is grown for the seed, which is used for feeding cage-birds. The sweet vernal grass, *Anthoxanthum odoratum*, is fragrant and gives a pleasant scent to hay. Some grasses are very troublesome weeds, such as couch-grass, *Agropyron repens*.

BIBLIOGRAPHY FOR STUDENTS

A FEW months before my first volume of this work was published in 1926, the late A. B. Rendle's *Classification of Flowering Plants,* vol. ii, appeared (Cambridge University Press, 1925). This contained an abridged account of the Dicotyledons arranged according to the Engler and Prantl system. That system has more recently been followed by G. H. M. Lawrence in his book *Taxonomy of Vascular Plants* (Macmillan Co., New York, 1951), and students should consult it, especially for the *bibliography* given for each family.

In addition students also have the advantage of another book, *Families of Dicotyledons* by Gunderson (Chronica Botanica Co., 1950).

Rendle's first volume dealing with Gymnosperms and Monocotyledons was published as long ago as 1904.

Other books of primary importance to taxonomists and students of phylogeny are the following:

C. ERDTMAN, *An Introduction to Pollen Analysis* (Chronica Botanica Co., 1943).
—— *Pollen Morphology and Plant Taxonomy, Angiosperms* (Chronica Botanica Co., 1952).
C. R. METCALFE and L. CHALK, *Anatomy of Dicotyledons* (Clarendon Press, Oxford, 1950).
C. D. DARLINGTON and JANAKI-AMMAL, *Chromosome Atlas of Cultivated Plants* (George Allen & Unwin Ltd., 1945); 2nd edn. DARLINGTON AND A. P. WYLIE (1955).
—— *Chromosome Botany* (George Allen & Unwin Ltd., 1956).
R. GOOD, *Geography of Flowering Plants* (Longmans, Green & Co., 1947); 2nd edn. (1953).
—— *Features of Evolution in the Flowering Plants* (Longmans, Green & Co., 1956).
J. HUTCHINSON, *A Botanist in Southern Africa* (Gawthorn, 1946).
—— *British Flowering Plants* (Gawthorn, 1948).

LIST OF FAMILIES
WITH CERTAIN MORE OR LESS
CONSTANT CHARACTERS

SOMETIMES a botanist is faced with the determination of imperfect material consisting perhaps of leaves only. As a help in the identification of such specimens, which can often be best brought about by a process of exclusion, I give below some lists of families in which certain macroscopic characters are constant or predominant.

Leaves. Opposite (or verticillate) leaves constant

Families with *constantly opposite* (or verticillate) leaves:
Aceraceae. Antoniaceae. Batidaceae. Buddleiaceae.[1] Calycanthaceae. Caprifoliaceae. Caryophyllaceae. Casuarinaceae. Ceratophyllaceae. Chloranthaceae. Clusiaceae. Columelliaceae. Coriariaceae. Cunoniaceae. Dipsacaceae. Elatinaceae. Eucryphiaceae. Frankeniaceae. Gomortegaceae. Grubbiaceae. Hydrangeaceae. Hypericaceae. Labiatae. Loganiaceae. Melastomaceae. Penaeaceae. Phrymaceae. Plocospermaceae. Potaliaceae. Quiinaceae. Rubiaceae. Salvadoraceae. Spigeliaceae. Staphyleaceae. Stilbeaceae. Strychnaceae. Valerianaceae.

Leaves. Opposite (or verticillate) leaves predominant

Families in which *opposite* (or verticillate) leaves are *predominant*:
Acanthaceae. Apocynaceae. Asclepiadaceae. Bignoniaceae. Chloanthaceae. Cistaceae. Ficoidaceae. Gentianaceae. Illecebraceae. Loranthaceae. Lythraceae. Malpighiaceae. Martyniaceae. Molluginaceae. Monimiaceae. Myrtaceae. Nyctaginaceae. Oleaceae. Pedaliaceae. Periplocaceae. Rhizophoraceae. Rutaceae. Santalaceae. Scrophulariaceae.

Leaves. Compound leaves constant

Families with *constantly compound* (sometimes 1-foliolate) *leaves*:
Caryocaraceae. Connaraceae. Juglandaceae. Lardizabalaceae. Lepidobotryaceae. Melianthaceae. Moringaceae. Oxalidaceae. Sapindaceae. Tovariaceae.

Leaves. Compound leaves predominant

Families in which *compound leaves* are *predominant*:
Ampelidaceae. Araliaceae. Bignoniaceae. Burseraceae. Caesalpiniaceae. Meliaceae. Mimosaceae. Papilionaceae. Rosaceae. Rutaceae. Simaroubaceae. Umbelliferae. Valerianaceae. Zygophyllaceae.

Leaves. Leaves sometimes compound

Families in which compound leaves sometimes occur (those marked with an * rather frequently):

[1] Except *Buddleia alternifolia*.

Aceraceae. Berberidaceae. Bombacaceae.* Capparidaceae. Caprifoliaceae. Convolvulaceae. Crassulaceae. Cucurbitaceae. Dipsacaceae.* Euphorbiaceae. Geraniaceae. Hydrophyllaceae. Menispermaceae. Menyanthaceae. Oleaceae. Passifloraceae. Polemoniaceae. Proteaceae.* Ranunculaceae. Sabiaceae. Saxifragaceae.* Staphyleaceae.* Sterculiaceae. Verbenaceae.

Stipules. Leaves always stipulate

Stipules are *constant* in the following families:
Begoniaceae. Caesalpiniaceae. Chailletiaceae. Chloranthaceae. Cunoniaceae. Dipterocarpaceae. Droseraceae. Elatinaceae. Eucryphiaceae. Irvingiaceae. Magnoliaceae. Malvaceae. Mimosaceae. Ochnaceae. Papilionaceae. Polygonaceae. Resedaceae. Rhamnaceae. Rubiaceae. Zygophyllaceae.

Stipules. Leaves mostly stipulate

Families in which the leaves are *mostly stipulate*:
Araliaceae. Chlaenaceae. Hamamelidaceae. Linaceae. Molluginaceae. Moringaceae. Portulacaceae. Quiinaceae. Rhizophoraceae. Rosaceae. Sterculiaceae. Vitaceae.

Glandular leaves

Families in which glandular or pellucid dots occur or sometimes occur in the leaves:[1]
Acanthaceae. Aegicerataceae. Alangiaceae. Anacardiaceae. Annonaceae. Balsaminaceae. Bixaceae. Burseraceae. Cochlospermaceae. Calycanthaceae. Canellaceae. Capparidaceae. Chloranthaceae. Clusiaceae. Combretaceae. Compositae. Cornaceae. Crassulaceae. Dilleniaceae. Euphorbiaceae. Fagaceae. Flacourtiaceae. Geraniaceae. Hypericaceae. Lacistemaceae. Lauraceae. Lythraceae. Magnoliaceae. Meliaceae. Monimiaceae. Myoporaceae. Myricaceae. Myristicaceae. Myrsinaceae. Myrtaceae. Nymphaeaceae. Nyssaceae. Olacaceae. Phytolaccaceae. Piperaceae. Polygalaceae. Polygonaceae. Portulacaceae. Primulaceae. Rhamnaceae. Rubiaceae. Rutaceae. Sabiaceae. Samydaceae. Santalaceae. Sapindaceae. Saxifragaceae. Simaroubaceae. Theaceae. Theophrastaceae. Thymelaeaceae. Tropaeolaceae. Urticaceae. Verbenaceae. Violaceae. Vitaceae.

Stamens opposite the petals

Families in which the stamens are the same number as and *opposite* the petals:
Ampelidaceae. Berberidaceae. Corynocarpaceae. Ebenaceae. Heteropyxidaceae. Lardizabalaceae. Menispermaceae (some). Myrsinaceae. Nandinaceae. Olacaceae (some). Plumbaginaceae. Portulacaceae (some). Primulaceae. Rhamnaceae. Sabiaceae.[2] Sapotaceae. Sterculiaceae (some).

Inferior ovary.

Families in which the ovary is *inferior*:
Alangiaceae. Araliaceae. Balanophoraceae. Begoniaceae. Bruniaceae

---

[1] This list is taken from Blenk, in *Flora*, 1884: 385.
[2] In this family sometimes some anthers are aborted.

(most). Cactaceae. Calyceraceae. Caprifoliaceae. Chloranthaceae. Columelliaceae. Combretaceae. Compositae. Cornaceae. Cucurbitaceae. Cytinaceae. Datiscaceae. Dipsacaceae. Elaeagnaceae. Ficoidaceae (some). Gesneriaceae (some). Goodeniaceae. Grossulariaceae. Grubbiaceae. Haloragidaceae. Hamamelidaceae. Juglandaceae. Loasaceae. Lobeliaceae. Loranthaceae. Melastomaceae (most). Myrsinaceae (few). Myrtaceae (most). Nymphaeaceae (some). Nyssaceae. Oliniaceae. Onagraceae. Portulacaceae (few). Punicaceae. Rhizophoraceae (many). Rosaceae (some). Rubiaceae. Santalaceae. Saxifragaceae (some). Stylidiaceae. Styracaceae. Umbelliferae. Vacciniaceae. Valerianaceae.

KEY TO THE
FAMILIES OF DICOTYLEDONES

Up to the middle of last century, and even later, the practice of determining plants by means of a *key* was very much discouraged as tending to superficial observation. Thus no analytical keys are to be found in de Candolle's *Prodromus*, which through lack of them failed to fulfil the purpose for which it was intended. In those days once the name of a plant was ascertained nothing more was thought to be required. But we have come to realize that to identify a plant is but a means to an end, and not the end itself. Botanists now want to know something more than the mere name, something about its habitat, its distribution, its structure and affinities from a phylogenetic point of view, and so on; and although the old method of wading through innumerable descriptions may have conduced to accurate and painstaking observation, many mistakes were no doubt made for want of a good analytical key.

As time went on the known species became more numerous and confusing, and a compromise appeared in the shape of the *conspectus*. In most floristic works the conspectus is all that is provided for the determination of the family. But if the family is not easily ascertainable, then it is not possible to determine the genus, and least of all the species. It seems highly desirable, therefore, that a floristic work should now be prefaced by a key based on macroscopic and easily observed characters.

The following is an attempt in this direction. Like most keys it will not prove infallible, but it will achieve its purpose if it brings to the student that preliminary knowledge of the families of flowering plants which is so necessary for work in the field, the garden, the herbarium, or the laboratory.

HINTS FOR USING THE KEY TO THE BEST ADVANTAGE

Do not start to use the key before you have examined your plant thoroughly. If you do you may easily go wrong. Make out (1) whether the carpels are *free* from each other or *united*; (2) if united, then make quite sure whether the ovules are on the *walls* (parietal placentation) or at the *apex*, *base*, or *centre* of the ovary (apical, basal, and central placentation respectively). Then note the number of stamens, and if few, whether *opposite to* or *alternate with* the petals. Then see whether there are *stipules*. The stipules may have fallen off; if so, you will be able to detect a *scar*, and then the leaves *are* stipulate. You must use a lens for these characters, and a razor or sharp pen-knife for the ovary.

Do not be afraid to cut a section of the ovary to see the arrangement of the ovules; in any case, with this key, you need not trouble whether the ovule is *anatropous*, *orthotropous*, or *campylotropous*, or whether it has one or two coats, which is something to be thankful for.

Do not, in using this key, read only the paragraph which seems to fit the plant you wish to determine. You will be much more sure if you read also the contrasting paragraph further on. Do not always blame the key if you cannot arrive at the family readily. You may have misread it, or your own observation may be at fault.

KEY TO THE ARTIFICIAL GROUPS[1]

Gynoecium (pistil) composed of 2 or more *separate* or nearly
    quite separate carpels with *separate styles* and stigmas
    (rarely the free carpels immersed in the expanded torus
    (*Nymphaeaceae*) or enclosed by a large disk . . 'APOCARPAE'

Petals present, free from each other, sometimes consider-
    ably modified . . . . Group 1 (p. 41)
Petals present, more or less united . . . . Group 2 (p. 45)
Petals absent . . . . Group 3 (p. 45)

Gynoecium (pistil) composed of 1 carpel or of 2 or more
    united carpels with free or united styles, or if carpels
    free below, then the styles or stigmas united . . 'SYNCARPAE'

Ovules attached to the wall or walls of the ovary . . 'PARIETALES'

Ovary superior:
    Petals present, free from each other . . . . Group 4 (p. 47)
    Petals present, more or less united . . . Group 5 (p. 52)
    Petals absent . . . . Group 6 (p. 54)

Ovary inferior or semi-inferior:
    Petals present, free from each other . . . . Group 7 (p. 55)
    Petals present, more or less united . . . Group 8 (p. 56)
    Petals absent . . . . . . Group 9 (p. 57)

Ovules attached to the central axis or to the base or apex
    of the ovary . . . . 'AXILES'

Ovary superior:
    Petals present, free from each other . . . . Group 10 (p. 58)
    Petals present, more or less united . . . Group 11 (p. 75)
    Petals absent . . . . . . Group 12 (p. 83)

Ovary inferior:
    Petals present, free from each other . . . . Group 13 (p. 92)
    Petals present, more or less united . . . Group 14 (p. 96)
    Petals absent . . . . . . Group 15 (p. 99)

[1] The names used for these groups are applied here for convenience. The 'Parietales'
in this sense are not the *Parietales* of either Bentham and Hooker or of Engler. The student
should on no account mistake this artificial grouping for the new system of classification
proposed in this work, the conspectus and sequence of which appears on p. 104.

GROUP I

Two or more free carpels; petals present, free from each other

Leaves opposite or verticillate (never all radical) (to p. 42):
  Stamens numerous (15 or more):
  Stamens arranged all to one side of the flower; seeds arillate; trailing or
      climbing shrubs   *Dilleniaceae*
  Stamens arranged symmetrically around the carpels:
    Leaves stipulate; fruits follicular or indehiscent, sometimes arranged on a
        large fleshy torus; style often lateral or basal
            Rosaceae; see also *Cunoniaceae* (part) and *Austrobaileyaceae*
    Leaves without stipules:
    Herbs or succulents, sometimes slightly woody only at the base:
      Carpels more or less free from the beginning; leaves often fleshy and
          connate at the base; flowers usually 5-merous   *Crassulaceae*
      Carpels connivent at first, then free and torulose; lower leaves alternate,
          not fleshy; sepals 3; petals 6   *Papaveraceae*
    Trees, shrubs, or woody climbers:
      Receptacle more or less campanulate or deeply concave; no tendrils:
      Anthers opening by valves or slits; carpels at or towards the base of a
          hollow receptacle; seeds with endosperm; mainly tropical
                                                                Monimiaceae
      Anthers opening by slits; sepals and petals in several series; carpels
          numerous, lining the hollow receptacle; seeds without endosperm;
          temperate regions   *Calycanthaceae*
      Receptacle neither hollow nor concave; petals numerous, linear; anthers
          opening by longitudinal slits; petiole acting as a tendril
                                                               Ranunculaceae
  Stamens up to 15 in number:
  Herbs, often succulent; leaves mostly connate at the base, exstipulate;
      flowers often cymose; carpels the same number as the petals; seeds
      minute, with fleshy endosperm   *Crassulaceae*
  Trees, shrubs, or woody climbers:
    Carpels inserted at or near the base of a hollow receptacle (calyx-tube); an-
        thers opening by valves or slits; seeds with endosperm *Monimiaceae*
    Carpels inserted on a more or less convex or slightly concave torus:
    Carpels 3–7; flowers large; petals yellow, not clawed, inserted at the base
        of a fleshy torus; stipules paired, axillary; anthers opening by short
        or long pores   *Ochnaceae*
    Carpels 5–10; petals persistent and thickened after flowering; shrubs
        with angular branchlets; stipules absent; flowers small, green;
        anthers large, opening by slits   *Coriariaceae*
    Carpels 1–3; petals often clawed, thin, not thickened after flowering;
        stipules mostly intrapetiolar, often connate at the base; sepals often
        biglandular at the base, anthers opening by slits   *Malpighiaceae*
    Carpels 2; petals not clawed, scarious; flowers in axillary heads; calyx
        not glandular; stipules caducous; anthers with slits   *Cunoniaceae*

Leaves alternate or all radical:

Leaves stipulate, sometimes the stipules minute or adnate to the petiole, or enclosing the young buds:

Carpels numerous, spirally arranged on a somewhat elongated receptacle; sepals often 3 or indistinguishable from the 6 or more petals; flowers solitary, mostly large and conspicuous; seeds with copious endosperm and minute embryo; trees or shrubs *Magnoliaceae*

Carpels few or numerous on a small globose or hollow receptacle; sepals or calyx-lobes often 5, usually quite distinct from the petals:

Stamens free from one another or nearly so or shortly united into separate bundles; calyx imbricate or valvate:

Carpels completely immersed in the greatly enlarged disk which envelops them in fruit; stamens 5 *Capusiaceae*

Carpels not as above:

Herbs, more or less scapigerous, with mostly radical leaves; seeds not arillate; endosperm usually copious; sepals mostly imbricate *Saxifragaceae*

Habit various; seeds not arillate; fruits follicular or indehiscent, often achenes arranged on a large fleshy torus; endosperm absent or very scanty; sepals mostly imbricate *Rosaceae*

Trees, shrubs, or climbers, rarely herbs, with often scabrid prominently pinnately nerved leaves; stipules adnate to the petiole; seeds arillate, aril often laciniate; calyx imbricate, often hardened in fruit *Dilleniaceae*; see also *Austrobaileyaceae*

Trees with large leaves and with stellate hairs; seeds not arillate; endosperm copious; calyx valvate *Tiliaceae*

Stamens more or less united into a column; calyx valvate; hairs on the leaves often stellate or lepidote *Sterculiaceae*

Leaves without stipules:

Carpels completely sunk in the tissue of the large broad torus:

Aquatic plants with floating leaves; endosperm not ruminate *Nymphaeaceae*

Not aquatic; branched trees or shrubs; endosperm ruminate *Eupomatiaceae*

Carpels not sunk in the tissue of the torus or only very slightly so:

Stamens the same number as and opposite to the petals; carpels usually 3 or rarely numerous:

Leaves compound; petals smaller than the sepals, sometimes minute; fruit usually baccate; endosperm never ruminate:

Carpels few (up to 9), in whorls *Lardizabalaceae*

Carpels numerous, spirally arranged *Sargentodoxaceae*

Leaves simple; fruit drupaceous; endosperm sometimes ruminate *Menispermaceae*

Stamens alternate with the petals or monadelphous or more numerous (rarely fewer) than the petals:

Stamens numerous, more than 12, or more than double the number of petals (to p. 44)

Sepals and petals connate into a calyptra:

Styles connate into a mass; endosperm ruminate; carpels sunk in the
  torus   *Eupomatiaceae*
Styles free; seeds not arillate; endosperm smooth; carpels sessile, not
  sunk in the torus:
  Indumentum not lepidote; leaves often gland-dotted; carpels remain-
    ing free in fruit   *Winteraceae*
  Indumentum lepidote; carpels concrescent in fruit *Himantandraceae*
Styles free; seeds covered with a multifid aril; carpels on a short
  common stipe; leaves neither gland-dotted nor lepidote
                                                   Crossosomataceae
Sepals and petals not connate into a calyptra; styles free or rarely
  slightly connivent at the base:
Sepals and petals in 3 distinct series (3+3+3), rarely in 2 series:
  Anthers usually with a broad truncate connective; flowers usually
    bisexual; seed with copious ruminate endosperm and minute
    embryo; trees, shrubs, or woody climbers   *Annonaceae*
  Anthers with a narrow connective; flowers dioecious *Menispermaceae*
Sepals and petals in 2 series or rarely the sepals gradually passing into
  the petals, usually in fours or fives, or rarely the petals numerous;
  endosperm not ruminate:
Herbs, sometimes rather woody at the base:
  Carpels in a single whorl and elevated on a stipe-like torus; petals 3
    or more times divided   *Resedaceae*
  Carpels not elevated on the torus, usually spirally arranged; petals
    entire, bifid, or tubular:
    Carpels free from the beginning; sepals and petals usually 5 each
      or the latter more numerous; flowers actinomorphic or zygo-
      morphic; rarely aquatics; fruit an achene, follicle, or rarely a
      berry:
      Disk present; stamens centrifugal, numerous; seeds arillate
                                                     Paeoniaceae
      Disk absent; stamens centripetal; seeds not arillate:
      Carpels with more than 1 ovule; fruits follicular or baccate
                                                     Helleboraceae
      Carpels with 1 ovule; fruit a bunch of dry achenes, rarely berry-
        like   *Ranunculaceae*
    Carpels free from the beginning; sepals and petals 3 each; flowers
      actinomorphic; aquatic herbs with peltate floating leaves
                                                     Cabombaceae
    Carpels at first connivent, at length free and torulose; sepals 3;
      petals 6; flowers actinomorphic; not aquatics *Papaveraceae*
Trees, shrubs, or woody climbers:
  Petals and stamens hypogynous:
  Flowers bisexual or very rarely polygamous:
    Calyx imbricate:
    Leaves aromatic, pellucid-punctate; sepals deciduous; seeds not
      arillate; petals numerous   *Illiciaceae*
    Leaves not aromatic; lateral nerves prominent and parallel;

sepals persistent and often accrescent; seeds often arillate

Dilleniaceae

Calyx valvate:

Trees covered with scales (lepidote); flowers with subulate staminodes; connective of anthers petaloid   *Himantandraceae*

Trees and shrubs without scales but sometimes with stellate
hairs; connective rarely petaloid:

Endosperm smooth   *Winteraceae*

Endosperm ruminate   *Annonaceae*

Flowers unisexual:

Leaves simple; seeds with copious endosperm and small embryo

Schisandraceae

Leaves pinnate or simple; seeds with or without endosperm and
fairly large embryo   *Simaroubaceae*

Petals and stamens perigynous:

Disk absent:

Endosperm present, fleshy; seeds arillate   *Crossosomataceae*

Endosperm absent; seeds not arillate   *Rosaceae*

Disk present, adnate to the inside of the calyx-tube; anthers often
opening by valves; leaves mostly pellucid-dotted; calyx-lobes
in 2 or more series; carpels arranged on the inside of the
hollow receptacle   *Monimiaceae*

Stamens 12 or fewer, or double the number of petals when more than 6:

Leaves gland-dotted:

Leaves simple; carpels in a spiral, mostly numerous; stamens more or
less united in a mass; fruiting carpellary axis elongated; flowers
solitary   *Schisandraceae*

Leaves often compound; carpels whorled; the axis in fruit not elongated; stamens more or less free from one another   *Rutaceae*

Leaves not gland-dotted:

Leaves compound:

Flowers unisexual or polygamous; carpels usually 3, rarely 6 or 9;
stamens often monadelphous   *Lardizabalaceae*

Flowers bisexual:

Herbs; seeds with copious endosperm and small embryo

Ranunculaceae

Herbs, shrubs or trees; seeds usually without endosperm:

Wood with resin ducts; seeds not arillate   *Anacardiaceae*

Wood without resin ducts; seeds often arillate   *Connaraceae*

Wood without resin ducts; seeds not arillate   *Rosaceae*

Leaves simple (sometimes the submerged ones of aquatics dissected):

Stamens free or slightly united at the base:

Flowers bisexual:

Shrubs or trees; seeds usually arillate:

Leaves reduced to scales; aril laciniate   *Dilleniaceae*

Leaves not reduced to scales; seeds not arillate; leaves pinnatisect;
carpels 5–10, with 2 ovules in the middle; stamens 5 or 10

Helleboraceae

Leaves not reduced to scales; aril entire, more or less cupular;
  carpels with 2 basal collateral ovules   *Connaraceae*
Leaves not reduced, not pinnatisect; no aril   *Anacardiaceae*
Herbs; seeds not arillate:
  Aquatics with peltate floating leaves   *Cabombaceae*
  Not aquatics:
    Carpels at the top of a gynophore   *Resedaceae*
    Carpels not on a gynophore, but sometimes on an elongated axis:
      Torus elongated or cone-like; annual herbs with entire leaves;
        carpels usually very numerous   *Ranunculaceae*
      Torus flat or concave; carpels few:
        Carpels the same number as the petals   *Crassulaceae*
        Carpels fewer than the petals   *Saxifragaceae*
Flowers unisexual, dioecious; petals and stamens in threes or multiples
  of 3   *Menispermaceae*
Stamens united into a column; flowers unisexual:
  Carpels numerous   *Schisandraceae*
  Carpels definite, often 3, rarely 6 or 9   *Menispermaceae*

GROUP 2

Two or more free carpels; petals present, more or less united

Leaves simple; flowers dioecious; seeds sometimes with ruminate endosperm,
  not arillate; fruit a drupe; mostly climbers with soft wood and broad
  medullary rays   *Menispermaceae*
Leaves usually pinnate or unifoliolate; flowers bisexual; seeds often arillate;
  fruit a capsule; trees, shrubs, or climbers   *Connaraceae*
Leaves 1–7-foliolate; flowers somewhat zygomorphic, bisexual; fruit a
  capsule; seeds not arillate; trees or shrubs; leaves often punctate
          Rutaceae
Leaves simple, opposite or scattered, often fleshy, not punctate; flowers actinomorphic, bisexual; fruits dehiscent; herbs or shrubs   *Crassulaceae*

GROUP 3

Two or more free carpels; petals absent

Trees, shrubs, or hard-wooded climbers; leaves simple or rarely compound;
  sepals not or rarely slightly petaloid:
  Leaves stipulate:
    Stamens free or slightly connate at the base:
      Calyx imbricate:
        Stipules free from or adnate to the petiole; fruits achenial or drupaceous,
          often included by the tubular calyx; disk usually present; flowers
          bisexual or polygamo-dioecious   *Rosaceae*
        Stipules laterally adnate to the petiole; fruits follicular; disk absent;
          flowers unisexual, dioecious   *Cercidiphyllaceae*

Stipules intrapetiolar, amplexicaul; fruits follicular; disk absent; flowers
unisexual, polygamo-monoecious *Lactoridaceae*
Calyx valvate:
Leaves alternate, simple, covered with stellate hairs; disk absent from
the flowers, the latter bisexual *Sterculiaceae*
Leaves opposite or verticillate, usually compound; disk present in the
flowers, the latter dioecious; male flowers with a rudimentary ovary
Brunelliaceae
Leaves opposite or verticillate, simple; male flowers without a rudimen-
tary ovary *Cunoniaceae*
Stamens united into a column; anthers in a ring or unequally arranged:
Sepals valvate; carpels not enclosed by the disk *Sterculiaceae*
Sepals imbricate; carpels numerous, enclosed by the enlarged fleshy disk
Scyphostegiaceae
Leaves exstipulate:
Leaves compound; stamens often 6 and monadelphous *Lardizabalaceae*
Leaves simple:
Seeds with ruminate endosperm; stamens numerous, mostly with broad
more or less truncate connective; carpels usually numerous, free in
fruit *Annonaceae*
Seeds sometimes with ruminate endosperm; stamens definite, often in threes
with narrow connective; carpels few, free; mostly climbers
Menispermaceae
Seeds with uniform endosperm; stamens usually with a narrow connective:
Stamens hypogynous:
Carpels in several series or in an irregular series, concrescent in fruit;
trees or shrubs with lepidote leaves *Himantandraceae*
Carpels mostly 3, free; woody climbers; not lepidote *Menispermaceae*
Carpels in a single series, free or nearly so in fruit; mostly herbs; not
lepidote *Phytolaccaceae*
Stamens more or less perigynous or on a widened or hollow receptacle:
Receptacle obscure and solid, bearing the stamens on its outside;
carpels in a single whorl, connate towards the base; anthers opening
lengthwise by slits *Trochodendraceae*
Receptacle more or less hollow, bearing the stamens on its inside;
anthers often opening by valves *Monimiaceae*
Herbs with radical or alternate leaves (or very soft-wooded climbers with
opposite leaves and broad medullary rays):
Carpels usually numerous, achenial and 1-seeded in fruit or follicular with
several seeds, often with long hairy tails; flowers mostly bisexual; sepals
usually petaloid, valvate or imbricate:
Carpels with more than 1 ovule *Helleboraceae*
Carpels with 1 ovule *Ranunculaceae*
Carpels mostly few; sepals not petaloid, sometimes rather scarious:
Flowers bisexual; stamens free amongst themselves; leaves alternate:
Carpels in a single whorl; sepals more or less free; style terminal or nearly
so:
Leaves not modified into pitchers *Phytolaccaceae*

Leaves modified into pitchers   *Cephalotaceae*
Carpels in more than 1 whorl; sepals free; style terminal or nearly so:
Carpels with more than 1 ovule   *Helleboraceae*
Carpels with 1 ovule   *Ranunculaceae*
Carpels 1–4; sepals united into a tube; style basal or lateral   *Rosaceae*
Carpels 1–4; sepals free; style absent; stigma terminal; small annual herb
                                                                  Circaeasteraceae
Flowers unisexual; sepals usually biseriately imbricate; stamens free or
      variously connate:
Climbers; carpels mostly 3 or 6   *Menispermaceae*
Low, often annual herbs; fruiting carpels 5   *Molluginaceae*

GROUP 4

*One carpel or more than one united carpels with parietal placentation;
ovary superior; petals present, free from each other*

Leaves opposite (to p. 48):
Stamens more or less united into three or more separate bundles; leaves
      often gland-dotted or with resin canals:
Mostly herbaceous or suffruticose; leaves often with pellucid dots; styles
      free or nearly so   *Hypericaceae*
Trees or shrubs; leaves with lines of resin canals and very numerous lateral
      nerves; stigma sessile or subsessile   *Clusiaceae*
Stamens free or more or less united at the base into not more than two
      separate bundles (diadelphous), sometimes adnate to a gynophore;
      leaves not or rarely glandular:
Connective of the anthers produced above the loculi; flowers often some-
      what zygomorphic (irregular), the lower petal often gibbous or saccate
      at the base   *Violaceae*
Connective of the anthers not produced; flowers usually actinomorphic
      (regular):
Stamens 6, tetradynamous; sepals 4; petals 4, often clawed; ovary of 2
      carpels   *Cruciferae*
Stamens not tetradynamous, often many:
  Stamens more than double the number of the petals:
    Ovary stipitate:
    Stamens hypogynous   *Capparidaceae*
    Stamens perigynous, inserted on the calyx-tube   *Lythraceae*
    Ovary sessile:
    Petals and stamens hypogynous:
      Sepals imbricate:
      Style or sessile stigma 1; indumentum when present often stellate;
            leaves not gland-dotted; petals fugacious   *Cistaceae*
      Styles or sessile stigmas 2 or more; leaves often gland-dotted
                                                                  Hypericaceae
      Sepals induplicate-valvate; leaves mostly subconnate at the base,
            often small and ericoid   *Frankeniaceae*

Petals and stamens perigynous; leaves not gland-dotted　*Flacourtiaceae*
Stamens the same as or double the number of the petals:
　Stamens and petals hypogynous; style 1, divided into as many stigmas
　　as placentas; no corona:
　　Leaves small, often more or less connate at the base; flowers usually
　　　sessile　　　　　　　　　　　　　　　　　　　　　　*Frankeniaceae*
　　Leaves not small, not connate at the base; flowers stalked
　　　　　　　　　　　　　　　　　　　　　　　　　　　Flacourtiaceae
　Stamens and petals more or less perigynous; no corona present:
　　Stamens not diadelphous; flowers actinomorphic:
　　　Styles free; seeds with endosperm; stamens erect in bud:
　　　　Herbs with fleshy exstipulate leaves; carpels as many as the petals
　　　　　　　　　　　　　　　　　　　　　　　　　　　Crassulaceae
　　　　Shrubs with deciduous bark and thin leaves; carpels fewer than the
　　　　　petals; no gynophore:
　　　　　Indumentum stellate　　　　　　　　　　　　*Philadelphaceae*
　　　　　Indumentum not stellate, or absent　　　　　　*Hydrangeaceae*
　　　　Mostly climbers with tendrils; leaves usually stipulate; ovary on a
　　　　　gynophore　　　　　　　　　　　　　　　　　*Passifloraceae*
　　　Styles united; seeds without endosperm; stamens often inflexed in
　　　　bud　　　　　　　　　　　　　　　　　　　　　　*Lythraceae*
　　Stamens diadelphous or monadelphous; flowers zygomorphic
　　　　　　　　　　　　　　　　　　　　　　　　　　　Papilionaceae
　Stamens hypogynous to perigynous; corona present; stamens adnate
　　to a gynophore　　　　　　　　　　　　　　　　　　*Passifloraceae*
Leaves alternate or all radical:
　Stamens numerous (more than 12) (to p. 50):
　　Filaments connate into a tube or column:
　　　Anthers free, small; petals often valvate; flowers mostly in heads or
　　　　dense spikes　　　　　　　　　　　　　　　　　*Mimosaceae*
　　　Anthers extrorse, adnate to the tube; glabrous aromatic trees; leaves
　　　　pellucid-punctate; flowers cymose　　　　　　　*Canellaceae*
　　Filaments connate into separate bundles:
　　　Bundles of filaments opposite the sepals　　　　　　*Tiliaceae*
　　　Bundles of filaments opposite the petals　　　　*Flacourtiaceae*
　　Filaments free or partially adnate to a gynophore, or shortly connate only
　　　at the base:
　　　Ovary supported on a gynophore　　　　　　　　*Capparidaceae*
　　　Ovary sessile or very nearly so:
　　　　Anthers horseshoe-shaped; ovary placentas 2; ovules numerous; stipules
　　　　　caducous, leaving a wide scar; leaves large; pedicels often with
　　　　　5 large glands below the sepals　　　　　　　　*Bixaceae*
　　　　Anthers straight or nearly so:
　　　　　Anthers opening by apical pores or short pore-like slits:
　　　　　　Seeds hairy; ovary entire; leaves digitately nerved or lobed
　　　　　　　　　　　　　　　　　　　　　　　　Cochlospermaceae
　　　　　　Seeds not hairy; ovary often deeply lobed, especially in fruit; leaves
　　　　　　　pinnately nerved　　　　　　　　　　　　　*Ochnaceae*

Anthers opening by longitudinal slits:
Flowers actinomorphic:
Fleshy plants, often spiny and with reduced or fleshy leaves; no
    stipules; stigmas often many   *Cactaceae*
Above characters not associated:
Stipules present, sometimes soon deciduous, free or adnate to the
    petiole:
Sepals contorted; petals very fugacious, often 4; placentas 3–5,
    parietal or adnate to the partially intrusive septa   *Cistaceae*
Sepals imbricate or valvate; petals often 5:
Corona absent:
Ovary of more than 1 carpel, i.e. with 2 or more placentas:
Petals and stamens hypogynous:
Leaves simple; sepals at length reflexed or deciduous
            Flacourtiaceae
Leaves mostly pinnate; sepals not or rarely reflexed, not
    deciduous   *Anacardiaceae*
Petals and stamens perigynous:
Sepals persistent, accrescent   *Flacourtiaceae*
Sepals not accrescent or only very slightly so   *Rosaceae*
Ovary of 1 carpel and with 1 placenta; stamens and petals hypo-
    gynous; sepals persistent, very imbricate   *Dilleniaceae*
Corona present   *Passifloraceae*
Stipules absent:
Trees, shrubs, or woody climbers:
Leaves simple:
Flowers mostly solitary; endosperm of seeds ruminate; stamens
    and petals hypogynous   *Annonaceae*
Flowers rarely solitary, sometimes spicate-racemose; endo-
    sperm smooth:
Ovary wholly superior:
Leaves rather small or very small; flowers often spicate or
    racemose   *Tamaricaceae*
Leaves rather large; flowers rarely spicate   *Flacourtiaceae*
Ovary semi-inferior   *Flacourtiaceae*
Leaves mostly bipinnate; petals valvate; calyx tubular, often
    valvate; flowers often in heads or spikes   *Mimosaceae*
Herbs:
Sepals more than 2; juice not milky:
Leaves ternately compound; sepals petaloid; carpel 1, baccate
    in fruit   *Helleboraceae*
Leaves pinnatisect; sepals not petaloid, 4; petals 4, clawed;
    ovary of 2 carpels   *Cruciferae* (Megacarpaea)
Sepals 2; juice milky; petals often 4, fugacious, not clawed;
    ovary of more than 1 carpel   *Papaveraceae*
Flowers zygomorphic:
Petals and stamens hypogynous; petals often considerably modified;
    ovary of 1 carpel   *Ranunculaceae*

Petals and stamens hypogynous or slightly perigynous; petals mostly laciniate; ovary of more than 1 carpel   *Resedaceae*
Petals and stamens perigynous or subperigynous; petals not laciniate:
  Fleshy plants with thick or reduced leaves; ovary of more than 1 carpel   *Cactaceae*
  Not fleshy; leaves not reduced; ovary of 1 carpel:
    Upper (adaxial) petal outermost   *Papilionaceae*
    Upper (adaxial) petal innermost   *Caesalpiniaceae*
Stamens 12 or fewer (from p. 48):
  Stamens 6, four long and two short (tetradynamous); sepals 4; petals 4; ovary of 2 carpels, often divided by a false septum   *Cruciferae*
  Stamens not as above, rarely 6:
   Flowers markedly zygomorphic:
    Stamens 4 or 6, opposite the petals, more or less united into 2 bundles; inflorescence often leaf-opposed   *Fumariaceae*
    Stamens with at least one row alternate with the petals:
      Fertile stamens about 2; ovary often supported on a short or long gynophore:
        Ovary of more than 1 carpel   *Capparidaceae*
        Ovary of 1 carpel (1 placenta); leaves usually pinnate *Caesalpiniaceae*
      Fertile stamens more than 2:
        Fleshy plants with numerous petals   *Cactaceae*
        Not fleshy:
          Herbs or rarely shrubs or trees; anthers often with produced connective, mostly connivent or connate around the style *Violaceae*
          Herbs, shrubs, or trees; anther-connective not produced or only glandular:
            Placentas 3; 5 fertile stamens, with the same number of staminodes   *Moringaceae*
            Placenta 1:
              Upper petal outermost; corolla of standard, wings, and keel (papilionaceous)   *Papilionaceae*
              Upper petal innermost; corolla not as above; anthers opening by slits   *Caesalpiniaceae*
              Petals imbricate; anthers opening by pores   *Polygalaceae*
   Flowers actinomorphic or nearly so:
    Parasitic leafless plants destitute of chlorophyll; anthers elongated, opening lengthwise by slits   *Monotropaceae*
    Not parasitic; leaves more or less green:
      Flowers with a distinct corona, this sometimes membranous or represented by a definite ring of hairs towards the base of the calyx-tube: ovary of more than 1 carpel:
       Styles connate or continuous at the base, or style 1:
        Ovary 1-locular; fruit opening loculicidally (if capsular)
                Passifloraceae
        Ovary imperfectly 5-locular; capsule opening septicidally; leaves sheathing at base   *Greyiaceae*

Styles widely separated at the base; calyx-tube long

Malesherbiaceae

Flowers without a corona:

Stamens completely united into a column with the anthers extrorse on the outside; leaves pellucid-punctate; endosperm not ruminate

Canellaceae

Stamens united, the anthers in a ring around the apex of the column; leaves not punctate; endosperm often ruminate

Menispermaceae

Stamens free or united only at the base or rarely only the anthers connivent:

Leaves stipulate:

Anthers with the connective produced above the loculi:

Anthers connivent around the style or subsessile   *Violaceae*

Anthers not connivent around the style   *Flacourtiaceae*

Anthers without a produced connective:

Staminodes present, sometimes petaloid; stipules sometimes pectinate   *Ochnaceae*

Staminodes absent:

Leaves with numerous very sticky gland-tipped hairs, mostly circinate in bud; seeds not carunculate   *Droseraceae*

Leaves without sticky hairs, not circinate; seeds often carunculate or arillate:

Styles free to the base   *Turneraceae*

Style single, shortly divided:

Mostly climbers with tendrils   *Passifloraceae*

Shrubs or trees without tendrils   *Flacourtiaceae*

Leaves exstipulate:

Stamens the same number as and opposite the petals:

Sepals and petals usually in threes; anthers mostly opening by valves:

Leaves 2–3 times pinnately compound, with swollen joints; erect shrubs   *Nandinaceae*

Leaves mostly all radical, peltate, palminerved or lobed or 2–3-foliolate; perennial herbs   *Podophyllaceae*

Leaves simple or pinnate, often with prickly margins; shrubs or shrublets with hard wood   *Berberidaceae*

Sepals and petals 2 and 4 respectively; flowers solitary or terminal or leaf-opposed; anthers opening by slits   *Fumariaceae*

Stamens with one row alternate with the petals:

Herbs:

Calyx-tube long; stamens usually perigynous   *Turneraceae*

Calyx-tube short; stamens hypogynous   *Parnassiaceae*

Trees, shrubs, or climbers:

Leaves simple, but sometimes deeply divided:

Leaves very small and more or less ericoid   *Tamaricaceae*

Leaves not small:

Leaves digitately lobed   *Caricaceae*

Leaves pinnately lobed or subdigitately nerved; calyx-tube
very short; stamens hypogynous:
No staminodes
Pittosporaceae; see also *Philadelphaceae (Dichroa)*
Ring of staminodes outside the stamens   *Greyiaceae*
Leaves pinnately nerved or lobed; calyx-tube long; stamens
mostly perigynous   *Turneraceae*
Leaves compound:
Flowers in heads or dense spikes; petals valvate; ovary of 1
carpel; ovules more than 1   *Mimosaceae*
Flowers not in heads or dense spikes; ovary usually of more
than 1 carpel; ovule solitary
Anacardiaceae; see also *Connaraceae* (in part)
Flowers racemose; ovary of 5 carpels with numerous ovules
Caricaceae

GROUP 5

One carpel or two or more united carpels with parietal placentation;
ovary superior; petals present, more or less united

Stamens free from the corolla-tube (to p. 53):
Ovary composed of more than one carpel:
Stamens numerous, more than twice the number of the corolla-lobes:
Anthers opening by a longitudinal slit, with broadened truncate con-
nective; seeds with copious ruminate endosperm; shrubs, trees, or
climbers with exstipulate simple leaves   *Annonaceae*
Anthers without a broadened connective; fleshy plants with reduced leaves
and often very spiny   *Cactaceae*
Anthers without a broadened connective; not fleshy; leaves coriaceous:
Flowers spicate-racemose; petals with induplicate margins
Flacourtiaceae
Flowers cymose-paniculate; corolla-lobes overlapping
Hoplestigmataceae
Stamens definite in relation to the corolla-lobes; anthers opening by terminal
pores or pore; leaves mostly opposite with longitudinal main nerves
Melastomataceae
Stamens 4, connate at the base or up to the middle; anthers opening by a
terminal pore; leaves primately nerved, alternate   *Polygalaceae*
Stamens 5–12; anthers neither appendaged nor opening by pores; leaves
alternate or fasciculate, exstipulate; erect trees or shrubs:
Branches with hooks; climbers   *Ancistrocladaceae*
Branches without hooks:
Leaves fairly large; flowers more or less corymbose or paniculate:
Not or rarely spiny; leaves not fasciculate; sepals 5, imbricate in bud;
stamens 5; petals 5, at most connivent   *Pittosporaceae*

Spiny shrubs; leaves often fasciculate   *Fouquieriaceae*

Leaves very small and scale-like; flowers in slender spikes or racemes

Tamaricaceae

Stamens 5; glabrous marsh herbs with verticillate leaves; flowers axillary, solitary   *Droseraceae*

Ovary composed of a single carpel (usually a legume); stamens free or more usually diadelphous or monadelphous, often 10, rarely numerous:

Stamens connate into a sheath, or free; flowers mostly bisexual:

Flowers actinomorphic; petals valvate; calyx gamosepalous or valvate; leaves usually bipinnate, rarely simply pinnate or reduced to phyllodes; flowers often collected into heads   *Mimosaceae*

Flowers zygomorphic or rarely actinomorphic; sepals imbricate or rarely valvate; petals imbricate, the upper (adaxial) one inside the others; leaves often pinnate or bipinnate

Caesalpiniaceae; see also some *Connaraceae* (with united petals)

Flowers zygomorphic; petals imbricate, the upper (adaxial) one (the standard) outside the others, the lateral two (the wings) outside the abaxial pair (the keel) which are more or less united along their lower edges; leaves simple, digitate or simply pinnate   *Papilionaceae*

Stamens connate into a column with the anthers in a ring at the top; flowers dioecious; fruit a drupe; slender climbers   *Menispermaceae*

Stamens inserted on the corolla-tube, sometimes near the base (from p. 52):

Stamens double the number of the corolla-lobes:

Flowers zygomorphic   *Polygalaceae*

Flowers actinomorphic   *Caricaceae*

Stamens the same number as the corolla-lobes; corolla actinomorphic or nearly so:

Leaves opposite:

Carpels 2, more or less free; pollen granular   *Plocospermaceae*

Carpels 2, free; styles separate up to the common thickened apex; pollen agglutinated into masses; corona usually present   *Asclepiadaceae*

Carpels 2, connate into a 1- or 2-locular ovary; pollen not agglutinated:

Stamens 5 or more; ovules numerous:

Corolla-lobes valvate   *Gentianaceae*

Corolla-lobes imbricate or contorted:

Herbs   *Hydrophyllaceae*

Trees or shrubs   *Potaliaceae*

Stamens 4; ovules numerous   *Bignoniaceae*

Stamens 4; ovules 1–2 in each loculus   *Verbenaceae*

Leaves alternate or radical:

Corolla-lobes without opposite glands; flowers bisexual:

Corolla-lobes imbricate or rarely contorted   *Hydrophyllaceae*

Corolla-lobes induplicate-valvate; leaves simple or trifoliolate

Menyanthaceae

Corolla-lobes with glands opposite to them; flowers unisexual

Achariaceae

Stamens fewer than the corolla-lobes, 4 or 2; corolla zygomorphic or rarely subactinomorphic:

Leafless parasitic (on roots), never green herbs; seeds minute, very numer-
ous, with endosperm *Orobanchaceae*
Leafy and not or rarely parasitic:
  Ovules numerous on each placenta:
    Mostly trees; seeds transverse, winged *Bignoniaceae*
    Mostly herbaceous; seeds minute, not winged *Gesneriaceae*
    Herbs; seeds not winged:
      Flowers mostly with characteristic glands (metamorphosed flowers)
        at the base of the pedicels; Old World *Pedaliaceae*
      Flowers without glands as above; New World *Martyniaceae*
  Ovules 1–2 on each placenta; stem and branches often 4-sided
Verbenaceae

GROUP 6

*One carpel or more than one united carpels with parietal placentation;
ovary superior; petals absent*

Leaves modified into pitchers; flowers dioecious; stamens united into a
  column; ovary 3–4-locular with numerous ovules in each loculus; seeds
  elongate-fusiform; embryo straight *Nepenthaceae*
Leaves not modified into pitchers:
  Submerged aquatic moss- or alga-like herbs; flowers dioecious; ovules
    numerous in each loculus; seeds microscopic, compressed
Hydrostachyaceae
  Not submerged, etc., as in preceding:
    Stamens 6, 4 long and 2 short (tetradynamous); fruits often with a thin
      membranous false septum between the placentas; seeds without endo-
      sperm, with accumbent or incumbent cotyledons; sepals usually 4
Cruciferae
    Stamens rarely 6, and then not tetradynamous:
    Stamens more than 1 (to p. 55):
      Ovary composed of 1 carpel; fruit usually a legume:
        Stamens more than 4; sepals not or rarely valvate:
          Stamens 10 or fewer by abortion:
            Leaves usually compound; flowers zygomorphic *Caesalpiniaceae*
            Leaves mostly simple; flowers actinomorphic:
              Leaves stipulate:
                Anthers erect in bud *Ulmaceae*
                Anthers inflexed in bud *Moraceae*
              Leaves exstipulate; flowers in catkins *Leitneriaceae*
          Stamens numerous:
            Flowers zygomorphic; fruit mostly a legume *Papilionaceae*
            Flowers actinomorphic; fruit a berry *Flacourtiaceae*
          Stamens 4, opposite the valvate calyx-segments *Proteaceae*
      Ovary composed of more than 1 carpel; at least with 2 or more placentas
        or more than 1 ovule:
      Ovary and fruit stipitate:
        Flowers not in catkins:
          Stamens more than 4; sepals rarely valvate *Capparidaceae*

Stamens 4; sepals valvate, often coloured   *Proteaceae*
Flowers in catkins   *Salicaceae*
Ovary sessile:
  Flowers without a corona but sometimes with a hypogynous disk:
  Stamens hypogynous or flowers unisexual:
    Filaments connate into a tube, anthers up to 20, adnate to the
        outside of the tube; leaves pellucid-punctate   *Canellaceae*
    Filaments free or slightly connate at the base:
      Seeds with endosperm:
        Leaves opposite; mostly shrubs; stipules mostly present
                              Cistaceae; see also *Austrobaileyaceae*
        Leaves alternate; trees or shrubs; stipules small, caducous or
            absent   *Flacourtiaceae*
        Leaves alternate; more or less herbaceous, with large pinnately
            or digitately nerved leaves; flowers paniculate; no stipules
                                                            Papaveraceae
      Seeds without endosperm; torus not dilated; fruit a capsule;
          branches leafy   *Salicaceae*
      Seeds without endosperm; torus dilated at the back; stamens 10–
          20; fruit a berry; often spiny shrubs more or less aphyllous
                                                            Resedaceae
  Stamens distinctly perigynous:
    Anthers inflexed in bud; staminodes rarely present; filaments free
                                                            Lythraceae
    Anthers not inflexed in bud; staminodes often alternating with the
        fertile stamens; filaments free or connate; indumentum some-
        times stellate   *Flacourtiaceae*
    Anthers not inflexed in bud; no staminodes; stamens 4, opposite
        the valvate sepals   *Proteaceae*
  Flowers with a distinct corona, more or less perigynous   *Passifloraceae*
Stamen 1:
  Stems not articulated; leaves well developed; flowers bisexual, spicate;
      anther erect in bud   *Lacistemaceae*
  Stems articulated; leaves reduced to scales; flowers unisexual, male
      spicate; anther inflexed in bud   *Casuarinaceae*

GROUP 7

*One carpel or two or more united carpels with parietal placentation;
ovary inferior; petals present, free from each other*

Aquatic herbs with floating or submerged leaves; petals numerous in several
    series; fruit a several-locular berry   *Nymphaeaceae*
Not aquatic, rarely marsh plants:
Flowers bisexual:
  Anthers opening by pores; leaves mostly opposite with longitudinal main
      nerves; stamens definite, often double the number of the petals
                                                            Melastomataceae

Anthers not opening by pores:
  Ovary-loculi not superposed:
    Stamens numerous, more than twice as many as the petals:
      Shrubs or trees with gland-dotted mostly opposite leaves   *Myrtaceae*
      Leaves not gland-dotted, sometimes reduced or fleshy:
        Fleshy herbs or shrubs; leaves reduced   *Cactaceae*
        Herbs with rough hairs; stamens often in bundles opposite the petals
              Loasaceae
        Trees or shrubs:
          Sepals gradually passing into the petals; endosperm ruminate
              Eupomatiaceae
          Sepals distinct from the petals   *Flacourtiaceae*
    Stamens 4–12; shrubs or trees; calyx imbricate or valvate:
      Leaves alternate:
        Leaves often gland-dotted, not stipulate   *Escalloniaceae*
        Leaves not glandular, mostly stipulate   *Grossulariaceae*
        Leaves opposite, not stipulate   *Hydrangeaceae*
    Stamens definite; usually herbs or weak climbers:
      Sepals and petals imbricate   *Philadelphaceae*
      Sepals valvate; petals contorted; ovary usually 4-locular
              Onagraceae
      Sepals imbricate or valvate; petals imbricate or induplicate-valvate;
        herbs or climbers with often rough stinging hairs   *Loasaceae*
  Ovary-loculi superposed in two series; leaves opposite or subopposite
              Punicaceae
Flowers unisexual:
  Leaves gland-dotted; style simple   *Myrtaceae*
  Leaves not gland-dotted; styles or stigmas usually 3:
    Shrubs, often armed with spines; leaves plicate or convolute in bud
              Grossulariaceae
    Herbs or herbaceous climbers:
      Stamens numerous; leaves stipulate; no tendrils; ovary closed, often
        winged   *Begoniaceae*
      Stamens 3 or 5; no stipules; often with tendrils; ovary closed at the top
              Cucurbitaceae
      Stamens 4 to many; stipules absent; no tendrils; ovary often gaping at
        the top   *Datiscaceae*

GROUP 8

One carpel or two or more united carpels with parietal placentas;
ovary inferior; petals present, more or less united

Stamens numerous; leaves often gland-dotted, mostly opposite   *Myrtaceae*
Stamens usually definite, rarely numerous, rarely more than twice the number
  of the corolla-lobes:
  Fleshy plants (often) usually with minute leaves; calyx-lobes, petals, and
    stamens numerous; style radiate at the apex   *Cactaceae*

Above characters never combined; stamens mostly the same number, double, or fewer than the petals:

Flowers unisexual; leaves alternate; tendrils often present; stamens mostly 3; anthers often twisted — *Cucurbitaceae*

Flowers bisexual; leaves opposite or verticillate, without stipules; anthers mostly opening by terminal pores — *Melastomataceae*

Flowers bisexual, very rarely unisexual; leaves opposite or alternate, often stipulate; anthers not opening by pores, sometimes connivent at the apex:

Leaves with interpetiolar or intrapetiolar stipules; flowers actinomorphic; stamens usually the same number as the corolla-lobes:

Ovules numerous on the walls of the ovary; branches not hooked — *Rubiaceae*

Ovule solitary; branches hooked — *Ancistrocladaceae*

Leaves exstipulate (sometimes the leaves anisophyllous, the smaller appearing like a stipule):

Evergreen trees or shrubs; corolla subactinomorphic; stamens 2, with very broad connective and sinuous anther-loculi — *Columelliaceae*

Shrubs; corolla actinomorphic; stamens numerous, with narrow connective; anther-loculi straight — *Flacourtiaceae*

Usually herbaceous, rarely subwoody plants; corolla more or less zygomorphic:

Stamens 4 or 2, often didynamous — *Gesneriaceae*

Stamens numerous; plants often roughly hairy — *Loasaceae*

GROUP 9

One carpel or two or more united carpels with parietal placentas; ovary inferior; petals absent

Leaves gland-dotted, opposite or alternate; stipules absent; stamens numerous; shrubs or trees rarely herbaceous — *Myrtaceae*

Leaves not gland-dotted or the leaves reduced to scales; mostly herbs:

Root parasites with scale-like leaves; stamens monadelphous:

Flowers unisexual — *Cytinaceae*

Flowers bisexual — *Hydnoraceae*

Green plants with well-developed leaves:

Leaves alternate:

Leaves stipulate, stipules sometimes adnate to the petiole:

Flowers bisexual:

Inflorescence not leaf-opposed; calyx present — *Saxifragaceae*

Inflorescence leaf-opposed; calyx absent — *Saururaceae*

Flowers unisexual; stamens usually numerous; ovary often winged — *Begoniaceae*

Leaves exstipulate; ovary often gaping at the top; stamens 4 to many; calyx not unilateral — *Datiscaceae*

Leaves exstipulate; ovary closed at the top; stamens 6 to many; calyx unilateral, coloured; climbers — *Aristolochiaceae*

Leaves opposite, ericoid; flowers crowded — *Grubbiaceae*

GROUP 10

One carpel or two or more united carpels with axile, basal, or apical placentation; ovary superior; petals present, free from each other

Perfect stamens the same number as the petals and opposite to them; leaves alternate or rarely opposite or all radical (to p. 59):
  Leaves not gland-dotted; petals and stamens more or less hypogynous or subperigynous; disk usually conspicuous:
  Calyx-lobes or sepals imbricate:
  Petals imbricate or biseriately imbricate:
  Ovary 1-locular; ovules basal:
  Petals often biglandular towards the base; ovules few; leaves simple or compound; anthers opening by valves   *Berberidaceae*
  Petals not glandular at the base; anthers opening by longitudinal slits:
  Ovules more than 1 in the ovary   *Primulaceae*
  Ovule 1 in the ovary   *Portulacaceae*
  Ovary 2–3-locular; ovules 2 in each loculus, horizontal or pendulous; stamens 4–5, sometimes only about 2 bearing anthers; no petaloid staminodes   *Sabiaceae*
  Ovary 1–2-locular; ovule solitary, pendulous from near the top:
  Sepals free or only shortly united:
  Stamens alternating with petaloid staminodes   *Corynocarpaceae*
  No staminodes; shrubs or small trees   *Flacourtiaceae*
  Sepals united high up; leaves often crowded; mostly undershrubs   *Thymelaeaceae*
  Petals valvate, mostly climbers with swollen nodes and leaf-opposed inflorescences:
  Fruits not enclosed by the calyx; ovary 6–2-locular; fruit baccate   *Vitaceae*
  Fruits completely enclosed by the enlarged calyx; ovary 1-locular; fruit drupaceous   *Erythropalaceae*
  Calyx-lobes valvate:
  Disk absent from the flowers:
  Trees and shrubs or rarely herbs; flowers not scapose:
  Leaves stipulate; stamens hypogynous:
  Ovary 8-locular, deeply and laterally lobed; stamens 8, opposite the petals   *Dirachmaceae*
  Ovary and other characters not as above; if stamens few then not opposite the petals   *Sterculiaceae*
  Ovary 1-locular with a free central placenta, the ovules attached at the top; fertile stamens opposite the petals   *Medusandraceae*
  Leaves exstipulate; stamens perigynous   *Lythraceae*
  Herbs, mostly with rosettes of leaves; flowers in scapose inflorescences   *Plumbaginaceae*
  Disk present, perigynous; leaves mostly stipulate; ovary 2–4-locular; ovules erect; seeds mostly with copious endosperm and large straight embryo   *Rhamnaceae*

Disk present; leaves exstipulate:
  Ovules erect   *Olacaceae*
  Ovules pendulous   *Opiliaceae*
Leaves pellucid-punctate:
  Leaves simple, without stipules; ovules numerous; trees or shrubs; no tendrils:
    Petals and stamens hypogynous; ovary 1-locular; ovules numerous on a free-central placenta   *Myrsinaceae*
    Petals and stamens perigynous; ovary 2–3-locular; ovules numerous on an axile placenta   *Heteropyxidaceae*
  Leaves mostly compound, usually stipulate; inflorescence leaf-opposed; ovules 1–2 in each loculus; mostly climbers with tendrils   *Vitaceae*
Perfect stamens the same number as the petals and alternate with them or more numerous, very rarely fewer:
  Stamens 6, tetradynamous (4 long and 2 short); flowers usually actinomorphic; petals 4, often clawed; placentas 2   *Cruciferae*
  Stamens not as above, rarely 6:
    Style basal; stipules mostly persistent:
      Leaves simple; stamens numerous; stomata of the leaves usually with special subsidiary cells   *Rosaceae*
      Leaves pinnate; stamens 10; disk large   *Simaroubaceae*
    Style or styles terminal or subterminal, sometimes gynobasic:
      Flowers markedly zygomorphic:
        Stamens definite in number, 12 or fewer:
          Lower sepal not spurred; sepals 5, the inner 2 larger and often petaloid, wing-like; anthers often opening by an apical pore; seeds mostly with endosperm:
            Ovary 2- or more-locular; fruits not bristly   *Polygalaceae*
            Ovary 1-locular; fruits bristly   *Krameriaceae*
          Lower sepal not spurred; sepals 4–5 or rarely up to 12, subequal; anthers opening by longitudinal slits; seeds mostly with copious endosperm   *Saxifragaceae*
          Lower sepal subsaccate; trees or shrubs with pinnate stipulate leaves; stamens 4–5, free, inserted within the disk   *Melianthaceae*
          Lower sepal more or less elongated into a spur:
            Sepals usually 3; anthers connivent around the ovary, opening lengthwise; seeds without endosperm   *Balsaminaceae*
            Sepals 5, anthers free, opening lengthwise; seeds usually without endosperm:
              Stamens about 8; leaves alternate   *Tropaeolaceae*
              Stamens 3–12, unilateral; leaves sometimes opposite   *Trigoniaceae*
              Stamens 1–2 (rarely a few staminodes); leaves opposite *Vochysiaceae*
        Stamens more than 12:
          Stamens and petals hypogynous   *Tamaricaceae*
          Stamens and petals perigynous or epigynous   *Rosaceae*
      Flowers actinomorphic or very slightly zygomorphic:
        Stamens united into more than one separate bundle (phalanges) often opposite the petals (to p. 60):

Leaves opposite, often gland-dotted or with resinous lines, exstipulate; calyx imbricate:

Herbs or shrubs; styles free from the base or nearly so; flowers bisexual
Hypericaceae

Trees or shrubs; styles mostly more or less united or stigma one and sessile or subsessile; flowers mostly unisexual   *Clusiaceae*

Leaves alternate (or if opposite then stipulate) or all radical:

Sepals imbricate:

Trees or shrubs:

Flowers hypogynous:

Leaves neither very small nor fleshy:

Petals contorted   *Bonnetiaceae*

Petals imbricate   *Theaceae*

Leaves often small and crowded or fleshy   *Tamaricaceae*

Flowers perigynous: *Flacourtiaceae*

Herbs or very small undershrubs:

Carpels 5, completely united   *Geraniaceae*

Carpels 3, only partially united   *Dilleniaceae*

Sepals valvate; hairs on the leaves, &c., often stellate:

Stamens free or monadelphous, or if united into bundles then some sterile   *Sterculiaceae*

Stamens in separate bundles, all fertile   *Tiliaceae*

Stamens free or at least not united into several bundles, sometimes more or less united at the base or into one bundle (monadelphous) (from p. 59):

Leaves opposite or verticillate or rarely fasciculate, never all radical or completely reduced (to p. 65):

Leaves compound, rarely unifoliolate and then with a distinctly tumid petiole, sometimes sessile (to p. 61):

Stamens numerous, more than twice the number of the petals:

Leaves digitate:

Leaves large; flowers in terminal racemes   *Caryocaraceae*

Leaves very small, sessile; flowers axillary, solitary   *Baueraceae*

Leaves pinnate; petals and stamens subhypogynous   *Eucryphiaceae*

Stamens definite, not more than twice as many as the petals; disk usually present:

Leaves gland-dotted; disk usually present between the stamens and ovary; ovary often deeply lobed; loculi 2-ovuled; ovules pendulous; stipules rarely present   *Rutaceae*

Leaves not gland-dotted, sometimes fleshy:

Leaves stipulate (to p. 61):

Ovules pendulous from the central axis, 2 or more in each loculus; disk often fleshy, rarely absent:

Stipules persistent and often paired; shrubs or herbs; leaves mostly 2-foliolate or pinnate; filaments often with a scale or gland attached to the base   *Zygophyllaceae*

Stipules often deciduous; leaves 3–8-foliolate; disk perigynous
Cunoniaceae

Ovule pendulous, solitary in each loculus; disk usually within the
 stamens; trees or shrubs; leaves mostly pinnate; filaments
 nude, pilose, or with a scale at the base *Simaroubaceae*
Ovules ascending; stamens inserted outside the disk
             Staphyleaceae

Leaves exstipulate:
 Stamens with free filaments, mostly twice as many as the petals:
  Leaves digitately 3-foliolate, sessile *Saxifragaceae*
  Leaves pinnate, stalked:
   Ovules mostly 2 in each loculus *Burseraceae*
   Ovule 1 in each loculus *Simaroubaceae*
 Stamens with more or less connate filaments, often double the
  number of the petals *Meliaceae*
 Stamens free, fewer than the petals; ovules 2 or rarely up to 8 in
  each loculus *Oleaceae*
 Stamens as many as the petals, free; ovules numerous in each
  loculus, at least more than 2 *Staphyleaceae*
 Stamens as many as or more than the petals; ovules 2 in each
  loculus, collateral; ovary compressed at right angles to the
  septum *Aceraceae*
Leaves simple, but sometimes deeply and variously divided:
 Ovary stipitate on a gynophore; stamens usually numerous, mostly
  more than twice as many as the petals, or if fewer then leaves gland-
  dotted; seeds without endosperm or very little; petals often clawed:
  Leaves not gland-dotted:
   Ovules on the walls or on the intrusive septa *Capparidaceae*
   Ovules on the central axis or from the base of the ovary
            Caryophyllaceae
  Leaves gland-dotted *Rutaceae*
 Ovary sessile or rarely very slightly stipitate:
  Stamens more than twice as many as the petals (to p. 62):
   Calyx imbricate or calyptrate (to p. 62):
    Sepals mostly 2, caducous; petals 4, often crumpled in bud;
     filaments free *Papaveraceae*
    Sepals more than 2, mostly persistent; petals usually 5:
     Stipules absent:
      Stamens united into 5 bundles which are connate nearly to the
       top; style single *Hypericaceae*
      Stamens free or united into a mass; flowers usually dioecious or
       polygamous:
       Leaves opposite, not fasciculate; unarmed *Clusiaceae*
       Leaves fasciculate; spiny fleshy shrubs *Didiereaceae*
     Stipules present:
      Leaves pinnately nerved:
       Stamens free or very shortly connate only at the base; styles
        2–3, free; leaves with numerous very fine transverse veins;
        stipules mostly paired, lateral, rigid; flowers paniculate
        or fascicled *Quiinaceae*

Stamens free, very numerous:
  Styles 5–12; leaves with small caducous intrapetiolar stipules;
    flowers solitary, showy   *Eucryphiaceae*
  Styles 20–25; ovary with as many loculi; flowers paniculate
                                  Medusagynaceae
  Style 1; stigma 3-lobed   *Theaceae*
  Stamens 10–15, free; style with 2–6 stigmas; leaves rather
    fleshy, with small persistent stipules; flowers in cymes
                                  Zygophyllaceae
Leaves with 3 or more longitudinally parallel main nerves
                                  Melastomataceae
Calyx valvate:
  Stamens free or very shortly connate at the base:
  Stamens not inflexed in bud:
    Stipules paired, not interpetiolar   *Tiliaceae*
    Stipules single, interpetiolar   *Rhizophoraceae*
    Stipules absent   *Philadelphaceae*
  Stamens inflexed in bud:
    Leaves stipulate; indumentum often stellate   *Euphorbiaceae*
    Leaves exstipulate; indumentum rarely stellate:
      Flowers sometimes large and showy, petals clawed; ovary
        few-locular   *Lythraceae*
      Flowers with small sessile petals; ovary many-locular
                                  Sonneratiaceae
  Stamens monadelphous or in fascicles opposite the petals, the
    latter contorted or imbricate; leaves usually stipulate; hairs
    often stellate   *Sterculiaceae*
Stamens not more than twice as many as the petals:
  Trees, shrubs, or woody climbers (to p. 64):
  Leaves stipulate, sometimes stipules rudimentary or of hairs (to
    p. 63):
  Stipules intrapetiolar, often connivent into one or adnate to the
    petiole:
    Sepals not glandular outside and not accrescent in fruit; hairs
      not medifixed   *Erythroxylaceae*
    Sepals usually glandular outside or accrescent in fruit; hairs
      medifixed; leaves often biglandular at the base
                                Malpighiaceae
  Stipules not intrapetiolar, sometimes rudimentary:
  Disk absent or inconspicuous or of separate glands; calyx often
    glandular:
    Stamens free or shortly united at the base:
    Calyx mostly with a pair of glands outside; trees, shrubs, or
      climbers; filaments of stamens without a scale
                                  Malpighiaceae
    Calyx not glandular; anther-loculi collateral:
    Filaments of stamens often with a scale attached
                                  Zygophyllaceae

Filaments without a scale *Cunoniaceae*

Calyx not glandular; anther-loculi back to back; trees or shrubs; filaments without a scale; petals 4; stamens 4
Salvadoraceae

Stamens united into a long tube; sepals not glandular; ovary 5-locular with 2 ovules in each; calyx valvate
Rhizophoraceae

Disk present, conspicuous; calyx not glandular:

Flowers bisexual:

Stamens inserted on or below the margin of the disk; filaments subulate:

Stamens 3–5 *Celastraceae*

Stamens 8–10:

Sepals imbricate; filaments on the inside of the disk
Ctenolophonaceae

Sepals valvate; filaments on the edge or on the outside of the disk *Rhizophoraceae*

Stamens usually 3, inserted on the disk; filaments flattened or connivent, often adnate to the ovary *Hippocrateaceae*

Flowers unisexual; ovules pendulous from the apex of each loculus:

Seeds often carunculate; flowers rarely in heads
Euphorbiaceae

Seeds not carunculate; flowers arranged in dense heads; hairs stellate *Hamamelidaceae*

Leaves exstipulate or stipules gland-like:

Stamens united into a tube:

Stamens more than 4; flowers bisexual *Meliaceae*

Stamens 4; flowers unisexual *Clusiaceae*

Stamens free or very shortly united at the base:

Anthers opening at the apex by a pore; stamens as many as or twice as many as the petals:

Leaves often with 3–9 longitudinally parallel main nerves; anthers often appendaged at the base *Melastomataceae*

Leaves with a single main nerve; anthers not appendaged at the base *Tremandraceae*

Anthers opening by slits lengthwise:

Ovules numerous in each loculus:

Petals and stamens hypogynous; flowers bisexual:

Stamens 10; embryo large, the endosperm very scanty
Ledocarpaceae

Stamens 5; embryo small, with copious endosperm
Pittosporaceae

Petals and stamens hypogynous; flowers unisexual
Clusiaceae

Petals and stamens perigynous; flowers bisexual
Lythraceae; see also small part of *Philadelphaceae* and *Hydrangeaceae*

Ovules few in each loculus:
  Sepals 2-glandular outside; hairs on the leaves (when present)
      medifixed; shrubs or climbers:
    Fruits usually winged; styles often 3   *Malpighiaceae*
    Fruits drupaceous; style one   *Simaroubaceae*
  Sepals not glandular; hairs not medifixed:
    Ovules pendulous from the apex of each loculus, or axile:
      Sepals imbricate or open:
        Sepals free or calyx-tube very short:
          Stamens hypogynous:
            Petals imbricate   *Linaceae*
            Petals valvate   *Icacinaceae*
          Stamens perigynous:
            Ovary 5-locular; ovules 2 in each loculus
                          Escalloniaceae
            Ovary 4-locular; ovule solitary   *Cunoniaceae*
          Sepals connate into a long or rather long tube
                          Thymelaeaceae
      Sepals valvate:
        Stamens hypogynous:
          Petals contorted   *Vivianiaceae*
          Petals induplicate-valvate   *Tremandraceae*
        Stamens perigynous   *Combretaceae*
    Ovules erect or ascending from the base of each loculus:
      Calyx imbricate:
        Filaments subulate or filiform:
          Leaves mostly palmately lobed, or if not so then disk
              absent; ovary and fruit flattened at right angles to
              the septum   *Aceraceae*
          Leaves pinnately lobed; disk present:
            Flowers bisexual   *Celastraceae*
            Flowers dioecious or polygamous   *Clusiaceae*
          Filaments flattened   *Hippocrateaceae*
      Calyx valvate; stamens 3–5; style short:
        Leaves not gland-dotted:
          Sepals free or nearly so   *Anacardiaceae*
          Sepals united into a long tube; the 2 posticous petals
              often larger than the others   *Lythraceae*
          Sepals united into a short tube; petals equal   *Podoaceae*
        Leaves gland-dotted   *Rutaceae*
Herbs, sometimes woody at the base (from p. 62):
  Ovary incompletely septate with free-central or basal placentation;
      leaves mostly stipulate:
    Sepals the same number as the petals, 3–5, free or connate; petals
        3–5, often clawed   *Caryophyllaceae*
    Sepals the same number as the petals but often with as many
        accessory lobes, connate into a tube; anthers inflexed in bud
                          Lythraceae

Sepals fewer than the petals, usually 2; petals 4–5 or more
Portulacaceae
Ovary completely septate:
Leaves stipulate:
Stipules paired:
Branches not articulate; ovules numerous, attached to the central axis *Elatinaceae*
Branches usually not articulated; ovules few, pendulous; sepals often unequal *Geraniaceae*
Branches articulated; ovules few, pendulous or ascending; sepals equal *Zygophyllaceae*
Stipules solitary, sometimes minute:
Stamens distinctly perigynous; capsule circumscissile
Ficoidaceae
Stamens hypogynous, or slightly perigynous:
Ovules pendulous; fruit a capsule or drupe, not circumscissile
Linaceae
Ovules basal or axile and spreading; fruit a valvular capsule, not circumscissile *Molluginaceae*
Leaves exstipulate:
Leaves with 3 or more longitudinally parallel nerves; anthers usually appendaged and opening by a terminal pore
Melastomataceae
Leaves not as above; anthers opening by longitudinal slits:
Stamens hypogynous or nearly so *Molluginaceae*
Stamens perigynous:
Anthers erect in bud *Ficoidaceae*
Anthers inflexed in bud:
Ovary superior; terrestrial or semi-aquatic herbs; cotyledons equal *Lythraceae*
Ovary semi-inferior; floating aquatic herbs with leaves of two kinds, the lower much divided; fruit spiny
Trapaceae
Leaves alternate or all radical (from p. 60):
Stamens more than twice the number of the sepals or petals (to p. 69):
Sepals valvate or open in bud (to p. 66):
Anthers 2-locular (to p. 66):
Anthers narrowly horseshoe-shaped, the loculi bent on themselves
Gonystylaceae
Anthers straight:
Stamens free or slightly united at the base:
Petals and stamens hypogynous or flowers unisexual:
Stipules present:
Flowers bisexual; indumentum often stellate *Tiliaceae*
Flowers unisexual; indumentum rarely stellate
Euphorbiaceae
Stipules absent; calyx cupular; stamens in several series; anthers opening by a pore or short slit *Scytopetalaceae*

Petals and stamens perigynous or epigynous:
  Leaves stipulate; stipules mostly paired; ovary 2-locular; styles
    subulate, free   *Hamamelidaceae*
  Leaves exstipulate:
    Anthers inflexed in bud; calyx tubular   *Lythraceae*
    Anthers erect in bud:
      Leaves simple; wood not resinous:
        Ovary incompletely septate, wholly superior   *Olacaceae*
        Ovary completely septate, partly inferior   *Styracaceae*
      Leaves compound or unifoliolate; wood resinous
                     Anacardiaceae
Stamens more or less united into a tube or into bundles, hypo-
  gynous; indumentum usually stellate:
  Anthers opening longitudinally   *Sterculiaceae*
  Anthers opening by pore-like short slits   *Scytopetalaceae*
Anthers 1-locular; stamens monadelphous; calyx with or without an
  epicalyx:
  Trees or rarely shrubs; leaves digitately compound or simple;
    carpels not or very rarely splitting away from the central axis
    in fruit   *Bombacaceae*
  Mostly herbs; leaves simple; carpels often splitting away from the
    central axis or becoming free in fruit   *Malvaceae*
Sepals imbricate or rarely completely connate or calyptrate or
  cupular:
  Anthers narrowly horseshoe-shaped, the loculi bent on themselves
               Gonystylaceae
  Anthers straight:
   Petals and stamens perigynous:
    Leaves stipulate:
     Seeds with endosperm and a curved embryo; mostly herbs
                  Portulacaceae
     Seeds without endosperm or with very little:
       Ovary with usually more than 2 carpels or sometimes only one;
         flowers not or very rarely capitate   *Rosaceae*
       Ovary of 2 carpels; flowers often capitate   *Hamamelidaceae*
    Leaves exstipulate:
     Stamens free from the petals:
       Flowers not capitate:
         Petals not crumpled in bud; ovules pendulous from the apex
           of each loculus:
           Leaves stipulate   *Rhizophoraceae*
           Leaves without stipules   *Flacourtiaceae*
         Petals often crumpled in bud; ovules basal or from the inner
           angle of each loculus; sepals valvate   *Lythraceae*
       Flowers capitate, asymmetric; involucre coloured
                    Hamamelidaceae
     Stamens inserted on the base of the petals   *Styracaceae*

Petals and stamens more or less hypogynous or flowers unisexual; disk often present:
Trees, shrubs, or woody climbers (to p. 68):
Leaves compound or rarely unifoliolate and then with a tumid petiole:
Leaves pinnate; petals not calyptrate:
Ovule ascending:
Leaves gland-dotted; style or styles central   *Rutaceae*
Leaves rarely gland-dotted; styles or stigmas often separated:
    Wood resinous   *Anacardiaceae*
    Wood not resinous, not bitter   *Sapindaceae*
    Wood not resinous, very bitter   *Simaroubaceae*
Ovule or ovules pendulous:
Stamens free; wood with resin ducts   *Anacardiaceae*
Stamens more or less free from one another; wood without resin ducts   *Simaroubaceae*
Stamens united into a tube   *Meliaceae*
Leaves digitate 3–5-foliolate; petals calyptrately connate; styles short, 8–20; embryo spiral   *Caryocaraceae*
Leaves simple:
Leaves stipulate:
Flowers unisexual:
Disk present   *Euphorbiaceae*
Disk absent   *Flacourtiaceae*
Flowers bisexual:
Torus enlarged after flowering; ovary mostly deeply lobed, the carpels becoming separated in fruit; anthers often opening by pores   *Ochnaceae*
Torus not enlarged:
Ovary stipitate; sepals more or less connate into a tube   *Capparidaceae*
Ovary sessile; sepals usually free:
Sepals 3; stipules caducous; flowers cymose or paniculate; petals contorted; stamens 10 or more, inside a ring of staminodes; ovary 3-locular; Mascarene Islands   *Schizolaenaceae*
Sepals 4; ovary 2-locular   *Sphaerosepalaceae*
Sepals 5; no staminodes:
Calyx enlarged and wing-like in fruit:
Flowers mostly rather small and not showy; petals much contorted   *Dipterocarpaceae*
Flowers showy; ovary 1-locular with a basal placenta   *Ochnaceae*
Calyx not enlarged:
Leaves digitately lobed; flowers large, handsome; anthers opening by short pore-like confluent slits at the apex; petals imbricate or slightly contorted   *Cochlospermaceae*

Leaves not lobed; flowers small:
 Sepals contorted; stipules very small *Ixonanthaceae*
 Sepals imbricate; stipules large and intrapetiolar
            Irvingiaceae
Leaves not stipulate:
 Ovary and fruit stipitate   *Capparidaceae*
 Ovary and fruit not stipitate:
  Seeds arillate; ovary composed of 1 carpel; leaves mostly
   with very prominent pinnately parallel lateral nerves;
   stamens usually persistent   *Dilleniaceae*
  Seeds not arillate; ovary usually composed of 2 or more
   carpels:
   Sterile flowers with modified pitcher-like saccate or spurred
    bracts   *Marcgraviaceae*
   Sterile flowers not present; no modified bracts:
    Ovary 1-locular, composed of 1 carpel:
     Stamens more than 10, free:
      Leaves pellucid-punctate, rather large and coriaceous
              Winteraceae
      Leaves usually very small and crowded *Tamaricaceae*
    Ovary 2- or more-locular:
     Anthers basifixed; seeds usually few:
      Petals contorted   *Bonnetiaceae*
      Petals imbricate   *Theaceae*
     Anthers versatile; seeds numerous, small:
      Climbers; flowers often unisexual; sepals scarcely im-
       bricate; styles numerous, free *Actinidiaceae*
      Erect trees or shrubs; flowers mostly bisexual; sepals
       very much imbricate; styles 3–5, free or connate
       at the base; anthers opening by pores
              Saurauiaceae
     Trees or shrubs; flowers bisexual; style simple, slender,
      entire or minutely dentate *Humiriaceae*
     Anthers versatile; seed solitary; leaves fasciculate; spiny
      plants   *Didiereaceae*
Herbs, rarely somewhat woody at the base (from p. 67):
 Carpels not sunk in the torus:
  Leaves neither sticky glandular, setose-ciliate, nor modified into
   pitchers:
   Anthers opening by longitudinal slits:
    Stamens quite free from one another:
     Sepals more than 2   *Helleboraceae*
     Sepals 2   *Portulacaceae*
    Stamens connate at the base; leaves pinnate *Oxalidaceae*
   Anthers opening by a short pore-like terminal slit
            Cochlospermaceae
  Leaves very sticky—glandular or ciliate with setose teeth, not
   modified into pitchers   *Droseraceae*

Leaves modified into tubes or pitchers; stamens numerous, free; ovary 3–5-locular; ovules numerous   *Sarraceniaceae*

Carpels sunk in the torus; aquatic plants with peltate leaves
Nymphaeaceae

Stamens definite in number in relation to the sepals or petals, often the same number or twice as many or fewer (from p. 65):

Leaves compound, rarely unifoliolate and then with a distinctly tumid petiole (to p. 70):

Stamens united into a tube; leaves pinnate or rarely unifoliolate:

Leaves exstipulate   *Meliaceae*

Leaves with intrapetiolar stipules   *Melianthaceae*

Stamens free or united only at the base:

Leaves stipulate:

Herbaceous or slightly woody; leaves digitately or pinnately compound:

Stamens without a scale at the base of the filaments; flowers actinomorphic   *Oxalidaceae*

Stamens with a scale at the base of the filaments; flowers actinomorphic   *Zygophyllaceae*

Stamens without a scale at the base; flowers more or less zygomorphic   *Melianthaceae*

Trees, shrubs, or climbers:

Ovules axile   *Lepidobotryaceae*

Ovules pendulous; stipules convolute, axillary, often very long; leaves simple   *Irvingiaceae*

Ovules ascending; leaves compound; habit often climbing:

Stipules lateral   *Sapindaceae*

Stipules intrapetiolar   *Melianthaceae*

Leaves exstipulate:

Leaves gland-dotted   *Rutaceae*

Leaves not gland-dotted:

Ovules pendulous from towards the apex of each loculus:

Ovules 8–12, 2-seriate; flowers small, paniculate   *Meliaceae*

Ovules solitary or collateral:

Leaves 2-foliolate   *Balanitaceae*

Leaves not 2-foliolate:

Ovary of more than 1 carpel; wood mostly resinous
Burseraceae

Ovary of more than 1 carpel; wood with bitter bark but not resinous   *Simaroubaceae*

Ovary of 1 carpel; wood resinous   *Anacardiaceae*

Ovules paired, superposed   *Akaniaceae*

Ovules ascending or horizontal:

Ovules numerous on axile placentas, horizontally spreading:

Sepals, petals, and stamens 8, rarely 5; leaves trifoliolate; stigmas sessile, 8-rayed   *Tovariaceae*

Sepals 5, petals 5; stamens 10 or 5; leaves pinnate
Averrhoaceae

Ovules mostly few or one; above characters not associated:
 Herbs with sensitive leaves   *Oxalidaceae*
 Trees or shrubs:
  Ovules mostly 2 in each loculus, superposed; styles various
       Rutaceae
  Ovules about 8 in each loculus; style 1   *Meliaceae*
  Ovules 2 in each loculus, collateral; style simple
       Connaraceae
  Ovules 1 or more in each loculus, erect or ascending; style
   simple or divided   *Sapindaceae* and *Hippocastanaceae*
  Ovule 1 in each loculus; style lobed or styles separate; wood
   with resin ducts   *Anacardiaceae*
Leaves simple, rarely completely reduced:
 Anthers opening by valves:
  Leafless parasitic herbs on roots of trees   *Monotropaceae*
  Leafy trees or shrubs; but sometimes leafless at time of flowering:
   Ovary composed of 2 carpels; stipules often present, mostly paired;
    flowers often capitate   *Hamamelidaceae*
   Ovary composed of 1 carpel; stipules absent   *Lauraceae*
 Anthers opening by apical pores:
  Leaves with 3 or more longitudinally parallel main nerves; con-
   nective of the anthers often produced at the base
        Melastomataceae
  Leaves pinnately nerved or nerves obscure:
   Petals induplicate-valvate; ovary 2-locular; anthers 2- or 4-locular
        Tremandraceae
   Petals imbricate or contorted:
    Ovary deeply lobed:
     Torus enlarging in fruit and the carpels often becoming separate;
      ovules 1–2 in each loculus   *Ochnaceae*
     Torus not enlarged; herbs, leaves mostly radical, rounded
          Pyrolaceae
    Ovary not deeply lobed; torus not enlarged:
     Ovules numerous in each loculus; leaves fairly large and broad
          Clethraceae
     Ovules 1–3; fruits winged   *Cyrillaceae*
     Ovules several in each loculus or in the ovary; leaves narrow
          Pittosporaceae
     Ovule usually solitary; leaves very narrow; not glandular
          Polygalaceae
     Ovules 1–2
      Leaves very glandular-pilose, circinate in bud   *Byblidaceae*
      Leaves not as above   *Pentaphylacaceae*
 Anthers opening by slits lengthwise:
  Shrubs or trees (to p. 74):
   Leaves stipulate (to p. 71):
    Calyx persistent and wing-like in fruit; leaves often with prominent
     parallel lateral nerves; petals contorted   *Dipterocarpaceae*

Calyx not wing-like in fruit; petals rarely contorted:
Flowers unisexual:
  Disk absent; petals not bilobed:
    Ovules more than 1 in each ovary   *Flacourtiaceae*
    Ovule 1 in each ovary   *Pandaceae*
  Disk present; petals bilobed   *Chailletiaceae*
  Disk present:
    Stipules conspicuous, persistent   *Euphorbiaceae*
    Stipules very inconspicuous, caducous   *Celastraceae*
Flowers bisexual:
  Stamens perigynous, inserted on the calyx-tube:
    Ovary 1-locular, composed of one carpel   *Rosaceae*
    Ovary 2-locular, composed of 2 or more carpels
                           Hamamelidaceae
    Ovary 3-locular at the base, 1-locular at apex
                         Dipentodontaceae
  Stamens hypogynous or inserted on or at the base of a disk:
    Stipules axillary, convolute in bud, often very long:
      Petals not appendaged inside:
        Sepals contorted   *Ixonanthaceae*
        Sepals imbricate:
          Flowers in panicles; sepals 5   *Irvingiaceae*
          Flowers solitary, axillary; sepals 10–8 *Strasburgeriaceae*
      Petals appendaged inside   *Erythroxylaceae*
    Stipules not axillary:
      Disk absent, or torus sometimes enlarging in fruit but not
        glandular:
        Sepals 3, much imbricate; petals imbricate-contorted; sta-
          mens inserted inside a cup of staminodes; Mascarene
          Islands   *Schizolaenaceae*
        Sepals 5; no cup of staminodes present:
          Sepals valvate; anthers 4-locular   *Huaceae*
          Sepals imbricate; anthers 2-locular:
            Stamens 10, in 2 series; hairs of the leaves when present not
              medifixed; petiole not glandular *Erythroxylaceae*
            Stamens 8; hairs not medifixed; petiole not glandular;
              ovary 4-locular; racemes catkin-like *Stachyuraceae*
            Stamens 10, in 1 series; hairs of leaves often medifixed;
              petiole often glandular like the sepals *Malpighiaceae*
            Stamens usually numerous; hairs of leaves when present
              not medifixed; petiole not glandular *Ochnaceae*
      Disk present, annular or of separate glands:
        Petals entire or emarginate; ovules erect:
          Petals valvate   *Goupiaceae*
          Petals imbricate   *Celastraceae*
        Petals often deeply lobed; ovules pendulous *Chailletiaceae*
Leaves exstipulate:
  Stamens united into a tube   *Meliaceae*

Stamens united into a column *Aptandraceae*
Stamens free or connate only at the base:
Stamens hypogynous or very slightly perigynous (to p. 73):
Sterile flowers with modified pitcher-like bracts; mostly epi-
phytes *Marcgraviaceae*
Sterile flowers without modified bracts, or sterile flowers not
present:
Stamens double the number of the petals or fewer only by the
abortion of some anthers (to p. 73):
Sepals usually with two large glands outside; hairs of leaves
medifixed; ovary 3-locular, with 1 ovule in each loculus,
seeds without endosperm; fruit often winged
Malpighiaceae
Sepals not glandular; hairs rarely medifixed:
Ovary 1-locular:
Ovary of 1 carpel:
Torus forming a stipe
Anacardiaceae; see also *Podoaceae*
Torus not forming a stipe *Phytolaccaceae*
Ovary of more than 1 carpel:
Leaves very small; flowers spicate-racemose
Tamaricaceae
Leaves not very small; ovary 1-locular with 1 free central
placenta *Stegnospermaceae*
Ovary completely 2- or more-locular (or nearly completely
5-locular):
No disk; leaves reduced or scale-like; placenta basal
Molluginaceae
Disk present; leaves not gland-dotted; petals mostly
valvate:
Flowers bisexual *Olacaceae*
Flowers polygamo-dioecious *Sapindaceae*
Disk present, often intrastaminal; leaves gland-dotted
Rutaceae
Disk extrastaminal, cupular, crowned with 10 gland-like
staminodes; ovary imperfectly 5-locular; soft-wooded
trees with geranium-like leaves *Greyiaceae*
Disk intrastaminal, closely girding the ovary, not lobed;
leaves not gland-dotted:
Ovary 5–7-locular *Humiriaceae*
Ovary 2–5-locular *Cyrillaceae*
Disk absent:
Flowers unisexual; ovary 3–4-locular:
Male petals imbricate *Pentadiplandraceae*
Male petals valvate *Pandaceae*
Flowers bisexual; ovary 2-locular; petals imbricate
Koeberliniaceae

Stamens the same number as the petals or fewer:
  Disk absent; flowers polygamous, axillary, solitary or fas-
    ciculate:
  Carpels not on a gynophore:
    Ovules numerous; anthers opening lengthwise or by apical
      pores; style simple; embryo minute in copious endo-
      sperm   *Pittosporaceae*
    Ovules 6 in each of the 2 loculi   *Koeberliniaceae*
    Ovules 1–2 in each loculus, pendulous:
      Petals imbricate or contorted, clawed; anthers opening
        by slits   *Linaceae*
      Petals imbricate, not clawed:
        Anthers opening by an apical pore   *Theaceae*
        Anthers opening by slits   *Pellicieraceae*
      Petals imbricate, sessile; anthers opening by slits length-
        wise   *Aquifoliaceae*
    Ovule 1 in each loculus, basal   *Tetrameristaceae*
  Carpels on a gynophore   *Cneoraceae*
  Disk present:
    Petals valvate; ovules pendulous:
      Stamens opposite the petals   *Olacaceae*
      Stamens the same number as and alternate with the petals
                                                 Icacinaceae
    Petals imbricate or contorted:
      Petals more or less spreading:
        Leaves not gland-dotted but sometimes lepidote:
          Stamens usually 5:
            Ovules 1–3 in each loculus:
              Ovule solitary; wood resinous   *Anacardiaceae*
              Ovules mostly 2 in each loculus; wood not resinous:
                Leaves not lepidote   *Celastraceae*
                Leaves densely lepidote   *Aextoxicaceae*
              Ovules 1–3; wood not resinous; flowers in slender
                racemes   *Cyrillaceae*
              Ovules several to many   *Pittosporaceae*
          Stamens 3, with flattened filaments; wood not resinous;
            flowers cymose   *Hippocrateaceae*
        Leaves gland-dotted   *Rutaceae*
      Petals erect, more or less connivent:
        Petals connivent in the upper part; small herbs with a
          woody branched rhizome   *Stackhousiaceae*
        Petals free in the upper part; shrubs or small trees
                                                Epacridaceae
Stamens very distinctly perigynous (from p. 72):
  Leaves with 3 or more longitudinally parallel main nerves
                                              Melastomataceae
  Leaves with more or less pinnate nervation:
    Carpels free at the apex; leaves stipulate *Hamamelidaceae*

Carpels completely united; stipules absent:
  Anthers inflexed in bud   *Lythraceae*
  Anthers erect in bud:
    Petals scale-like, opposite the sepals; ovary wholly superior:
      Fruit a capsule   *Aquilariaceae*
      Fruit indehiscent   *Thymelaeaceae*
    Petals not scale-like, alternate with the sepals:
      Ovary wholly superior; petals more or less clawed; stamens only slightly perigynous; woody only at the base   *Molluginaceae*
      Ovary semi-inferior; stamens very clearly perigynous; flowers often in heads; low shrubs with small leaves *Bruniaceae*
      Ovary quite superior; trees or shrubs with fairly large leaves   *Escalloniaceae*
Herbs, rarely slightly woody at the base (from p. 70):
  Parasites destitute of chlorophyll; leaves reduced to scales   *Monotropaceae*
  Not parasitic; leaves green:
  Leaves densely covered with sticky gland-tipped processes or setose-ciliate and bilobed, stipulate, often circinate in bud   *Droseraceae*
   Leaves not glandular:
   Leaves stipulate:
   Stamens and petals hypogynous or flowers unisexual:
    Flowers bisexual:
    Sepals more than 2:
     Sepals valvate   *Tiliaceae*
     Sepals imbricate:
      Ovary more or less deeply lobed   *Geraniaceae*
      Ovary entire:
       Stipules not scarious; petals contorted   *Linaceae*
       Stipules scarious; petals imbricate or small   *Molluginaceae*
    Sepals 2, very much imbricate   *Portulacaceae*
    Flowers unisexual   *Euphorbiaceae*
   Stamens and petals perigynous; anthers inflexed in bud   *Lythraceae*
   Leaves exstipulate:
   Sepals 2, much imbricate   *Portulacaceae*
   Sepals more than 2:
    Petals connivent in the upper part; small herbs from a woody branched rhizome   *Stackhousiaceae*
    Petals not connivent:
     Petals and stamens hypogynous or very slightly perigynous:
      Petals contorted, fugacious, mostly large and conspicuous; embryo straight:
       Ovules pendulous; leaves entire or nearly so   *Linaceae*

    Ovules ascending; leaves dissected   *Limnanthaceae*
    Petals imbricate or very small and inconspicuous; embryo
        curved   *Molluginaceae* and *Francoaceae*
  Petals and stamens perigynous:
  Seeds with endosperm:
    Ovules more than 1 in each loculus, axile *Saxifragaceae*
    Ovule 1 in each loculus, basal   *Eremosynaceae*
  Seeds without endosperm; carpels with a gland or scale at
    the base; anthers erect in bud   *Crassulaceae*
  Seeds without endosperm; carpels without a gland or scale;
    anthers inflexed in bud   *Lythraceae*

GROUP 11

*One carpel or two or more united carpels with axile, basal, or apical
placentation; ovary superior; petals present, more or less united*

Stamens the same number as and opposite to the corolla-lobes (to p. 76):
  Ovules solitary in the whole ovary or in each loculus of the ovary; style often
    lobed:
  Trees or shrubs, often with hard wood:
    Flowers mostly dioecious; petals imbricate or valvate; stamens mostly
      free from or attached to the base of the corolla   *Ebenaceae*
    Flowers bisexual; stamens epipetalous:
    Petals imbricate; hairs often stellate or medifixed:
    Flowers fasciculate in the leaf-axils or at the nodes; leaves alternate
                                 Sapotaceae
    Flowers in racemes or panicles; leaves opposite or subopposite
                            Sarcospermaceae
    Petals valvate; hairs usually simple:
    Inflorescence not leaf-opposed; leaves simple   *Olacaceae*
    Inflorescence leaf-opposed; leaves often compound   *Vitaceae*
  Herbs or climbers:
    Corolla-lobes valvate; tendrils often present; inflorescence usually cymose-
      paniculate, leaf-opposed; leaves usually with the stipules adnate to
      the petiole   *Vitaceae*
    Corolla-lobes imbricate:
    Stamens connate into a column, free from the petals; stipules absent
                          Menispermaceae
    Stamens free from each other and from the petals; stipules scarious, rarely
      absent   *Portulacaceae*
    Stamens more or less adnate to or inserted on the corolla *Plumbaginaceae*
  Ovules 2 or more in each loculus; style undivided; placentas often basal:
  Trees or shrubs often with gland-dotted leaves:
    Seeds with endosperm and short embryo; cotyledons not connate; anthers
      not transversely septate:
    Anthers introrse; no staminodes   *Myrsinaceae*

Anthers extrorse; staminodes present, alternating with the corolla-lobes
Theophrastaceae

Seeds without endosperm, elongated; embryo long and arcuate, germinating in the fruit; cotyledons connate into a tube; anthers transversely septate *Aegicerataceae*

Herbs or climbers usually with compound leaves and leaf-opposed inflorescence *Vitaceae*

Herbs, often with rosettes of leaves; leaves not gland-dotted *Primulaceae*

Stamens the same number as the corolla-lobes and alternate with them or more numerous or fewer:

Stamens more thantwice as many as the corolla-lobes:

Anthers opening by apical pores or short pore-like slits:

Corolla-tube very short; stamens numerous, adnate to the base of the corolla; anthers not tailed *Saurauiaceae*

Corolla-tube usually fairly long; stamens rarely many more than double the number of the corolla-lobes, not adnate to the corolla-tube; anthers often with tails *Ericaceae*

Anthers opening by longitudinal slits:

Flowers bisexual:

Leaves simple, sometimes deeply divided:

Bracts more or less pouch-like and adnate to the pedicels; stems climbing or epiphytic *Marcgraviaceae*

Bracts and habit not as above:

Stamens hypogynous:

Sepals imbricate:

Trees or shrubs *Theaceae*

Herbs or slightly woody at the base *Molluginaceae*

Sepals valvate:

Stamens free or nearly so *Tiliaceae*

Stamens monadelphous *Malvaceae*

Stamens perigynous or epigynous; sepals usually imbricate:

Leaves often gland-dotted and opposite *Myrtaceae*

Leaves not gland-dotted, alternate *Lecythidaceae*

Leaves digitately compound, opposite or alternate *Caryocaraceae*

Flowers unisexual:

Disk absent; leaves without stipules *Ebenaceae*

Disk present; leaves usually with stipules *Euphorbiaceae*

Stamens as many as or up to twice as many as the corolla-lobes or fewer:

Stamens as many as or more than the corolla-lobes (to p. 82):

Flowers zygomorphic:

Ovary deeply 4-lobed; style gynobasic *Labiatae*

Ovary not 4-lobed; style not gynobasic:

Lower sepal elongated into a tubular spur; ovary 5-locular
Balsaminaceae

Lower sepal not spurred; ovary usually 2-locular:

Ovules numerous:

Leaves simple:

Corolla-lobes induplicate or contorted *Solanaceae*

Corolla-lobes imbricate or folded *Scrophulariaceae*
Leaves compound or 1-foliolate *Bignoniaceae*
Ovules few:
  Anthers 2-locular, opening by a longitudinal slit *Verbenaceae*; see
    also *Chailletiaceae* (*Tapura*), *Stilbeaceae*, and *Chloanthaceae*
  Anthers 1-locular, opening by a longitudinal slit *Selaginaceae*
  Anthers 1–2-locular, opening by a terminal pore *Polygalaceae*
Flowers actinomorphic:
  Leaves opposite or verticillate, mostly exstipulate (to p. 78):
    Anthers opening by apical pores or pore-like slits:
      Filaments of the stamens often geniculate and inflexed; anthers mostly
        opening by a single (rarely 2) pore; leaves mostly with the main
        nerves longitudinally parallel *Melastomataceae*
      Filaments of the stamens neither geniculate nor inflexed; anthers
        opening by 2 pores; leaves without longitudinally parallel nerves:
        Woody plants with usually evergreen leaves; stamens hypogynous
Ericaceae
        Herbs; stamens epipetalous *Gentianaceae*
    Anthers opening by longitudinal slits:
      Leaves gland-dotted or pustulate; petals usually shortly united:
        Styles terminal; stamens epipetalous *Loganiaceae*
        Style not inserted at the inner base of the carpels; stamens not epi-
        petalous *Rutaceae*
        Style inserted at the very inner base of the carpels; stamens epipetalous
Boraginaceae
      Leaves not gland-dotted; petals usually joined high up:
        Style single entire, with often a large more or less capitate stigma:
          Pollen granular:
            Corolla scarious; mostly herbs with radical leaves and dense spikes
              of flowers *Plantaginaceae*
            Corolla not scarious; flowers not in dense spikes:
              Trees or shrubs; leaves often stipulate:
              Stamens 4 or more, rarely 1:
                Ovary of united carpels:
                  Corolla-lobes contorted; fruit a berry *Potaliaceae*
                  Corolla-lobes imbricate; fruit usually a capsule:
                    Intraxylary phloem present; indumentum when present
                      neither glandular, stellate, nor lepidote *Loganiaceae*
                  Intraxylary phloem absent; indumentum when present
                      glandular, stellate, or lepidote *Buddleiaceae*
                Corolla-lobes valvate:
                  Fruit a capsule; seeds winged at each end *Antoniaceae*
                  Fruit indehiscent, drupaceous or baccate; seeds not winged
Strychnaceae
                Ovary of 2 separate carpels but stigmas united *Periplocaceae*
               Stamens usually 2; petals or corolla-lobes imbricate *Oleaceae*
             Mostly herbs or scramblers; leaves not stipulate:
                Embryo straight *Spigeliaceae*

Embryo curved or annular *Solanaceae*
Pollen agglutinated in wax-like masses; flower usually with a corona; leaves exstipulate *Asclepiadaceae*
Pollen granular; flower without a corona; leaves exstipulate:
Corolla-lobes contorted or rarely valvate *Apocynaceae*
Corolla-lobes imbricate:
Leaves not verticillate *Scrophulariaceae*
Leaves verticillate or very crowded:
Seeds without endosperm *Verbenaceae*
Seeds with endosperm; leaves linear or acicular; flowers in dense terminal spikes *Stilbeaceae*
Styles with more than 1 separate stigmas:
Stamens double the number of the corolla-lobes; petals united only at the base:
Mostly herbaceous; flowers bisexual:
Petals not numerous *Lythraceae*
Petals numerous *Molluginaceae*
Trees or shrubs; flowers dioecious *Ebenaceae*
Stamens the same number as the corolla-lobes:
Rudimentary stipules often present; stamens and corolla-lobes 4 *Salvadoraceae*

Stipules absent:
Style gynobasic *Boraginaceae*
Style terminal:
Trees or shrubs:
Ovules numerous in each loculus, or if solitary then corolla-lobes valvate *Loganiaceae*
Ovules 1–2 in each loculus; corolla-lobes imbricate:
Seeds without endosperm *Verbenaceae*
Seeds with endosperm; indumentum often dense and consisting of stellate or dendriform hairs, rarely lepidote *Chloanthaceae*
Herbs or herbaceous climbers:
Ovary imperfectly locular by the intrusive parietal placentas *Gentianaceae*
Ovary perfectly locular with axile placentas:
Ovary 3–5-locular; style 3–5-lobed *Polemoniaceae*
Ovary 2-locular; style simple *Solanaceae*
Leaves alternate or all radical or reduced to scales, rarely absent:
Leafless parasites destitute of chlorophyll; flowers bisexual:
Ovary 1–4–6-lobed and -locular; ovules very numerous in each loculus *Monotropaceae*
Ovary 10–14-lobed, 20–28-locular; ovules solitary in each loculus *Lennoaceae*
Ovary more or less 2-locular; ovules 4 in the ovary *Cuscutaceae*
Not parasitic or rarely so; leaves more or less green and normally developed:
Leaves stipulate, stipules sometimes soon falling off:

Leaves densely covered with viscid processes, mostly all radical; often stemless herbs; flowers mostly in simple circinate cymes; placentas subbasal; styles 3–5, mostly free *Droseraceae*
Leaves not as above:
Flowers unisexual; petals not bifid; ovary usually 3-lobed and 3-locular; calyx not wing-like in fruit *Euphorbiaceae*
Flowers bisexual or unisexual; petals bifid or bilobed; calyx not wing-like in fruit *Chailletiaceae*
Flowers bisexual; petals not bilobed; ovary 1-locular, 1-ovulate; stamens 5 or 10; calyx wing-like in fruit *Ancistrocladaceae*
Flowers bisexual; ovary 3-locular; leaves with tendrils *Cobaeaceae*
Leaves exstipulate:
Stamens hypogynous or perigynous, free from the corolla or slightly adnate to its base (to p. 80):
Anthers opening by terminal pores, often with appendages; calyx persistent, sometimes petaloid; corolla-lobes contorted or imbricate; woody plants *Ericaceae*
Anthers opening by pores; without appendages:
Ovary 3–2-locular; stamens 5; leaves linear, glandular-pilose; pollen grains not united in tetrads *Byblidaceae*
Ovary partially 5-locular; stamens 10–8; leaves not as above; pollen grains in tetrads *Pyrolaceae*
Anthers opening by longitudinal slits:
Stamens 4–6:
Leaves gland-dotted; ovary mostly deeply lobed; petals connivent by their claws; disk usually conspicuous between the stamens and ovary *Rutaceae*
Leaves not gland-dotted; ovary mostly entire:
Petals only slightly united at the base:
Disk present in the flowers, usually conspicuous, not adherent to the ovary:
Corolla-segments valvate; ovules 2–5 in each loculus:
Stamens opposite the petals or more numerous than them *Olacaceae*
Stamens the same number as and alternate with the petals *Icacinaceae*
Corolla-segments and sepals imbricate; ovules numerous:
Leaves not small and ericoid *Pittosporaceae*
Leaves small and ericoid *Tamaricaceae*
Disk absent, or if present, adherent to the ovary:
Ovules numerous; sepals imbricate; not epiphytic *Pittosporaceae*
Ovules numerous; sepals very imbricate; epiphytic or scandent; bracts 3-lobed *Marcgraviaceae*
Ovules 1–2 in each loculus; indumentum not stellate or lepidote; calyx-lobes imbricate; leaves simple *Aquifoliaceae*
Ovules 2 in each loculus, collateral, ascending; leaves pinnate *Connaraceae*

Ovules few in each loculus; indumentum often stellate or
　　　lepidote; calyx-lobes valvate or open   *Styracaceae*
Petals united high up; sometimes free at the base:
Calyx-lobes valvate, herbaceous; anthers connivent around the
　　style:
　　Herbs; not aquatic   *Campanulaceae*
　　Trees or shrubs   *Burseraceae*
Calyx-lobes imbricate, rather leathery; shrubs or shrublets;
　　anthers free   *Epacridaceae*
Calyx-lobes imbricate; herbs from a woody rhizome
　　　　　　　　　　　　　　　　　　　　　　　Stackhousiaceae
Calyx-lobes very imbricate; aquatic herbs   *Plantaginaceae*
Stamens more than 6:
Stamens connate into a tube   *Meliaceae*
Stamens free or slightly connate only at the base:
Disk absent; corolla long and tubular:
　Calyx very much imbricate; flowers bisexual   *Fouquieriaceae*
　Calyx not or very slightly imbricate; flowers unisexual
　　　　　　　　　　　　　　　　　　　　　　　　　Ebenaceae
Disk present, or if inconspicuous or absent then the corolla-tube
　　very short:
Leaves gland-dotted, often compound or unifoliolate *Rutaceae*
Leaves not gland-dotted, simple or very rarely compound:
　Disk present in the flowers:
　　Leaves well developed, not small and ericoid:
　　　Leaves simple; bark not bitter:
　　　　Petals contorted   *Cyrillaceae*
　　　　Petals valvate   *Olacaceae*
　　　Leaves compound or unifoliolate; bark usually bitter
　　　　　　　　　　　　　　　　　　　　　　　Simaroubaceae
　　Leaves small and ericoid; flowers in spikes or racemes
　　　　　　　　　　　　　　　　　　　　　　　Tamaricaceae
　Disk absent:
　　Trees or shrubs:
　　　Ovules 1–2 in each loculus; indumentum not stellate; calyx-
　　　　lobes imbricate:
　　　　Calyx-tube very short   *Aquifoliaceae*
　　　　Calyx-tube long and slender   *Thymelaeaceae*
　　　Ovules few in each loculus, indumentum often stellate or
　　　　lepidote; calyx-lobes valvate or open   *Styracaceae*
　　　Ovules numerous in each loculus   *Pentadiplandraceae*
　　Herbs; sepals often scarious   *Molluginaceae*
Stamens inserted on the corolla-tube or in a column adnate to the
　　stigma (from p. 79):
Style gynobasic:
Style 1; fruit composed of pyrenes or nutlets:
Flowers axillary; corolla-lobes plicate; ovary 5-locular
　　　　　　　　　　　　　　　　　　　　　　　　Nolanaceae

Flowers mostly in scorpioid cymes; corolla-lobes contorted or imbricate; ovary 2–4-locular   *Boraginaceae*

Styles 2; fruit mostly capsular   *Convolvulaceae*

Style not gynobasic, terminal:

Corolla valvate or plaited in bud (in the latter case the limb may be somewhat twisted but is not truly imbricate):

Ovules 1–4 in each ovary loculus:

Ovules basal, erect:

Anthers not united   *Convolvulaceae*

Anthers united into a tube   *Brunoniaceae*

Ovules pendulous from the top of the ovary   *Icacinaceae*

Ovules numerous in each ovary loculus:

Flowers with a corona; pollen agglutinated in wax-like masses

    Asclepiadaceae

Flowers without a corona; pollen not agglutinated in wax-like masses   *Solanaceae*

Corolla imbricate or contorted in bud:

Corolla contorted; ovary mostly 3-locular with axile placentas

    Polemoniaceae

Corolla contorted; ovary 1–2-locular:

Carpels completely united   *Hydrophyllaceae*

Carpels more or less free:

Pollen agglutinated in wax-like masses   *Asclepiadaceae*

Pollen not agglutinated in wax-like masses   *Apocynaceae*

Corolla imbricate; ovary 1–2- (rarely up to 5-) locular:

Flowers arranged in a dense leafy head; shrubs with sessile imbricate leaves; ovary 2-locular   *Bruniaceae*

Flowers in dense spikes; herbs with radical leaves and broad sheathing petioles   *Plantaginaceae*

Flowers neither in heads nor in spikes, sometimes corymbose or cymose:

Ovary 3–10-locular; leaves evergreen:

Stamens 4–5:

Anthers 2-locular   *Diapensiaceae*

Anthers 1-locular   *Epacridaceae*

Stamens 10   *Polygalaceae*

Ovary 1–2- or spuriously 4-locular:

Herbs:

Style undivided or very shortly lobed; lower leaves opposite

    Gentianaceae

Style deeply 2-lobed or styles 2; all the leaves alternate or radical   *Hydrophyllaceae*

Style undivided; stigmas terminal, small or more or less dilated; all the leaves alternate   *Solanaceae*

Trees or shrubs; fruits a pyrene or nut:

Fruits winged   *Cardiopteridaceae*

Fruits not winged   *Ehretiaceae*

Stamens fewer than the corolla-lobes; leaves mostly opposite (from p. 76):
Flowers actinomorphic:
Stamens more than 1:
Ovules numerous; corolla not dry and scarious:
Ovary constantly and completely 2-locular:
Herbs:

Corolla-lobes induplicate or contorted-plicate	*Solanaceae*
Corolla-lobes imbricate	*Scrophulariaceae*
Shrubs; stamens 2	*Oleaceae*

Ovary 1-locular or imperfectly 2-locular by the intrusive placentas
Gesneriaceae
Ovules 1–8 in each loculus of the ovary; capsule circumscissile; corolla
scarious with 4 lobes; mostly herbs with radical leaves and spicate
inflorescences   *Plantaginaceae*
Ovules 1–2 in each loculus of the ovary; corolla not scarious:
Corolla-lobes not more than the calyx-lobes:
Corolla-lobes quite equal; ovules mostly pendulous   *Oleaceae*
Corolla-lobes slightly unequal or limb oblique; ovules erect
Verbenaceae
Corolla-lobes about 3 times as many as the calyx-lobes   *Sapotaceae*
Stamen 1; corolla articulating above the base; flowers in corymbose
panicles   *Antoniaceae*
Flowers zygomorphic:
Placenta free-basal, more or less globose; ovules numerous; ovary 1-
locular; stamens 2, anthers 1-locular; stigma sessile or style very
short; aquatic or swamp plants   *Lentibulariaceae*
Placentas axile, or if subbasal then ovules very few:
Ovules numerous in the whole ovary or in each loculus of the ovary, or
if 2 then superposed:
Anthers mostly free from each other; ovary completely 2-locular, with
the placentas on the septum; loculi ad- and abaxial
Scrophulariaceae
Anthers often coherent; ovary imperfectly 2-locular by the variously
intrusive parietal placentas, the latter placed right and left of the
floral axis   *Gesneriaceae*
Anthers free but connivent; ovary mostly 2-locular and then the loculi
ad- and abaxial (antero-posterior); leaves often compound; woody
plants, very rarely herbaceous; seeds often winged, transverse
Bignoniaceae
Anthers often connivent in pairs; ovary 1–4-locular; fruit usually with
a hard endocarp; seeds not winged:
Herbs with vesicular glands; leaves opposite or alternate; fruit sometimes prickly; disk mostly inconspicuous   *Pedaliaceae*
Herbs or rarely shrubs with tumid nodes and opposite or verticillate
leaves; seeds inserted on hardened outgrowths from the central
placentas; leaves often prominently marked with cystoliths;
valves of the capsule opening elastically from the apex; disk
cupular or annular   *Acanthaceae*

Shrubs; nodes not tumid; leaves alternate; 2 inner lobes of the corolla broadly emarginate or bifid; fruit a drupe; disk subannular or lobed *Chailletiaceae*
Ovule solitary in each loculus of the ovary, or if 2 then collateral:
Leaves opposite or verticillate:
Ovary entire; style terminal:
Filaments free from each other:
Calyx not bilabiate; ovary 9–2-locular; calyx-lobes not hooked *Verbenaceae*
Calyx bilabiate; ovary 1-locular with 1 erect ovule; 3 calyx-lobes hooked *Phrymaceae*
Filaments forming a sheath split on its upper edge *Polygalaceae*
Ovary 4-lobed; style gynobasic *Labiatae*
Leaves alternate:
Filaments free from each other:
Anthers 2-locular; leaves usually studded with resinous glands *Myoporaceae*
Anthers 1-locular opening by a slit; leaves not studded with glands:
Ovary 2-locular *Selaginaceae*
Ovary 1-locular *Globulariaceae*
Filaments more or less monadelphous and split along the top; anthers 1- or rarely 2-locular, opening by a pore at the top *Polygalaceae*

GROUP 12

One carpel or two or more united carpels with axile, basal, or apical placentation; ovary superior; petals absent

Bisexual or male (and often the female) flowers without a calyx (perianth) (to p. 84)
Fleshy herbs parasitic on roots, without green colouring matter; ovule solitary in a 1-locular ovary *Balanophoraceae*
Moss-like or hepatic-like aquatic herbs with minute flowers; ovules 2 or more in a 1-locular ovary *Podostemaceae*
Neither parasites nor aquatic plants with above habit:
Leaves radical, palminerved; flowers in a slender spike; carpel 1; ovule 1, erect from the base of the loculus; herb with creeping rhizome *Podophyllaceae*
Leaves not all radical; above characters not associated:
Trees or shrubs with whorled scale-like leaves *Casuarinaceae*
Trees, shrubs, or herbs with normally developed leaves:
Leaves stipulate; stipules sometimes adnate to the petiole:
Ovary 1-locular:
Herbs or shrubs; leaves usually alternate; flowers in dense spikes; petiole not dilated and not enclosing the young bud
Piperaceae; see also *Myricaceae* (with glandular aromatic leaves)
Trees or shrubs with alternate leaves; flowers minute on a common open receptacle, the fruit becoming immersed in it *Moraceae*

Herbs, shrubs, or trees with opposite leaves   *Chloranthaceae*

Large trees; leaves alternate, palmately nerved and lobed, the dilated petiole enclosing the young bud   *Platanaceae*

Ovary 2- or more-locular; leaves alternate:

Ovules 1–2 in each loculus of the ovary; stipules rarely spinulose, often caducous:

Flowers various, sometimes in an involucre margined with fleshy glands; seeds usually with copious endosperm; ovary usually 2–3- or more-locular   *Euphorbiaceae*

Male flowers in catkins or slender spikes; endosperm absent from the seeds; ovary 2–6-locular:

Fruit with a cupular involucre or enclosed by the latter   *Fagaceae*

Fruit cone-like, with imbricate scales   *Betulaceae*

Fruits separate, not arranged as above; leaves trifoliolate
          Picrodendraceae

Ovules numerous; stipules not spinulose; large trees; leaves not plicately nerved   *Hamamelidaceae*

Ovules numerous; stipules spinulose when old; leaves opposite, plicately nerved; low shrubs   *Myrothamnaceae*

Leaves without stipules:

Trees or shrubs with hard wood:

Flowers in a cyathium   *Euphorbiaceae*

Flowers not in a cyathium:

Leaves not aromatic; flowers dioecious:

Males in catkins on the young branchlets or below the leaves
          Balanopsidaceae

Male and female flowers solitary, precocious   *Eucommiaceae*

Leaves aromatic, often glandular; flowers in dense spikes; mostly swamp plants; leaves simple   *Myricaceae*

Leaves not aromatic, pinnate; not swamp plants   *Oleaceae*

Leaves not aromatic, fleshy; flowers dioecious; ovary 4-locular; stamens 4; leaves simple; maritime plants   *Batidaceae*

Herbs, sometimes slightly woody at the base:

Ovary 1-locular:

No stinging hairs; stems not fibrous; epidermal cells without cysto-liths   *Chenopodiaceae*

No stinging hairs; stems not fibrous; flowers minute, usually densely spicate; epidermal cells often with cystoliths   *Piperaceae*

Stinging hairs often present; stems often fibrous; epidermal cells mostly with prominent cystoliths   *Urticaceae*

Ovary 2–3-locular; flowers much reduced, often arranged in a cyathium with glands on the margin   *Euphorbiaceae*

Ovary 4-locular; annual herbs with minute unisexual flowers; styles 2; stamen 1   *Callitrichaceae*

All the flowers (or at any rate the male) with a calyx, sometimes minute or petaloid and long tubular (from p. 83):

Moss-like or hepatic-like herbs with minute flowers (submerged in fresh water)   *Podostemaceae*

Not as above:

Leaves opposite or verticillate, never all radical (to p. 88):

Leaves stipulate (to p. 86):

Stamens more than twice the number of the sepals:

Flowers unisexual:

Style terminal   *Euphorbiaceae*

Style basal   *Cynocrambaceae*

Flowers bisexual:

Sepals free or nearly so; stamens hypogynous:

Filaments trifid at the apex, the two lateral lobes overlapping the anther; ovary 10-locular; stamens 10   *Zygophyllaceae*

Filaments entire; ovary 5-locular; stigma ligulate, thick   *Geraniaceae*

Filaments entire; ovary 1–5-locular; stigmas not ligulate:

Herbs or slightly woody at the base   *Molluginaceae*

Trees; stipules large and membranous   *Cunoniaceae*

Sepals united into a tube; stamens inserted on the tube, more or less perigynous:

Fruit capsular   *Ficoidaceae*

Fruit an achene   *Rosaceae*

Stamens definite, up to twice as many as the sepals:

Stamens the same number as and alternate with the sepals, 4 or 5:

Trees or shrubs, not fleshy; leaves often toothed   *Rhamnaceae*

Herbs or undershrubs with fleshy entire leaves   *Ficoidaceae*

Stamens the same number as and opposite the sepals or more numerous or fewer:

Ovary with free-central placentation; ovules usually several to numerous   *Caryophyllaceae*

Ovary with axile, basal, or apical placentation:

Flowers arranged in an involucre (cyathium) margined with fleshy often more or less similunar glands; male flower with only one stamen, jointed about the middle; ovary often stipitate, mostly 3-locular   *Euphorbiaceae*

Flowers not as above; stamens usually more than 1; ovary mostly sessile:

Flowers unisexual:

Ovary 2- or more-locular   *Euphorbiaceae*

Ovary 1-locular:

Ovule erect:

Filaments inflexed in bud; mostly herbaceous plants with fibrous stems and sometimes stinging hairs; juice not milky   *Urticaceae*

Filaments not inflexed in bud; mostly trees and shrubs, very rarely herbs; juice mostly milky; flowers often minute and arranged on or inside an enlarged 'receptacle'   *Moraceae*

Ovule pendulous:

Filaments not inflexed in bud:

Fruit a drupe; flowers monoecious or subdioecious   *Ulmaceae*

Fruit a small dry achene; flowers dioecious   *Cannabiaceae*

Filaments erect or inflexed in bud *Moraceae*
Flowers bisexual:
Sepals free or nearly so; stamens more or less hypogynous; ovary
3–10-locular:
Ovules numerous in each loculus; ovary 3–5-locular; stamens
often 5, rarely up to 10:
Stipules often lobed or lacerate, persistent; mostly herbs
Molluginaceae
Stipules membranous, deciduous; trees *Cunoniaceae*
Ovules 2 or more in each loculus; ovary 5–10-locular; stamens 5
or 10:
Filaments 3-fid at the apex; ovary 10-locular; ovules 2–3 in each
loculus, ascending; leaves opposite, connate, subterete
Zygophyllaceae
Filaments entire; ovary 5-locular, beaked; ovules pendulous
from the inner angle of the loculi; leaves opposite, entire
or 3-lobed *Geraniaceae*
Sepals free or nearly so; stamens hypogynous or perigynous; ovary
1-locular:
Stipules forming a tube (ochrea) around the stem; fruit a nut
Polygonaceae
Stipules not forming a tube round the stem, often scarious and
bilobed or more divided; leaves opposite *Illecebraceae*
Stipules minute; leaves verticillate *Molluginaceae*
Sepals connate into a tube; stamens perigynous; ovary 1–5-locular:
Flowers bisexual; leaves simple *Ficoidaceae*
Flowers dioecious; leaves 1–3-foliolate *Rosaceae*
Leaves without stipules:
Ovary 1-locular, with free-central placentation, not septate or only im-
perfectly septate at the base; ovules usually numerous
Caryophyllaceae
Ovary with axile, basal, or apical placentation:
Ovary and fruit compressed contrary to the septum, 2-locular; trees or
shrubs with perulate buds; leaves simple or palmately lobed or
pinnately foliolate; flowers andromonoecious or dioecious
Aceraceae
Ovary if compressed then not contrary to the septum or septa:
Ovules 2 or more in each loculus of the ovary or in a 1-locular
ovary:
Flowers bisexual:
Shrubs or trees with woody branches:
Calyx more or less spreading, or not tubular:
Large disk often present *Celastraceae*
No disk:
Calyx shortly tubular, segments petaloid; ovary 4-locular
Geissolomataceae
Calyx of free sepals, not petaloid; ovary 5- or 3-locular
Ledocarpaceae

Calyx tubular, lobes valvate; disk absent or inconspicuous:
  Ovary 2–4-locular; calyx not or rarely petaloid, often with accessory lobes *Lythraceae*
  Ovary many-locular *Sonneratiaceae*
  Ovary 4-locular; calyx petaloid, lobes valvate; stamens opposite the lobes; flowers often in heads *Proteaceae*
  Ovary 4-locular; calyx more or less petaloid; stamens alternate with the lobes *Penaeaceae*
Herbs:
  Sepals united into a tube; stamens perigynous:
    Sepals imbricate, without accessory lobes *Ficoidaceae*
    Sepals valvate, often with accessory lobes *Lythraceae*
  Sepals free or nearly so; stamens usually hypogynous:
    Style-branches or styles 2–3; leaves connate at the base; ovules 1–2 *Illecebraceae*
    Styles more or less free; leaves not connate at the base *Amaranthaceae*

Flowers unisexual:
  Leaves digitately compound *Euphorbiaceae*
  Leaves simple; ovary 3-locular *Buxaceae*
  Leaves simple; ovary 2-locular *Crypteroniaceae*
  Leaves simple; ovary 1-locular *Garryaceae*
Ovule solitary in each loculus of the ovary or in a 1-locular ovary:
  Stamens circinately involute in bud; calyx usually long-tubular, often coloured; bracts sometimes petaloid *Nyctaginaceae*
  Stamens sometimes inflexed but not circinate in bud; calyx often scarious but rarely petaloid; bracts often scarious:
    Submerged aquatics with verticillate divided leaves; flowers monoecious *Ceratophyllaceae*
    Not submerged aquatics; leaves very rarely verticillate:
      Flowers not arranged in a cyathium; mostly bisexual:
        Trees, shrubs, or undershrubs with woody stems; embryo straight, usually very small:
          Stamens numerous *Monimiaceae*; see also *Trimeniaceae*
          Stamens 6–9; flowers dioecious; calyx not petaloid, deeply lobed; flowers cymose *Barbeyaceae*
          Stamens definite (sometimes reduced to one); calyx often petaloid, usually long-tubular; flowers often in heads *Thymelaeaceae*
          Stamens 4; calyx membranous, campanulate, 2-lipped; flowers densely spicate *Batidaceae*
        Herbs sometimes a little woody at the base; embryo more or less curved:
          Sepals united into a tube; stamens perigynous *Ficoidaceae*
          Sepals free or nearly so; stamens mostly hypogynous:
            Calyx scarious only on the margin; stamens hypogynous; styles free or nearly so *Molluginaceae*
            Calyx often hyaline all over; stamens often slightly perigynous and connate at the base *Amaranthaceae*

Calyx herbaceous; stamens hypogynous or slightly perigynous, mostly free   *Chenopodiaceae*

Flowers ♂ ♀, arranged in a cyathium margined with glands   *Euphorbiaceae*

Leaves alternate or radical or reduced to scales, sometimes tubiform or pitcher-like (from p. 85):

Parasitic plants with the leaves reduced to scales:

Anthers opening by slits:

Flowers spicate; sepals imbricate   *Monotropaceae*

Flowers densely crowded; sepals valvate   *Balanophoraceae*

Anthers opening by valves   *Lauraceae*

Not parasitic; leaves normally developed:

Leaves stipulate (to p. 89):

Stamens monadelphous, usually numerous; calyx mostly valvate:

Anthers 2-locular; flowers bisexual

Sterculiaceae; see also *Gyrostemonaceae*

Anthers 1-locular; flowers bisexual   *Malvaceae*

Anthers 2-locular; flowers unisexual   *Euphorbiaceae*

Stamens free or shortly connate at the base:

Stamens the same number as the sepals and alternate with them:

Herbs   *Molluginaceae*

Trees, shrubs, or climbers   *Rhamnaceae*

Stamens the same number as the sepals and opposite to them or more numerous or fewer:

Leaves compound:

Flowers unisexual:

Ovary 1-locular, of 1 carpel   *Moraceae*

Ovary 2- or more-locular:

Leaves pinnate   *Rhoipteleaceae*

Leaves not pinnate   *Euphorbiaceae*

Flowers bisexual:

Flowers actinomorphic:

Seeds without endosperm; style basal or ventral on the 1-carpelled ovary   *Rosaceae*

Seeds usually with endosperm; style or styles more or less terminal; ovary of more than 1 carpel   *Saxifragaceae*

Flowers slightly zygomorphic; leaves pinnate   *Melianthaceae*

Leaves simple:

Ovary 2- or more-locular:

Flowers unisexual:

Ovary quite superior; anthers opening by slits:

Male flowers not in catkins   *Euphorbiaceae*

Male flowers in catkins   *Betulaceae*

Ovary semisuperior; anthers often opening by valves   *Hamamelidaceae*

Flowers bisexual:

Trees or shrubs; ovary 2-locular; carpels often free at the top; anther-loculi often opening by valves; stipules often paired:

Ovary quite superior; stipule single, adnate to the petiole
Tetracentraceae

Ovary inferior to semi-inferior; stipules paired, free
Hamamelidaceae

Herbs:
Stamens perigynous; ovary 1–3-locular *Saxifragaceae*
Stamens hypogynous; ovary 3–5-locular, very rarely 2-locular
Molluginaceae

Ovary 1-locular, mostly of 1 carpel:
Stipules ochreate, i.e. sheathing and more or less membranous around the stem *Polygonaceae*
Stipules not ochreate:
Ovary of 1 carpel; stamens inflexed in bud; flowers mostly unisexual:
Herbs *Urticaceae*
Trees or shrubs *Moraceae*
Ovary of 1 carpel; stamens erect in bud; flowers bisexual
Rosaceae

Ovary usually of more than 1 carpel; stamens erect in bud; flowers always unisexual:
Flowers in catkins *Salicaceae*
Flowers not in catkins *Euphorbiaceae*
Ovary usually of more than 1 carpel; stamens erect in bud; flowers bisexual:
Ovary 1-locular *Petiveriaceae*
Ovary 2- or more-locular *Phytolaccaceae*
Leaves exstipulate:
Stamens the same number as and alternating with the calyx-lobes:
Leaves compound, mostly pinnate:
Flowers mostly bisexual, not involucrate *Burseraceae*
Flowers dioecious, the females solitary, enclosed in and adnate to an involucre *Julianiaceae*
Leaves simple, minute; small shrubs *Ficoidaceae*
Leaves simple, dentate; annual herb; stamens 1–2 *Circaeasteraceae*
Stamens the same number as the calyx-lobes and opposite to them, or more numerous or fewer:
Leaves compound:
Herbs; ovary composed of 1 carpel; leaves ternately compound; flowers paniculate or racemose, usually very small *Ranunculaceae*
Shrubs or trees:
Stamens the same number as and opposite to the calyx-(perianth) segments; leaves often many times divided; flowers often in heads or dense spikes or racemes; calyx mostly petaloid *Proteaceae*
Stamens usually more numerous than the calyx-lobes; calyx rarely petaloid:
Flowers unisexual; leaves digitate *Euphorbiaceae*
Flowers mostly polygamous; leaves pinnate; bark bitter, not resinous *Simaroubaceae*

Flowers mostly polygamo-dioecious; leaves pinnate; bark not
bitter; wood not resinous   *Sapindaceae*
Flowers various; leaves pinnate or trifoliolate; wood resinous
Anacardiaceae
Leaves simple:
Leaves modified into pitchers or tubes:
Flowers dioecious; stamens united into a column   *Nepenthaceae*
Flowers bisexual; stamens free   *Sarraceniaceae*
Leaves not modified as above:
Stamens circinately involute in bud; calyx-tube often rather long;
ovary 1-locular; ovule 1, basal   *Nyctaginaceae*
Stamens sometimes inflexed but not circinate in bud:
Stamens more or less connate into a central column:
Herbs or weak climbers; calyx (perianth) often long-tubular and
oblique; ovules numerous; seeds with smooth endosperm;
flowers bisexual   *Aristolochiaceae*
Habit various; flowers unisexual; calyx not oblique; disk or disk-
glands often present; ovules pendulous; endosperm smooth
Euphorbiaceae
Trees or shrubs; calyx mostly small, not oblique; ovule erect; seeds
with ruminate endosperm   *Myristicaceae*
Stamens free or the filaments shortly connate only at the base:
Stamens distinctly perigynous or flowers unisexual; sepals connate
into a tube below:
Herbs or twiners; anthers opening by longitudinal slits:
Twiners; flowers in axillary spikes, racemes, or panicles; ovule
solitary, basal:
Anthers opening by slits lengthwise; embryo not spirally
twisted   *Agdestidaceae*
Anthers opening by terminal pores or pore-like slits; embryo
spirally twisted   *Basellaceae*
Not twiners; herbs:
Calyx long and tubular, many-ribbed; stamens about 11,
unequal; ovules 2 or more   *Lythraceae*
Calyx-tube short or almost absent:
Ovary quite superior; leaves often thick and fleshy
Crassulaceae
Ovary semisuperior; leaves not fleshy   *Ficoidaceae*
Trees or shrubs; anthers opening by valves or longitudina
slits:
Small shrubs; stamens numerous, in bundles alternate with the
calyx-lobes   *Ficoidaceae*
Mostly undershrubs with often rather long and usually petaloid
calyx (perianth); leaves frequently small and evergreen,
sometimes much divided; stamens definite:
Calyx-lobes imbricate:
Fruit indehiscent   *Thymelaeaceae*
Fruit a capsule   *Aquilariaceae*

Calyx-lobes valvate:

Stamens the same number as and opposite the calyx-lobes
Proteaceae

Stamens more than the primary lobes of the calyx
Lythraceae

Trees or shrubs; leaves usually large; stamens mostly numerous
Monimiaceae

Trees or shrubs; leaves large, very rarely reduced; stamens usually double the number of the calyx-lobes, in 2 or 4 rows *Lauraceae*

Stamens hypogynous or slightly perigynous if accompanied by a disk, or flowers unisexual:

Flowers in a cyathium margined by bracts *Euphorbiaceae*

Flowers not in a cyathium:

Trees or shrubs:

Leaves glandular; flowers in catkin-like spikes or racemes; berry often warted *Myricaceae*

Leaves not glandular; flowers not in catkin-like inflorescences:

Leaves very small and ericoid; fruit drupaceous, succulent; ovary 2–9-locular with 1 axile ovule in each loculus; stamens 2–3 *Empetraceae*

Leaves not as above and other characters not associated:

Ovules 6–8, pendulous *Peridiscaceae*

Ovules 2–1:

Flowers unisexual; ovule solitary, pendulous; seeds with straight embryo *Euphorbiaceae*; see also *Trimeniaceae* and *Daphniphyllaceae*

Flowers bisexual; ovule solitary, pendulous; embryo straight *Olacaceae*

Flowers unisexual or polygamous; ovules 2 in each loculus, collateral or the lower ascending; seeds without endosperm and spirally twisted embryo
Sapindaceae

Flowers bisexual or unisexual; ovule solitary, basal; seeds with the embryo curved around the endosperm:

Fruit a capsule; anthers introrse *Barbeuiaceae*

Fruit indehiscent, fleshy or drupe-like:

Ovary of 12–4 free or more or less connate carpels; anthers introrse *Phytolaccaceae*

Ovary 1-locular; anthers extrorse *Achatocarpaceae*

Herbs:

Ovule 1 or more in each carpel *Molluginaceae*

Ovule 1 in each carpel or ovary; ovary of several subdistinct carpels *Phytolaccaceae*

Ovule 1: ovary 1-locular:

Perianth herbaceous *Chenopodiaceae*

Perianth more or less scarious *Amaranthaceae*

GROUP 13

*One carpel or more than one carpel with axile, basal, or apical placentas;
ovary inferior; petals present, free*

Leaves opposite or verticillate, never all radical, rarely reduced to scales (to
   p. 93):
 Leaves compound, much divided or unifoliolate; flowers mostly umbellate or
    capitate, rarely racemose; calyx small, entire or toothed; petals usually
    5, valvate or slightly imbricate; disk on top of the ovary, often confluent
    with the style or styles; ovule solitary in each loculus, pendulous; seeds
    with copious endosperm and small embryo:
  Trees or shrubs; petals usually valvate; ovary 1–many-locular; fruit usually
     a berry or drupe   *Araliaceae*
  Herbs; petals imbricate, rarely valvate; ovary 2-locular; styles 2; fruit of
     dry indehiscent mericarps   *Umbelliferae*
 Leaves simple:
  Leaves stipulate:
   Stamens the same number as and opposite the petals   *Rhamnaceae*
   Stamens alternate with the petals or more numerous:
    Ovary composed of 2 carpels, more or less free at the apex; flowers mostly
       capitate; ovules pendulous; trees or shrubs; anthers often opening
       by valves   *Hamamelidaceae*
    Ovary mostly 2-locular; flowers rarely capitate; anthers opening by slits
                                                               Cunoniaceae
    Ovary composed of 2–6 carpels, 2–6-locular or 1-locular by suppression
       of the septa; flowers rarely congested:
     Ovules pendulous; mostly maritime trees or shrubs   *Rhizophoraceae*
     Ovules axile; stipules intrapetiolar   *Dialypetalanthaceae*
    Ovary various; flowers rarely in heads; ovules ascending or attached to
       the central axis; trees, shrubs, or herbs   *Rosaceae*
  Leaves exstipulate:
   Trees, shrubs, or climbers:
   Stamens numerous:
    Ovary loculi not superposed:
     Leaves gland-dotted; style simple with a small capitate stigma or very
        rarely 3–4-lobed   *Myrtaceae*
     Leaves with pellucid lines or often with stellate hairs; style 5–10-lobed
        or styles 2–5 and more or less free; ovary 2–10-locular
                                                               Philadelphaceae
     Leaves not gland-dotted, with longitudinally parallel nerves; stamens
        jointed, the connective often produced at the base; anthers open-
        ing by a terminal pore   *Melastomataceae*
    Ovary loculi superposed; leaves not gland-dotted; style simple
                                                               Punicaceae
   Stamens as many to twice as many as the petals:
    Stamens the same number as and opposite to the petals; mostly parasitic
       shrubs or trees; calyx usually much reduced   *Loranthaceae*

Stamens the same number as and alternate with the petals or more
   numerous:
   Anthers opening by a terminal pore; filaments often jointed; leaves
      often with 3–9 longitudinally parallel nerves   *Melastomataceae*
   Anthers opening by longitudinal slits; calyx mostly valvate:
      Ovule solitary; fruits mostly drupaceous; endosperm copious; petals
         without alternate scales   *Cornaceae*
      Ovules up to 3 in each loculus; fruit a drupe, not winged; flowers
         small, in cymes; petals with alternating scales
                              Oliniaceae; see also *Escalloniaceae* (*Grevea*)
      Ovules numerous; fruit a capsule or berry; flowers conspicuous; no
         scales   *Hydrangeaceae*
      Ovules 2 or more; fruits mostly winged; endosperm absent; flowers
         in heads, spikes, racemes, or panicles   *Combretaceae*
      Ovules numerous; stamens double the number of the petals
                                                          Onagraceae
Herbs; sometimes slightly woody, but then often with fleshy leaves:
   Anthers opening by a terminal pore; leaves mostly with longitudinally
      parallel nerves; connective of anthers usually produced at the base
      and jointed to the filament   *Melastomataceae*
   Anthers opening by longitudinal slits:
      Flowers in umbels or heads; ovary 2-locular; carpels separating in fruit
         and suspended by the divided thread-like central axis (carpophore)
                                                          Umbelliferae
      Flowers in heads surrounded by bracts; ovary 2–3-locular; carpels not
         as above   *Cornaceae*
      Flowers not in umbels or heads; carpels not separating in fruit:
         Placenta pendulous from the apex of the 1-locular ovary; ovules
            numerous   *Vahliaceae*
         Ovules 1–4, pendulous from the top of the ovary-loculi
                                                          Haloragidaceae
         Placentas axile with numerous ovules, or ovules very few and pendulous
            from the apex of the usually 4-locular ovary:
            Cotyledons equal   *Onagraceae*
            Cotyledons very unequal; floating herbs   *Trapaceae*
         Placentas at the bottom of the ovary-loculi; petals numerous
                                                          Ficoidaceae
Leaves alternate or all radical:
Flowers unisexual (to p. 94):
   Flowers not in heads or umbels, sometimes paniculate or racemose:
      Leaves stipulate; stipules paired; no tendrils; stamens mostly numerous,
         straight; flowers often somewhat zygomorphic   *Begoniaceae*
      Leaves without stipules; tendrils often present; stamens definite or rarely
         many, anthers often conduplicate or twisted, mostly 3; flowers actino-
         morphic, conspicuous   *Cucurbitaceae*
      Leaves without stipules or if present then adnate to the petiole, sometimes
         anisophyllous and then the smaller leaf appearing like a stipule; no
         tendrils; anthers straight:

Styles 4; petals 4, involute in bud; leaves with 3–5 main nerves; ovary 4-locular; flowers not minute; trees or shrubs   *Rhizophoraceae*

Styles 1–4, separate; petals 2 or 4, valvate in bud; ovary 1–4-locular; flowers mostly minute; mostly herbs, sometimes with large radical leaves or often aquatic   *Haloragidaceae*

Flowers arranged in heads, umbels, or corymbs:

Fruit of dry indehiscent mericarps; ovary 2-locular; styles 2; herbs with usually much dissected leaves   *Umbelliferae*

Characters not as above:

Anthers opening by a single lateral valve; petals linear-spathulate; ovary 2-locular; ovules solitary; leaves stipulate   *Hamamelidaceae*

Anthers opening by slits; petals usually not linear-spathulate:

Leaves usually stipulate; flowers usually umbellate   *Araliaceae*

Leaves without stipules; flowers capitate or corymbose:

Petals imbricate   *Nyssaceae*

Petals valvate   *Cornaceae*

Leaves without stipules; male flowers corymbose, female solitary   *Onagraceae*

Flowers bisexual:

Stamens numerous:

Aquatic herbs with floating leaves; flowers usually large and showy; ovules numerous   *Nymphaeaceae*

Not aquatic:

Herbs:

Leaves exstipulate; sepals more than 2:

Styles more or less free; low herbs often with rosettes of leaves   *Saxifragaceae*

Styles more or less united; erect or climbing, mostly roughly hispid-pilose herbs   *Loasaceae*

Leaves stipulate, stipules often laciniated and thread-like; seeds with more or less copious endosperm; sepals 2   *Portulacaceae*

Leaves stipulate, not laciniate; seeds without endosperm; sepals more than 2   *Rosaceae*

Trees or shrubs:

Leaves gland-dotted; stamens mostly very numerous:

Fruits not winged   *Myrtaceae*

Fruits broadly winged   *Lecythidaceae*

Leaves not gland-dotted:

Style more or less divided or styles separate; rarely maritime; leaves often compound, stipulate:

Stipules not intrapetiolar   *Rosaceae*

Stipules intrapetiolar and connate; leaves digitate   *Araliaceae*

Style simple; usually maritime; leaves simple   *Rhizophoraceae*

Stamens definite in relation to the sepals and petals, the same number as or about twice as many, rarely fewer:

Stamens the same number as and opposite the petals:

Leaves stipulate or not; not parasites; flowers often crowded into heads; ovary 3-locular:

Fruit not enclosed by the calyx; ovules erect from the base of the ovary
 Rhamnaceae

Fruit enclosed by the greatly enlarged calyx; ovules pendulous from the
 apex of the ovary *Erythropalaceae*

Leaves exstipulate; often parasitic; ovary 1-locular *Loranthaceae*

Stamens the same number as and alternate with the petals or more
 numerous or fewer:

Anthers opening by apical pores; leaves often with very prominent
 longitudinally parallel nerves; anthers often unequal, with the
 connective produced at the base *Melastomataceae*

Anthers not opening by pores; leaves usually not as above:

Leaves stipulate:

Herbs:

Leaves simple; sepals 2; fruit a capsule *Portulacaceae*

Leaves usually compound or much dissected, sometimes peltate;
 sepals obsolete or more than 2; fruit of 2 indehiscent mericarps
 Umbelliferae

Trees or shrubs:

Flowers actinomorphic; corolla not gibbous at the base; stamens not
 unilateral:

Leaves simple; stipules paired; flowers often capitate; fruit woody;
 stamens up to twice as many as the petals
 Hamamelidaceae

Leaves compound, rarely simple; stamens as many as the petals;
 fruit a berry or drupaceous; flowers often umbellate
 Araliaceae

Leaves compound or simple; stamens more than the petals; fruit
 not woody:

Filaments not toothed at the top *Rosaceae*

Filaments broad and toothed at the top *Pterostemonaceae*

Flowers zygomorphic; corolla often gibbous at the base; stamens
 unilateral *Trigoniaceae*

Leaves exstipulate:

Flowers arranged in heads surrounded by a brightly coloured involucre
 simulating a single flower; petals very unequal, fewer than the
 stamens; styles subulate, elongate *Hamamelidaceae*

Flowers not as above and other characters not associated:

Herbs:

Flowers umbellate; ovules solitary, pendulous:

Ovary 2-locular; carpels separating in fruit into 2 indehiscent
 mericarps *Umbelliferae*

Ovary 3–4-locular; carpels not separating in fruit *Araliaceae*

Flower not umbellate:

Ovules more than 1 in each loculus or in a 1-locular ovary:

Mostly scapigerous herbs; ovary 1–3-locular:

Fruit a capsule; flowers rarely solitary *Saxifragaceae*

Fruit indehiscent; flowers solitary *Donatiaceae*

Leafy-stemmed herbs; ovary mostly 4-locular *Onagraceae*

Ovules solitary in each loculus of the ovary:
Style 1, with a capitate or shortly lobed stigma; flowers mostly fairly large and conspicuous:
Neither rough-setose nor scabrid; ovules 1 or more *Onagraceae*
Usually rough-setose or scabrid; ovules solitary from the apex of a one-locular ovary *Loasaceae*
Styles more than 1:
Styles 5–10; carpels 5–10, radiating; stigmas capitate *Rosaceae*
Styles up to 4; ovary up to 4-locular; carpels not radiating; stigmas not capitate *Halorrhagaceae*
Shrubs, trees, or climbers:
Flowers umbellate; fruit a berry or drupe *Araliaceae*
Flowers not umbellate:
Leaves 3-foliolate; petals 5; stamens 5, alternating with glands; anthers opening by valves *Hernandiaceae*
Leaves simple; anthers opening by slits:
Petals contorted; stamens mostly 4 or 8 *Onagraceae*
Petals valvate or imbricate:
Filaments not toothed at the top:
Petals loriform, valvate *Alangiaceae*
Petals not loriform:
Petals imbricate; stamens various *Combretaceae*
Petals valvate, or if slightly imbricate then stamens usually 5:
Fruit a capsule or berry; shrubs or trees *Escalloniaceae*
Fruit a drupe; shrubs or trees *Cornaceae*
Fruit indehiscent, 1-seeded; climber *Loasaceae*
Filaments broad and toothed at the top *Pterostemonaceae*
Petals convolute or inflexed; leaves anisophyllous
Rhizophoraceae

GROUP 14

One carpel or two or more united carpels with axile, basal, or apical placentation; ovary inferior; petals present, more or less united

Leaves opposite (to p. 97):
Leaves stipulate, stipules mostly inter- or intra-petiolar; anthers free from each other:
Leaves simple, entire; corolla actinomorphic *Rubiaceae*
Leaves pinnate; flowers actinomorphic or zygomorphic *Caprifoliaceae*
Leaves exstipulate:
Leaves usually with longitudinally parallel main nerves; stamens often double the number of the corolla-lobes, mostly jointed, the connective produced at the base into an appendage *Melastomataceae*
Leaves and stamens not as above:
Anthers free from each other; ovules mostly pendulous:
Leaves not gland-dotted; mostly herbaceous plants, rarely shrubs; stamens definite:

Stigma not indusiate:
  Herbaceous or woody at the base:
    Flowers zygomorphic:
      Ovary with 1 perfect 1-ovulate loculus and often 2 empty loculi
                                            Valerianaceae
      Ovary 1-locular, without additional empty loculi; flowers often capitate   *Dipsacaceae*
    Flowers actinomorphic:
      Anthers 2-locular; stamens usually 5   *Campanulaceae*
      Anthers 1-locular; stamens appearing to be double the number of the corolla-lobes by division of the filaments   *Adoxaceae*
  Trees, shrubs, or woody climbers or parasites; corolla often saccate or spurred at the base:
    Stamens double the number of the corolla-lobes; ovary 6-locular; a large tree   *Lythraceae*
    Stamens the same number as the corolla-lobes:
      Stamens alternate with the usually imbricate corolla-lobes; not parasitic   *Caprifoliaceae*
      Stamens opposite the valvate corolla-lobes; often parasitic
                                            Loranthaceae
  Stigma indusiate; ovary 1–2-locular; flowers not capitate   *Goodeniaceae*
  Leaves gland-dotted; stamens mostly numerous; trees or shrubs   *Myrtaceae*
Anthers mostly connivent or in pairs around the style:
  Ovule solitary; flowers mostly in heads:
    Ovule erect; calyx usually modified into a pappus of barbellate or plumose bristles   *Compositae*
    Ovule pendulous; calyx not modified into a pappus   *Calyceraceae*
  Ovules numerous; flowers usually not in heads:
    Flowers actinomorphic; stamens the same number as the corolla-lobes
                                            Campanulaceae
    Flowers zygomorphic; stamens usually fewer (4 or 2) than the corolla-lobes   *Gesneriaceae*
Leaves alternate or radical:
  Stamens 1–2:
    Flowers bisexual:
      Anthers with a narrow connective or the loculi divergent; filaments free from each other   *Gesneriaceae*
      Anthers with very broad connective; filaments free from each other
                                          Columelliaceae
      Anthers with narrow connective; filaments connate   *Stylidiaceae*
    Flowers unisexual; tendrils often present   *Cucurbitaceae*
  Stamens 3 or more:
    Anthers free from one another or very slightly connate only at the base:
      Stamens the same number as and opposite the corolla-lobes:
        Herbaceous; leaves not gland-dotted   *Primulaceae*
        Trees and shrubs:
          Not parasitic; leaves gland-dotted   *Myrsinaceae*
         Often parasitic; leaves not gland-dotted   *Loranthaceae*

Stamens alternate with the corolla-lobes or more numerous or fewer:
  Corolla actinomorphic:
    Herbaceous plants with often milky juice:
      Flowers unisexual; stems usually climbing by the tendrils; anthers often sinuous or twisted   *Cucurbitaceae*
      Flowers bisexual; no tendrils; anthers usually straight:
        Leaves stipulate; sepals 2   *Portulacaceae*
        Leaves exstipulate; sepals more than 2:
          Filaments free or nearly so; ovary usually 2- or more-locular   *Campanulaceae*
          Filaments monadelphous; ovary 1-locular   *Calyceraceae*
    Woody, rarely subherbaceous; juice not milky:
      Leaves gland-dotted; stamens mostly numerous   *Myrtaceae*
      Leaves not gland-dotted:
        Stamens free from the corolla:
          Petals valvate; stipules present, often adnate to the petiole   *Araliaceae*
          Petals valvate; stipules absent   *Lecythidaceae*
          Petals imbricate, rarely valvate:
            Stipules absent; leaves simple   *Vacciniaceae*
            Stipules present, adnate to the petiole; leaves compound *Araliaceae*
          Petals contorted; small stipules present; branches hooked   *Ancistrocladaceae*
        Stamens epipetalous:
          Ovary 1–2- (rarely 3-) locular; ovules 2, pendulous; flowers in a leafy capitulum   *Bruniaceae*
          Ovary 3–5-locular; ovule 1, or when more axile; flowers not in a capitulum:
            Stamens numerous; filaments free or partially connate   *Symplocaceae*
            Stamens mostly 5 or 10; filaments not united at the base   *Styracaceae*
          Stamens 8, connate   *Lissocarpaceae*
          Ovary 1–2-locular; ovule solitary, pendulous; flowers in cymes   *Alangiaceae*
  Corolla zygomorphic:
    Ovule solitary, pendulous   *Valerianaceae*
    Ovule 1 or more, erect or ascending; stigma indusiate   *Goodeniaceae*
    Ovules numerous, axile   *Lobeliaceae*
Anthers more or less united into a ring around the style:
  Anthers straight, not flexuous:
    Flowers not in heads surrounded by a common involucre:
      Flowers bisexual, zygomorphic; no tendrils   *Lobeliaceae*
      Flowers unisexual, actinomorphic; tendrils usually present   *Cucurbitaceae*
    Flowers in heads surrounded by a common involucre:
      Ovule erect from the base of the ovary-loculus; filaments usually free from each other; calyx modified into a pappus   *Compositae*

Ovule pendulous from the top of the ovary-loculus; filaments more or less connate; calyx not modified into a pappus   *Calyceraceae*

Anthers flexuous or conduplicate; plants often with tendrils
Cucurbitaceae

GROUP 15

One carpel or two or more united carpels with axile, basal, or apical placentation; ovary inferior; petals absent

Parasitic herbs destitute of chlorophyll, the leaves reduced to scales; ovules nude or with a single integument:

Ovules 3 from the apex of a central placenta; flowers dioecious
Myzodendraceae

Ovules solitary, pendulous; flowers densely crowded into inflorescences; fruits nut-like, 1-seeded; anthers opening by slits   *Balanophoraceae*

Ovules solitary, pendulous; flowers spicate, racemose, or capitate; anthers opening by valves   *Lauraceae*

Ovules very numerous; flowers large, solitary or rarely spicate; fruit with very numerous minute seeds:

Flowers unisexual   *Cytinaceae*

Flowers bisexual   *Hydnoraceae*

Not parasitic, or if so then more or less woody and often with normally developed leaves (at least with chlorophyll):

Leaves stipulate:

Flowers unisexual; stipules often paired:

Stamens and ovules numerous; fruit often winged; outer pair of calyx-lobes valvate; herbs, often with obliquely shaped leaves *Begoniaceae*

Stamens and ovules few, the latter solitary or paired:

Trees or shrubs; stipules not adnate:

Male flowers with a calyx:

Ovule 1 in the ovary   *Moraceae*

Ovules 2 in each loculus   *Fagaceae*

Male flowers without a calyx   *Corylaceae*

Herbs; stipules adnate to the petiole   *Halorrhagaceae*

Flowers bisexual, often solitary or racemose:

Stamens the same number as and alternate with the sepals *Rhamnaceae*

Stamens the same number as and opposite or more numerous than the sepals:

Leaves alternate; ovules 2, pendulous; flowers racemose   *Rosaceae*

Leaves alternate or opposite; ovules 2 to many; flowers solitary or in short racemes   *Rhizophoraceae*

Flowers rarely unisexual, spicate or capitate, often precocious; leaves alternate; ovule 1, pendulous:

Trees or shrubs; calyx sometimes absent   *Hamamelidaceae*

Herbs, sometimes with large leaves   *Halorrhagaceae*

Leaves exstipulate; but somctimes when opposite connate and sheathing at the base:

Flowers usually in catkins or slender spikes, or rarely the males in panicles, unisexual:

Leaves pinnate; ovule 1, erect   *Juglandaceae*

Leaves simple, alternate; ovules 1–2, descending   *Fagaceae*
Leaves simple, opposite; ovules 2, collateral, pendulous   *Garryaceae*
Leaves simple, opposite; ovule 1 in each loculus, pendulous
                                                                Chloranthaceae
Flowers not in catkins, mostly bisexual:
  Calyx calyptrate; leaves opposite, gland-dotted   *Myrtaceae*
  Calyx not calyptrate; leaves not gland-dotted:
    Flowers in simple or compound umbels; herbs; leaves sheathing at the
      base; ovary 2-locular, separating in fruit into 2 mericarps with
      resinous lines   *Umbelliferae*
    Flowers not or rarely in umbels; fruit not separating into mericarps:
      Ovules numerous on axile placentas:
        Calyx actinomorphic:
          Ovary many-locular   *Sonneratiaceae*
          Ovary 1–4-locular   *Onagraceae*
          Calyx zygomorphic   *Aristolochiaceae*
      Ovules solitary or few, inserted at the top or base of the ovary, rarely
        axile:
        Ovules pendulous from the apex of the ovary or at the apex of a basal
          placenta, usually more than 1:
          Mostly trees, shrubs, or woody climbers; sepals mostly valvate:
            Anthers opening by valves:
              Ovary 1-locular:
                Leaves simple; calyx-lobes imbricate   *Lauraceae*
                Leaves simple or compound; calyx-lobes valvate *Hernandiaceae*
                Ovary 2–3-locular: *Gomortegaceae*
            Anthers opening by longitudinal slits:
              Stamens erect in bud, often double the number of the sepals
                                                                Nyssaceae
              Stamens inflexed in bud, often double the number of the sepals:
                Ovules at the apex of the ovary   *Combretaceae*
                Ovules on a free-basal placenta   *Grubbiaceae*
              Stamens erect in bud, the same number as and opposite the sepals:
                Placenta not reaching the top of the ovary; hairs not stellate
                  (tufted in *Exocarpus*)   *Santalaceae*
                Placenta reaching to the top of the ovary and adnate to it; hairs
                  stellate   *Octoknemaceae*
          Herbaceous; sepals mostly imbricate   *Ficoidaceae*
        Ovule 1, erect, or axile:
          Mostly maritime trees and shrubs with often lepidote leaves; flowers
            not capitate   *Elaeagnaceae*
          Not maritime; leaves not lepidote; flowers capitate or densely
            crowded; ovule well developed at flowering time   *Rhamnaceae*
          Mostly parasitic; flowers not capitate; ovule scarcely developed at
            time of flowering   *Loranthaceae*
          Twining herb with twisted petioles; flowers paniculate; calyx wing-
            like in fruit   *Agdestidaceae*

INDEX TO FAMILIES OF DICOTYLEDONES FOR READY REFERENCE

(Also included in general index at end of volume)

Acanthaceae, 489.
Aceraceae, 364.
Achariaceae, 241.
Achatocarpaceae, 210.
Actinidiaceae, 274.
Adoxaceae, 466.
Aegicerataceae, 347.
Aextoxicaceae, 318.
Agdestidaceae, 437.
Akaniaceae, 368.
Alangiaceae, 173.
Amaranthaceae, 440.
Ampelidaceae (*see* Vitaceae).
Anacardiaceae, 363.
Ancistrocladaceae, 286.
Annonaceae, 133.
Antoniaceae, 375.
Apocynaceae, 380.
Aptandraceae, 322.
Aquifoliaceae, 311.
Aquilariaceae, 213.
Araliaceae, 177.
Aristolochiaceae, 414.
Asclepiadaceae, 383.
Austrobaileyaceae, 137.
Averrhoaceae, 356.

Balanitaceae, 267.
Balanophoraceae, 340.
Balanopsidaceae, 189.
Balsaminaceae, 499.
Barbeuiaceae, 434.
Barbeyaceae, 203.
Basellaceae, 443.
Batidaceae 442.
Baueraceae, 166.
Begoniaceae, 244.
Berberidaceae, 412.
Betulaceae, 191.
Bignoniaceae, 389.
Bixaceae, 205.
Bombacaceae, 253.
Bonnetiaceae, 271.
Boraginaceae, 502.
Brunelliaceae, 147.
Bruniaceae, 185.

Brunoniaceae, 479.
Buddeeiaceae, 373.
Burseraceae, 355.
Buxaceae, 184.
Byblidaceae, 220.

Cabombaceae, 406.
Cactaceae, 247.
Caesalpiniaceae, 153.
Callitrichaceae, 449.
Calycanthaceae, 151.
Calyceraceae, 475.
Campanulaceae, 476.
Canellaceae, 128.
Cannabiaceae, 201.
Capparidaceae, 224.
Caprifoliaceae, 178.
Capusiaceae, 325.
Cardiopteridaceae, 314.
Caricaceae, 246.
Caryocaraceae, 279.
Caryophyllaceae, 429.
Casuarinaceae, 197.
Celastraceae, 320.
Cephalotaceae, 458.
Ceratophyllaceae, 405.
Cercidiphyllaceae, 132.
Chailletiaceae, 150.
Chenopodiaceae, 438.
Chlaenaceae (*see* Sarco-laenaceae).
Chloanthaceae, 396.
Chloranthaceae, 421.
Circaeasteraceae, 412.
Cistaceae, 206.
Clethraceae, 288.
Clusiaceae, 298.
Cneoraceae, 314.
Cobaeaceae, 387.
Cochlospermaceae, 208.
Columelliaceae, 493.
Combretaceae, 307.
Compositae, 481.
Connaraceae, 145.
Convolvulaceae, 484.
Coriariaceae, 147.
Cornaceae, 171.

Corylaceae, 193.
Corynocarpaceae, 321.
Crassulaceae, 457.
Crossosomataceae, 145.
Cruciferae, 425.
Crypteroniaceae, 167.
Ctenolophonaceae, 265.
Cucurbitaceae, 242.
Cunoniaceae, 158.
Cuscutaceae, 501.
Cynocrambaceae, 441.
Cyrillaceae, 316.
Cytinaceae, 416.

Daphniphyllaceae, 184.
Datiscaceae, 245.
Dialypetalanthaceae, 384.
Diapensiaceae, 293.
Dichapetalaceae = Chailletiaceae, 150.
Diclidantheraceae (*see* Polygalaceae).
Didiereaceae, 369.
Dilleniaceae, 143.
Dipentodontaceae, 333.
Dipsacaceae, 474.
Dipterocarpaceae, 285.
Dirachmaceae, 248.
Donatiaceae, 462.
Droseraceae, 467.

Ebenaceae, 348.
Ehretiaceae, 393.
Elaeagnaceae, 342.
Elatinaceae, 427.
Empetraceae, 317.
Epacridaceae, 292.
Eremosynaceae, 460.
Ericaceae, 290.
Erythropalaceae, 324.
Erythroxylaceae, 263.
Escalloniaceae, 165.
Eucommiaceae, 204.
Eucryphiaceae, 300.
Euphorbiaceae, 270.
Eupomatiaceae, 134.

Fagaceae, 192.

Ficoidaceae, 430.
Flacourtiaceae, 207.
Fouquieriaceae, 229.
Francoaceae, 462.
Frankeniaceae, 228.
Fumariaceae, 423.

Garryaceae, 174.
Geissolomataceae, 214.
Gentianaceae, 450.
Geraniaceae, 495.
Gesneriaceae, 491.
Globulariaceae, 505.
Gomortegaceae, 140.
Gonystylaceae, 212.
Goodeniaceae, 478.
Goupiaceae, 322.
Greyiaceae, 164.
Grossulariaceae, 162.
Grubbiaceae, 338.
Guttiferae (see Clusiaceae).
Gyrostemonaceae, 436.

Halorrhagaceae, 448.
Hamamelidaceae, 180.
Helleboraceae, 401.
Hernandiaceae, 141.
Heteropyxidaceae, 341.
Himantandraceae, 130.
Hippocastanaceae, 365.
Hippocrateaceae, 324.
Hoplestigmataceae, 209.
Huaceae, 262.
Humiriaceae, 259.
Hydnoraceae, 415.
Hydrangeaceae, 161.
Hydrophyllaceae, 501.
Hydrostachyaceae, 470.
Hypericaceae, 297.

Icacinaceae, 316.
Ilicaceae (see
    Aquifoliaceae).
Illecebraceae, 432.
Illiciaceae, 125.
Irvingiaceae, 261.
Ixonanthaceae, 256.

Juglandaceae, 195.
Julianiaceae, 368.

Koeberliniaceae, 313.
Krameriaceae, 233.

Labiatae, 506.
Lacistemaceae, 211.
Lactoridaceae, 131.

Lardizabalaceae, 408.
Lauraceae, 139.
Lecythidaceae, 303.
Ledocarpaceae, 263.
Leitneriaceae, 188.
Lennoaceae, 295.
Lentibulariaceae, 492.
Lepidobotryaceae, 266.
Limnanthaceae, 496.
Linaceae, 260.
Lissocarpaceae, 168.
Loasaceae, 237.
Lobeliaceae, 477.
Loganiaceae, 372.
Loranthaceae, 337.
Lythraceae, 445.

Magnoliaceae, 123.
Malesherbiaceae, 240.
Malpighiaceae, 258.
Malvaceae, 254.
Marcgraviaceae, 278.
Martyniaceae, 392.
Medusagynaceae, 280.
Medusandraceae, 335.
Melastomataceae, 308.
Meliaceae, 356.
Melianthaceae, 359.
Menispermaceae, 410.
Menyanthaceae, 451.
Mimosaceae, 154.
Molluginaceae, 428.
Monimiaceae, 136.
Monotropaceae, 294.
Moraceae, 201.
Moringaceae, 225.
Myoporaceae, 503.
Myricaceae, 189.
Myristicaceae, 142.
Myrothamnaceae, 181.
Myrsinaceae, 345.
Myrtaceae, 302.
Myzodendraceae, 339.

Nandinaceae, 411.
Nepenthaceae, 417.
Nolanaceae, 486.
Nyctaginaceae, 216.
Nymphaeaceae, 403.
Nyssaceae, 175.

Ochnaceae, 282.
Octoknemaceae, 331.
Olacaceae, 329.
Oleaceae, 378.
Oliniaceae, 163.
Onagraceae, 446.
Opiliaceae, 330.

Orobanchaceae, 492.
Oxalidaceae, 497.

Paeoniaceae, 400.
Pandaceae, 311.
Papaveraceae, 422.
Papilionaceae, 155.
Parnassiaceae, 465.
Passifloraceae, 240.
Pedaliaceae, 389.
Pellicieraceae, 275.
Penaeaceae, 214.
Pentadiplandraceae, 319.
Pentaphylacaceae, 276.
Peridiscaceae, 252.
Periplocaceae, 381.
Petiveriaceae, 438.
Philadelphaceae, 159.
Phrymaceae, 398.
Phytolaccaceae, 435.
Picrodendraceae, 196.
Piperaceae, 419.
Pittosporaceae, 219.
Plantaginaceae, 455.
Platanaceae, 182.
Plocospermaceae, 379.
Plumbaginaceae, 453.
Podoaceae, 361.
Podophyllaceae, 404.
Podostemaceae, 470.
Polemoniaceae, 500.
Polygalaceae, 232.
Polygonaceae, 431.
Portulacaceae, 430.
Potaliaceae, 371.
Primulaceae, 453.
Proteaceae, 217.
Pterostemonaceae, 157.
Punicaceae, 306.
Pyrolaceae, 289.

Quiinaceae, 301.

Ranunculaceae, 402.
Resedaceae, 426.
Rhamnaceae, 343.
Rhizophoraceae, 304.
Rhoipteleaceae, 194.
Rosaceae, 149.
Rubiaceae, 386.
Rutaceae, 353.

Sabiaceae, 361.
Salicaceae, 187.
Salvadoraceae, 312.
Samydaceae (see
    Flacourtiaceae).
Santalaceae, 339.

Sapindaceae, 360.
Sapotaceae, 350.
Sarcolaenaceae, 283.
Sarcospermaceae, 351.
Sargentodoxaceae, 407.
Sarraceniaceae, 468.
Saurauiaceae, 274.
Saururaceae, 420.
Saxifragaceae, 459.
Schisandraceae, 129.
Scrophulariaceae, 488.
Scyphostegiaceae, 326.
Scytopetalaceae, 249.
Selaginaceae, 505.
Simaroubaceae, 354.
Solanaceae, 484.
Sonneratiaceae, 306.
Sphaerosepalaceae, 284.
Spigeliaceae, 376.
Stachyuraceae, 183.
Stackhousiaceae, 322.

Staphyleaceae, 367.
Stegnospermaceae, 222.
Sterculiaceae, 251.
Stilbeaceae, 395.
Strasburgeriaceae, 281.
Strychnaceae, 377.
Stylidiaceae, 480.
Styracaceae, 168.
Symplocaceae, 170.

Tamaricaceae, 228.
Tetracentraceae, 179.
Tetrameristaceae, 277.
Theaceae, 272.
Theophrastaceae, 346.
Thymelaeaceae, 215.
Tiliaceae, 250.
Tovariaceae, 226.
Trapaceae, 447.
Tremandraceae, 223.
Trigoniaceae, 234.

Trimeniaceae, 138.
Trochodendraceae, 131.
Tropaeolaceae, 498.
Turneraceae, 236.

Ulmaceae, 199.
Umbelliferae, 471.
Urticaceae, 202.

Vacciniaceae, 296.
Vahliaceae, 461.
Valerianaceae, 473.
Verbenaceae, 395.
Violaceae, 230.
Vitaceae, 344.
Vivianiaceae, 223.
Vochysiaceae, 234.

Winteraceae, 126.

Zygophyllaceae, 268.

SEQUENCE OF ORDERS[1] AND FAMILIES

DICOTYLEDONES

Division I. Lignosae

Notes on affinity (origin and further development)	Sequence of Orders and Families (a cross-line indicates the climax of a group)	General characteristics and tendences of Orders[2]
	1. Magnoliales	
Entirely woody groups, probably the most ancient types of existing Dicotyledons and basic for the succeeding also predominantly woody groups beginning respectively with *Dilleniales, Rosales, Bixales, Tiliales,* and the rest of the predominantly woody families ending with *Verbenaceae.*	1. Magnoliaceae, p. 123. 2. Illiciaceae, p. 125. 3. Winteraceae, p. 126. 4. Canellaceae, p. 128. 5. Schisandraceae, p. 129. 6. Himantandraceae, p. 130. 7. Lactoridaceae, p. 131. 8. Trochodendraceae, p. 131. 9. Cercidiphyllaceae, p. 132.	Hypogynous, bisexual, becoming unisexual with reduction of perianth; apocarpous; petals rarely absent; stamens numerous, usually free; endosperm copious, not ruminate; embryo minute; stipules present or absent.
	2. Annonales	
Closely related to the *Magnoliales,* but more advanced; probably little more evolution from this stock; tropical distribution.	10. Annonaceae, p. 133. 11. Eupomatiaceae, p. 134.	Hypogynous to rarely perigynous; mostly bisexual; apocarpous to very rarely syncarpous with parietal placentation; petals present, rarely united; stamens numerous, free; endosperm copious, markedly ruminate; embryo minute; leaves without stipules.
	3. Laurales	
Reductions from the *Magnoliales,* approaching most nearly to the *Winteraceae;* becoming perigynous; mainly tropics.	12. Monimiaceae, p. 136. 13. Austrobaileyaceae, p. 137. 14. Trimeniaceae, p. 138. 15. Lauraceae, p. 139. 16. Gomortegaceae, p. 140. 17. Hernandiaceae, p. 141. 18. Myristicaceae, p. 142.	Hypogynous to perigynous, bisexual or unisexual; apocarpous to monocarpous; no petals; stamens definite in number, free; endosperm copious, rarely ruminate or absent; embryo minute; leaves without stipules.

[1] The orders (cohorts) here recognized are usually much smaller concepts than those of either Bentham and Hooker or of Engler, and often approximate more to the suborders (*Unterreihe*) of the latter.

[2] The characteristics given are quite general and do not account for exceptions which occur in several of the orders.

Notes on affinity (origin and further development)	Sequence of Orders and Families (a cross-line indicates the climax of a group)	General characteristics and tendences of Orders
	4. DILLENIALES	
Woody to rarely herbaceous basal group rather remotely related to the *Magnoliales* and perhaps showing a connecting link between that group and the *Rosales*, *Bixales*, *Theales*, and *Guttiferales*.	19. Dilleniaceae, p. 143. 20. Connaraceae, p. 145. 21. Crossosomataceae, p. 145. 22. Brunelliaceae, p. 147.	Hypogynous; bisexual; apocarpous; petals present; stamens numerous, rarely few; endosperm copious, plain; embryo minute to fairly large; seeds often arillate; leaves alternate, with strong pinnate nerves or pinnately compound; usually no stipules.
	5. CORIARIALES	
Difficult to place in any system, and doubtfully arranged here.	23. Coriariaceae, p. 147.	More or less as in *Dilleniales*, but stamens 10, with large anthers; seeds with thin endosperm, not arillate; petals accrescent; leaves opposite or verticillate.
	6. ROSALES	
A prolific group mainly spread into temperate regions, woody to herbaceous, but the herbs clearly related to woody ancestors; derived from the *Dilleniales*, passing into amentiferous families culminating in the *Urticales*.	24. Rosaceae, p. 149. 25. Dichapetalaceae, p. 150. 26. Calycanthaceae, p. 151.	Perigynous to epigynous, mostly apocarpous to syncarpous, with central placentation; no endosperm; leaves simple to compound, stipulate.
	7. LEGUMINALES	
Prolific and highly successful group derived from the *Rosales* stock, through the mainly tropical *Caesalpiniaceae* and *Mimosaceae*, ending in the very homogeneous *Papilionaceae*, the latter more abundantly represented in temperate regions.	27. Caesalpiniaceae, p. 153. 28. Mimosaceae, p. 154. 29. Papilionaceae, p. 155.	Progressive group with increasing zygomorphy of the flower; free to variously united stamens; carpel 1; no endosperm, the embryo filling the seed.
	8. CUNONIALES	
Woody to rarely herbaceous group allied to the early *Dilleniales* and *Rosales* and even *Celastrales*; intermediate between the *Rosales* and the higher evolved *Hamamelidales* and the so-called 'Amentiferae'.	30. Pterostemonaceae, p. 157. 31. Cunoniaceae, p. 158. 32. Philadelphaceae, p. 159. 33. Hydrangeaceae, p. 161. 34. Grossulariaceae, p. 162. 35. Oliniaceae, p. 163. 36. Greyiaceae, p. 164. 37. Escalloniaceae, p. 165. 38. Baueraceae, p. 166. 39. Crypteroniaceae, p. 167.	Perigynous to epigynous; apocarpous to syncarpous with central or parietal placentation; endosperm copious, embryo mostly small; leaves simple or compound; stipules present or absent.

Notes on affinity (origin and further development)	Sequence of Orders and Families (a cross-line indicates the climax of a group)	General characteristics and tendences of Orders
	9. STYRACALES	
A small group probably derived from the *Cunoniales*.	40. Lissocarpaceae, p. 168. 41. Styracaceae, p. 168. 42. Symplocaceae, p. 170.	Corolla mostly sympetalous; stamens inserted on the corolla, rarely free; ovary superior to inferior, 5–2-locular with axile few to many ovules; seeds with endosperm and straight embryo. Trees or shrubs often with stellate indumentum; leaves alternate, stipules absent.
	10. ARALIALES	
Probably derived from the *Rosales* via the *Cunoniales*, *Cornaceae* being connected with *Philadelphaceae* through the genus *Broussaisia* in the latter family. *Nyssaceae* approach *Hamamelidaceae*.	43. Cornaceae, p. 171. 44. Alangiaceae, p. 173. 45. Garryaceae, p. 174. 46. Nyssaceae, p. 175. 47. Araliaceae, p. 177. 48. Caprifoliaceae, p. 178.	Woody; complete epigyny, syncarpous; stamens definite in number; specialization of inflorescence into a climax type more or less comparable with that of *Umbelliferae* in *Herbaceae* division; some sympetaly; leaves simple to compound; stipules present or absent.
	11. HAMAMELIDALES	
Closely allied to the *Rosales*, with increasing reduction and unisexuality of the flowers with specialization of the inflorescence towards the catkin-bearing families, the 'Amentiferae'.	49. Tetracentraceae, p. 179. 50. Hamamelidaceae, p. 180. 51. Myrothamnaceae, p. 181. 52. Platanaceae, p. 182. 53. Stachyuraceae, p. 183. 54. Buxaceae, p. 184. 55. Daphniphyllaceae, p. 184. 56. Bruniaceae, p. 185.	More or less as in *Rosales*, but the flowers often crowded into heads or catkins; ovary often reduced to 2 carpels; tendency to apetaly; leaves alternate, mostly stipulate, nerves plicate.
	12. SALICALES	
Salicaceae seems to find its true place here and not with *Tamaricaceae* or *Flacourtiaceae* as sometimes suggested; resemblance to these families regarded as superficial.	57. Salicaceae, p. 187.	Flowers always in catkins and usually insect-pollinated, rarely wind-pollinated; placentation parietal; no endosperm; leaves alternate, mostly stipulate.
	13. LEITNERIALES	
This and the five following orders regarded as reductions from the *Rosales* stock via the *Hamamelidales*.	58. Leitneriaceae, p. 188.	As above but 'catkins' erect; perianth absent or rudimentary; ovary superior; placenta parietal; leaves alternate, no stipules.

Notes on affinity (origin and further development)	Sequence of Orders and Families (a cross-line indicates the climax of a group)	General characteristics and tendences of Orders
	14. MYRICALES	
See note above.	59. Myricaceae, p. 189.	More or less as in preceding but leaves aromatic and gland-dotted; placenta basal.
	15. BALANOPSIDALES	
See note above.	60. Balanopsidaceae, p. 189.	Resembling the preceding but with two parietal placentas; no stipules.
	16. FAGALES	
See note above.	61. Betulaceae, p.191. 62. Fagaceae, p. 192. 63. Corylaceae, p. 193.	Perianth small or none; ovary inferior or nude, 6–2-locular, loculi 2–1-ovuled; endosperm absent; flowers in catkins or spikes, ♂ ♀; stipules present.
	17. JUGLANDALES	
See note above.	64. Rhoipteleaceae, p. 194. 65. Juglandaceae, p. 195. 66. Picrodendraceae, p. 196.	Flowers mostly in catkins, apetalous; ♂ ♀; ovary inferior or superior, 2–1-locular; ovule solitary; no endosperm; stipules present or absent.
	18. CASUARINALES	
See note above; a climax family.	67. Casuarinaceae, p. 197.	Male flowers spicate, female capitate; no perianth; male with only 1 stamen; seed solitary, no endosperm; leaves completely reduced.
	19. URTICALES	
An extremely reduced group of families, from mostly woody to more rarely herbaceous, but remaining fibrous.	68. Ulmaceae, p. 199. 69. Cannabiaceae, p. 201. 70. Moraceae, p. 201. 71. Urticaceae, p. 202. 72. Barbeyaceae, p. 203. 73. Eucommiaceae, p. 204.	Ovary usually 1-locular; ovule 1, rarely 2, erect or pendulous; endosperm present; leaves usually stipulate, mostly alternate.
	20. BIXALES	
Woody to rarely subherbaceous group in which syncarpy with parietal placentation has remained a fixed character; the basic group for *Passiflorales* and allies, and a step towards the *Theales, Guttiferales,* and especially the *Tiliales*.	74. Bixaceae, p. 205. 75. Cistaceae, p. 206. 76. Flacourtiaceae, p. 207. 77. Cochlospermaceae, p. 208. 78. Hoplestigmataceae, p. 209. 79. Achatocarpaceae, p. 210. 80. Lacistemaceae, p. 211.	Hypogynous to perigynous, ♀ to ♂ ♀; syncarpous with parietal placentation; increasing unisexuality of flowers; stamens numerous to few; seeds with copious endosperm and small embryo.

Notes on affinity (origin and further development)	Sequence of Orders and Families (a cross-line indicates the climax of a group)	General characteristics and tendences of Orders
	21. THYMELAEALES	
Apetalous relations of *Bixales*; *Gonystylaceae* allied to *Flacourtiaceae*.	81. Gonystylaceae, p. 212. 82. Aquilariaceae, p. 213. 83. Geissolomataceae, p. 214. 84. Penaeaceae, p. 214. 85. Thymelaeaceae, p. 215. 86. Nyctaginaceae, p. 216.	Mostly apetalous and mono-carpellary; ovules few to solitary; flowers often capitate; endosperm present or absent; calyx imbricate or valvate; stipules absent or minute and glandular.
	22. PROTEALES	
Clearly related to *Thymelaeaceae*; mostly an austral type with no parallel group in the northern hemisphere; a few stragglers in the Malaya; a completely climax group with flowers often in heads equivalent to *Compositae*.	87. Proteaceae, p. 217.	Perigynous; actinomorphic or zygomorphic; calyx valvate, often split down one side; stamens equal to and opposite the sepals; ovary superior, 1-locular; no endosperm; stipules absent.
	23. PITTOSPORALES	
Might be equally well placed near the *Cunoniales*.	88. Pittosporaceae, p. 219. 89. Byblidaceae, p. 220. 90. Stegnospermaceae, p. 222. 91. Vivianiaceae, p. 223. 92. Tremandraceae, p. 223.	Hypogynous; mostly ☿; syncarpous with axile or parietal placentation; stamens definite in number, free; petals imbricate to induplicate-valvate; endosperm copious; embryo minute; stipules absent.
	24. CAPPARIDALES	
Woody to herbaceous, derived from the *Bixales* stock; some with flowers and fruits bearing superficial resemblance to *Cruciferae*; here regarded as parallel evolution.	93. Capparidaceae, p. 224. 94. Moringaceae, p. 225. 95. Tovariaceae, p. 226.	Hypogynous or subperigynous; ☿; petals present; syncarpous with parietal placentation; carpels 2; stamens numerous to few, mostly equal; endosperm absent; embryo variously folded; flowers actinomorphic to zygomorphic; leaves rarely stipulate.
	25. TAMARICALES	
Probably derived from the large and mostly tropical *Bixaceous* stock.	96. Frankeniaceae, p. 228. 97. Tamaricaceae, p. 228. 98. Fouquieriaceae, p. 229.	Hypogynous; syncarpous, with parietal placentation; tendency to catkin-like inflorescences; small flowers; petals free to connate; stamens mostly definite in number; seeds often hairy, endosperm present or absent; no stipules.

Notes on affinity (origin and further development)	Sequence of Orders and Families (a cross-line indicates the climax of a group)	General characteristics and tendences of Orders
	26. VIOLALES 99. Violaceae, p. 230.	Hypogynous to perigynous; ♀ rarely ♂ ♀; petals present; syncarpous with parietal placentation; stamens several to few; endosperm present or absent; embryo straight or curved; flowers mostly zygomorphic; leaves with stipules.
More or less woody group with herbs mostly in more temperate regions; gradually more zygomorphic with reduction in number of stamens and ovules.		
	27. POLYGALALES 100. Polygalaceae, p. 232. 101. Krameriaceae, p. 233. 102. Trigoniaceae, p. 234. 103. Vochysiaceae, p. 234.	Axile or apical placentation; stamens 8 or less, some infertility and cohesion; stipules mostly absent.
Woody to herbaceous families, the stock of which has not given rise to further evolution; gradual reduction in number of stamens and ovules.	28. LOASALES 104. Turneraceae, p. 236. 105. Loasaceae, p. 237.	Hypogynous to epigynous; stamens numerous and sometimes united into bundles, or few; syncarpous with parietal placentation; endosperm copious; embryo straight; seeds often strophiolate; flowers actinomorphic; stipules absent.
Mostly climbing types related to the *Bixales* and becoming herbaceous, probably some derived from the Papaverian stock.	29. PASSIFLORALES 106. Malesherbiaceae, p. 240. 107. Passifloraceae, p. 240. 108. Achariaceae, p. 241.	More or less as in *Bixales*, but no endosperm and corona often present; fruit often stipitate; habit mostly climbing and becoming herbaceous; stipules present or absent.
Undoubtedly closely related to *Passifloraceae* and better placed here than in the *Metachlamydeae* to which Engler assigned the *Cucurbitaceae*.	30. CUCURBITALES 109. Cucurbitaceae, p. 242. 110. Begoniaceae, p. 244. 111. Datiscaceae, p. 245. 112. Caricaceae, p. 246.	Constantly unisexual; ovary inferior with parietal placentation; endosperm scanty or often absent; corolla sometimes sympetalous; stipules present or absent.
Rather a problem group highly modified ecologically, but perhaps best placed here.	31. CACTALES 113. Cactaceae, p. 247.	Succulent or woody; sepals, petals, and stamens mostly numerous and in several series on a tubular axis; ovary inferior, 1-locular with parietal placentas.

Notes on affinity (origin and further development)	*Sequence of Orders and Families (a cross-line indicates the climax of a group)*	*General characteristics and tendences of Orders*
	32. TILIALES	
A fairly advanced group whence considerable evolution is evident, i.e. to *Celastrales, Rhamnales* (petaliferous disciform types) and much of the *Euphorbiaceae* (apetalous types). *Tiliales* evolved probably from the *Dilleniales* and *Bixales* stocks.	114. Dirachmaceae, p. 248. 115. Scytopetalaceae, p. 249. 116. Tiliaceae, p. 250. 117. Sterculiaceae, p. 251. 118. Peridiscaceae, p. 252. 119. Bombacaceae, p. 253.	Hypogynous, actinomorphic; ♀ or ♂ ♀; syncarpous with axile (very rarely apical) placentation; stamens rarely few and then opposite the petals, free to partially united; anthers 2–1-locular; endosperm copious, rarely absent; embryo fairly large, straight or curved; calyx mostly valvate; leaves alternate, stipulate; indumentum often stellate; trees, shrubs, or shrublets.
	33. MALVALES	
A very natural family and clearly a climax in this line of evolution.	120. Malvaceae, p. 254.	Mostly as above, but mainly herbaceous or softly woody and fibrous; calyx always valvate; anthers split in two and therefore '1-locular'.
	34. MALPIGHIALES	
Advanced and specialized groups derived from the *Tiliales*, with special types of indumentum, fruits, &c.	121. Ixonanthaceae, p. 256. 122. Malpighiaceae, p. 258. 123. Humiriaceae, p. 259. 124. Linaceae, p. 260. 125. Irvingiaceae, p. 261. 126. Huaceae, p. 262. 127. Ledocarpaceae, p. 263. 128. Erythroxylaceae, p. 263. 129. Ctenolophonaceae, p. 265. 130. Lepidobotryaceae, p. 266. 131. Balanitaceae, p. 267. 132. Zygophyllaceae, p. 268.	Hypogynous; actinomorphic to subzygomorphic; ♀; syncarpous with subapical placentation; ovules few; stamens usually definite in number; endosperm mostly absent. Often climbers with opposite leaves.
	35. EUPHORBIALES	
A composite (heterogeneous) family probably derived from several stocks such as *Bixales, Tiliales, Malvales, Celastrales*, and perhaps *Sapindales*.	133. Euphorbiaceae, p. 270.	Hypogynous; actinomorphic; ♂ ♀; petals usually absent, if present sometimes quite sympetalous (*Jatropha*); syncarpous with 1–2 ovules pendulous from the inner angle; stamens various; seeds often with a conspicuous caruncle: endosperm mostly copious; stipules mostly present.

Notes on affinity (origin and further development)	*Sequence of Orders and Families (a cross-line indicates the climax of a group)*	*General characteristics and tendences of Orders*
	36. THEALES	
Related to *Dilleniales* and *Bixales* and probably the direct syncarpous line developed from those groups. *Celastrales* perhaps also closely connected, but more advanced.	134. Bonnetiaceae, p. 271. 135. Theaceae, p. 272. 136. Saurauiaceae, p. 274. 137. Actinidiaceae, p. 274. 138. Pellicieraceae, p. 275. 139. Pentaphylacaceae, p. 276. 140. Tetrameristaceae, p. 277. 141. Marcgraviaceae, p. 278. 142. Caryocaraceae, p. 279. 143. Medusagynaceae, p. 280.	Hypogynous to rarely subperigynous, mostly ♀; syncarpous with axile placentas; stamens often in several series, mostly free; seeds with scanty or no endosperm; embryo large, straight, or curved, rarely spiral; leaves usually alternate, without stipules.
	37. OCHNALES	
Derivatives of *Theales*. Tropics and subtropics.	144. Strasburgeriaceae, p. 281. 145. Ochnaceae, p. 282. 146. Rhodolaenaceae, p. 283. 147. Sphaerosepalaceae, p. 284. 148. Dipterocarpaceae, p. 285. 149. Ancistrocladaceae, p. 286.	More or less as in *Theales*, but leaves with stipules; calyx-lobes often enlarged and wing-like in fruit or involucrate with bracts.
	38. ERICALES	
Clearly one of the most primitive groups of families with sympetalous corollas (the stamens having remained hypogynous) and derived from the *Theales*, especially through the family *Clethraceae*, which has retained free petals. Most highly represented in the S. Hemisphere.	150. Clethraceae, p. 288. 151. Pyrolaceae, p. 289. 152. Ericaceae, p. 290. 153. Epacridaceae, p. 292. 154. Diapensiaceae, p. 293. 155. Monotropaceae, p. 294. 156. Lennoaceae, p. 295. 157. Vacciniaceae, p. 296.	Corolla sympetalous, actinomorphic to slightly zygomorphic; stamens hypogynous, often double the number of the corolla-lobes; anthers often opening by pores; ovary superior to inferior, with axile, very rarely parietal, placentation; seeds with fleshy endosperm and straight embryo. Trees or shrubs, very rarely herbs and then parasitic; leaves mostly alternate, simple, without stipules.
	39. GUTTIFERALES	
Related to *Theales* and showing the same tendency as in the *Malvales*, the stamens becoming connate into bundles.	158. Hypericaceae, p. 297. 159. Clusiaceae, p. 298. 160. Eucryphiaceae, p. 300. 161. Quiinaceae, p. 301.	More advanced hypogynous types of the *Theales*, with opposite leaves often gland-dotted or lined with resin; stamens united into bundles; seeds without endosperm; sepals always imbricate; stipules rare.

Notes on affinity (origin and further development)	Sequence of Orders and Families (a cross-line indicates the climax of a group)	General characteristics and tendences of Orders
	40. MYRTALES	
Related to and derived from the same stock as the *Guttiferales*.	162. Myrtaceae, p. 302. 163. Lecythidaceae, p. 303. 164. Rhizophoraceae, p. 304. 165. Sonneratiaceae, p. 306. 166. Punicaceae, p. 306. 167. Combretaceae, p. 307. 168. Melastomataceae, p. 308.	Mostly epigynous relatives of *Theales* and *Guttiferales*, with opposite often gland-dotted leaves; stamens becoming specialized and dissimilar; some in maritime habitats; calyx becoming valvate.
	41. CELASTRALES	
An association of mostly small families usually with a floral disk, perhaps mostly descended from the *Tiliales* and *Theales*; probably affinity with *Escalloniaceae*.	169. Pandaceae, p. 311. 170. Aquifoliaceae, p. 311. 171. Salvadoraceae, p. 312. 172. Koeberliniaceae, p. 313. 173. Cneoraceae, p. 314. 174. Cardiopteridaceae, p. 314. 175. Cyrillaceae, p. 316. 176. Icacinaceae, p. 316. 177. Empetraceae, p. 317. 178. Aextoxicaceae, p. 318. 179. Pentadiplandraceae, p. 319. 180. Celastraceae, p. 320. 181. Corynocarpaceae, p. 321. 182. Stackhousiaceae, p. 322. 183. Goupiaceae, p. 322. 184. Hippocrateaceae, p. 324. 185. Erythropalaceae, p. 324. 186. Capusiaceae, p. 325. 187. Scyphostegiaceae, p. 326.	More or less perigynous disk present, often adnate to the base of the calyx-tube or lining it; stamens alternate with the petals; petals mostly imbricate; ovules 2–1, erect; endosperm present; leaves simple, not glandular.
	42. OLACALES	
More advanced types of the preceding group.	188. Olacaceae, p. 329. 189. Opiliaceae, p. 330. 190. Octoknemaceae, p. 331. 191. Aptandraceae, p. 332. 192. Dipentodontaceae, p. 333. 193. Medusandraceae, p. 335.	As above but petals mostly valvate, rarely absent.

Notes on affinity (origin and further development)	Sequence of Orders and Families (a cross-line indicates the climax of a group)	General characteristics and tendences of Orders
	43. SANTALALES	
Mostly parasitic derivatives of the preceding groups, some of rather doubtful relationship.	194. Loranthaceae, p. 337. 195. Grubbiaceae, p. 338. 196. Santalaceae, p. 339. 197. Myzodendraceae, p. 339. 198. Balanophoraceae, p. 340.	Flowers mostly epigynous; calyx valvate or open or absent; stamens opposite to the corolla-lobes when latter present; endosperm present; embryo straight.
	44. RHAMNALES	
Closely related to *Celastrales*, and probably the basic group for *Myrsinaceae* (sympetalous) which also have stamens opposite the petals.	199. Heteropyxidaceae, p. 341. 200. Elaeagnaceae, p. 342. 201. Rhamnaceae, p. 343. 202. Vitaceae, p. 344.	More or less as in *Celastrales*, but often of climbing habit, and the stamens always opposite the petals; leaves simple or compound; petals imbricate or valvate; endosperm often scanty or ruminate.
	45. MYRSINALES	
Probably derived from the same stock as the *Rhamnales* and *Celastrales*, but all sympetalous.	203. Myrsinaceae, p. 345. 204. Theophrastaceae, p. 346. 205. Aegicerataceae, p. 347.	Sympetalous families related to the preceding, also with stamens opposite to the corolla-lobes, usually epipetalous; ovary superior to half inferior, with numerous ovules on a free basal placenta.
	46. EBENALES	
A climax sympetalous group in the tropics, the flowers sometimes unisexual.	206. Ebenaceae, p. 348. 207. Sapotaceae, p. 350. 208. Sarcospermaceae, p. 351.	Sympetalous; corolla-lobes imbricate; stamens epipetalous or rarely hypogynous, 1–4 times as many as the corolla-lobes; petaloid staminodes often present; anthers opening lengthwise; ovary superior; ovules 1–2 in each loculus, axile; seeds often with shining hard testa and conspicuous hilum. Trees or shrubs, leaves alternate, rarely with stipules.

Notes on affinity (origin and further development)	Sequence of Orders and Families (a cross-line indicates the climax of a group)	General characteristics and tendences of Orders
	47. RUTALES	Hypogynous to slightly perigynous; ☿ or ♂ ♀; apocarpous to syncarpous with axile, basal, or apical placentation; ovules mostly few; stamens definite in number, free; petals contorted to valvate; disk mostly conspicuous; leaves often gland-dotted; endosperm present or absent.
	209. Rutaceae, p. 353.	
	210. Simaroubaceae, p. 354.	
	211. Burseraceae, p. 355.	
	212. Averrhoaceae, p. 356.	
A large mainly tropical series of families of woody plants often spoken of as the 'Pinnatae', characterized by mostly pinnate or rarely palmate leaves; origin and early affinities not very evident; *Sapindaceae* and *Anacardiaceae* especially related to some *Euphorbiaceae*, from the stock of which part of the latter may have arisen.	48. MELIALES	More or less as in preceding group but leaves not gland-dotted and stamens connate into a tube.
	213. Meliaceae, p. 356.	
	49. SAPINDALES	Flowers often ♂ and ♀; petals mostly present, free; stamens more or less perigynous; ovules 1–2 in each ovary-loculus; endosperm mostly 0; embryo often curved or crumpled. Trees or shrubs.
	214. Melianthaceae, p. 359.	
	215. Sapindaceae, p. 360.	
	216. Podoaceae, p. 361.	
	217. Sabiaceae, p. 361.	
	218. Anacardiaceae, p. 363.	
	219. Aceraceae, p. 364.	
	220. Hippocastanaceae, p. 365.	
	221. Staphyleaceae, p. 367.	
	222. Akaniaceae, p. 368.	
	223. Julianiaceae, p. 368.	
	224. Didiereaceae, p. 369.	
A rather mixed group either mimicking or having direct affinity with several other families.	50. LOGANIALES	Corolla sympetalous, actinomorphic; stamens epipetalous, alternate with the corolla-lobes; ovary superior, 4–2-locular; ovules numerous, axile or ascending; seeds with endosperm and straight embryo. Trees, shrubs, or herbs; leaves opposite, simple, with or without stipules.
	225. Potaliaceae, p. 371.	
	226. Loganiaceae, p. 372.	
	227. Buddleiaceae, p. 373.	
	228. Antoniaceae, p. 375.	
	229. Spigeliaceae, p. 376.	
	230. Strychnaceae, p. 377.	
	231. Oleaceae, p. 378.	
Advanced climax types derived from the preceding group, the tendency to free	51. APOCYNALES	Corolla sympetalous, actinomorphic; stamens epipetalous, alternate with the
	232. Plocospermaceae, p. 379.	
	233. Apocynaceae, p. 380.	

Notes on affinity (origin and further development)	Sequence of Orders and Families (a cross-line indicates the climax of a group)	General characteristics and tendences of Orders
carpels is probably secondary and not primitive because of the common style or stigma.	234. Periplocaceae, p. 381. 235. Asclepiadaceae, p. 383.	corolla-lobes; pollen becoming waxy and collecting into masses as in orchids; ovary superior, carpels 2, free or becoming free in fruit; styles united; ovules mostly numerous, parietal or on the septa; seeds usually with endosperm and straight embryo. Leaves opposite, simple; no stipules.
A very large and natural assemblage derived from the *Loganiales* stock. Mostly Tropical, with more advanced group (*Galieae*) in Temperate Regions.	**52. RUBIALES** 236. Dialypetalanthaceae, p. 384. 237. Rubiaceae, p. 386.	Corolla sympetalous, actinomorphic; stamens 5, rarely more, epipetalous, alternate with the corolla-lobes; anthers free, opening lengthwise; ovary inferior; axile placentation, rarely parietal; style 1; ovules numerous to solitary; seeds with endosperm. Leaves opposite, simple, entire; stipules inter- or intrapetiolar.
A climax group probably derived from the *Loganiales* and *Apocynales*, mostly climbing shrubs with compound leaves and leaf-tendrils, culminating in a few herbs.	**53. BIGNONIALES** 238. Cobaeaceae, p. 387. 239. Bignoniaceae, p. 389. 240. Pedaliaceae, p. 389. 241. Martyniaceae, p. 392.	Corolla sympetalous, more or less zygomorphic; stamens 5, 4, or 2, epipetalous, alternate with the corolla-lobes, the fifth often reduced to a staminode; ovary superior, 2- or 1-locular; ovules numerous; seeds without endosperm, often winged. Leaves opposite, mostly compound; stipules very rare.
Another climax group of the *Lignosae*, forming a parallel with the *Labiatae* at the top of the *Herbaceae*.	**54. VERBENALES** 242. Ehretiaceae, p. 393. 243. Verbenaceae, p. 395. 244. Stilbeaceae, p. 395. 245. Chloanthaceae, p. 396. 246. Phrymaceae, p. 398.	Corolla sympetalous, actinomorphic to zygomorphic; stamens 5, 4, or 2, epipetalous; ovary superior, entire, bicarpellate; ovules solitary or paired; style terminal on the ovary. Leaves alternate, opposite or verticillate; no stipules.

DIVISION II. Herbaceae

Notes on affinity (origin and further development)	Sequence of Orders and Families (a cross-line indicates the climax of a group)	General characteristics and tendences of Orders
	55. RANALES	
Herbaceous (some with scattered vascular bundles as in Monocotyledons) to softly woody groups (wood of special type probably derived from herbaceous), from which may have been derived the following herbaceous groups beginning with *Rhoeadales, Saxifragales,* culminating in *Umbelliferae,* and the reduced apetalous *Aristolochiaceae* and *Piperaceae.* Considerable affinity with Monocotyledons, especially with apocarpous families such as *Alismataceae.*	247. Paeoniaceae, p. 400. 248. Helleboraceae, p. 401. 249. Ranunculaceae, p. 402. 250. Nymphaeaceae, p. 403. 251. Podophyllaceae, p. 404. 252. Ceratophyllaceae, p. 405. 253. Cabombaceae, p. 406.	Hypogynous to rarely perigynous; ♀; hemicyclic to rarely cyclic; apocarpous; petals usually present; stamens free, often numerous; seeds rich in endosperm; embryo minute. Herbs to softly woody, some aquatics.
	56. BERBERIDALES	
Derived from the *Ranales* with great reduction in number of carpels (to one); great diversity of morphological characters.	254. Sargentodoxaceae, p. 407. 255. Lardizabalaceae, p. 408. 256. Menispermaceae, p. 410. 257. Nandinaceae, p. 411. 258. Circaeasteraceae, p. 412. 259. Berberidaceae, p. 412.	Hypogynous; ♀ to ♂ ♀; cyclic; one or few carpels; petals present, small, free; endosperm copious, sometimes ruminate; embryo small to large; herbaceous to woody or climbing habit; wood often with broad medullary rays.
	57. ARISTOLOCHIALES	
See note under *Ranales*; probably reduced *Berberidales* by way of *Menispermaceae* and with very similar wood; accompanying reduction is parasitic habit.	260. Aristolochiaceae, p. 414. 261. Hydnoraceae, p. 415. 262. Cytinaceae, p. 416. 263. Nepenthaceae, p. 417.	Hypogynous to epigynous; apetalous; ovary superior to inferior; stamens numerous to few; parietal to axile placentation; endosperm present or absent; small to large embryo; herbaceous to climbing habit with wood as in *Berberidales*; some parasites with reduction of leaves.
	58. PIPERALES	
Reduced types from the *Ranales*, often with scattered vascular bundles as in Monocotyledons.	264. Piperaceae, p. 419. 265. Saururaceae, p. 420. 266. Chloranthaceae, p. 421.	Usually no perianth; ovary mostly superior; placentas parietal to subaxile; endosperm copious; embryo minute.

Notes on affinity (origin and further development)	Sequence of Orders and Families (a cross-line indicates the climax of a group)	General characteristics and tendences of Orders
	59. RHOEADALES	
Herbaceous and closely related to the *Ranunculaceae*; basic group for *Cruciferae*.	267. Papaveraceae, p. 422. 268. Fumariaceae, p. 423.	Petals present, becoming zygomorphic; stamens numerous to few; syncarpous, with parietal placentation; endosperm copious; embryo minute.
	60. CRUCIALES	
A large and completely climax family derived from the *Papaveraceae*.	269. Cruciferae, p. 425.	Stamens reduced to 6, 4 long and 2 short; petals 4; ovary usually divided by a false septum; no endosperm.
	61. RESEDALES	
More or less as in *Cruciales* but flowers mostly zygomorphic and with a variable number of stamens.	270. Resedaceae, p. 426.	Hypogynous; calyx mostly zygomorphic, 4–7-lobed; petals small and inconspicuous or absent, valvate; stamens 40–3; ovary of 2–6 free or connate carpels, ovules numerous, parietal or basal; fruits capsular or baccate.
	62. CARYOPHYLLALES	
A prolific herbaceous group which has given rise to apetalous orders such as *Polygonales, Chenopodiales*, and perigynous petaliferous families as *Lythrales*, besides sympetalous groups as *Gentianales* and *Primulales*.	271. Elatinaceae, p. 427. 272. Molluginaceae, p. 428. 273. Caryophyllaceae, 429. 274. Ficoidaceae, p. 430. 275. Portulacaceae, p. 430.	Hypogynous to perigynous; mostly ⚥; cyclic, syncarpous; axile to free-central placentation; stamens mostly definite in number; endosperm copious; embryo curved.
	63. POLYGONALES	
Reduced from *Caryophyllales*.	276. Polygonaceae, p. 431. 277. Illecebraceae, p. 432.	More or less as in *Caryophyllales* but apetalous; ovary 1-locular, 1-ovuled; embryo straight to curved; endosperm still copious; stipules often sheathing, intrapetiolar, membranous or scarious.

Notes on affinity (origin and further development)	Sequence of Orders and Families (a cross-line indicates the climax of a group)	General characteristics and tendences of Orders
	64. CHENOPODIALES	
Further reductions from the *Caryophyllaceous* stock.	278. Barbeuiaceae, p. 434. 279. Phytolaccaceae, p. 435. 280. Gyrostemonaceae, p. 436. 281. Agdestidaceae, p. 437. 282. Petiveriaceae, p. 438. 283. Chenopodiaceae, p. 438. 284. Amaranthaceae, p. 440. 285. Cynocrambaceae, p. 441. 286. Batidaceae, p. 442. 287. Basellaceae, p. 443.	As in *Polygonales* but stipules absent or very small; carpels numerous to solitary, free or connate; embryo curved.
	65. LYTHRALES	
Herbaceous, rarely woody, probably advanced perigynous types derived from the *Caryophyllales* through the subfamily *Sileneae*.	288. Lythraceae, p. 445. 289. Onagraceae, p. 446. 290. Trapaceae, p. 447. 291. Haloragidaceae, p. 448. 292. Callitrichaceae, p. 449.	Actinomorphic; perigynous to epigynous; calyx tubular, valvate; petals present; stamens as many or twice as many as petals; ovules numerous to solitary; placentation axile; no endosperm; several aquatic forms.
	66. GENTIANALES	
Another group very closely related to the *Caryophyllales* and maybe to *Saxifragales*, of which they appear to be sympetalous representatives; mostly herbaceous.	293. Gentianaceae, p. 450. 294. Menyanthaceae, p. 451.	Corolla actinomorphic; stamens epipetalous, alternate with the corolla-lobes; anthers free; disk often present; ovary superior, 1-locular with parietal placentation; ovules numerous; seeds with copious endosperm and small embryo. Herbs.
	67. PRIMULALES	
Closely related to *Caryophyllaceae* and perhaps to *Saxifragaceae* (*sensu stricto*).	295. Primulaceae, p. 453. 296. Plumbaginaceae, p. 453.	More or less as above, but stamens usually opposite the corolla-lobes; ovary mostly 1-locular with free basal placentation; seeds usually with copious endosperm. Herbs often with radical leaves.
	68. PLANTAGINALES	
Climax family of the alliance.	297. Plantaginaceae, p. 453.	Stamens alternate with the corolla-lobes; flowers anemophilous.

Notes on affinity (origin and further development)	Sequence of Orders and Families (a cross-line indicates the climax of a group)	General characteristics and tendences of Orders
	69. SAXIFRAGALES	
Herbaceous groups closely connected with the *Ranales* but more advanced; several small families with very special leaf-morphology and/or habitat.	298. Crassulaceae, p. 457. 299. Cephalotaceae, p. 458. 300. Saxifragaceae, p. 459. 301. Eremosynaceae, p. 460. 302. Vahliaceae, p. 461. 303. Francoaceae, p. 462. 304. Donatiaceae, p. 462. 305. Parnassiaceae, p. 465. 306. Adoxaceae, p. 466.	More or less perigynous to rarely epigynous; ♀; apocarpous to syncarpous, with axile placentation; stamens definite in number, free; endosperm copious; embryo small, straight.
	70 SARRACENIALES	
Derived from *Saxifragales*.	307. Droseraceae, p. 467. 308. Sarraceniaceae, p. 468.	More or less as in *Saxifragales*, but plants mostly insectivorous; syncarpous; placentation parietal to axile; stamens numerous to few.
	71. PODOSTEMALES	
A very advanced and specialized group.	309. Podostemaceae, p. 470. 310. Hydrostachyaceae, p. 470.	Probably very much reduced types of *Saxifragales*, with peculiar habit and habitat.
	72. UMBELLALES	
A climax family possibly derived from the *Saxifragales* stock; regarded as a parallel with *Araliaceae*.	311. Umbelliferae, p. 471.	Flowers in umbels; ovary inferior, of 2 carpels. Herbs, often with hollow stems; leaves without stipules.
	73. VALERIANALES	
An advanced group probably derived from the *Saxifragales*.	312. Valerianaceae, p. 473. 313. Dipsacaceae, p. 474. 314. Calyceraceae, p. 475.	Corolla usually zygomorphic; calyx and corolla epigynous; inflorescence cymose to capitate or verticillate, sometimes with an involucre of bracts; ovary 3–1-locular, only 1 loculus fertile; ovule 1, pendulous.
	74. CAMPANALES	
Perhaps derived from early *Gentianales*, the genus *Cyananthus* (*Campanulaceae*) having a superior ovary.	315. Campanulaceae, p. 476. 316. Lobeliaceae, p. 477.	Corolla actinomorphic to zygomorphic; epigynous; stamens free or inserted low on the corolla; anthers free to connivent; ovary inferior; ovules numerous to few on axile placentas. Herbaceous.

Notes on affinity (origin and further development)	*Sequence of Orders and Families (a cross-line indicates the climax of a group)*	*General characteristics and tendences of Orders*
	75. GOODENIALES	
Probably derived from the preceding but relationships rather problematical.	317. Goodeniaceae, p. 478. 318. Brunoniaceae, p. 479. 319. Stylidiaceae, p. 480.	More or less as above, but with indusiate stigma.
	76. ASTERALES	
Rather sharply cut off from other existing families, but perhaps derived mainly from the Campanulaceous stock; completely climax group.	320. Compositae, p. 481.	Ovary inferior, 1-locular, 1-ovulate; anthers united into a tube. Herbaceous or woody; flowers collected into heads, surrounded by an involucre of bracts.
	77. SOLANALES	
Advanced sympetalous families but not yet reduced in the number of stamens as in higher families.	321. Solanaceae, p. 484. 322. Convolvulaceae, p. 484. 323. Nolanaceae, p. 486.	Corolla actinomorphic to very slightly zygomorphic; stamens the same number and alternate with the corolla-lobes, epipetalous; ovary superior, 4–1-(mostly 2)- locular with numerous ovules on axile placentas, or rarely basal. Herbaceous to rarely woody, often climbing.
	78. PERSONALES	
A large natural order showing progressive reduction in the number of stamens accompanied by increasing zygomorphy of the corolla.	324. Scrophulariaceae, p. 488. 325. Acanthaceae, p. 489. 326. Gesneriaceae, p. 491. 327. Orobanchaceae, p. 492. 328. Lentibulariaceae, p. 492. 329. Columelliaceae, p. 493.	Corolla nearly always zygomorphic with stamens fewer than the corolla-lobes. Mostly herbaceous; leaves alternate to opposite.
	79. GERANIALES	
Here regarded as advanced more or less fixed types from *Caryophyllales* or direct from *Ranales*; considerable gap between these groups, but affinity evident through *Limnanthaceae* especially.	330. Geraniaceae, p. 495. 331. Limnanthaceae, p. 496. 332. Oxalidaceae, p. 497. 333. Tropaeolaceae, p. 498. 334. Balsaminaceae, p. 499.	Hypogynous; ⚥; ovary entire to lobed, syncarpous; ovules mostly 2–1 in each loculus; stamens definite in number; disk-glands often present; no endosperm; leaves frequently much divided, stipulate; higher types have zygomorphic flowers and tendency to syngenesious anthers.

Notes on affinity (origin and further development)	Sequence of Orders and Families (a cross-line indicates the climax of a group)	General characteristics and tendences of Orders
Regarded as most nearly related to the *Geraniales*, of which they may be advanced representatives.	80. POLEMONIALES 335. Polemoniaceae, p. 500. 336. Hydrophyllaceae, p. 501. 337. Cuscutaceae, p. 501. 81. BORAGINALES 338. Boraginaceae, p. 502.	Corolla actinomorphic; stamens epipetalous; anthers free; ovary superior, not lobed; placentas parietal or axile; ovules numerous to few. Herbaceous. More or less as in preceding group, but ovary deeply lobed, with gynobasic style, composed of 2 carpels and with paired ovules.
The climax development of the fundamentally herbaceous line of evolution, parallel with *Verbenaceae*.	82. LAMIALES 339. Myoporaceae, p. 503. 340. Selaginaceae, p. 505. 341. Globulariaceae, p. 505. 342. Labiatae, p. 506.	As in the preceding but leaves mostly opposite or whorled; corolla zygomorphic; stamens 4 or 2; ovary becoming deeply lobed with a gynobasic style; ovules mostly paired. Largely herbaceous, with inflorescence tending to capitula or verticillasters.

DESCRIPTIONS OF ORDERS AND FAMILIES, WITH KEYS TO GENERA OF SMALLER FAMILIES

Division I. LIGNOSAE

Order 1. MAGNOLIALES

Entirely woody group; flowers hypogynous, ☿, rarely ♂ ♀ accompanied by reduction, acyclic to cyclic; petals usually present; stamens numerous, free or rarely connate in a mass; carpels free or reduced to 1; endosperm copious, not ruminate; embryo minute. Leaves alternate, very rarely opposite, simple, stipulate or not.—Mainly in N. Temperate Regions.

A. Perianth present, conspicuous, never operculate; indumentum not lepidote:
  B. Flowers bisexual:
    C. Stamens free among themselves:
      D. Leaves stipulate, the stipules large and enclosing and protecting the young growths, but soon deciduous and leaving an annular scar around the stem; flowers large, solitary, terminal or axillary; axis usually elongated and cone-like; stamens and carpels spirally arranged
        Magnoliaceae
      DD. Leaves exstipulate, pellucid-punctate; flowers small or medium-sized, rarely solitary; axis short and never cone-like in fruit; carpels more or less in a single whorl:
        E. Sepals imbricate   *Illiciaceae*
        EE. Sepals valvate   *Winteraceae*
    CC. Stamens united; ovary 1-locular, with parietal placentas
        Canellaceae
  BB. Flowers unisexual; stamens partially or wholly connate into a globose mass; leaves exstipulate; climbing shrubs   *Schisandraceae*
AA. Perianth present, operculate; indumentum lepidote; stamens petaloid
        Himantandraceae
AAA. Perianth absent or much reduced and bract-like; indumentum never lepidote; stamens not petaloid:
  F. Carpels 3; stipules large and intrapetiolar, membranous leaves minutely pellucid-punctate; flowers polygamous-monoecious   *Lactoridaceae*
  FF. Carpels more than 3; stipules absent or small; leaves not pellucid-punctate:
    G. Flowers bisexual, clustered or racemose-paniculate; seeds not winged
        Trochodendraceae
    GG. Flowers dioecious, solitary on short arrested branchlets; stipules adnate to the petiole; seeds winged   *Cercidiphyllaceae*

1. Magnoliaceae

Trees or shrubs; leaves alternate, simple; *stipules large*, deciduous, leaving an annular scar on the shoot, enclosing the young buds; flowers large, solitary, terminal or axillary, usually ♀; sepals and petals often similar, in *several series*, imbricate; stamens numerous, *hypogynous*, free; anthers long, 2-locular, opening lengthwise; pollination by insects; carpels usually numerous, 1-locular, *spirally arranged* on an often elongated axis, rarely consolidated in fruit; ovules 2 or more; 2-seriate on the ventral suture; fruiting carpels splitting

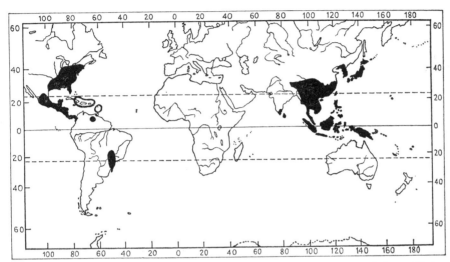

Approximate range of the family Magnoliaceae, probably the most ancient of living Dicotyledons; the discontinuous distribution of members of this family, considered in conjunction with the anatomical and floral structure, indicates that it is of great antiquity.

longitudinally or transversely, or indehiscent and samaroid, more rarely united into a fleshy syncarp; seeds large, suspended (when carpel dehiscent) by a *silky thread-like funicle*; testa externally *arilloid* or rarely adherent to the endocarp; endosperm copious, oily; *embryo minute*. B.H. **1**, 16, partly; E.P. **3**, 2, 12, partly. Southeast N. and Central America, West Indies, Venezuela, Brazil, E. Asia, Malay Archipelago.

Useful Products: *Tulip-tree wood* (Liriodendron tulipifera L.). Many handsome garden trees and shrubs.

Key to genera by J. E. Dandy

A. Anthers introrse or latrorse; fruiting carpels not samaroid: **B.** Flowers terminal: **C.** Flowers bisexual (rarely abnormally female by tepalody of the stamens); tepals 9 or more, the outer whorl sometimes much reduced in size or texture; fruiting carpels dorsally dehiscent, circumscissile or indehiscent: **D.** Fruit not capsular, the carpels separate or in a fleshy syncarp and usually numerous: **E.** Fruiting carpels dehiscent, not fleshy: **F.** Gynoecium sessile or shortly stipitate, more or less exserted from the androecium: **G.** Carpels free or rarely somewhat united, in fruit dehiscent along the dorsal suture: **H.**

Ovules 4 or more in each carpel—MANGLIETIA (E. Himal. to S. China, Malay Archip.). **HH.** Ovules 2 in each carpel (rarely 3–4 in the lower carpels)—MAGNOLIA (E. Asia, Malay Archip., Southeastern U.S.A., Cent. Amer., Greater Antilles, Venez.). **GG.** Carpels concrescent at least at the base, in fruit circumscissile and woody, the upper portions falling away either singly or in irregular masses, the lower portions persistent with the suspended seeds; stipules adnate to the petiole—TALAUMA (E. Himal. to Indo-China and

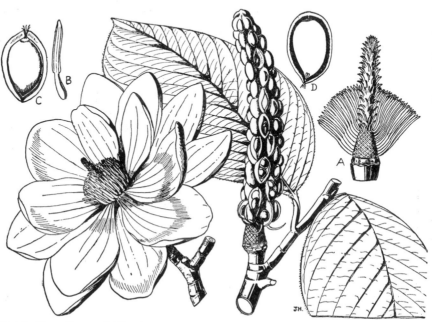

FIG. 1. Magnolia campbellii *Hk. f. & Thoms.* (Magnoliaceae). A, section showing arrangement of stamens and carpels. B, stamen. C, seed. D, section of seed. (After Hk. f.)

Malaya; Trop. Amer. and West Indies). **FF.** Gynoecium stipitate, not exserted from the androecium; tepals 9, subequal; carpels 2–5-ovulate, in fruit dehiscent along the dorsal suture; stipules free from the petiole—ALCIMANDRA (E. Himal. to Tongking). **EE.** Fruiting carpels indehiscent, concrescent to form a fleshy syncarp; tepals 18 or more, subequal; connective-appendage very long, subequalling or longer than the anther-loculi; ovules 2 in each carpel; stipules free from the petiole—AROMADENDRON (Malay Penin. and Archip.). **DD.** Fruit a woody loculicidal capsule composed of few (2–8) concrescent carpels; tepals 9–15, subequal; ovules about 4–8 in each carpel; stipules free from the petiole—PACHYLARNAX (Assam to Indo-China and Malay Penin.). **CC.** Flowers unisexual; tepals 6–7, subequal; fruiting carpels woody, dehiscent completely along the ventral suture and partly along the dorsal suture, thus finally becoming bifid; ovules 2 in each carpel; stipules adnate to the petiole—KMERIA (S. China to Indo-China). **BB.** Flowers axillary: **J.** Gynoecium sessile; anthers introrse; stipules free from the petiole—ELMERRILLIA (Malay Archip., Philipp. Is., New Guin.). **JJ.** Gynoecium stipitate; anthers latrorse or sublatrorse; stipules adnate to or free from the petiole—MICHELIA (Trop. and Subtrop. E. Asia to Malay Archip.). **AA.** Anthers extrorse; fruiting carpels indehiscent, samaroid (produced at the apex into a long wing-like beak), deciduous; leaves 2–10-lobed, the apex truncate or widely emarginate; stipules free from the petiole—LIRIODENDRON (SE. Asia and Southeastern N. Amer.).

NOTE: *Goniostoma* Elmer, *Leafl. Bot.* **5,** 1808 (1913) is error for *Geniostoma* (*Loganiaceae*).

2. ILLICIACEAE[1]

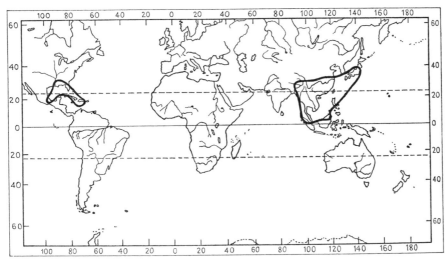

Range of Illicium, the sole genus of Illiciaceae, an ancient group formerly included in Winteraceae, to which it is closely related.

Shrubs or small trees; leaves alternate, simple, sometimes clustered or sub-verticillate, entire, pinnately nerved; *stipules absent*; flowers bisexual, solitary,

[1] A. C. Smith, *J. Arnold Arbor.* **24,** 120 (1943). See also the detailed account of the families *Illiciaceae* and *Schisandraceae* by the same author in *Sargentia*, **7,** 1 (1947). I doubt if any of the more widely experienced botanists of the past decades would have agreed with some of the rather sweeping statements in this paper. Examples are: 'It has long been realised by systematists who have looked into the matter that these three genera (i.e. *Illicium, Schisandra,* and *Kadsura*) have no close affinity to the *Magnoliaceae* (e.g. Dandy, Bailey, and Smith). On the basis of various morphological and anatomical characters, the *Magnoliaceae* form with their only close allies the *Himantandraceae* and *Degeneriaceae*, a compact group of families.' On p. 128 of the present work I have indicated that I consider, rightly or wrongly, that *Degeneria* (*Degeneriaceae*) is closely related to *Exospermum* and *Zygogynum* in the family *Winteraceae*.

Again to quote: 'In general usage at present is the family named *Schisandraceae*, usually taken to include *Schisandra* and *Kadsura*, but most students fail to consider the proximity of the genus *Illicium* to this family.' Yet in the key to the two families below this statement (p. 2) a multitude of differences are given, and it would have been more to the point if *Illicium* had been compared with *Winteraceae*, wherein it was formerly placed by all botanists, with the exception of van Tieghem, whose unorthodox views in the classification of other groups based mainly on anatomical characters have received little support up to the present. Too much reliance on anatomical characters alone seems to me to result, sometimes, not in classification, but *declassification*.

axillary or supra-axillary, rarely lateral and below the leaves or on the trunk; pedicels bracteate; sepals and petals numerous to 7, free, imbricate, usually *several-seriate*, the outermost often small and bracteole-like, inner gradually larger, becoming ligulate and thin to fleshy and ovate to suborbicular, the innermost often reduced; stamens numerous to 4, several to 1-seriate, connective sometimes glandular, loculi introrsely lateral, dehiscing lengthwise; carpels 21–5, *free, in a single whorl*, mostly closely appressed laterally, erect or somewhat spreading, narrowed into a slender or stout style stigmatic on the ventral side;

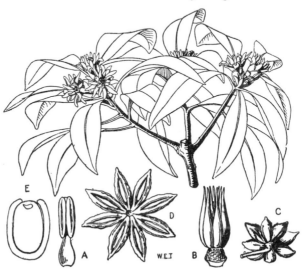

FIG. 2. Illicium anisatum *L.* (Illiciaceae). A, stamen. B, carpels. C, fruit. D, the same from above. E, section of seed. (After Bentl. & Trim.)

ovule 1, attached ventrally near the base; fruits *follicular*, dehiscing ventrally; seeds glossy, with copious endosperm and minute embryo. E. Asia, Indo-Malaya, China, Japan, Southeastern U.S., and West Indies.—ILLICIUM.

USEFUL PRODUCTS: *Star Anise* (Illicium verum *Hk. f.*), S. China; *Japanese Star Anise* (Illicium anisatum *L.*), Japan.

3. WINTERACEAE

Trees or shrubs with aromatic alternate pellucid-dotted leaves; *stipules absent*; flowers small, mostly *cymose* or *fasciculate*, ♀ or rarely polygamous; sepals 2–6, free and valvate or united (*Drimys*); petals 2- or more-seriate, mostly conspicuous in bud, imbricate; stamens several, hypogynous; anthers introrse, 2-locular, short, opening lengthwise; carpels several to one, more or less in a *single whorl*, free or partially united, 1- to many-ovuled; stigma sessile or styles distinct; fruit dehiscent or a berry; seeds with copious endosperm and minute embryo. B.H. **1**, 17; E.P. **3**, 2, 12 (under *Magnoliaceae*). Tropics and Subtropics, absent from Africa.

USEFUL PRODUCTS: *Winter's Bark* (Drimys winteri *Forst.*), S. Amer.

A small family, more tropical than *Magnoliaceae*, but evidently derived from it; no stipules, and the carpels mostly reduced to a single whorl.

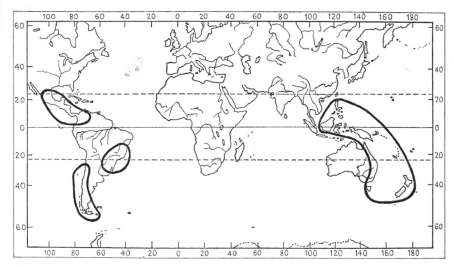

Range of the family Winteraceae (*sensu stricto*). Though the wood structure has ancient features, the floral structure is more advanced than Magnoliaceae, to which it is closely related though on parallel lines and more austral in distribution.

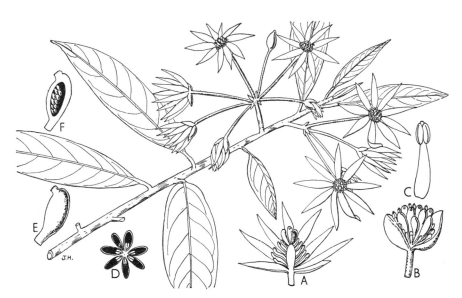

FIG. 3. Drimys winteri *Forst*. (Winteraceae). A, vertical section of flower. B, flower with petals removed. C, stamen. D, cross-section of carpels. E, one carpel. F, the same in vertical section. (Partly after *Bot. Mag.*)

A. Carpels remaining free from one another in fruit: **B.** Calyx enclosing the petals in bud and at length rupturing—DRIMYS (Malay Archip. to E. Austral., New Caled., Cent. and S. Amer., Juan Fernandez). **BB.** Calyx exposing the petals in bud, small and more or less cup-like or short and dentate: **C.** Flowers solitary and axillary; petals 5–6—PSEUDOWINTERA (New Zeal.). **CC.** Flowers in a terminal cluster of many-flowered cymes; petals 14–10: **D.** Inner series of petals 6–4; stamens with two widely divergent anther-loculi—BUBBIA (New Guin., E. Austral., New Caled., Lord Howe's Is.). **DD.** Inner petals 10; stamens with linear and parallel contiguous anther-loculi—BELLIOLUM (New Caled., Solomon Is.). **AA.** Carpels more or less united, especially in fruit, or carpel solitary: **E.** Stamens numerous: **F.** Staminodes absent: **G.** Carpels 8–7, with conspicuous grooves between them in fruit, partially united—EXOSPERMUM (New Caled.). **GG.** Carpels 4–1, closely united, each separated by a very thin wall—ZYGOGYNUM (New Caled.). **FF.** Staminodes present; carpel solitary—DEGENERIA[1] (Fiji). **EE.** Stamens about 12—TETRATHALAMUS (New Guin.).

4. CANELLACEAE

Glabrous *aromatic* trees; leaves simple, alternate, *gland-dotted*; stipules absent; flowers ☿, actinomorphic, cymose; bracts 3, imbricate, persistent; sepals

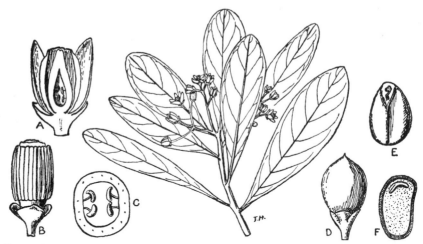

FIG. 4. Canella winterana (*L.*) *Gaertn.* (Canellaceae). A, section of flower. B, staminal tube. C, cross-section of ovary. D, fruit. E, seed. F, section of same. (Orig.)

4–5, free, thick, imbricate; petals thin, imbricate; stamens hypogynous, up to 20; filaments *connate into a tube* with the anthers adnate to its outer side, opening lengthwise by valves; ovary superior, 1-locular; placentas 2–5, *parietal*; ovules several; style thick; stigmas 2–5; ovules subanatropous; fruit a berry; seeds 2 or more, shining; endosperm oily and fleshy; embryo straight or

---

[1] Regarded as the type of a separate family, *Degeneriaceae*, by I. W. Bailey and A. C. Smith; see *J. Arnold Arbor.* **23**, 357 (1942). I consider *Degeneria* to be closely related to *Zygogynum*, &c., as placed in the key above. See footnote on p. 125.

nearly so. B.H. **1**, 121; E.P. **3**, 6, 314. Tropical America and E. and S. Africa.

USEFUL PRODUCTS: *Canella bark* (Canella winterana (*L.*) *Gaertn.*), West Indies and S. Florida.

A. Petals free; stamens 20–10: **B.** Flowers axillary: **C.** Petals 12, in 4 series; stamens 1–2; stigma 6-lobed; leaves with numerous much-branched lateral nerves—PLEODENDRON (West Indies). **CC.** Petals 10, the 5 inner narrower than the outer: **D.** Ovules 2-seriate on the 2–6 placentas; stamens 20–10—CINNAMODENDRON (*Capsicodendron*) (West Indies, Trop. S. Amer.). **DD.** Ovules 1-seriate on each of the 5 placentas; stamens 10—WARBURGIA (*Dawea*) (Trop. E. Afr., N. Transvaal). **BB.** Flowers in a terminal cyme; stamens 10; petals free—CANELLA (Florida, West Indies). **AA.** Petals united into a tube; stamens 9–7; flowers axillary, solitary, subsessile—CINNAMOSMA (Madag.).

5. SCHISANDRACEAE

Climbing or trailing shrubs; leaves simple, alternate, often *pellucid-dotted*; stipules absent; flowers ♂ ♀, small, axillary, solitary; sepals and petals 9–15,

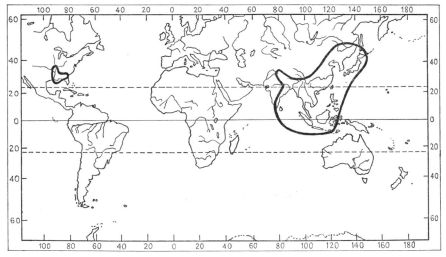

Range of the small family Schisandraceae, closely related to Magnoliaceae and with a similar discontinuous but less wide distribution. Schisandra occurs both in E. Asia and the Southeastern U.S.A., Kadsura only in E. Asia.

scarcely distinguishable from one another, the inner gradually petaloid, imbricate; stamens numerous, short, *partially or wholly united into a fleshy globose mass*; anthers small, 2-locular; carpels numerous, with 2–3 ovules, in fruit either *spread on the much elongated axis* or crowded into a fleshy mass; fruit baccate; seeds immersed in the fleshy pulp; endosperm oily, copious; embryo small. B.H. **1**, 17; E.P. **3**, 2, 12 (under *Magnoliaceae*). See revision by A. C. Smith, *Sargentia*, **7**, 79 (1947). Southeastern N. America and E. Asia.

A very small and ancient family (see map) which, together with the separation of the sexes, has adopted a climbing habit. The distribution is almost identical with that of *Magnoliaceae*, from which it has apparently been derived.

FIG. 5. Schisandra glabra (*Brickell*) *Rehder*.
(male) (Schisandraceae). A, stamens. B, carpels. C, section of carpel. D, fruiting carpels
E, seed. (After Le Maout & Decne.)

A. Carpels scattered on an elongated axis after flowering—SCHISANDRA.
AA. Carpels remaining crowded in a head after flowering—KADSURA.

6. HIMANTANDRACEAE

Aromatic trees covered with *peltate scaly indumentum*; leaves alternate, entire, penninerved; *stipules absent*; flowers bisexual, solitary or paired on short

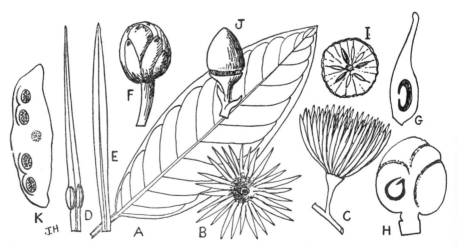

FIG. 6. Himantandra belgraveana *F. Muell.* (Himantandraceae). A, leaf. B, scale from same.
C, open flower. D, stamen. E, staminode. F, fruit. G, section of one carpel. H, longitudinal
section of fruit. I, cross-section of fruit. J, opening flower bud. K, cross-section of anther.
(Partly after Diels.)

axillary branches, at first involucrate by two *calyptriform leathery deciduous sepals*; inner sepals the one within the other; petals about 7, lanceolate, very similar in size and shape to the numerous (about 40) stamens which have the anther-loculi separated on each side towards the base, opening lengthwise; *staminodes several*, subulate; carpels 7–10, contiguous, free except at the base; ovule solitary in each, pendulous from the apex, anatropous; fruit globose, gall-like, fleshy, 7–10-locular by the *coalescence of the carpels*; seed pendulous, with oily endosperm and small embryo. N.E. Australia, New Guinea, Moluccas.—HIMANTANDRA (Fig. 6).

A small and curious *relic*, with petaloid stamens; remarkable in its group in having peltate scaly indumentum.

7. LACTORIDACEAE

Shrubs with alternate small, obovate, emarginate, entire leaves and numerous minute *pellucid dots*; stipules large, membranous, united within the petiole;

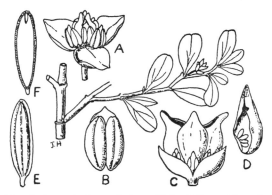

FIG. 7. Lactoris fernandeziana *Philippi* (Lactoridaceae).
A, flower. B, anther. C, fruit. D, one carpel. E, seed.
F, section of seed. (After Hk. *Ic. Pl.*)

flowers polygamo-monoecious, small, solitary or up to 3, axillary; sepals 3, imbricate; *petals absent*; stamens 6, in 2 whorls; anthers short, extrorse, 2-locular, carpels 3, *free*, stigma beak-like; ovules 6 in each carpel, in 2 vertical series on the intruded placentas; fruit follicular, beaked; seeds 4–6; endosperm copious, oily; embryo minute. B.H. **3**, 127 (under *Piperaceae*); E.P. **3**, 2, 19. Juan Fernandez Is.—LACTORIS (Fig. 7.).

A monotypic family closely related to the *Winteraceae*, of which it is probably a reduced derivative.

8. TROCHODENDRACEAE

Trees with *whorled* long-petiolate serrate leaves; *buds perulate*; stipules absent; flowers ♀ or polygamous, racemose or subfasciculate, rather small; *sepals absent* or very minute; *petals absent*; stamens numerous, hypogynous or subperigynous on the *expanded torus*; anthers short or linear, extrorse, on slender filaments; carpels 6–10, more or less in a *single whorl*, rather loosely united (*Trochodendron*) or quite free and stipitate (*Euptelea*); stigmas free; ovules 1 to several in each carpel, pendulous; fruit dehiscent or samaroid; seeds with endosperm and minute embryo. B.H. **1**, 954 (under *Magnoliaceae*); E.P. **3**, 2. 21. Assam to Formosa and Japan.

A small family with a restricted distribution, related to but more advanced and reduced than the *Illiciaceae* which occurs in the same area. This family may show the path of development to part of the *Hamamelidales*.

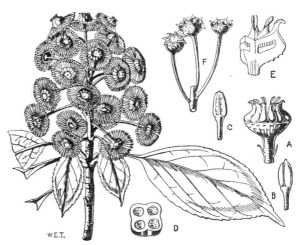

FIG. 8. Trochodendron aralioides *Sieb. & Zucc.* (Trochodendraceae). A, flower with stamens removed. B and C, anthers. D, section of anther. E, section of carpels. F, fruits. (After *Bot. Mag.*)

A. Carpels free and stipitate—Euptelea (Himal. to Japan). **AA.** Carpels loosely united and sessile—Trochodendron (Japan).

9. CERCIDIPHYLLACEAE

Trees; leaves deciduous, *opposite or alternate*, stipulate; *stipules adnate to the petiole*, caducous; flowers *dioecious*, males subsessile, axillary, solitary or fascicled, female pedicellate; sepals 4, small; *petals absent*; stamens 15–20; filaments long and slender, on a conical torus; anthers oblong-linear, basifixed, opening lengthwise; carpels 4–6, *slightly stipitate*, gradually narrowed into elongated slender styles stigmatic on their inner face; ovules in two rows, descending, anatropous; fruit a cluster of 2–6 follicles splitting down the ventral suture, which by twisting becomes external; endocarp woody and shining within; seeds compressed, nearly square, winged at one end; embryo medium-sized in copious endosperm; cotyledons flat. See Swamy and Bailey, 'The Morphology and Relationships of Cercidiphyllum', *J. Arnold Arbor.* **30**, 187 (1949). China and Japan.—Cercidiphyllum.

USEFUL PRODUCTS: C. japonicum (see Fig. 9), the only species, is a magnificent tree up to 55 ft. in girth in its native habitat; valuable timber.

A monotypic family of the *Magnoliales* and approaching the *Hamamelidales*, to some members of which it bears considerable external resemblance.

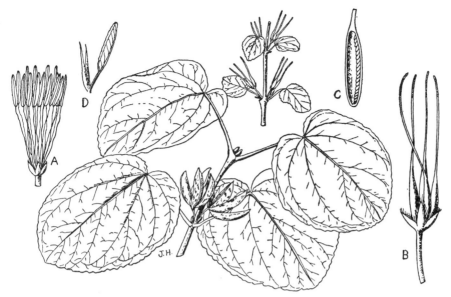

FIG. 9. Cercidiphyllum japonicum *Sieb. & Zucc.* (Cercidiphyllaceae). A, male flower. B, female flower. C, section of carpel. D, young leaf and stipules.

ORDER 2. ANNONALES

Entirely woody group; flowers hypogynous to perigynous, ♀; apocarpous to rarely syncarpous with parietal placentation; petaliferous with occasional gamopetaly; stamens ∞, free; endosperm constantly and markedly ruminate; embryo minute. Leaves alternate, simple, exstipulate.—Tropics and Subtropics.

A. Carpels numerous or few, rarely solitary, free or rarely united and with parietal placentas, inserted on a flat or conical receptable; styles usually free; fruit superior, of several free units or rarely united into a mass; sepals and petals not connate into a calyptra *Annonaceae*

AA. Carpels numerous, immersed in the turbinate receptacle; styles connate into a mass; fruit a several-locular berry; sepals and petals connate into a calyptra *Eupomatiaceae*

10. ANNONACEAE

Trees, shrubs, or climbers with aromatic wood and leaves; leaves alternate, entire; *stipules 0*; flowers mostly ♀, rarely ♂♀, variously arranged; sepals usually 3, separate or partly united, slightly imbricate or valvate; petals hypogynous, often 6 in 2 series, rarely 4 or 3, imbricate or valvate in each series; stamens hypogynous, numerous, spirally arranged; filaments very short; anthers 2-locular, opening lengthwise, often *overtopped by the truncate enlarged connective*; carpels numerous or few, free or rarely united into a

1-locular ovary; styles separate; ovules 1 to many, basal or parietal; carpels usually *stipitate in fruit*, free, rarely united into a 1- or many-locular mass, dry or fleshy, rarely dehiscent; seeds often arillate, with copious and markedly *ruminate endosperm* and minute embryo. B.H. **1**, 20; E.P. **3**, 2, 23. Tropics and Subtropics.—UVARIA, GUATTERIA, ARTABOTRYS, ASIMINA, MONODORA, ROLLINIA, ANNONA, XYLOPIA, &c.

FIG. 10. Asimina triloba (*L.*) *Dunal* (Annonaceae). A, section of flower. B and C, anthers. D, section of anther. E, carpel. F, longitudinal section of carpel. G, cross-section of carpel. H, fruit. I, longitudinal section of seed. (After Le Maout & Decne.)

USEFUL PRODUCTS: Various *Lancewoods* (Duguetia quitarensis *Bth.*), S. Amer.; (Bocagea laurifolia *B. & H.* and B. virgata *B. & H.*), West Indies. Fruits: *Cherimoyer* (Annona cherimolia *Mill.*), W.S. Amer.; *Sour Sop* (Annona muricata *L.*), Trop. Amer.; *Sweet Sop* (Annona squamosa *L.*), Malaya; *Custard Apple* (Annona reticulata *L.*), Trop. Amer.

A large tropical family, related to but a more advanced and fixed type than the *Magnoliaceae*.

11. EUPOMATIACEAE

Shrubs; leaves alternate, simple; stipules 0; *flowers perigynous*, solitary, ☿, fairly large; sepals and petals not differentiated from one another, forming a deciduous calyptra on the rim of the expanded concave torus; stamens numerous, perigynous, the *inner ones sterile and petaloid*, the outer with two linear extrorse anther-loculi and acuminate connective; carpels numerous, *immersed in the turbinate receptacle*; styles connate into a mass; ovules several on the ventral side; fruit a berry, truncate at the apex, girt with the remains of the perianth, several-locular; seeds 1–2 in each loculus, angular, with

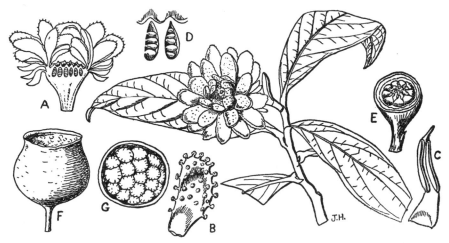

FIG. 11. Eupomatia laurina *R. Br.* (Eupomatiaceae). A, section of flower showing carpels immersed in the receptacle. B, petal. C, stamen. D, section of two carpels. E, receptacle with petals, &c., removed. F, fruit. G, section of fruit. (Partly after *Bot. Mag.*)

copious ruminate endosperm and very small embryo. B.H. **1,** 29 (under *Annonaceae*); E.P. **3,** 2, 39. Australia.—EUPOMATIA.

USEFUL PRODUCTS: Timber prettily marked (E. laurina *R. Br.*).

A remarkable type formerly included in the *Annonaceae*, but better treated as a separate family. The immersion of the otherwise free carpels in the expanded receptacle is probably a parallel to the similar condition found in *Nymphaeaceae*, in the herbaceous Ranalean phylum.

ORDER 3. LAURALES

Entirely woody group; flowers hypogynous to perigynous, ♀ or ♂♀; cyclic; apocarpous to one carpel; apetalous; stamens definite, free; endosperm uniform to rarely ruminate or absent; embryo often minute. Leaves alternate or opposite, simple, exstipulate.—Mainly Tropics.

A. Carpels free among themselves or rarely single; leaves often pellucid-punctate, mostly opposite; endosperm not ruminate:
  B. Style entire   *Monimiaceae*
  BB. Style 2-lobed   *Austrobaileyaceae*
AA. Carpels united into a single ovary:
  C. Stamens free among themselves:
    D. Ovary superior, rarely inferior; fruit not winged, either baccate or drupaceous:
      E. Anthers opening from the base upwards by valves   *Lauraceae*
      EE. Anthers opening by slits lengthwise   *Trimeniaceae*
    DD. Ovary inferior:
      F. Fruits winged or enclosed in the inflated perianth; leaves alternate
                                               Hernandiaceae

FF. Fruits neither winged nor enclosed in the perianth; leaves opposite
Gomortegaceae

CC. Stamens connate into a column; seeds with copious often ruminate endosperm; leaves often with pellucid dots   *Myristicaceae*

12. MONIMIACEAE

Trees or shrubs, rarely climbers, usually fragrant, with opposite, or rarely alternate, entire or serrate, coriaceous leaves with pellucid dots; *stipules absent*; flowers actinomorphic, rarely oblique, bisexual, polygamous or uni-

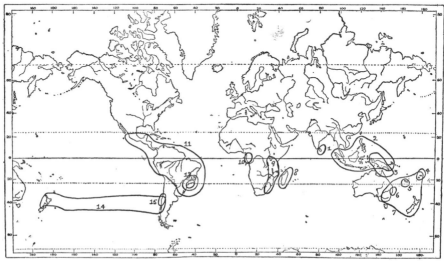

Distribution of some genera* of Monimiaceae. 1, Hortonia; 2, Matthaea; 3, Levieria; 4, Trimenia; 5, Amborella, Carnegiea, Nemualon; 6, Piptocalyx; 7, Hedycarya; 8, Ephippiandra; 9, Xymalos; 10, Glossocalyx; 11, Mollinedia; 12, Macropeplus; 13, Macrotorus; 14, Laurelia; 15, Peumus.

sexual, cymose or racemose, rarely solitary, small or medium-sized; inflorescence axillary or rarely terminal; calyx inferior, with 4–many often connivent teeth or lobes in 2–many series, and imbricate, equal, or the outer sepaloid and the inner petaloid, rarely obsolete; disk adnate to the perianth-tube; stamens numerous or few in 1–2 series; filaments very short, often flattened, *with or without glands* at the base; anthers erect, 2-locular, opening by a longitudinal slit or by *valves* from the base upwards. Female fl.: staminodes present or none; carpels several or rarely solitary, 1-locular; style short or elongated, stigma terminal; ovule solitary, erect or pendulous; carpels *separate in fruit*, enclosed by the perianth, or the latter deciduous, indehiscent, often drupaceous; seed erect or pendulous; testa membranous; endosperm fleshy; embryo small to half as large as the endosperm; cotyledons erect or spreading. B.H. **3**, 137; E.P. **3**, 2, 94. Tropics and Subtropics.—MONIMIA, TAMBOURISSA, MOLLINEDIA, KIBARA, HEDYCARYA, SIPARUNA, LAURELIA, AMBORELLA, ATHEROSPERMA, &c.

* Nos. 4, 6, and 9 are here transferred to *Trimeniaceae*, p. 138.

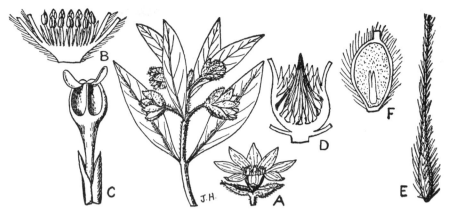

FIG. 12. Atherosperma moschatum *Labill.* (Monimiaceae). A, flower. B, section of flower. C, stamen. D, fruit. E, single carpel. F, section of seed.

ECONOMIC PRODUCTS: *Boldo* (Peumus boldus *Mol.*), Chile; *Australian Sassafras* (Doryphora sassafras *Endl.*), New South Wales.

A very interesting, mostly tropical family, showing strong tendency to perigyny; probably an apetalous parallel to the *Rosaceae*. It is interesting that the valvular dehiscent anthers also occur in the *Hamamelidales*, themselves a further development of the *Rosales*.

13. AUSTROBAILEYACEAE

Large *climbing shrubs*; leaves opposite or subopposite, coriaceous, entire, reticulate, and pinnately looped-nerved; stipules small, deciduous; flowers

FIG. 13. Austrobaileya maculata *C. T. White* (Austrobaileyaceae). A, flower from below. B, stamen from within. C, the same from the outside. D, carpel.

bisexual, axillary, solitary, pedicellate; pedicels bracteate at the base and bracteolate in the upper part; sepals and petals together about 12, pale green, free, imbricate, gradually larger from the outer sepaloid to the inner petaloid and obovate or suborbicular with thin margins; stamnes 25–12, *petaloid* (pale green), outer fertile, *inner gradually smaller and sterile* (densely purple-spotted); anthers 2-locular, loculi adnate to the connective, dehiscing lengthwise; carpels several (about 8), free on a slightly upraised torus; *style 2-lobed*; stigmas introrse, about half as long as the carpels; ovules 14–8, in 2 collateral series on the adaxial side; fruits not known. See Bailey and Swamy, 'Morphology and Relationships of *Austrobaileya*', *J. Arnold Arbor.* **30**, 211 (1949). Queensland.—Austrobaileya.

Austrobaileya, a genus of two species found in recent years on the Atherton Tableland, Queensland, Australia; its opposite leaves, single axillary flowers, the sepals and petals graded into each other (Fig. 13 A, flower from below), numerous petaloid introrse stamens (B) covered with large resinous warts, and several free carpels with a bilobed style, form a combination of characters probably unique among flowering plants; for want of a better place included here near *Monimiaceae*, and not in *Magnoliales* as originally suggested by the late C. T. White.

14. Trimeniaceae

Trees, shrubs, or climbers; leaves alternate or opposite, simple, entire or toothed, sometimes *glandular-toothed*; *stipules absent*; flowers bisexual or uni-sexual, sometimes polygamous or dioecious, small, arranged in axillary or

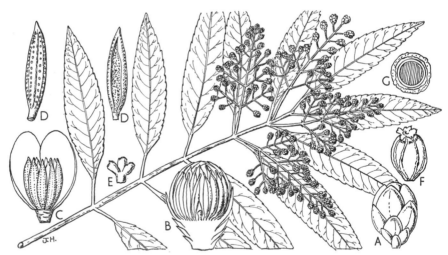

Fig. 14. Trimenia weinmannifolia *Seem.* (Trimeniaceae), male flowering shoot. A, male flower. B, vertical section of male flower. C, male flower showing stamens and 2 sepals. D, stamens. E, stigmas. F, fruit. G, transverse section of fruit.

terminal *racemes* or *racemes of cymules or panicles*; bracts small or absent; calyx-lobes or sepals 6 or 4, 2–1-seriate, imbricate, small; *petals absent*; stamens free, numerous to 6; anthers opening by slits lengthwise; loculi parallel, *extrorse*; rudimentary ovary present in the male flowers; ovary superior, *2–1-locular*; stigma sessile; ovule solitary, *pendulous* from the top of the ovary, anatropous; fruit baccate (mostly not known), ellipsoidal or subglobose; seeds compressed; cotyledons equal. See Money, Bailey, and Swamy, *J. Arnold Arbor.* **31,** 399 (1950). Tropical and S. Africa, New Guinea, New Caledonia, Fiji, New South Wales.

A. Trees or shrubs; leaves serrate or dentate: **B.** Stamens numerous; inflorescence axillary—XYMALOS (Trop. and S. Afr.). **BB.** Stamens 12–6: **C.** Racemes only terminal—SPHENOSTEMON (*Idenburgia, Nouhuysia*) (New Caled., New Guin.). **CC.** Racemes both terminal and axillary—TRIMENIA (Fiji Is.). **AA.** Scandent shrubs; stamens numerous; flowers polygamous, racemose; leaves opposite, entire—PIPTOCALYX (*Muellerothamnus*) (New South Wales).

15. LAURACEAE

Trees or shrubs, very rarely twining parasitic herbs, all parts with *aromatic oil-glands*; leaves alternate, rarely opposite or subopposite, coriaceous and evergreen, variously nerved; *stipules absent*; flowers small, greenish or yellow-

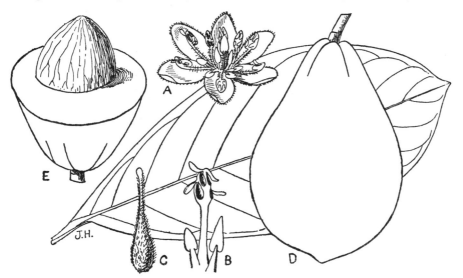

FIG. 15. Persea americana *Mill.* (Lauraceae). A, flower. B, stamen. C, ovary. D, fruit. E, section of fruit.

ish, usually cymose or racemose, bisexual, polygamous or dioecious, actinomorphic; calyx usually inferior; tube sometimes enlarging in fruit; lobes usually 6, imbricate; stamens typically in 4 whorls, often the fourth row suppressed or reduced to staminodes; filaments sometimes glandular at the base, very rarely the glands fused into a disk; anthers continuous with the filament, 2- or 4-valved, valves superimposed or more or less collateral, opening from the base upwards by flaps, introrse or sometimes the third whorl extrorse; ovary of 1 carpel, superior, rarely inferior, 1-locular; style terminal, simple; stigma small; ovule solitary, pendulous; fruit baccate or drupaceous; seed pendulous; without endosperm; testa membranous; embryo straight;

cotyledons thick, fleshy; radicle superior. B.H. **3,** 146; E.P. **3,** 2, 106. Mainly Tropics, and Subtropics. CRYPTOCARYA, BEILSCHMIEDIA, AYDENDRON, CINNA-MOMUM, MACHILUS, PERSEA, OCOTEA, NECTANDRA, SASSAFRAS, ACTINO-DAPHNE, LITSEA, UMBELLULARIA, LINDERA, LAURUS, CASSYTHA, &c.

USEFUL PRODUCTS: Many beautiful evergreen trees. *Sweet Bay Laurel* (Laurus nobilis *L.*); *Cinnamon* (Cinnamomum zeylanicum *Breyn*), Ceylon; *Camphor* (Cinnamomum camphora *Nees*), Japan and China; *Sassafras* (Sassa-fras officinale *Nees*), N. Amer.; *Avocado Pear* (Persea gratissima *Gaertn.*), Trop. Amer. Timbers: *Nan-Mu* wood (Persea nanmu *Oliv.*), China; *Green-heart wood* (Nectandra rodiaei *Schk.*), British Guiana.

A large tropical family (much in need of revision by an experienced taxonomist) appar-ently showing the extreme limit of reduction in the Magnolian alliance. The tendency to valvular dehiscence of the anthers shown partly in the *Berberidaceae* is here almost a constant character and is probably due to parallel development and not a sign of true affinity.

16. GOMORTEGACEAE

Large tree, wood[1] heavy, durable, and beautifully figured; leaves *opposite,* petiolate, shining and aromatic, narrowly elliptic, pinnately nerved; *stipules*

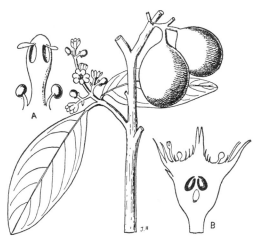

FIG. 16. Gomortega nitida *Ruiz & Pavon* (Gomorte-gaceae). A, stamen and glands. B, vertical section of flower. (After R. & P.)

absent; racemes axillary and terminal; flowers bisexual, subtended by 2 oppo-site bracts; sepals 6–10, *spirally arranged,* epigynous; petals absent; stamens

[1] The wood of this little-known and puzzling tree has been described in detail by W. L. Stern in *Amer. J. Bot.* **42,** 874 (1955), and he has also correlated the various descriptions of botanists since the genus was first described by Ruiz and Pavon in 1794. I have therefore extended the description compiled for my first edition to accord with that of Stern. After a careful investigation based on floral morphology, including the pollen grains, and the xylem anatomy, Stern (last sentence of his summary) considers 'that most likely *Gomor-tegaceae* is closely allied to *Monimiaceae* through a *Hortonia*-like forbear with valvular ("valvate") anthers'.

Flowering and fruiting specimens with seeds are still much desired for the Kew herbarium.

described as varying from 2 to 11, epigynous; filaments free; anthers 2-locular, introrse, *dehiscing by valves*; inner stamens with 2 shortly stalked glands at the base of each filament; ovary *inferior*, 2–3-locular; style 2–3-lobed; ovule 1 in each loculus, pendulous; fruit with a bony endocarp and fleshy exocarp; seed with large embryo in abundant oily endosperm. B.H. **3,** 149 (under *Lauraceae*); E.P.N. 172, 347; Hutch. *Fam. Fl. Pl.* **1,** 91. Chile.— GOMORTEGA. Recorded from the environs of Concepción, Araucó, Tomé, Collipulli, and near the Rio Quele in Chile. Common name 'Quele'.

17. HERNANDIACEAE

Trees or shrubs, sometimes scandent, with alternate, simple or *digitately compound* leaves; stipules absent; flowers bisexual, or monoecious or polygamous by abortion, actinomorphic, arranged in axillary corymbose or paniculate

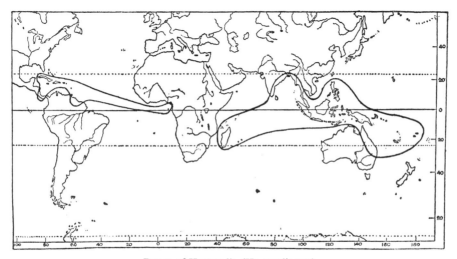

Range of Hernandia (Hernandiaceae).

cymes, bracteate or not; calyx superior, with 3–5 valvate subequal segments in two whorls or rarely 4–8 in one whorl; stamens 5–3, often 4, in a single whorl, opposite the outer segments when the calyx is double; anthers 2-locular. opening introrsely or laterally by *2 valves*; *staminodes gland-like*, in one or two whorls outside the stamens, or absent, those of the outer whorl in pairs at the base of the filaments, those of the inner whorl alternate with the stamens; ovary *inferior*, 1-locular; ovule solitary, pendulous; fruit dry, more or less ribbed, either with 2–4 wings on the body or with 2 terminal wings formed by enlarged perianth-segments, or wingless but enclosed in the inflated receptacle; seed solitary, *without endosperm*; testa leathery; embryo straight; cotyledons large, plano-convex or flat and twisted around the radicle. B.H. **3,** 164; (under *Lauraceae*); E.P. **3,** 2, 126. Tropics.

A small family, perhaps not very homogeneous and probably of mixed derivation. An imperfectly known Queensland genus, *Valvanthera* C. T. White, may prove to be better placed in *Lauraceae*.

A. Cymes bracteate; fruits with lateral wings or not winged: **B.** Leaves simple: **C.** Leaves not peltate, often triplinerved; fruits dry, ribbed—SPARAT-TANTHELIUM (Trop. Amer.). **CC.** Leaves often peltate; fruits surrounded by the inflated perianth—HERNANDIA (Tropics). **BB.** Leaves digitately com-

FIG. 17. Hernandia peltata *Meisn.* (Hernandiaceae).
A and B, flowers. C, stamen and glands. D, fruit. E,
same with receptacle removed.

pound; fruits with 2–4 broad lateral wings—ILLIGERA (Trop. Asia–Afr.). **AA.** Cymes ebracteate; fruits crowned by 2 terminal wings formed by the enlarged persistent calyx-segments; flowers unisexual—GYROCARPUS (Tropics).

18. MYRISTICACEAE

Trees, often large and frequently aromatic; leaves alternate, entire, penni-nerved, often with *pellucid dots*; stipules absent; flowers small, dioecious, apetalous, fascicled, corymbose or capitate; calyx 3- (rarely 2–5-) lobed, funnel-shaped to globose or saucer-shaped, lobes *valvate*; male flower: sta-mens 2–30; filaments *united into a column*; anthers 2-locular, free or united into a mass, dehiscing longitudinally; rudimentary ovary absent; female flower: staminodes absent; ovary superior, sessile, 1-locular; stigma sub-sessile; ovule 1, almost basal; fruit fleshy, usually dehiscing by two valves; seed erect, with a thin or fleshy sometimes laciniate often coloured aril; endosperm copious, replete with fat and often starch, mostly *ruminate*; embryo small; cotyledons ascending or spreading, sometimes connate. B.H. **3**, 135; E.P. **3**, 2, 40. Tropics.—MYRISTICA, PYCNANTHUS, &c.[1]

[1] This family formerly consisted of a single genus *Myristica*, but was divided into 15 engera by Warburg, 'Monogr. Myristicac.', *Nova Acta Leop. Carol.* **68** (1897).

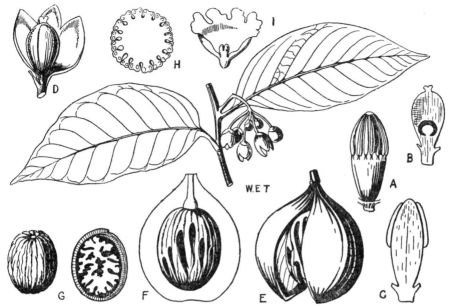

FIG. 18. Myristica fragrans *Houtt.* (Myristicaceae). A, anther-column. B, vertical section of ovary. C, anther. D, open female flower. E, fruit. F, section of fruit. G, seed. H, same transverse. I, embryo. (After Köhler.)

USEFUL PRODUCTS: *Nutmeg* (Myristica fragrans *Houtt.*), Indian Archip., and much cultivated in Tropics.

ORDER 4. DILLENIALES

Trees or shrubs, rarely herbs; flowers hypogynous, ♂, actinomorphic; calyx imbricate; petals imbricate, often crumpled in bud; stamens numerous, free; apocarpous; seeds with copious plain endosperm and small to fairly large embryo, often arillate. Leaves usually alternate with marked pinnate nervation; stipules absent or adnate to the petiole, rarely free.

A. Leaves alternate (very rarely opposite), often with strong parallel lateral nerves; stipules absent or wing-like and adnate to the petiole; seeds often arillate:
  B. Stamens hypogynous:
    C. Leaves simple   *Dilleniaceae*
    CC. Leaves pinnate, trifoliolate or unifoliolate   *Connaraceae*
  BB. Stamens perigynous, inserted on the calyx-tube   *Crossosomataceae*
AA. Leaves opposite or verticillate, simple to trifoliolate or pinnate; stipules present; seeds not arillate   *Brunelliaceae*

19. DILLENIACEAE

Trees, shrubs, or twiners, rarely undershrubs or herbs with radical leaves; leaves alternate, rarely opposite, entire or dentate, rarely pinnatifid or trilobed, usually with numerous prominent *parallel lateral nerves*; stipules absent or wing-like and *adnate* to the petiole, mostly deciduous; flowers small to medium-sized, rarely large, ♀ or ♂♀; sepals 5, *much imbricate, persistent*;

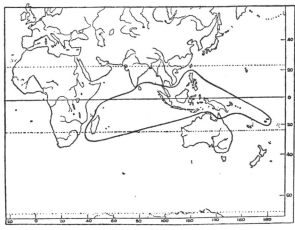

Range of Wormia.

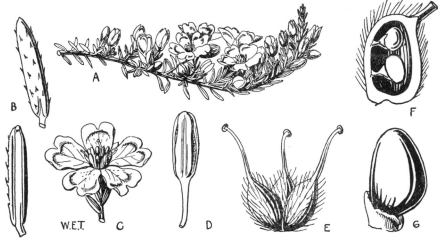

FIG. 19. Hibbertia ericifolia *Hk. f.* (Dilleniaceae). A, branch with flowers. B, leaves. C, flower. D, stamen. E, ovary. F, vertical section of same. G, fruit. (After Hook.)

petals 5 or fewer, imbricate, often *crumpled* in bud, deciduous; stamens *numerous*, rarely definite, *hypogynous*, free or variously united into bundles at the base, *usually persistent*; anthers with lateral or introrse loculi, opening lengthwise or by apical pores; carpels free, rarely one; ovules 1 or more, erect from the base or from the inner angle; styles free; fruiting carpels dehiscent or baccate; seeds mostly with a *crested or laciniate aril*; *endosperm copious*, fleshy; *embryo minute*. B.H. **1**, 10; E.P. **3**, 6, 100. Mostly Tropical and Subtropical Regions.—DAVILLA, DOLIOCARPUS, TETRACERA, ACROTREMA, WORMIA, DILLENIA, HIBBERTIA, CANDOLLEA, &c.

20. CONNARACEAE

Erect trees or shrubs or scandent; leaves alternate, compound, *imparipinnate* or 1–3-*foliolate*; stipules absent; flowers ♀, rarely ♂♀, actinomorphic or slightly zygomorphic; calyx imbricate or valvate; petals 5, free or sometimes slightly connate, imbricate or rarely valvate; stamens hypogynous to perigynous, often declinate, 5 or 10; filaments often united at the base; anthers 2-locular, opening lengthwise; disk absent or thin; carpels 1–5, *free*, 1-locular;

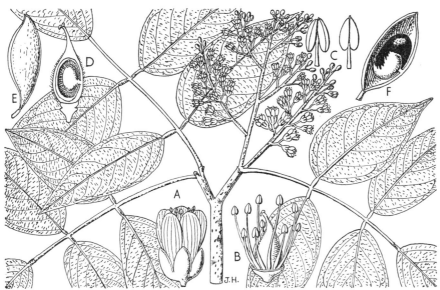

Fig. 20. Connarus monocarpus *L.* (Connaraceae). A, flower. B, the same with calyx and petals removed. C, anthers, back and front. D, vertical section of ovary. E, fruit. F, vertical section of fruit showing the single arillate seed.

ovules 2, collateral, ascending from the inner angle; fruit dehiscent, sessile or stipitate, usually 1-seeded; seeds *often arillate*, with or without endosperm. B.H. **1**, 430; E.P. **3**, 3, 61. Tropics.—BYRSOCARPUS, AGELAEA, ROUREA, CONNARUS, CNESTIS, &c.

USEFUL PRODUCTS: *Zebra wood* (Connarus guianensis *Lamb.*), British Guiana.

This family is here moved from near *Sapindaceae*, where it was placed in my first edition, following Bentham and Hooker. I now regard it as probably representing a pinnate-leaved group derived from the same stock as the *Dilleniaceae*. The free carpels and arillate seeds are common features of both families. The family is comprehensively dealt with by Schellenberg in Engl. *Pflanzenr.* (1938).

21. CROSSOSOMATACEAE

Small shrub; leaves alternate, simple; flowers solitary, terminal, showy, ♀, sepals 5, *connate* at the base into a turbinate tube; petals 5, imbricate, nervose, orbicular; stamens *numerous*, free, inserted on the calyx-tube; filaments slender, anthers oblong, 2-locular, opening lengthwise; carpels 3–5, *free from one another*, with 1–2 series of ovules, narrowed into a short style; stigma

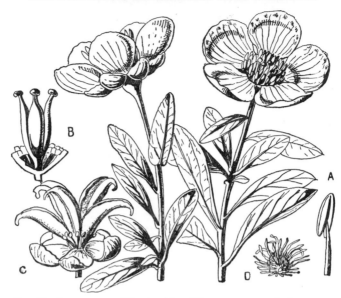

FIG. 21. Crossosoma californica *Nutt.* (Crossosomataceae). A, stamen.
B, ovary. C, fruit. D, seed. (Orig.)

oblique, discoid; fruit a bivalved capsule; seeds numerous, globose, girt by a *multifid aril*; testa shining; endosperm thin and fleshy; embryo medium-sized, slightly curved. B.H. **1,** 15 (under *Dilleniaceae*). E.P.N. 185. California. —CROSSOSOMA.

FIG. 22. Brunellia comocladifolia *H.B. & K.* (Brunelliaceae). A, flower. B, stamen. C, fruit.
D, seed. (Orig.)

22. Brunelliaceae

Trees, sometimes spiny, often tomentose; leaves *opposite* or verticillate, simple, *trifoliolate or imparipinnate*; stipules present; flowers small, in axillary or terminal panicles, *dioecious*, actinomorphic; calyx 4–5-partite, *valvate*; petals absent; disk hirsute, adnate to the calyx, 8–10-lobed; stamens 8–10, inserted at the base of the disk; ovary rudimentary, sessile; rudiments of stamens in the ♀ flowers; carpels 4–5, *free*, sessile, 1-locular; styles subulate, recurved, with simple stigmas; ovules paired, collateral; fruits 4–5 or fewer, spreading, 2-valved, 1–2-seeded; seeds with fleshy endosperm and flat cotyledons. B.H. **1**, 313 (under *Simarubaceae*). E.P.N. 182. Tropical America.—BRUNELLIA (Fig. 22).

Order 5. CORIARIALES

Shrubs with scaly buds; flowers hypogynous, ♂ or ♂ ♀, actinomorphic; sepals imbricate; petals persistent; stamens 10, free; apocarpous, with solitary pendulous ovule; seeds with straight embryo and thin endosperm. Leaves opposite or verticillate, simple, without stipules.

23. Coriariaceae

Shrubs with *angular* branchlets and *opposite* or verticillate simple leaves and *scaly buds*; stipules 0; flowers ♂ or ♂♀, small, green, axillary or racemose;

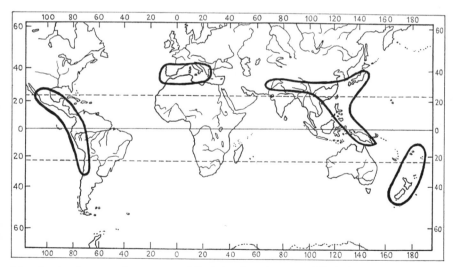

Map showing the approximate range of Coriaria, the sole genus of Coriariaceae, a very distinct family difficult to place satisfactorily in any system.

sepals 5, imbricate; petals 5, shorter than the sepals, *keeled inside*; stamens 10, hypogynous, free, or those opposite the petals adnate to the keel; anthers large, exserted, opening lengthwise; carpels 5–10, *free*, 1-locular; *styles free*,

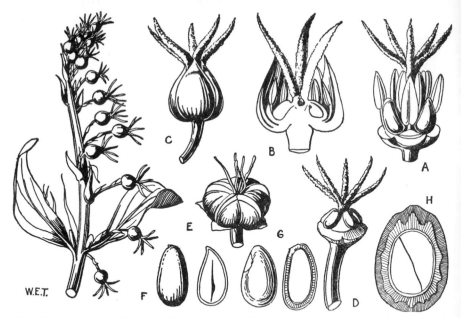

Fig. 23. Coriaria myrtifolia *L.* (Coriariaceae). A, flower with perianth removed. B, vertical section of flower. C, flower. D, ovary. E, fruit. F, G, seeds. H, section of seed. (After Le Maout & Decne.)

long; ovule solitary in each carpel, pendulous from the apex, anatropous; cocci 5–8, enclosed by the much *accrescent* petals; seed compressed, with thin endosperm and straight embryo. B.H. **1**, 429; E.P. **3**, 5, 128. Warm Temperate and Tropical Regions.—CORIARIA.

ORDER 6. ROSALES

Trees, shrubs, or herbs; leaves alternate or rarely opposite, simple or compound; stipules rarely absent; flowers mostly ♂, actinomorphic; petals free; stamens perigynous to epigynous, mostly free; carpels free or variously united and then ovary often inferior; seeds without endosperm.—Mainly Temperate Regions.

A. Leaves with stipules, these sometimes adnate to the petiole, alternate or very rarely opposite; stamens all fertile:
  B. Stamens usually numerous and free among themselves; sepals, petals, and stamens mostly perigynous or epigynous; petals entire or at most shortly bilobed; leaves simple or compound   *Rosaceae*
  BB. Stamens 5 or 3, free or united; sepals, petals, and stamens hypogynous; petals often deeply bilobed or bipartite; leaves simple
                                                       Dichapetalaceae
AA. Leaves without stipules, opposite; stamens numerous, the inner ones sterile   *Calycanthaceae*

24. ROSACEAE

Trees, shrubs, or herbs; leaves various, simple or compound, alternate or rarely opposite, sometimes with glandular teeth; stipules mostly present and paired, sometimes adnate to the petiole; flowers mostly actinomorphic and ☿;

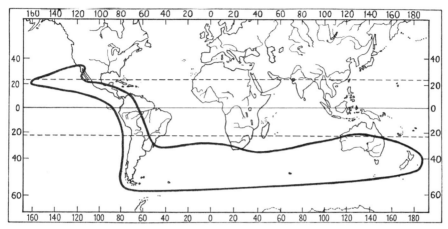

The distribution of the genus Acaena (Rosaceae) suggests its origin in the S. Hemisphere, reaching as far north as California in N. America. It occurs as an alien in other parts of the N. Hemisphere.

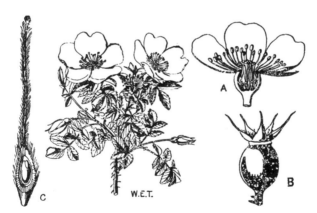

FIG. 24. Rosa spinosissima *L.* (Rosaceae). A, vertical section of flower. B, fruit. C, single carpel. (After Baill.)

calyx free or adnate to the ovary; lobes mostly 5, imbricate, the fifth lobe adaxial; disk lining the tube of the calyx; petals the same number as the calyx-lobes, rarely absent, equal or rarely unequal, imbricate; stamens numerous, rarely definite or reduced to 1 or 2; filaments free, rarely connate; anthers small, 2-locular, opening lengthwise; carpels 1 or more, free or variously connate, often more or less adnate to the calyx-tube; styles free or rarely connate; ovules in each carpel 2 or more, superposed; fruit superior or inferior, drupaceous, pomaceous, follicular, or achenial, sometimes on an enlarged fleshy torus; seeds without (very rarely with a little) endosperm. B.H. **1**, 600; E.P. **3**, 3, 1. Distribution cosmopolitan, but mainly N. Temperate Regions.—LICANIA, PARINARI, HIRTELLA, PRUNUS, PYGEUM, NUTTALLIA, SPIRAEA, EXOCHORDA, KERRIA, LINDLEYA, RUBUS, DRYAS, GEUM, FRAGARIA, POTENTILLA, ALCHEMILLA, AGRIMONIA, ACAENA, POTERIUM, CLIFFORTIA, ROSA, NEURADA, PYRUS, SORBUS, CRATAEGUS, COTONEASTER, AMELANCHIER, LYONOTHAMNUS, &c.

USEFUL PRODUCTS: Many important fruits and some of the most orna-mental of garden plants. Amongst the former are the *Apple* (Malus pumila *Mill.*); *Pear* (Pyrus communis *L.*); *Plum* (Prunus domestica *L.*); *Prunes* (P. domestica var. juliana *DC.*), France; *Peach* (P. persica *Stokes*); *Apricot* (P. armeniaca *L.*); *Sweet Almonds* (Prunus amygdalus, var. dulcis *Baill.*), Medi-terr.; *Bitter Almonds* (P.a. var. amara *Baill.*); *Strawberry* (Fragaria vesca *L.*), *Blackberry* (Rubus spp.); *Loquat* (Eriobotrya japonica *Lindl.*); and the *Coco Plum* (Chrysobalanus icaco *L.*), &c. *Cherry Laurel* (Laurocerasus officinalis *Roemer*), widely cultivated; *Cusso* (Brayera anthelmintica *Kunth*), NE. Trop. Afr.

25. CHAILLETIACEAE (Dichapetalaceae)

Small trees or shrubs, sometimes climbing; leaves alternate, simple; stipules present; flowers small, ♀, rarely ♂♀, actinomorphic or slightly zygomorphic;

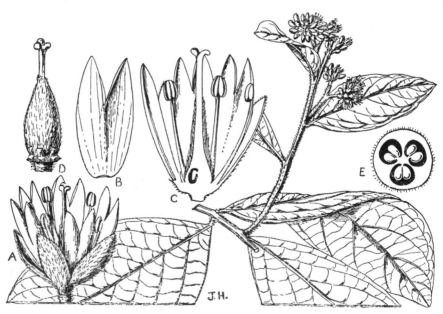

FIG. 25. Dichapetalum thonneri *De Wild*. (Dichapetalaceae). A, flower. B, petal. C, vertical section of flower. D, ovary. E, cross-section of same. (After De Wild.)

sepals 5, free or partially connate, imbricate; petals mostly *2-lobed* or 2-parted, free or united with the stamens into a tube; stamens 5, alternate with the petals, free or united; anthers 3–5, 2-locular, opening lengthwise, the connective often *dorsally thickened*; hypogynous glands *opposite* to the petals, free or connate; ovary superior to quite inferior, 2–3-locular; style mostly simple, 2–3-fid at the apex; ovules 2 in each loculus, pendulous from the apex; fruit a drupe, dry or rarely fleshy, sometimes the epicarp splitting; seeds without endosperm; embryo large, straight. B.H. **1**, 340; E.P. **3**, 4, 345. Tropics.

PRODUCTS: Some poisonous plants.

A. Fertile stamens 5: **B.** Petals usually free from one another; anthers not sessile—DICHAPETALUM (*Chailletia*) (Tropics). **BB.** Petals united; anthers sessile—STEPHANOPODIUM (Trop. S. Amer.). **AA.** Fertile stamens 3; anthers on slender filaments; petals united into a somewhat zygomorphic corolla—TAPURA (*Gonypetalum*) (Trop. Afr. and Amer.).

26. CALYCANTHACEAE

Shrubs; leaves *opposite*, simple; stipules absent; flowers axillary, solitary, fragrant, ☿; sepals and petals in *several series*, imbricate, inserted on the outside of the *thick urceolate receptacle*; stamens numerous, inserted at the top

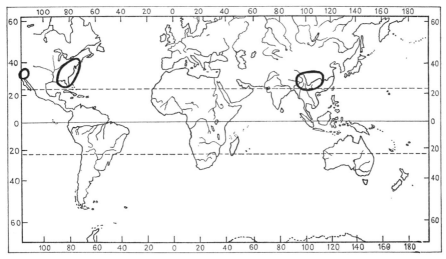

The discontinuous distribution of the Calycanthaceae recalls that of Liriodendron in Magnoliaceae.

of the receptacle, the inner ones *sterile*; anthers 2-locular, dehiscing lengthwise; carpels numerous, free, inserted on the inside of the receptacle; styles filiform; ovules solitary, or 2 superposed in each carpel, anatropous, ascending; fruit an *achene*, 1-seeded, enclosed in the fleshy enlarged receptacle; seed erect, without endosperm; cotyledons leafy, convolute. B.H. **1**, 16; E.P. **3**, 2, 94. E. Asia, N. America.

USEFUL PRODUCTS: Aromatic early-flowering garden shrubs.

A. Stamens in several rows, only about 12 of the outer ones fertile; flowers

FIG. 26. Calycanthus occidentalis *Hook. & Arn.* (Calycanthaceae).
A, flower with perianth removed. B, vertical section of same.
C, stamen. D, carpel. (After *Bot. Mag.*)

greenish purple or reddish brown—CALYCANTHUS (E. Asia, N. Amer.). **AA.**
Stamens in 2 rows, the outer row sterile; flowers yellowish—CHIMONANTHUS
(China).

ORDER 7. LEGUMINALES[1]

Trees, shrubs, or herbs; leaves simple to bipinnate; stipules present or absent;
flowers actinomorphic to zygomorphic; petals free or some partially united;
stamens numerous to few, free or variously connate, often diadelphous;
carpel solitary, superior; fruit often a *legume* or indehiscent, sometimes
winged; seeds without endosperm. World-wide distribution.

[1] This **Order** is perhaps best split up into three separate families; the fruit is often any-
thing but a *legume*, which is defined by Asa Gray as 'a fruit formed of a single carpel and
dehiscent by both the ventral and dorsal sutures so as to separate into two valves'.

A. Flowers more or less zygomorphic; petals imbricate, the adaxial (upper) petal within the adjacent lateral petals; anthers dehiscing lengthwise or by terminal pores *Caesalpiniaceae*

AA. Flowers actinomorphic; petals valvate or very rarely imbricate, free or connate into a tube; anthers opening lengthwise, sometimes with a deciduous gland at the apex *Mimosaceae*

AAA. Flowers very zygomorphic; petals imbricate, the adaxial (upper) petal outside the adjacent lateral (wing) petals; stamens monadelphous or diadelphous *Papilionaceae*

27. CAESALPINIACEAE

Trees, shrubs, or rarely herbs; leaves pinnate or bipinnate, rarely simple or 1-foliolate; stipels mostly absent; flowers mostly showy, racemose, spicate, or rarely cymose, *zygomorphic*, rarely subactinomorphic; sepals 5 or the 2

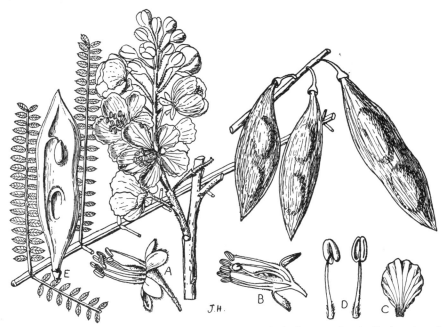

FIG. 27. Peltophorum vogelianum *Benth*. (Caesalpiniaceae). A, flower. B, longitudinal section of same. C, petal. D, stamens. E, pod showing seed. (After Martius.)

upper ones connate, mostly free, imbricate or rarely valvate; petals 5 or fewer or absent, the adaxial (upper) one *inside*, the others variously imbricate; stamens mostly 10, very rarely numerous, often free or variously connate; anthers various, sometimes opening by terminal pores; ovary superior, 1-locular; fruit a legume or indehiscent, often winged; seeds with copious, thin or no endosperm and large embryo. B.H. **1**, 562; E.P. **3**, 3, 125 (under *Leguminosae*). Mainly Tropics.—PELTOPHORUM, MEZONEURUM, CAESALPINIA, PTEROLOBIUM, GLEDITSCHIA, POINCIANA, PARKINSONIA, CASSIA, DIALIUM, CERATONIA, BAUHINIA, CERCIS, BROWNEA, AMHERSTIA, MACROLOBIUM,

BERLINIA, AFZELIA. TAMARINDUS, BAIKIAEA, BRACHYSTEGIA, HYMENAEA, SARACA, CRUDIA, DETARIUM, COPAIFERA, CYNOMETRA, DIMORPHANDRA, ERYTHROPHLOEUM, &c.

USEFUL PRODUCTS: *Sassy bark* (Erythrophloeum guineense *G. Don*), W. Afr.; *Cassia pods* (Cassia fistula *L.*), India, &c.; *Senna* (Alexandrian) (Cassia acutifolia *Del.*), N. Afr., Egypt, and E. Trop. Afr.; *Indian Senna* (Cassia angustifolia *Vahl*), Arabia to India; *Tamarind* (Tamarindus indica *L.*), Tropics; *Locust* (West Indian) (Hymenaea courbaril *L.*); *Purple Heart wood* (Copaifera pubiflora *Benth.*), British Guiana; and many other timber trees.

28. MIMOSACEAE

Trees or shrubs, very rarely herbs; leaves mostly *bipinnate*, rarely simply pin-nate; flowers ☿, small, spicate, racemose or capitate, actinomorphic, 3–6-usually 5-merous; calyx tubular, *valvate* or very rarely (*Parkieae*) imbricate,

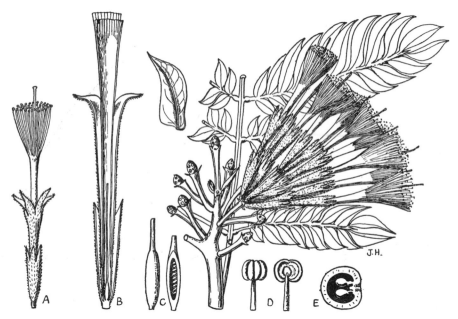

FIG. 28. Pithecellobium spruceanum *Benth.* (Mimosaceae). A, flower. B, vertical section of same. C, ovary. D, anthers. E, cross-section of ovary. (After Martius.)

5-lobed or toothed; petals *valvate*, free or connate into a short tube, mostly hypogynous; stamens equal in number to the sepals or more numerous or indefinite, free or monadelphous; anthers small, 2-locular, opening length-wise, often with a *deciduous gland* at the apex; ovary superior; fruit a *legume* or indehiscent; seeds with scanty or no endosperm. B.H. **1**, 588; E.P. **3**, 3, 99 (under *Leguminosae*). Tropics and Subtropics, many in dry regions.— PENTACLETHRA, PARKIA, ENTADA, PIPTADENIA, PROSOPIS, MIMOSA, ACACIA, CALLIANDRA, ALBIZZIA, PITHECELLOBIUM, INGA, &c.

USEFUL PRODUCTS: *Cacoon, Mackay* or *Sea Bean* (Entada gigas (*L.*)

Fawc. & Rendle, E. phaseoloides (*L.*) *Merrill*, and E. pursaetha *DC.*), Tropics; *Mesquit Tree* (Prosopis juliflora *DC.*), West Indies, Cent. Amer.; *Ironwood* (Xylia dolabriformis *Benth.*), India; *Gum Arabic* (Acacia senegal *Willd.*, &c.), Trop. Afr.; *Cutch* (Acacia catechu *Willd.* and A. suma *Kurz*), India and Burma; *Australian Blackwood* (Acacia melanoxylon *R. Br.*); *Wattle barks* (various Australian spp. of *Acacia*); *Sabicu* (Lysiloma sabicu *Benth.*); *Rain Tree* (Pithecellobium saman *Benth.*), &c. Many other valuable timbers.

29. PAPILIONACEAE (Fabaceae)

Herbs, shrubs, or trees; leaves simple or compound; flowers zygomorphic, mostly ♂; sepals usually 5, more or less connate into a tube; petals 5, imbricate, free, the upper (adaxial) exterior and forming the standard, the two

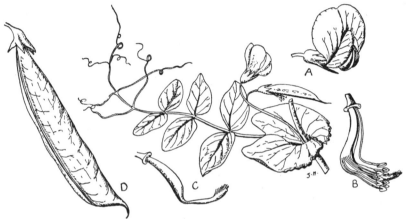

Fig. 29. Pisum sativum *L.* (Papilionaceae). A, flower. B, same with perianth removed. C, ovary. D, fruit. (After Baill.)

lateral (*wings*) more or less parallel with each other, the lower two interior and connate by their lower margins into a *keel*; stamens inserted with the petals, often 10, monadelphous or diadelphous, mostly all perfect; anthers mostly opening lengthwise; fruit usually a legume or indehiscent, sometimes jointed and breaking up into 1-seeded segments; seeds without or with very scanty endosperm. B.H. **1**, 465; E.P. **3**, 3, 184 (under *Leguminosae*). General distribution.—PODALYRIA, OXYLOBIUM, CHORIZEMA, GASTROLOBIUM, PULTENAEA, BOSSIAEA, RAFNIA, LOTONONIS, LEBECKIA, ASPALATHUS, CROTALARIA, LUPINUS, ARGYROLOBIUM, ADENOCARPUS, LABURNUM, GENISTA, SPARTIUM, ULEX, CYTISUS, ONONIS, PAROCHETUS, TRIGONELLA, MEDICAGO, MELILOTUS, TRIFOLIUM, ANTHYLLIS, LOTUS, HOSACKIA, PSORALEA, AMORPHA, INDIGOFERA, GALEGA, TEPHROSIA, MILLETTIA, WISTARIA, ROBINIA, SESBANIA, CARMICHAELIA, CLIANTHUS, LESSERTIA, SWAINSONA, COLUTEA, CARAGANA, ASTRAGALUS, OXYTROPIS, GLYCYRRHIZA, CORONILLA, HEDYSARUM, ONOBRYCHIS, AESCHYNOMENE, STYLOSANTHES, ARACHIS, DESMODIUM, LESPEDEZA, VICIA, LATHYRUS, ABRUS, CENTROSEMA, CLITORIA, KENNEDYA, HARDENBERGIA, &c.

USEFUL PRODUCTS: Very many valuable commodities, the most impor-
tant being: *Peas* (Pisum sativum *L.*); *Broad Bean* (Vicia faba *L.*); *Ground Nuts*
(Arachis hypogaea *L.*); *Soy Beans* (Glycine max *Merr.*), Orient; *Lentils* (Lens
culinaris *Medicus*); *Clover* (Trifolium pratense *L.* and T. repens *L.*); *Tagasaste*
(Cytisus palmensis *Christ*), Canaries; *Calabar Beans* (Physostigma veneno-
sum *Balf.*), W. Afr.; *Tonka Bean* (Dipteryx odorata?); *Common Broom*
(Cytisus scoparius *Link*), Europe; *Liquorice Root* (Glycyrrhiza glabra *L.*),
Eur., Asia; *Indigo Dyes* (Indigofera tinctoria *L.*, &c.); *Gum Tragacanth*
(Astragalus gummifer *Lab.*, &c.), Orient; *Tolu Balsam* (Myroxylon balsamum
(*L.*) *Harms*), S. Amer.; *Kino* (Pterocarpus marsupium *Roxb.*), S. India,
Ceylon. *Rotenone* (Derris and Lonchocarpus spp.). Many valuable timbers,
including *American Rosewood* (Dalbergia spp.); *Indian Rosewood* (D. latifolia
Roxb.); *Bastard Teak* (Pterocarpus marsupium *Roxb.*), India; *Camwood*
(Baphia nitida *Lodd*), W. Afr.; *Moreton Bay Chestnuts* (Castanospermum
australe *A. Cunn.*), Austral., and many others.

ORDER 8. CUNONIALES

Trees or shrubs; leaves alternate, opposite or whorled, simple or compound;
stipules mostly present; flowers mostly ♀, perigynous to epigynous; petals
usually present, free; stamens numerous to few; carpels free or united, with
parietal or axile placentation; seeds with mostly copious endosperm and
small embryo.—Temperate and Subtropical Regions.

NOTE: An exceptionally difficult and rather heterogeneous group, much in need of
monographic treatment and possibly reassessment into families; the following key should
therefore be regarded as tentative.

A. Petals present, though sometimes small and scale-like:
  B. Stipules present, though sometimes minute, never adnate to the petiole:
    C. Stamens 10, the filaments toothed near the apex, only 5 fertile; stipules
       very small, not intrapetiolar; style single; leaves simple; ovary inferior;
       capsule septicidal   *Pterostemonaceae*
    CC. Stamens various in number, filaments not toothed at the apex, all
       bearing anthers; stipules often large and united in pairs within the
       petiole; styles 2 or more, free; leaves trifoliolate or pinnate, rarely
       simple   *Cunoniaceae*
  BB. Stipules absent, or if present adnate to the petiole, the latter sometimes
     sheathing at the base:
    D. Disk absent:
      E. Stamens 8 or more; fruit a loculicidal capsule, rarely a berry:
        F. Indumentum mostly of stellate hairs; filaments often toothed near
           the apex; flowers in racemes, cymes, heads, or panicles
                                                            Philadelphaceae
        FF. Indumentum absent or of simple hairs; filaments not toothed;
           flowers cymose or corymbose   *Hydrangeaceae*
      EE. Stamens 5–4; fruit a drupe or berry:
        G. Flowers racemose or subsolitary; fruit a pulpy berry; leaves alter-
           nate or fascicled; ovary 1-locular   *Grossulariaceae*

GG. Flowers in terminal clusters; fruit a drupe; leaves opposite; ovary 5–3-locular *Oliniaceae*

DD. Disk present:

H. Leaves simple:

J. Disk corona-like and crowned by 10 gland-like processes; stamens 10; petiole sheathing at the base; style simple; ovules parietal
Greyiaceae

JJ. Disk entire or lobed, the lobes alternating with the stamens; stamens usually 5, rarely 6 or 4; leaves often glandular-serrate, petiole not sheathing at the base; ovules axile or parietal; fruit a capsule, berry or drupe *Escalloniaceae*

HH. Leaves 3-foliolate, opposite, sessile; styles 2, free, filiform; fruit a subdidymous compressed truncate capsule *Baueraceae*

AA. Petals absent:

K. Stipules present; disk present; styles 2 or more; seeds with endosperm; anther-loculi more or less parallel *Cunoniaceae*

KK. Stipules absent; disk absent; style single; seeds without endosperm; anther-loculi oblique *Crypteroniaceae*

30. Pterostemonaceae

Shrubs with dichotomous branches; leaves alternate, glandular above; stipules small; flowers few in terminal *corymb-like cymes*, bisexual; calyx-tube turbinate, united with the ovary; lobes 5, triangular-subulate, *valvate*; petals

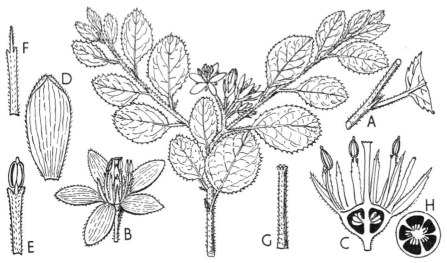

Fig. 30. Pterostemon mexicanus *Schauer* (Pterostemonaceae). A, part of leaf and stipule. B, flower. C, section of flower with petals removed. D, petal. E, stamen. F, staminode. G, style. H, cross-section of ovary.

5, free, imbricate, at length reflexed, white; stamens 10, inserted with the petals, erect, with broad filaments *toothed near the apex*, the 5 opposite the sepals bearing fertile anthers, *the other 5 without anthers*; ovary *inferior*,

5-locular; style erect, 5-fid at the apex, stigmas radiate, separating more with age; ovules 6–4 in each loculus, axile; capsule septicidal, woody, crowned by the erect sepals and reflexed petals; seed solitary, erect *without endosperm*. B.H. **1,** 615 (under *Saxifragaceae*); E.P. **3,** 2*a*, 78, fig. 42 (as tribe of *Saxifragaceae*). Mexico.—PTEROSTEMON.

This monotypic family differs from the *Philadelphaceae* by the alternate leaves, presence of small stipules, and the absence of endosperm from the seeds, and from *Rosaceae* by the *dehiscent* inferior fruits and toothed stamens.

Schauer, in describing the genus *Pterostemon*, was struck by its peculiarities, for he remarked: 'Genus perinsigne, nulli inter hucusque cognita propius affine, staminum cyclo altero sterili, stylo quasi simplici, fructuque tandem maturo carne fere destituto (nec tamen duro capsulari, sed herbaceo-molli) ordinem cum Myrtaceis iisque imprimis xerocarpicis proxime nectens, ceterum vero et habitum et characteres Pomacearum manifesto prae se ferens.'

FIG. 31. Cunonia capensis *L.* (Cunoniaceae). A, flower. B, stamens. C, ovary. (After *Bot. Mag.*)

31. CUNONIACEAE

Trees or shrubs; leaves *trifoliolate* or *pinnate*, rarely simple, mostly *opposite* or rarely verticillate; leaflets often *glandular-serrate*; stipules sometimes large and *united in pairs* within the petioles; flowers ☿ or dioecious, from solitary to paniculate or capitate; sepals imbricate or valvate, sometimes accrescent; petals present or absent, entire or toothed, or 2–3-lobed, the lobes sometimes gland-tipped; stamens numerous to few and then alternate with the petals; filaments free; anthers 2-locular, opening lengthwise; disk often annular; carpels superior, free or united into a 2–5-locular ovary with axile or apical placentas; styles free, straight or circinate in bud; ovules numerous or few; fruit dehiscent or not; seeds glabrous or long-pilose; endosperm usually copious with rather small straight embryo. B.H. **1,** 649 (under *Saxifragaceae*); E.P. **3,** 2*a*, 94. Mainly Australasia; a few in S. Africa and S. America.—CODIA, PANCHERIA, CALLICOMA, SPIRAEANTHEMUM, WEINMANNIA, CUNONIA, CERATOPETALUM, DAVIDSONIA, &c.

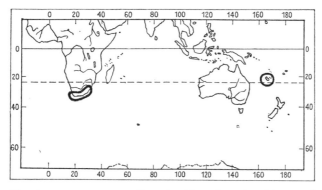

The homogeneous genus Cunonia (Cunoniaceae), with several species in New Caledonia and only one in S. Africa, is a remarkable example of discontinuous distribution.

USEFUL PRODUCTS: *Lightwood* (Ceratopetalum apetalum *D. Don*), New South Wales.

32. PHILADELPHACEAE

Shrubs or subshrubs, often with *opposite branches*, rarely small trees; indumentum mostly of *stellate hairs*; leaves usually deciduous, *opposite or verticillate*, dentate, sometimes 3-nerved from the base; *stipules absent*; flowers bisexual or polygamo-dioecious, in terminal racemes, cymes, or heads, rarely solitary; calyx-tube more or less adnate to the ovary, rarely free; lobes 5–4, imbricate or valvate; petals 7–5, contorted, imbricate or valvate, free, mostly white; stamens numerous to 4; filaments sometimes *lobed or toothed*, free or connate at the base; anthers short, 2-locular; ovary superior to inferior, 7–1-locular; styles 7–1, free or nearly so, rarely united; ovules numerous on axile or rarely parietal placentas or rarely solitary and pendulous; fruit a loculicidal capsule or rarely a berry; seeds small, with fleshy endosperm and small straight embryo. B.H. **1,** 641 (in *Saxifragaceae*); E.P. **3,** 2a, 69 (in *Saxifragaceae*).—S. Europe to E. Asia and N. America, south to the Philippines, New Guinea, and Sandwich Is.

A. Ovary superior or nearly completely so; leaves opposite: B. Styles 5–3, free to the base or nearly so: C. Sepals and petals 5 each; filaments not divided at the apex: D. Inflorescence a cyme or panicle: E. Leaves serrate— JAMESIA (N. Amer.). EE. Leaves entire—FENDLERELLA (N. Amer.). DD. Inflorescence a head-like long-pedunculate raceme—WHIPPLEA (Calif.). CC. Sepals and petals 4 each; filaments divided at the top and produced beyond the anther; leaves opposite, entire; flowers few, terminal—FENDLERA (N. Amer.). BB. Styles united, with 5–7 stigmas; anther-connective not produced at the apex—CARPENTERIA (Calif.). BBB. Style simple with undivided stigma; anther-connective produced at the apex—KANIA (New Guin.). AA. Ovary inferior or at least 2/3 inferior; leaves alternate, opposite or verticillate: F. Fruit a capsule; ovary inferior: G. Stamens numerous (20 or more); capsule obconic or obovoid: H. Petals imbricate—PHILADELPHUS (Temp. N. Hemisph.).

Fig. 32. Carpenteria californica *Torr.* (Philadelphaceae). A, stamen. B, ovary. C, cross-section of same. D, seed. E, vertical section of same. (After *Bot. Mag.* partly.)

HH. Petals 4, valvate; styles 2—Platycrater (Japan). **GG.** Stamens 15 or fewer: **J.** Stamens 12–15; filaments not toothed; petals imbricate—Neodeutzia (Mexico). **JJ.** Stamens 10; filaments often expanded or trifid at the apex—Deutzia (E. Asia, N. Amer.). **FF.** Fruit a berry; ovary 2/3 inferior: **K.** Styles free, clavate; flowers bisexual, in terminal panicles—Dichroa

(China, Indo-Malaya). **KK.** Styles connate; flowers polygamo-dioecious—
BROUSSAISIA (Sandwich Is.).

33. HYDRANGEACEAE

Herbs or softly wooded undershrubs, shrubs, or rarely climbers; leaves alternate or opposite, simple, *without stipules*; flowers cymose or corymbose, bi-

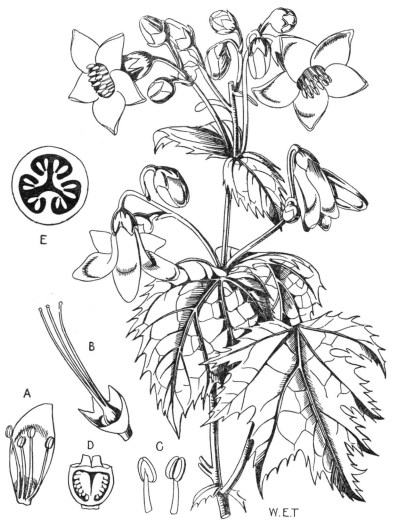

FIG. 33. Kirengeshoma palmata *Yatabe* (Hydrangeaceae). A, petal with adherent stamens.
B, part of calyx with ovary and styles. C, anthers. D, ovary in vertical section. E, ovary in cross-
section. (After *Bot. Mag.*)

sexual or sometimes the outer flowers sterile and with large petal-like sepals;
calyx-tube more or less *adnate to the ovary*, 5-lobed or toothed, lobes imbricate;

petals 5–4, free, contorted or valvate; stamens numerous and in *several series*, to 10 or 8; anthers basi- or medifixed, linear to very short and didymous; disk absent; ovary half-inferior to inferior, 6–3-locular, or incompletely so; styles as many as the loculi, free or partly connate; ovules numerous, on axile or intrusive parietal placentas; fruit a loculicidal capsule; seeds numerous, small, sometimes winged and reticulate, with endosperm and straight embryo. B.H. **1**, 640 (as tribe of *Saxifragaceae*); E.P. **3**, 2*a*, 74 (as subfamily of *Saxifragaceae*); Hutch., *Kew Bull.* 1927, 100).—Mostly in N. Hemisphere, from Himalayas to Japan and N. America; few in Western S. America.

A. Herbs with simple stems from a creeping rhizome; petals contorted or imbricate; stamens numerous, 15 or more; ovary semi-inferior to quite inferior: **B.** Ovary semi-inferior; petals contorted; stamens 15, in 3 series; flowers few in a terminal lax leafy cyme, none sterile; leaves opposite— KIRENGESHOMA (Japan). **BB.** Ovary quite inferior; petals imbricate; stamens numerous; flowers in spreading corymbose cymes, the outer flowers sterile with enlarged petaloid calyx-lobes: **C.** Leaves alternate, scattered on the stem, not lobed, coarsely serrate; styles 3, rather short: flowers small, numerous— CARDIANDRA (China, Japan). **CC.** Leaves opposite or subverticillate, mostly bilobed; styles connate high up—DEINANTHE (China, Japan). **AA.** Softly woody plants with branched stems, or rarely climbers; petals valvate; ovary inferior: **D.** Styles 4–5, free or connate only at the base; capsule open at the top between the styles; sterile flowers with 4–5 enlarged, more or less petaloid sepals, or if absent then leaves often gland-dotted and inflorescence enclosed in bud by large bracts; stamens 8–10 (rarely 15)—HYDRANGEA (E. Asia, N. to S. Amer.). **DD.** Style 1; sterile flowers absent or if present with only 1 enlarged ovate sepal; capsule opening laterally: **E.** Stamens 20–30; leaves deciduous; creeping or climbing shrubs; petals 7–10; no sterile flowers— DECUMARIA (China, N. Amer.). **EE.** Stamens 8–10; petals 4–5: **F.** Leaves evergreen; petals cohering into a cap; no sterile flowers—PILEOSTEGIA (India, China). **FF.** Leaves deciduous; petals valvate; sterile flowers with one enlarged ovate white sepal—SCHIZOPHRAGMA (China, India).

34. GROSSULARIACEAE

Shrubs, often armed with spines; leaves often fasciculate, simple, *plicate* or *convolute* in bud; stipules absent or adnate to the petiole; flowers often unisexual by abortion, racemose or subsolitary; calyx-tube adnate to the ovary, lobes imbricate or subvalvate; petals 4–5, mostly small or scale-like; stamens 4–5, alternate with the petals; anthers 2-locular, didymous or subglobose, opening lengthwise; ovary *inferior*, 1-locular, with 2 *parietal* placentas; styles 2, free or connate, with undivided stigmas; ovules few or numerous, 2- or more-seriate; fruit a pulpy berry, crowned by the persistent calyx; seed with endosperm and rather small embryo. B.H. **1**, 654; E.P. **3**, 2*a*, 88 (under *Saxifragaceae*). Temperate N. Hemisphere, Andes of S. America.—RIBES (Fig. 34).

USEFUL PRODUCTS: *Gooseberries* (Ribes uva-crispa *L.*); *Black currants, Red currants, White currants* (forms of R. rubrum *L.*). Some beautiful early-flowering shrubs.

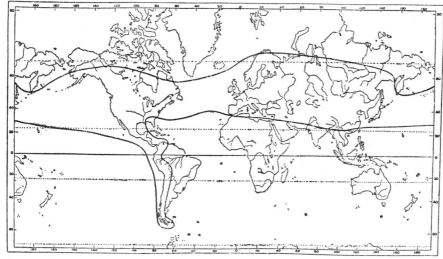

Range of genus Ribes (Grossulariaceae), almost absent from Africa and not represented in Malaya and Australasia.

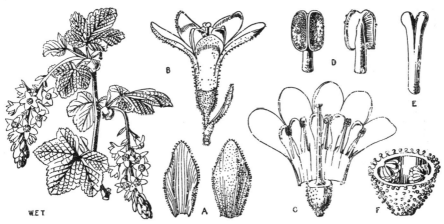

FIG. 34. Ribes sanguineum *L.* (Grossulariaceae). A, sepals. B, flower. C, same opened. D, front and back views of anther. E, stigmas. F, cross-section of ovary. (Orig.)

35. OLINIACEAE

Shrub or small tree; branches *quadrangular*; leaves *opposite*, simple, penni-nerved; stipules 0; calyx-tube adnate to the ovary; limb produced *beyond* the ovary, tubular, 4–5-toothed, deciduous; petals 5, rarely 4, inserted at the mouth of the calyx, spathulate, pilose within the base, alternating with as many *incurved scales*; stamens 4–5, inserted on the calyx-tube; filaments short; anthers small, didymous, with thickened connective; ovary *inferior*, 3–5-locular; style with a thickened stigma; ovules up to 3 in each loculus, axile, pendulous; fruit drupaceous, each loculus 1-seeded; seeds without

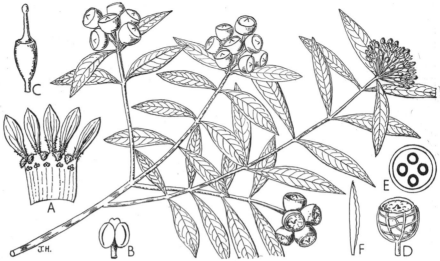

FIG. 35. Olinia acuminata *Kl.* (Oliniaceae). A, calyx spread out. B, stamen. C, ovary and style. D, fruit. E, section of fruit. F, seed.

endosperm; cotyledons irregularly convolute; radicle short. B.H. **1**, 785 (under *Lythraceae*); E.P. **3**, 6a, 213. S. and E. Tropical Africa.—OLINIA.

36. GREYIACEAE

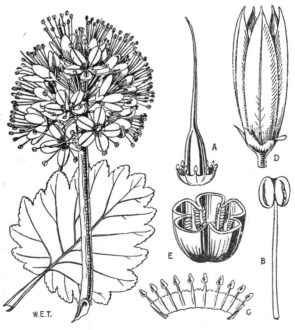

FIG. 36. Greyia sutherlandii *Harv*. (Greyiaceae). A, ovary. B, stamen. C, disk with staminodial gland-like appendages. D, fruit. E, cross-section of ovary. (Partly after Harv.)

Small trees with soft wood; leaves alternate, simple, currant-like; petiole sheathing at the base and clasping the branchlets; stipules absent; flowers actinomorphic, racemose, ♀; sepals 5, free, imbricate, persistent; petals 5, perigynous, imbricate; disk cupular, crowned by 10 gland-like processes (corona); stamens 10 within the disk, free; anthers 2-locular, didymous; ovary superior, deeply 5-grooved, 1-locular but nearly 5-locular by the intrusive margins of the carpels; style 1; ovules numerous, parietal; fruit a capsule opening between the carpels; seeds minute, with endosperm and very small embryo. B.H. **1**, 1000 (under *Sapindaceae*); E.P. **3**, 5, 382 (under *Melianthaceae*). S. Africa.—GREYIA.

37. ESCALLONIACEAE

Trees or shrubs; leaves simple, alternate, rarely subopposite or subverticillate, mostly with *gland-tipped teeth*; stipules absent; flowers ♂, rarely dioecious or polygamous, mostly racemose; sepals mostly united in the lower part, rarely

FIG. 37. Escallonia macrantha *Lindl.* (Escalloniaceae). A, sepals and ovary. B, ovary. C, cross-section of same. (After *Bot. Mag.*)

free; imbricate or valvate, often persistent; petals free or rarely connate into a short tube, imbricate or valvate; stamens 5, rarely 4 or 6, sometimes alternating with staminodes, perigynous, free; anthers 2-locular, opening lengthwise; disk-lobes alternating with the stamens; ovary *superior* to *quite inferior*, syncarpous or rarely apocarpous, 1–6-locular; ovules numerous, *parietal* in the 1-locular ovaries, otherwise on central placentas; fruit a capsule or berry; seeds with small embryo and copious endosperm. B.H. **1**, 644; E.P. **3**, 2a, 79 (under *Saxifragaceae*). Mainly S. Hemisphere, rare in Africa.—ESCALLONIA, BREXIA, ARGOPHYLLUM, CARPODETUS, POLYGONANTHUS, CHORISTYLIS,

ITEA, POLYOSMA, PHYLLONOMA, ANOPTERUS, MONTINIA,[1] GREVEA,[1] &c.—
Some useful garden shrubs.

38. BAUERACEAE

Erect or prostrate shrubs with slender leafy terete branches sometimes glandular-hairy; leaves small, *opposite*, sessile, evergreen, *3-foliolate*; leaflets sessile,
serrate; *stipules absent*; flowers axillary, solitary, sessile or pedicellate, white

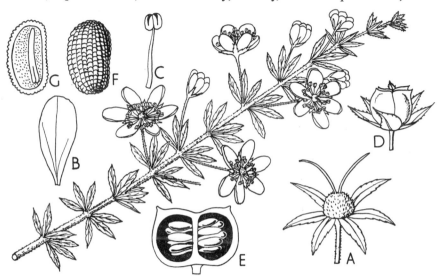

FIG. 38. Bauera rubioides *Andr*. (Baueraceae). A, flower with petals and stamens removed.
B, petal. C, stamen. D, fruit. E, vertical section of fruit. F, seed. G, vertical section of seed.

or pink, sometimes crowded towards the ends of the shoots; calyx 10–4-
partite, segments *valvate or subimbricate*, persistent; petals 10–4, free, imbricate, inserted at the base of the calyx around a thin disk; stamens 10–4 or
more, 1–2-seriate; filaments filiform, anthers didymous, opening by *pore-like
slits*; ovary free from the calyx or nearly so, ovoid-globose, 2-locular, hairy;
styles 2, free, filiform, recurved, stigma undivided; ovules numerous, axile,
spreading horizontally; fruit a capsule free from the calyx, subdidymous,
compressed, broadly ovate-quadrate, truncate, 2-locular, 2-valved from the
apex, valves often 2-partite; seeds spreading horizontally, obovate-oblong;
embryo terete, in the middle of fleshy endosperm. B.H. **1**, 655 (as anomalous
genus of *Saxifragaceae*); E.P. **3**, 2*a*, 93, fig. 53 (as subfamily of *Saxifragaceae*).
Australia, Tasmania.—BAUERA.

A single genus without any very close relatives, but perhaps nearest *Cunoniaceae*, some
of which also have pinnate or trifoliolate leaves.

[1] These two genera have been put into a separate family, *Montiniaceae*, by Milne-
Redhead in Hook. *Ic. Pl.* **6**, 2. 3 (1955). The family *Escalloniaceae* as at present constituted
shows a very wide range of characters which in my opinion amply cover the two genera in
question. In my *Botanist in Southern Africa*, p. 100, with fig., I gave my view on the position
of *Montinia*, supporting that of Harvey and Engler in including it in *Escalloniaceae* rather
than that of Bentham and Hook. f. in the *Onagraceae*.

39. Crypteroniaceae

Trees with 4-angled branches; leaves opposite, entire; stipules absent; flowers in axillary spiciform racemes or panicles, very small, white or green, actinomorphic, polygamo-dioecious; calyx-tube 4–5-lobed, lobes valvate; petals absent; stamens 4–5, *alternate* with the calyx-lobes; anthers didymous; disk none; ovary superior, 2-locular; style slender; ovules numerous, axile; fruit

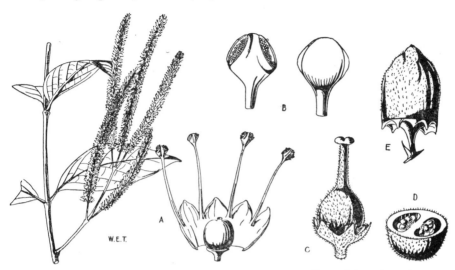

Fig. 39. Crypteronia paniculata *Bl.* (Crypteroniaceae). A, flower, dissected. B, anthers. C, ovary. D, cross-section of same. E, fruit. (Orig.)

a capsule, loculicidally 2-valved, valves connected by the persistent base of style; seeds minute, elongated, winged or not; endosperm none; embryo cylindrical. B.H. **1,** 782 (under *Lythraceae*); Engler and Gilg, *Syllabus,* edns. 9 and 10, 299 (1924). India, Malay Archipelago.—Crypteronia.

Order 9. STYRACALES

Trees or shrubs, often with stellate indumentum; leaves simple, alternate; stipules absent; flowers actinomorphic; sepals valvate; petals free to united, imbricate or valvate, rarely contorted; stamens free from or adnate to the corolla-tube, few and alternate with the lobes or more numerous; anthers opening lengthwise; ovary superior to inferior, with axile placentation; seeds with copious endosperm.—Warmer Regions.

A. Corolla-lobes contorted; calyx-lobes 4, imbricate; stamens 8, anthers linear, connective produced at the apex   *Lissocarpaceae*
AA. Corolla-lobes or petals imbricate or valvate; calyx-lobes valvate:
  B. Anthers linear; indumentum usually stellate or lepidote; stamens equal to or double the number of the corolla-lobes   *Styracaceae*

BB. Anthers didymous, ovoid or subglobose; indumentum when present not stellate; stamens mostly numerous   *Symplocaceae*

40. LISSOCARPACEAE

Small trees; leaves alternate, entire; stipules absent; flowers cymose; calyx-tube shortly adnate to the base of the ovary, campanulate, lobes 4, *imbricate*;

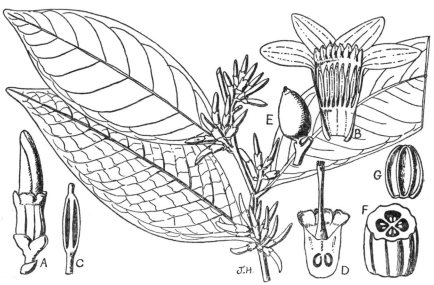

FIG. 40. Lissocarpa benthamii *Gürke* (Lissocarpaceae). A, bud. B, flower opened. C, stamen. D, ovary in vertical section. E, fruit. F, same in transverse section. G, seed. (After Hook. *Ic. Pl.*)

corolla-tube 4-lobed, lobes *contorted*; stamens 8, inserted towards the base of the corolla-tube, the filaments shortly connate; anthers linear, adnate within the middle of the tube, opening lengthwise, *apiculate*; ovary *inferior*, 4-locular; style club-shaped; ovules 2 in each loculus, *pendulous*; fruit *inde-hiscent*, 2-seeded; seed 3-ribbed, with copious endosperm and straight embryo about half as long. B.H. **2,** 671 (in *Styracaceae*). Tropical S. America.— LISSOCARPA.

41. STYRACACEAE

Trees or shrubs often with *stellate or lepidote* indumentum; leaves alternate, simple; *stipules absent*; flowers actinomorphic, ⚥, rarely polygamo-dioecious, racemose, paniculate, rarely solitary, axillary or terminal; calyx tubular, more or less *adnate to the ovary*; lobes or teeth *valvate* or open; corolla sympetalous or rarely of free petals, lobes 4–7, valvate or imbricate; stamens equal and alternate with or double the number of the corolla-lobes, adnate to the corolla-tube or rarely free; anthers 2-locular, opening lengthwise; ovary superior to inferior, 3–5-locular; style slender, 3–5-lobed; ovules 1 to many in each loculus. axile, anatropous; fruit drupaceous or capsular, calyx persistent;

seed with copious endosperm and straight or slightly curved embryo. B.H.
2, 667; E.P. **4,** 1, 172; Perkins, Engl. *Pflanzenr. Styracac.* (1907). Warmer
parts of N. Hemisphere; rare in Tropical Africa and Tropical S. America.

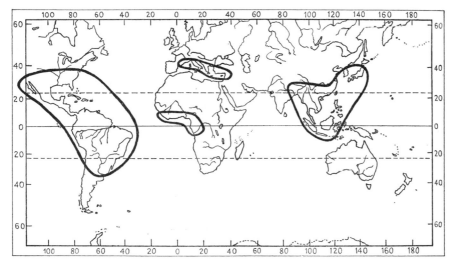

Discontinuous distribution of the family Styracaceae; only one genus represented in Tropical
Africa (Afrostyrax).

FIG. 41. Styrax benzoin *Dryand.* (Styracaceae). A, hair. B, bud. C, flower in vertical section.
D, calyx. E, flower with perianth removed. F, transverse section of ovary. G, fruits. H, same
showing stone. (Partly after Pierre.)

USEFUL PRODUCTS: *Storax* (Styrax officinale *L.*), S. Eur., Asia Minor;
Gum Benzoin (Styrax benzoin *Dry.*), Malaya, Indo-China. Some ornamental
garden shrubs.
    A. Stamens 10 or more (rarely 8 or 9): **B.** Flowers bisexual: **C.** Flowers in
racemes, cymes or panicles: **D.** Ovary completely or almost completely
superior: **E.** Seeds not winged; filaments free or connate only in the lower
part; fruit various—STYRAX (*Anthostyrax*) (S. Eur., Orient, Tropics except

Afr.). **EE.** Seeds winged at each end; filaments connate to the top into a tube; fruit a capsule—ALNIPHYLLUM (China). **DD.** Ovary $\frac{2}{3}$ to completely inferior: **F.** Filaments free or shortly connate at the base: **G.** Anther-connective not produced beyond the loculi. **H.** Fruits not 10-ribbed—PTEROSTYRAX (*Decavenia*) (E. Asia). **HH.** Fruits 10-ribbed—REHDERODENDRON (E. China, Indo-China). **GG.** Anther-connective produced beyond the loculi: **I.** Anther-connective 2–3-toothed; fruit a loculicidal capsule—HUODENDRON (China, Indo-China). **II.** Anther-connective entire; fruit indehiscent—SINOJACKIA (China). **FF.** Filaments connate into a cylindrical tube; fruit a drupe—PARASTYRAX (Burma). **CC.** Flowers solitary or fasciculate: **J.** Ovary superior, 1-locular—AFROSTYRAX (W. Trop. Afr.). **JJ.** Ovary inferior: **K.** Ovary imperfectly 5-locular—MELLIODENDRON (China). **KK.** Ovary 4–2-locular—HALESIA (E. Asia, N. Amer.). **BB.** Flowers polygamo-dioecious, in axillary and terminal panicles; fruit woody, indehiscent—BRUINSMIA (Malay Archip.). **AA.** Stamens 5; ovules solitary in each loculus of the 3-locular (at length 1-locular) ovary; flowers racemose; leaves entire, rusty-tomentose with stellate hairs—PAMPHILIA (Brazil).

42. SYMPLOCACEAE

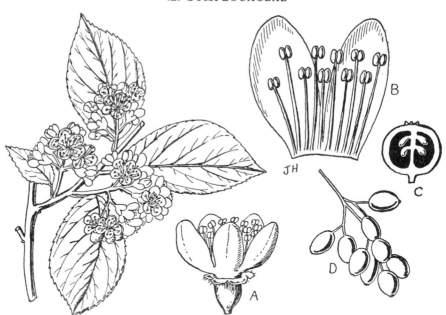

FIG. 42. Symplocos paniculata (*Thunb.*) *Miq.* (Symplocaceae). A, flower. B, petals and stamens. C, ovary in vertical section. D, fruits.

Trees or shrubs; leaves alternate, simple; indumentum when present not stellate; *stipules absent*; flowers axillary or terminal, solitary or in spikes, racemes, or fascicles, actinomorphic, ⚥, rarely polygamous; sepals 5, connate, *valvate*; petals 3–11, more or less connate; stamens *inserted on the corolla*, 4 to numerous, free or variously united, in 1–4 series; anthers subglobose, 2-locular, opening lengthwise; ovary *inferior* or *semi-inferior*, 2–5-locular; ovules 2–4, pendulous; style slender; fruit baccate, or drupaceous, crowned by the calyx-lobes, 1–5-locular; seed solitary in each loculus, with copious endosperm; embryo straight or curved; cotyledons very short. B.H. **2,** 668 (under *Styracaceae*); E.P. **4,** 1, 165. Warmer parts of Asia, Australia, and America; absent from Africa.—SYMPLOCOS.

USEFUL PRODUCTS: *Lodh bark* (Symplocos racemosa *Roxb.*), India.

ORDER 10. ARALIALES

Woody, or rarely reduced to herbs; leaves simple or compound; stipules present or absent; flowers mostly small and often arranged in umbels or heads; petals free or united; stamens definite, alternate with petals or corolla-lobes; ovary inferior; seeds with copious often ruminate endosperm.—World-wide distribution.

A. Petals free or absent, rarely coherent at the base; stamens usually free from the petals (when latter present); petals imbricate or valvate:
  B. Stipules absent:
   C. Petals valvate or absent:
    D. Flowers not in catkins:
     E. Ovules with 1 integument; flowers cymose to capitate, sometimes with petaloid bracts *Cornaceae*
     EE. Ovule with 2 integuments; flowers cymose *Alangiaceae*
    DD. Flowers in catkins *Garryaceae*
   CC. Petals imbricate; flowers sometimes subtended by petaloid bract-like upper leaves *Nyssaceae*
  BB. Stipules present; seeds with copious sometimes ruminate endosperm; flowers mostly in simple umbels, sometimes racemose or capitate; leaves often with stellate indumentum; petals or corolla-lobes usually valvate *Araliaceae*
AA. Petals united into a tube; stamens inserted on the corolla-tube; corolla-lobes imbricate; stipules absent or very small *Caprifoliaceae*

43. CORNACEAE

Trees, shrubs, or rarely perennial herbs; leaves opposite or alternate, simple; stipules absent; flowers small, in dichotomous panicles or racemes of panicles, or in heads, ♂ or dioecious, actinomorphic; calyx-tube adnate to the ovary, 4–5-lobed or subtruncate; petals 4–5, free, rarely absent, valvate or imbricate; stamens the same number as the petals and *alternate* with them; anthers short, 2-locular, opening lengthwise; disk cushion-shaped, central in the ♂ flower, epigynous in the ♀ flower; ovary *inferior*, 1–4-locular; style simple or lobed; ovule solitary and pendulous in each loculus, anatropous, with 1 integument; fruit a drupe or berry, 1–4-locular; seeds pendulous; embryo often small in copious endosperm. B.H. **1**, 947, partly; E.P. **3**, 8, 250; Wangerin, Engl. *Pflanzenr.* (1910). Hutch., *Annal. Bot.* **6**, 83 (1942). Scattered distribution.

USEFUL PRODUCTS: Ornamental garden shrubs. *Cornelian Cherry wood* (Cornus mas *L.*).

A. Petals imbricate; leaves alternate: **B.** Flowers bisexual; anthers basifixed; pedicels 2-bracteolate—MELANOPHYLLA (Madag.). **BB.** Flowers unisexual, dioecious; anthers dorsifixed; pedicels jointed, not bracteolate—GRISELINIA (New Zeal., Chile, Brazil). **AA.** Petals valvate: **C,** Leaves alternate

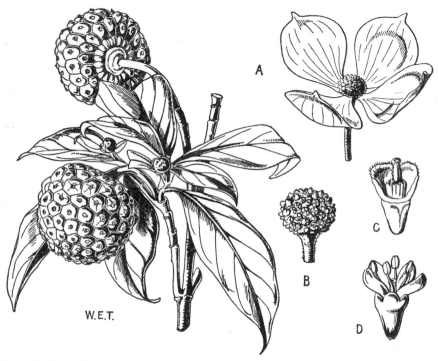

FIG. 43. Dendrobenthamia capitata (*Wall.*). *Hutch.* (Cornaceae). A, flower. B, flowers in bud. C, pistil. D, flower.

or fasciculate: **D.** Flowers bisexual: **E.** Ovary 2-locular: **F.** Flowers 7–5-merous—COROKIA (*Lautea*) (New Zealand and neighbouring islands). **FF.** Flowers 4-merous—THELYCRANIA (N. Hemisph.): **EE.** Ovary 1-locular; stigma undivided—MASTIXIA (Indo-Malaya, New Guin.). **DD.** Flowers unisexual: **G.** Flowers 5-merous; stamens 5—TORICELLIA (E. Himal., W. China). **GG.** Flowers 4-merous; stamens 8—KALIPHORA (Madag.). **CC.** Leaves opposite: **H.** Ovary 4-locular; indumentum of branched hairs—CURTISIA (S. Afr. and SE. Trop Afr.). **HH.** Ovary 1-locular: **J.** Flowers bisexual—MASTIXIA (see above). **JJ.** Flowers unisexual—AUCUBA (E. Asia). **HHH.** Ovary 2-locular: **K.** Inflorescence a corymbose cyme without bracts—THELYCRANIA (N. Hemisph.).

KK. Inflorescence capitate, with 4 or more herbaceous or petaloid bracts before or during flowering: **L.** Flowers pedicellate, in umbelliform cymules or umbels: **M.** Trees or large shrubs with precocious bisexual flowers arranged in umbels within the herbaceous involucral bracts—CORNUS (Temp. N. Hemisph.). **MM.** Trees; flowers dioecious, the males within the herbaceous early deciduous bracts in short cymules, the female fewer and umbellate—AFROCRANIA (E. Trop. Afr.). **MMM.** Herbs with annual stems from a perennial rhizome; bracts petaloid; flowers in small cymules or umbellate—CHAMAEPERICLYMENUM (*Arctocrania, Cornella*) (Cool N. Hemisph.). **LL.** Flowers sessile within the usually petaloid bracts: **N.** Calyces and fruits free from one another—CYNOXYLON (N. Amer. south to Costa Rica). **NN.** Calyces and fruits united into a fleshy syncarp—DENDROBEN-THAMIA (India to Japan).

For MASTIXIODENDRON (*Dorisia*) see *Rubiaceae*.

44. ALANGIACEAE

Trees or shrubs, sometimes spiny; leaves alternate, simple; stipules 0; flowers ♀, in axillary cymes; pedicels *articulated*; calyx *truncate* or with 4–10 teeth; petals 4–10, mostly linear, *valvate*, at length recurved, sometimes coherent

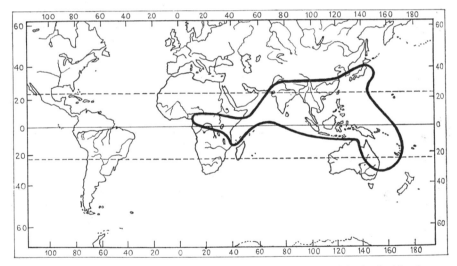

The distribution of the distinctive genus Alangium, the sole member of the family Alangiaceae, suggests that it spread across the Old World after America was separated.

at the base; stamens the same number as and alternate with the petals or 2–4 times as many, free or slightly connate at the base, more or less *villous inside*; anthers 2-locular, linear, opening lengthwise; disk cushion-like; ovary *inferior*, 1–2-locular; style simple, clavate or 2–3-lobed; ovule solitary, pendulous, with 2 integuments; fruit a drupe crowned by the sepals and disk, 1-seeded; seeds with the embryo about equal to the endosperm. B.H. **1,** 949 (under *Cornaceae*); E.P. **3,** 8, 260; Wangerin, Engl. *Pflanzenr. Alangiac.* (1910). Tropical Old World and Temperate E. Asia and E. Australia.— ALANGIUM.

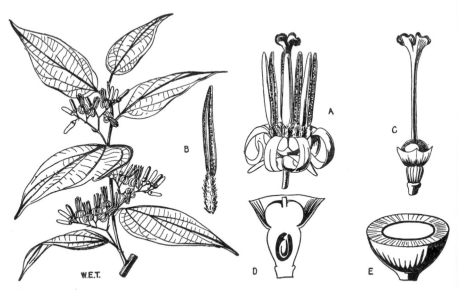

FIG. 44. Alangium chinense (*Lour.*) *Harms.* (Alangiaceae). A, flower. B, stamen, C, pistil. D, vertical section of ovary. E, cross-section of ovary. (Orig.)

45. GARRYACEAE

Trees or shrubs; leaves *opposite*, simple, evergreen, with petioles *connate at the base*; stipules absent; flowers dioecious; arranged in silky catkin-like racemes; ♂ sepals 4, *valvate*; stamens 4, *alternate* with the sepals, free; anthers 2-locular; rudimentary ovary present; female sepals 0; ovary 1-locular, inferior; styles 2, free, subulate; ovules 2, pendulous from the apex of the ovary, with a single integument; fruit a berry crowned by the styles, 1–2-seeded; seed ovoid or subglobose, with minute embryo at the apex of the *copious fleshy endosperm*. B.H. **1,** 951; E.P. **3,** 8, 255 (under *Cornaceae*); Wangerin, Engl. *Pflanzenr. Garryac.* (1910). N. America and West Indies.— GARRYA. Garden shrubs.

The genus *Garrya* was formerly included in the *Cornaceae*, its ovary being described as *inferior*. Up to the fourth edition of his *Syllabus*, Engler maintained this position for the genus, but in subsequent editions, after Wangerin's account of it as a separate family in the *Pflanzenreich* in 1910, Engler established a separate Reihe for it, **Garryales,** placing it in the 'Amentiferae' between the *Salicales* and *Myricales*. Wangerin considered the ovary to be *superior*, which, if correct, removed it far from the *Cornaceae*. Rendle followed Wangerin, as did the present author in his *Families of Flowering Plants*.

For this new edition, however, I have re-examined the material of the genus in the Kew Herbarium and now consider the ovary to be undoubtedly *inferior*, as there are 4 or 2 very small calyx-lobes below the base of the styles in several species, especially in *G. fremontii* Torr. Eastwood, 'Notes on Garrya', *Bot. Gaz.* **36,** 456 (1903), describes the females of several species as having minute calyx-teeth at the top of the ovary.

On this account the family is now replaced next to *Cornaceae*, with which it has much in common in its wood anatomy.

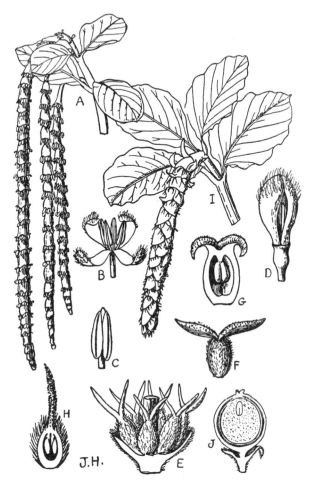

FIG. 45. Garrya elliptica *L.* (Garryaceae). A, male inflorescences. B, male flower. C, stamen. D, unopened male flower. E, whorl of female flowers. F, ovary. G, vertical section of same. H, another view of same. I, female inflorescence. J, vertical section of fruit.

46. NYSSACEAE

Trees or shrubs with alternate, simple leaves; stipules 0; flowers unisexual or ♀, capitate, racemose or umbellate, rarely solitary; male flowers: calyx *obsolete* or of very small teeth; petals 5 or more, *imbricate*, or absent; stamens up to double the number of the petals, often 2-seriate; anthers 2-locular, opening lengthwise; disk central, fleshy; female flowers: calyx *adnate to the ovary*; petals 5 or more, imbricate, small; ovary *inferior*, 1-locular or 6–10-locular

(*Davidia*); ovule solitary, pendulous from the apex, anatropous, with 2 integuments; disk pulvinate or absent; style simple or divided into as many lobes as ovary-loculi; fruit drupaceous or subsamaroid, 1–5-locular, loculi

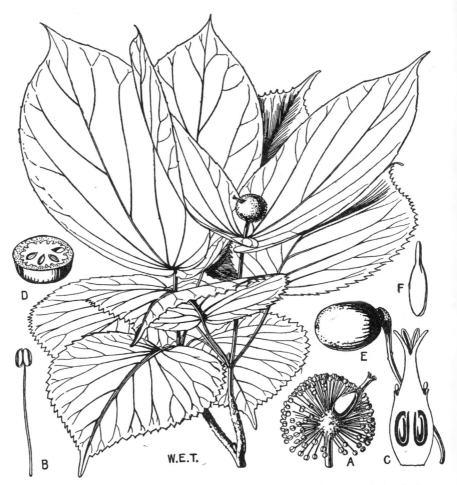

Fig. 46. Davidia involucrata *Baill.* (Nyssaceae). A, inflorescence. B, stamen. C, female flower. D, transverse section of fruit. E, fruit. F, embryo. (Flowers pendulous in nature.)

1-seeded; endosperm thin with fairly large embryo. B.H. **1**, 952 (under *Cornaceae*); E.P. **3**, 8, 257; Wangerin, Engl. *Pflanzenr. Nyssac.* (1910). E. Asia and Eastern U.S.A.—Including *Davidiaceae* Li (1955).

USEFUL PRODUCTS: Handsome garden trees. *Ogeechee Lime fruits* (Nyssa capitata *Walt.*), N. Amer.

A. Ovary 10–6-locular; male flowers without a perianth, female and bisexual with numerous segments; style divided into lobes; fruit a drupe— DAVIDIA (E. Asia). AA. Ovary 1-locular; all flowers with calyx and petals; style subulate: B. Style undivided; fruit a drupe with bony endocarp—

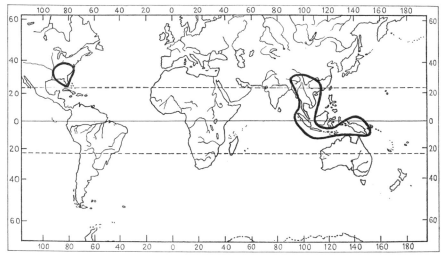

The distribution of the small but highly evolved family Nyssaceae is probably an indication of considerable antiquity, recalling that of the more ancient family Magnoliaceae.

NYSSA (E. Asia, Malaya, N. Amer.). **BB.** Style 2-fid; fruit samaroid, with corky mesocarp and thin endocarp—CAMPTOTHECA (Tibet).

47. ARALIACEAE

Mostly woody, sometimes climbing by means of aerial roots; leaves alternate or rarely opposite, simple, pinnate or digitate, often with *stellate indumentum*; stipules either adnate to and scarcely distinguishable from the base of the petiole, or intrapetiolar, rarely absent; flowers ⚥, polygamous or dioecious, actinomorphic, racemose, umbellate or capitate, rarely epiphyllous; calyx

FIG. 47. Acanthopanax henryi (*Oliv.*) *Harms* (Araliaceae). A, flower. B, ovary. C, same in transverse section. D, seed. (After *Bot. Mag.*)

superior, small, entire or toothed; petals 3 or more, often 5, *valvate* or slightly imbricate, free or united; stamens free, alternate with the petals and mostly the same number; anthers 2-locular, opening lengthwise; disk on top of the ovary, often confluent with the style in the middle; ovary *inferior*, 1- or more-locular; styles free or connate; ovule solitary in each loculus, pendulous from the apex, anatropous, raphe ventral; fruit a berry or drupe; seeds with copious, sometimes ruminate, endosperm and very small embryo. B.H. **1**, 931; E.P. **3**, 8, 1. Mainly Tropics.—ARALIA, HEDERA, PANAX, ACANTHO-PANAX, FATSIA, DIDYMOPANAX, HELWINGIA, SCIADOPHYLLUM, POLYSCIAS, HEPTAPLEURUM, DENDROPANAX, CUSSONIA, OREOPANAX, &c.

USEFUL PRODUCTS: *Virginian Sarsaparilla* (Aralia nudicaulis *L.*); *Ginseng Root* (Panax schinseng *Nees*), N. China; *Ivy* (Hedera helix *L.*).

48. CAPRIFOLIACEAE

Shrubs, mostly with rather soft wood and broad pith, rarely herbs; leaves *opposite*, simple or deeply divided; *stipules absent* or very small; flowers ⚥, actinomorphic or zygomorphic, mostly cymose; calyx *adnate to the ovary*,

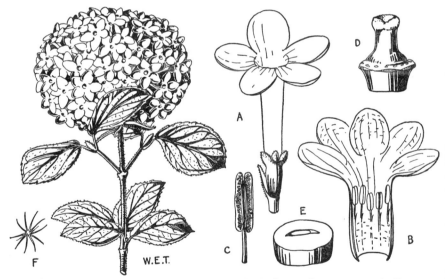

FIG. 48. Viburnum carlesii *Hemsl.* (Caprifoliaceae). A, flower. B, same opened. C, stamen. D, ovary. E, same in transverse section. F, hair. (Orig.)

5-fid or toothed; corolla epigynous, gamopetalous, sometimes *2-lipped*, lobes imbricate; stamens inserted on the corolla-tube and alternate with its lobes; anthers free, 2-locular, opening lengthwise; *ovary inferior*, 2–5-locular; style terminal, often slender; ovules 1 or more, pendulous or axile; fruit a fleshy berry; seeds often with bony testa, copious endosperm and often small or linear straight embryo. B.H. **2**, 1; E.P. **4**, 4, 156. Generally distributed.—SAMBUCUS, VIBURNUM, SYMPHORICARPOS, ABELIA, LINNAEA, LONICERA, LEYCESTERIA, DIERVILLA (*Weigelia*), &c.

USEFUL PRODUCTS: Beautiful ornamental shrubs and climbers. *Common Elder* (Sambucus nigra *L.*), Eur., &c.; *American Elder* (S. canadensis *L.*); *Snow-berry* (Symphoricarpos albus *Blake* (S. racemosus *Michx.*); *Honeysuckle* (Lonicera periclymenum *L.*), Eur., &c.

ORDER 11. HAMAMELIDALES

Trees or shrubs; leaves simple, alternate, rarely opposite, mostly stipulate; flowers usually ♂, actinomorphic, often collected into heads or pendulous catkins; petals present or absent; stamens perigynous or subepigynous; ovary semi-inferior to inferior, rarely quite superior, often bicarpellary; ovules pendulous from axile placentas; seeds with rather thin endosperm and straight embryo.

A. Stipules present:
  B. Calyx and usually the petals present; indumentum often stellate:
    C. Ovary quite superior; stipule single, adnate to the petiole
                              Tetracentraceae
    CC. Ovary inferior or semi-inferior; stipules paired, free
                              Hamamelidaceae
  BB. Calyx and petals absent:
    D. Leaves opposite; flowers in catkin-like spikes; ovules numerous; anthers apiculate   *Myrothamnaceae*
    DD. Leaves alternate; flowers in heads; ovules 1–2; anthers truncate
                              Platanaceae
AA. Stipules absent:
  E. Ovary superior:
    F. Petals 4; flowers bisexual   *Stachyuraceae*
    FF. Petals absent; flowers unisexual:
      G. Ovary 3-locular; styles 3   *Buxaceae*
      GG. Ovary imperfectly 2-locular; styles 2–1, very short or absent
                           Daphniphyllaceae
  EE. Ovary semi-inferior to inferior; flowers in spikes or heads; petals present   *Bruniaceae*

49. TETRACENTRACEAE

Tree with *long and* alternate *short shoots,* the latter conspicuously marked by the crowded concentric scars of fallen leaves and bud-scales and terminated by a bud enclosed by the stipule adnate to the petiole; each short shoot bearing a single subterminal leaf and a single inflorescence; leaves deciduous, simple, rounded-ovate, palmately nerved from the base, crenate-dentate; inflorescence a slender *catkin-like spike,* shortly pedunculate; flowers bisexual, very small and numerous, in clusters of 4, the clusters alternate, each flower sessile in the axil of a minute bract; sepals 4, imbricate; *petals absent;* stamens 4, each opposite a sepal; anthers basifixed, erect, connective truncate-rounded at the apex; loculi lateral, opening by slits lengthwise; ovary superior, of 4 united carpels alternate with the stamens, each carpel unilocular

with 2 placentas, the several ovules attached near the middle of the loculi, at
first horizontal; styles 4, at first connivent, at length becoming sharply recurved and sub-basal by elongation of the ventral surface; fruit composed of
4 *laterally coalescent carpels*, these loculicidally dehiscent along the entire
exposed portion of the ventral face to base of persistent deflexed style; seeds

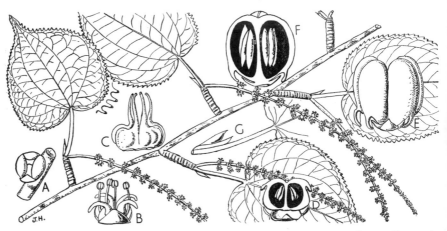

FIG. 49. Tetracentron sinense *Oliv.* (Tetracentraceae). A, flower bud. B, flower. C, carpels.
D, vertical section of carpels. E, fruit. F, vertical section of fruit. G, stipules and petiole.

pendulous from the apex of the loculus, with oily endosperm and minute
embryo obscurely cleft at the apex. Oliv., Hook. *Ic. Pl.* t. 1892 (1889); see
also A. C. Smith, 'Taxonomic Review of *Trochodendron* and *Tetracentron*',
J. Arnold Arbor. **26,** 135, with map and bibliography (1945). W. China,
Upper Burma.—TETRACENTRON.

50. HAMAMELIDACEAE

Trees or shrubs, often with *stellate indumentum*; leaves alternate, rarely opposite, deciduous or evergreen, simple, teeth sometimes glandular; *stipules
mostly paired*, often persistent, sometimes large; flowers small, sometimes
precocious, ⚲ or ♂♀, often capitate, actinomorphic or zygomorphic; calyx-
tube more or less *adnate to the ovary*; lobes imbricate or valvate; petals 4 or
more, rarely 0, perigynous or epigynous, imbricate or valvate, rarely circinate;
stamens 4 or more, perigynous, 1-seriate; filaments free; anthers oblong, 2-
locular, opening lengthwise or by valves, the connective often produced; disk
absent or annular or of separate glands between the stamens and ovary; ovary
inferior or nearly so, rarely superior, composed of 2 carpels often *free at the
apex*, 2-locular; styles subulate, free, often *recurved*; ovules 1 or more in each
loculus, pendulous from axile placentas; fruit a capsule, woody; seeds various,
with thin fleshy endosperm and straight embryo. B.H. **1,** 664; E.P. **3,** 2a, 115.
Asia, Africa, N. America.—PARROTIA, FOTHERGILLA, DISTYLIUM, SYCOPSIS,
CORYLOPSIS, DICORYPHE, HAMAMELIS, TRICHOCLADUS, LOROPETALUM,
RHODOLEIA, EXBUCKLANDIA (*Bucklandia, Symingtonia*), LIQUIDAMBAR,
DISANTHUS, &c.

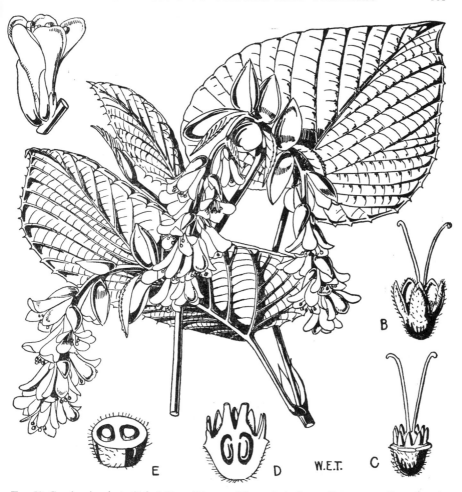

FIG. 50. Corylopsis spicata *Sieb. & Zucc.* (Hamamelidaceae). A, flower. B, same, corolla removed. C, ovary. D, vertical section of same. E, cross-section of same. (After *Bot. Mag.*)

USEFUL PRODUCTS: Timber trees: Altingia excelsa *Noronha*, E. India, &c.; Liquidambar formosana *Hance*, Formosa; *Satin Walnut* (L. styraciflua *L.*), N. Amer. Ornamental shrubs, some flowering in winter (*Hamamelis* spp.—Witch Hazels).

51. MYROTHAMNACEAE

Undershrub, resinous, rigid, with opposite branches, subspinulose with the persistent stipules and petioles; leaves opposite, *flabellate-cuneate, plicate-nerved*, articulate with the subvaginate petiole; stipules small, subulate on the sheathing base of the petiole; flowers *dioecious*, spicate; spikes catkin-like, erect, terminal; bracts 1-flowered; *no calyx or corolla*; stamens 4–8, often 5; filaments connate, free at the apex; anthers large, subquadrate. loculi opening

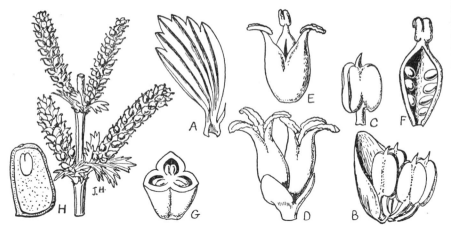

FIG. 51. Myrothamnus flabellifolius *Welw.* (Myrothamnaceae). A, leaf showing stipules. B, male flower. C, stamen. D, female flower. E, ovary. F, vertical section of same. G, cross-section of same. H, section of seed. (After Welw.)

laterally lengthwise, connective produced into a beak; no rudimentary ovary; ovary in the ♀ sessile, 3-locular; 3-lobed, styles free, recurved, subspathulate; ovules numerous, inserted on the inner angle of the loculi, 2-seriate; capsule small, leathery, the carpels divaricate, dehiscing on the inside, many-seeded; seeds minute, pendulous, with copious endosperm and minute embryo. B.H. **1**, 1005 (under *Hamamelidaceae*). E.P. **3**, 2*a*, 103. Tropical and S. Africa.— MYROTHAMNUS.

FIG. 52. Platanus orientalis *L.* (Platanaceae). A, male inflorescence. B, male flower. C, cross-section of anther. D, female inflorescence. E, fruit. F, pappus-seta. G, vertical section of fruit. H, female flower. I, vertical section of same. (Orig.)

52. PLATANACEAE

Trees often with deciduous bark; leaves alternate, *palmately nerved and lobed, the dilated petiole enclosing the young bud*; stipules membranous, caducous; flowers monoecious, densely arranged in *unisexual capitula*; bracts absent from the ♂ capitulum, present in the female; calyx 0; male capitula: anthers numerous, subsessile, each subtended by a minute scale, oblong or linear, 2-locular, opening lengthwise, the connective peltate at the apex; female capitula: carpels numerous, distinct, subsessile, here and there with linear bracts intermixed; ovary linear, 1-locular, with a unilateral stigma; ovule 1 or rarely 2, pendulous, orthotropous; carpels in fruit surrounded at the base by long hairs, indehiscent; seed one in each carpel, linear; endosperm thin; embryo linear, straight. B.H. **3**, 396; E.P. **3**, 2*a*, 137. N. Temperate and Subtropical Zone.—PLATANUS.

USEFUL PRODUCTS: *American Plane* (Platanus occidentalis *L.*), N. Amer.; *Lacewood* or *Oriental Plane* (P. orientalis *L.*), Near East; the *London Plane* (P. acerifolia *Willd.*) is a hybrid between these two species.

53. STACHYURACEAE

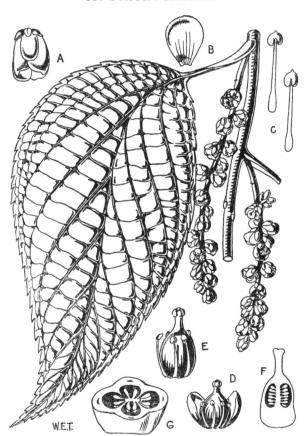

FIG. 53. Stachyurus praecox *Sieb. & Zucc.* (Stachyuraceae). A, flower. B, petal. C, stamens. D, ovary and stamens. E, another view of same. F, vertical section of ovary. G, cross-section of same. (After *Bot. Mag.*)

Shrubs or small trees; leaves alternate; *stipules 0*; flowers small, in axillary racemes or spikes; bracteoles 2, connate at the base; sepals 4, much imbricate; petals 4, free, imbricate; stamens 8, free; anthers 2-locular, opening lengthwise; ovary 4-locular; style simple, with a *capitate-peltate* stigma; ovules numerous, on axile placentas; fruit a 4-locular berry; seeds small; endosperm fleshy; embryo straight; cotyledons elliptic. B.H. **1**, 184 (under *Ternstroemiaceae*); E.P. **3**, 6, 192. E. Asia.—STACHYURUS.

54. BUXACEAE

Trees, shrubs, or rarely herbs; leaves evergreen, alternate or opposite, simple, coriaceous; *stipules absent*; flowers ♂♀ or rarely a few ♀, monoecious or dioecious, spicate or densely racemose, bracteate; sepals imbricate or absent, usually 4; *petals 0*; stamens 4 or 6, rarely more, when 4 then opposite the sepals, when 6 two pairs opposite the inner sepals; anthers large, sessile or borne on fairly long filaments; loculi 2-valved or opening lengthwise; rudimentary ovary present or absent in the ♂ flowers; female flowers often larger than the males and fewer or solitary, often pedicellate; sepals as in the ♂; ovary superior, 3-locular; styles contiguous or widely separated, undivided;

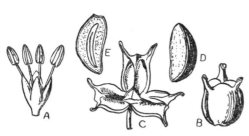

FIG. 54. Buxus sempervirens *L.* (Buxaceae). A, male flower. B, ovary. C, dehisced fruit. D, seed. E, section of same.

ovules 1–2, pendulous, anatropous; fruit capsular or drupaceous; seeds *black* and shining, with fleshy endosperm and straight embryo with flat or thick cotyledons. B.H. **3**, 265 (under *Euphorbiaceae*); E.P. **3**, 5, 130. Distribution rather scattered, rare in S. America.

USEFUL PRODUCTS: *Boxwood* (Buxus sempervirens *L.*), Eur. &c.; *Cape Boxwood* (B. macowanii *Oliv.*), S. Afr.

A. Stamens numerous; rudimentary ovary absent from the male flowers: **B.** Leaves alternate; fruit a drupe; ovary 6–4-locular—STYLOCERAS (S. Amer.). **BB.** Leaves opposite; fruit a 3-valved capsule; ovary 3-locular—SIMMONDSIA (Calif.). **AA.** Stamens definite, usually the same number as the sepals and opposite to them, or stamens 6: **C.** Woody shrubs with entire leaves: **D.** Sepals 4; stamens 4, opposite the sepals; filaments elongated, rarely the anthers sessile: **E.** Leaves alternate; female flowers at the base of the racemes; fruit indehiscent—SARCOCOCCA (China, Indo-Malaya). **EE.** Leaves opposite; female flowers terminal in the racemes; fruits capsular—BUXUS (Temp. N. Hemisph., Trop. and S. Afr., Madag., West Indies). **DD.** Sepals 4; stamens 6; anthers sessile—NOTOBUXUS (SE. Afr.). **CC.** Herbs with procumbent stems and alternate often coarsely toothed leaves; flowers spicate—PACHYSANDRA (E. Asia, N. Amer.).

55. DAPHNIPHYLLACEAE

Trees or shrubs; leaves crowded, alternate, entire, pinnately nerved; *stipules absent*; flowers small, *dioecious*, in axillary racemes; *petals absent*; bracts deciduous; male flowers: sepals 8–3, imbricate; stamens 12–6, free; anthers

2-locular, opening by lateral slits; no rudimentary ovary; female flowers: staminodes small or absent; ovary superior, *imperfectly 2-locular*; styles 2–1, very short or absent; stigmas 2, divaricate, recurved or circinate; ovules 2 in each loculus, anatropous, *pendulous*; fruit a 1-seeded *drupe*; seed with thick

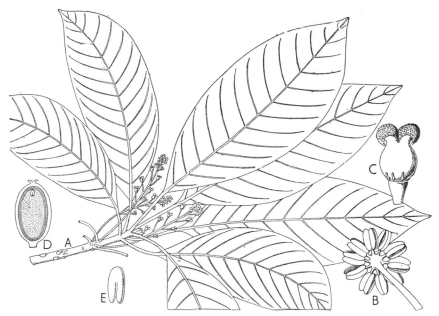

FIG. 55. Daphniphyllum macropodum *Miq.* (Daphniphyllaceae). A, female flowering shoot. B, male flower from below. C, female flower. D, vertical section of fruit. E, embryo.

fleshy bluish endosperm and minute apical embryo. B.H. **3**, 282 (in *Euphorbiaceae*); E.P. **3**, 5, 36; Rosenthal, Engl. *Pflanzenr. Daphniphyllac.* (1919). E. Asia, Malaya.—DAPHNIPHYLLUM.

56. BRUNIACEAE

Shrubs or undershrubs, often *heath-like*; leaves small, entire, usually imbricate; stipules absent; flowers ♀, small, actinomorphic, generally in a *spike* or *head*, sessile, 5-bracteate; calyx 4–5-partite, persistent or deciduous, imbricate; petals 4–5, usually free, sometimes connate with the stamens into a tube at the base, imbricate; stamens equal in number to and alternate with the petals; filaments free, or sometimes adnate to the claws of the petals; anthers introrse, 2-locular, loculi parallel or diverging at their base, opening lengthwise; ovary *semi-inferior* or *inferior*, very rarely free, 1–3-locular; styles 2–3, terminal, more or less cohering; stigmas minute, papillose; ovules 1–2, pendulous from near the top; fruit crowned by the calyx, and sometimes by the persistent corolla and androecium, dry, indehiscent or capsular, often with two 1–2-seeded cocci, dehiscence internal, lengthwise; seeds minute, with straight embryo at the top of a copious fleshy endosperm; cotyledons short; radicle conical, superior. B.H. **1**, 670; E.P. **3**, 2*a*, 131; Dümmer, 'Enumeration of Bruniaceae', *J. Bot.* 1912 *Suppl.*—S. Africa.

A. Petals free from one another: **B.** Ovary 3-locular; loculi 2-ovuled; inflorescence spike-like; petals long-clawed—AUDOUINIA. **BB** (see also **BBB** below). Ovary 2-locular; loculi 4–2-ovuled: **C.** Anthers linear or oblong, the connective not prolonged; flowers solitary, terminal or axillary: **D.** Calyx-tube shortly obconical, not verrucose; nut crowned by the annual disk and

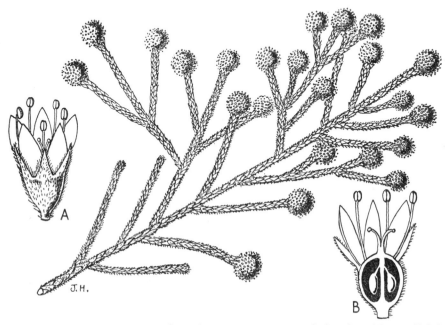

FIG. 56. Raspalia phylicoides *Presl* (Bruniaceae). A, flower. B, vertical section of flower. (Orig.)

style—THAMNEA. **DD.** Calyx-tube globose or turbinate, verrucose; nut crowned by the remains of the calyx and corolla—TITTMANNIA. **CC.** Anthers cordate or sagittate, their bases usually free and often divergent: **E.** Fruit dehiscent: **F.** Inflorescence spicate or rarely subcapitate; flowers scarious; petals clawed; connective of anthers produced at the apex—LINCONIA. **FF.** Inflorescence capitate or very rarely spike-like; flowers not scarious; petals not clawed; connective not produced: **G.** Styles 2; ovary half-inferior: **H.** Bracts leafy or absent; stamens very rarely exserted—RASPALIA. **HH.** Bracts scarious, pale flesh- or straw-coloured; stamens always exserted—NEBELIA. **GG.** Style 1, deeply grooved; ovary half-inferior—STAAVIA. **EE.** Fruit indehiscent: **J.** Stamens not exserted; anthers dorsifixed; styles short, stout—PSEUDO-BAECKEA. **JJ.** Stamens exserted; anthers versatile; styles filiform—BRUNIA. **BBB.** Ovary 1-locular, 1-ovuled; style 1: **K.** Stamens not exserted; flowers solitary, axillary or terminal, inconspicuous—MNIOTHAMNUS. **KK.** Stamens exserted; flowers crowded into ovoid or globose heads—BERZELIA. **AA.** Petals united at the base into a short tube; stamens subsessile, inserted on the corolla—LONCHOSTOMA.

ORDER 12. SALICALES

Trees or shrubs; leaves alternate, stipulate; flowers dioecious, in erect or pendulous catkins; calyx absent or much reduced; petals absent; stamens 2 or more; ovary 1-locular, with parietal placentas; ovules numerous, ascending; seeds covered with fine hairs; no endosperm; embryo straight.

57. SALICACEAE

Trees or shrubs; leaves alternate, simple, deciduous; stipules free, small or sometimes foliaceous and persistent; flowers ♂♀, dioecious, densely arranged in erect or pendulous catkins often produced before the leaves; bracts membranous, fugacious or persistent, each subtending a flower; calyx absent or

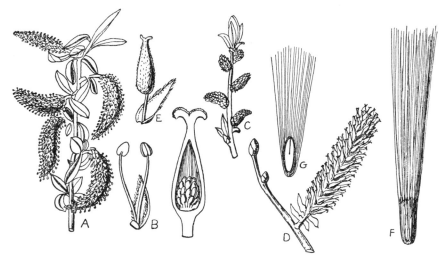

FIG. 57. Salix alba *L.* (Salicaceae). A, shoot with male inflorescences. B, male flower. C, female shoot. D, female inflorescence. E, female flower. F, seed. G, vertical section of same. (After Baill.)

represented by a small cupular disk or 2 glandular scales; male flowers: stamens 2 or more, filaments slender, free or more or less united; anthers 2-locular, opening lengthwise; female flowers: ovary sessile or shortly stipitate, 1-locular, with 2–4 *parietal or basal placentas*; style short or long, 2–4-fid; ovules numerous, ascending, anatropous; capsule 2–4-valved; seeds numerous, small or minute, with numerous *fine hairs arising from the funicle and enveloping the seed*; endosperm none; embryo straight. B.H. **3,** 411; E.P. **3,** 1, 29. Wide distribution, but absent from Australasia and Malay Archipelago.

USEFUL PRODUCTS: *Osiers* for basket-making (Salix spp.); *Cricket Bat Willow* (Salix coerulea *Sm.*); *Balsam Poplar* (Populus tacamahacca *Miller*).

A. Bracts of the catkins laciniate, very rarely entire; flowers with a cup-shaped disk; catkins pendulous; winter-buds covered by several scales—

POPULUS (*Turanga*) (Temp. N. Hemisph.). **AA.** Bracts of the catkins entire; flowers without a disk; winter-buds covered by a single scale: **B.** Styles 2, free, bifid; male catkins pendulous; stamens adnate to the bract; flowers without a gland at the base—CHOSENIA (NE. Asia). **BB.** Style 1, with 2 usually bifid stigmas or stigmas sessile; male catkins erect; stamens free from the bract; flowers with one or more glands at the base—SALIX (*Toisusu*) (Cosmopol.).

ORDER 13. LEITNERIALES

Shrubs; leaves alternate; no stipules; flowers dioecious, in erect catkin-like spikes; no calyx in the ♂ flowers, small in the ♀; stamens few; ovary superior, with 1 parietal ovule; seeds with thin endosperm and straight embryo.

58. LEITNERIACEAE

Shrubs with silky young parts; leaves alternate, simple; stipules 0; flowers dioecious, in catkin-like erect spikes, solitary in each bract, the lower bracts often sterile; ♂ flower: calyx 0; stamens 3–12; filaments free; anthers erect,

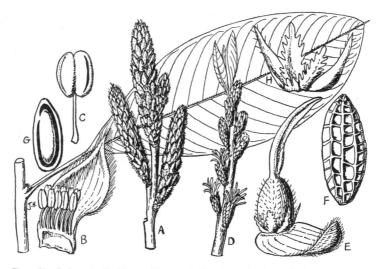

FIG. 58. Leitneria floridana *Chapm.* (Leitneriaceae). A, male inflorescences. B, male flower. C, stamen. D, female inflorescences. E, female flower. F, seed. G, section of same. H, female perianth. (Orig.)

basifixed, 2-locular, loculi opening lengthwise; rudimentary ovary 0; ♀ flower: calyx small, of unequal scales connate at the base; ovary sessile, 1-locular, narrowed into a long undivided style stigmatose on one side; ovule 1, attached to the *wall* of the ovary; drupe oblong, compressed, with a hard endocarp; endosperm thin, fleshy; embryo straight, slightly shorter than the seed; cotyledons flat. B.H. **3**, 396; E.P. **3**, 1, 28. Southeastern U.S.A.— LEITNERIA.

ORDER 14. MYRICALES

Trees or shrubs, aromatic; leaves alternate, with or without stipules; flowers unisexual, in axillary spikes; no sepals or petals; stamens 2 or more; ovary 1-locular, with 1 erect basal ovule; seed without endosperm.

59. MYRICACEAE

Trees or shrubs, often strongly *aromatic*; leaves alternate, simple, sometimes pinnately lobed; stipules present or absent; flowers unisexual, monoecious or dioecious, sometimes the sexes alternating on the same individual year by year, in axillary spikes, dense-flowered, when the inflorescence bisexual then the ♂ flowers below the ♀; sepals and petals absent, or the ♀ with a few sepal-like whorled bracteoles; ♂ flower subtended by a solitary bract; stamens 2 to many, usually 4–8; filaments free or connate; anthers 2-locular, opening lengthwise by slits; rudimentary ovary rarely present; ♀ flower: ovary sessile, 1-locular; style short, 2-branched; ovule 1, erect, basal, orthotropous; drupe small, often warted, warts waxy;

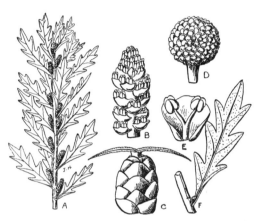

FIG. 59. Myrica quercifolia *L.* (Myricaceae). A, twig with male inflorescences. B, male inflorescence. C, female flower. D, fruit. E, male flower. F, female flower in leaf-axil. (Orig.)

endocarp hard; seed erect; endosperm 0; embryo straight. B.H. **3**, 400; E.P. **3**, 1, 26. Widely distributed, numerous and varied in S. Africa.

USEFUL PRODUCTS: *Sweet Gale* or *Bog Myrtle* (Myrica gale *L.*), used in medicine; *Sweet Fern* (Comptonia peregrina (*L.*) *Coulter*), N. Amer.

A. Leaves stipulate, pinnatifid—COMPTONIA (NE. Amer.). **AA.** Leaves without stipules, entire or toothed—MYRICA (*Canacomyrica*) (World-wide distrib.).

ORDER 15. BALANOPSIDALES

Trees or shrubs; leaves alternate; no stipules; flowers dioecious, male in catkins, female solitary in an involucre of bracts; no sepals or petals; stamens few; ovary imperfectly 2-locular, with two parietal sub-basal placentas; seeds with some endosperm and straight embryo.

60. BALANOPSIDACEAE

Trees or shrubs; leaves alternate, simple; stipules absent; flowers dioecious, the male in catkins on the young branchlets or below the leaves, the female solitary in an involucre of bracts; ♂ calyx represented by a single unilateral scale at the apex of the pedicel; stamens 2–12, often 5 or 6; anthers subsessile, ovoid, 2-locular, opening lengthwise; rudimentary ovary absent or minute; ♀ flowers without a perianth; ovary sessile, 3- or imperfectly 2-locular, with 3–2 parietal placentas; styles 3–2, 2-partite to near the base, branches, subulate; ovules 2 on each placenta, erect from near the base; drupe supported by the persistent involucre, ovoid, with 1 or 2 pyrenes; pericarp shining; seed solitary in each pyrene, erect, with fleshy endosperm and fairly large straight embryo. B.H. **3**, 341; E.P.N. 114. New Caledonia, Polynesia, Queensland.

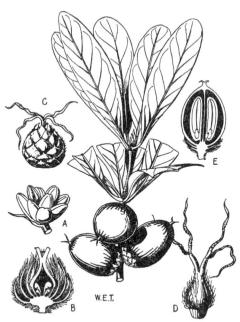

FIG. 60. Balanops vieillardii *Baill*. (Balanopsidaceae). A, male flower. B, vertical section of female flower. C, female flower. D, ovary. E, vertical section of fruit. (After Baill.)

A. Ovary 3-locular; styles 3, each deeply bipartite; ovules 2 in each loculus, superimposed— TRILOCULARIA (Polynesia). **AA.** Ovary imperfectly 2-locular; styles 2, bipartite nearly to the base; ovules 2 in each loculus, collateral—BALANOPS (New Caled., Queensland).

ORDER 16. FAGALES

Shrubs or trees with perulate buds; leaves alternate, simple, stipulate; flowers often precocious, ♂♀, monoecious, in erect or pendulous catkin-like spikes or the female like cones; calyx much reduced or absent, the female flower often surrounded by an involucre of bracts; stamens 2 to many; ovary inferior or nude, 2–6-locular; styles free or nearly so; ovules 1–2 in each loculus, pendulous; seeds without endosperm.—Mainly N. Temperate Zone.

A. Male flowers with a small calyx:
   B. Stamens 4–2; female flowers without a calyx, therefore ovary superior, 2-locular, loculi 1-ovulate   *Betulaceae*
   BB. Stamens numerous (more than 4); female calyx adnate to the ovary, therefore ovary inferior, loculi 2-ovulate; involucre in fruit cupular below or around the nut   *Fagaceae*
AA. Male flowers without a calyx; female calyx adnate to the ovary, therefore ovary inferior, 2-locular, loculi 1-ovulate; stamens 3 or more.
        Corylaceae

61. Betulaceae

Trees or shrubs with *perulate* buds; leaves alternate, prominately *penni-nerved*, mostly *serrate*; stipules free, often deciduous; flowers monoecious; male inflorescence a pendulous catkin, often *precocious*, terminal or lateral; female flowers in cylindrical cone-like *spikes* with imbricate bracts, 2–3 to

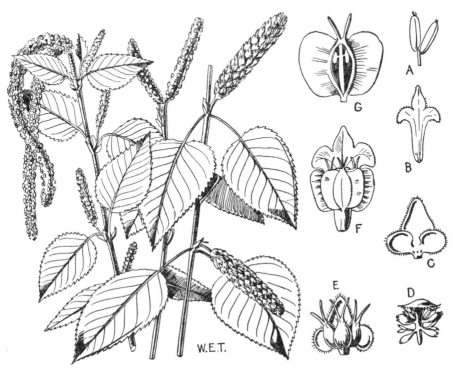

FIG. 61. Betula papyrifera *Michx.* (Betulaceae). A, stamen. B, fruit bract. C, bract of female flower. D, group of male flowers. E, female flowers. F, fruits. G, section of single fruit. (After De Wild.)

each bract; ♂ flower: bracteoles within each scale 2–5; calyx membranous, usually 4-partite, slightly imbricate; stamens 2 or 4; filaments very short; anthers 2-locular, loculi connate or separate, opening lengthwise; no rudimentary ovary; ♀ flower: perianth absent; ovary nude, compressed, 2-locular; styles 2, free, cylindrical; ovule solitary and attached near the apex of each loculus; fruiting spikes cylindrical or ovoid, the bracts falling off or persisting; nuts small, nude or winged, often crowned by the persistent styles; seed solitary, pendulous, without endosperm, with straight embryo and flat cotyledons. B.H. **3**, 404 (under *Cupuliferae*); E.P. **3**, 1, 38. Mainly N. Temperate Zone, also in S. America.

USEFUL PRODUCTS: Good timbers from *Black Birch* (Betula lenta *L.*), N. Amer.; B. utilis *D. Don*, Himal.; *White Birch*, B. alba *L.*, Eur.

A. Stamens 4; winter-buds usually stalked and with 2 valvate scales; scales of fruiting catkins 5-lobed, woody, persistent—ALNUS (Eur., N. and Cent.

Asia, N. and S. Amer.). **AA.** Stamens 2; winter-buds sessile, covered by 3 or more scales; scales of fruiting catkins thin, 3-lobed, deciduous—BETULA (Eur., N. and Cent. Asia, N. Amer.).

62. FAGACEAE

Trees; leaves alternate, evergreen or deciduous, simple, penninerved; stipules present, often soon falling; flowers unisexual, monoecious, the male in erect or catkin-like spikes; male calyx 4–6-lobed or rarely 7-lobed, lobes imbricate; stamens few to numerous, up to about 40; filaments free, filiform; anthers

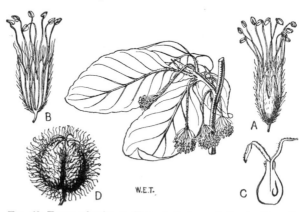

FIG. 62. Fagus sylvatica *L.* (Fagaceae). A, male flower. B, vertical section of same. C, female flower. D, female inflorescence. (After Baill.)

erect, 2-locular, loculi contiguous, opening lengthwise; rudimentary ovary present or obsolete; female flower *solitary* within an *involucre* of often numerous imbricate scales; staminodes present or absent; calyx adnate to the ovary, 4–6-lobed; ovary inferior, 3–6-locular; styles as many as the ovary-loculi; ovules 2 in each loculus; involucre in fruit often hardened, cupular or altogether closed, often tuberculate or echinate; fruit a nut, free or adnate to the involucre, sometimes completely enclosed by the latter, which opens like a pericarp; seed usually solitary by abortion, without endosperm. B.H. **3,** 407 (under *Cupuliferae*); E.P. **3,** 1, 47. Temperate and Tropical Regions, absent from Tropical and S. Africa (except cultivated).

USEFUL PRODUCTS: *Common Beech* (Fagus sylvatica *L.*), Eur., &c.; *Oaks* (Quercus spp.) provide valuable hardwoods; *Sweet* or *Spanish Chestnut* (Castanea sativa *Mill.*).

A. Male and female flowers solitary or in pedunculate heads; involucre regularly 2–4-lobed; nuts triangular; cotyledons appearing above ground after germination: **B.** Male and female flowers solitary or up to 3 together; leaves evergreen or deciduous; involucre with transverse entire or toothed scales—NOTHOFAGUS. **BB.** Male flowers many in heads; female flowers 2; leaves deciduous; involucre with prickly subulate or bract-like appendages, with 2 nuts—FAGUS. **AA.** Male flowers in slender spikes; female flowers solitary or in spikes; involucre not or only irregularly split; cotyledons remaining in the seed after germination: **C.** Male flowers in erect spikes: **D.** Leaves deciduous; ovary 6-locular; terminal bud absent—CASTANEA. **DD.** Leaves evergreen; ovary 3-locular; terminal bud present: **E.** Involucre usually spiny, asymmetrical, usually wholly enclosing the 1–3 fruits; leaves usually in 2 rows—CASTANOPSIS. **EE.** Involucre of fruits not spiny, mostly cup-shaped; nut always solitary; leaves not 2-ranked—LITHOCARPUS. **CC.** Male flowers in pendulous catkins; styles flattened, with the stigma on the upper surface; leaves deciduous or evergreen—QUERCUS.

63. CORYLACEAE

Shrubs or small trees with *perulate* buds; leaves alternate, prominently *penni-nerved*, mostly *serrate*; stipules present; flowers monoecious; spikes unisexual, the male in *catkins*, the female geminate in a short spike, bracteate;

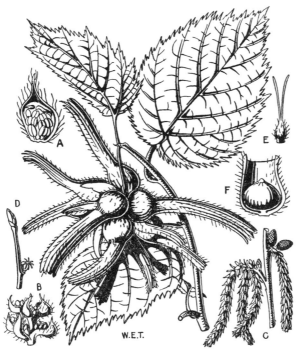

FIG. 63. Corylus mandshurica *Maxim.* (Corylaceae). A, male flower. B, group of male flowers. C, male inflorescences. D, female inflorescence. E, ovary. F, nut. (After *Bot. Mag.*)

male calyx absent; stamens several, inserted on the bract; filaments often divided; anthers with separate loculi often hairy at the apex; no rudimentary ovary; female calyx present, adnate to the ovary, irregularly lobed at the top; ovary inferior, rather imperfectly 2-locular; ovules 2 or by abortion 1, pendulous from the apex; styles 2, free or nearly so, linear; nut enclosed in the foliaceous accrescent involucre; seed solitary, without endosperm; embryo straight, with large fleshy cotyledons much longer than the small radicle. B.H.

3, 405 (under *Cupuliferae*); E.P. **3,** 1, 41 (under *Betulaceae*). N. Temperate Zone.

USEFUL PRODUCTS: *Hornbeam* (Carpinus betulus *L.*); *Filberts* and *Barcelona nuts* from varieties of the common *Hazel* (Corylus avellana *L.*), Eur., &c.; *Turkey Filberts* (C. colurna *L.*).

A. Fruits in pendulous slender catkins: **B.** Involucre of the fruit flat, 3-lobed or dentate, leafy; staminate catkins produced in spring—CARPINUS (Temp. N. Hemisph., Mexico). **BB.** Involucre a bladder-like closed bag; staminate catkins formed in autumn—OSTRYA (S. Eur. to E. Asia, N. and Cent. Amer.). **AA.** Fruits in clusters; staminate catkins naked during the winter: **C.** Anthers undivided, not hairy at the top; flowers produced with the leaves—OSTRYOPSIS (NE. Asia). **CC.** Anthers divided, with tufts of hairs at the top; flowers before the leaves—CORYLUS (Temp. N. Hemisph.).

ORDER 17. JUGLANDALES

Trees with hard wood; leaves alternate or rarely opposite, pinnate or trifoliolate; stipules present or absent; flowers bisexual or unisexual, spicate or paniculate; bracts often enlarged in fruit; calyx usually present; petals and disk absent; stamens numerous to few, erect in bud; ovary superior to inferior, 2–1-locular; ovules 2 or 1; fruit a drupe or nut; seeds without endosperm; cotyledons often much contorted.—Mostly Temperate Regions of N. Hemisphere.

A. Leaves pinnate:
  B. Stipules present; bisexual flowers fertile, female flowers sterile; ovary 2-locular, superior, one loculus empty, ovule axile; fruit 2-winged
  Rhoipteleaceae
  BB. Stipules absent; flowers unisexual, females fertile; ovary 1-locular, inferior, ovule erect; bracts or bracteoles often enlarged in fruit
  Juglandaceae
AA. Leaves trifoliolate; stipules minute and setiform; ovary 2-locular
  Picrodendraceae

64. RHOIPTELEACEAE

Tree up to 20 metres high, with hard wood; branchlets covered with numerous lenticels; leaves alternate, sessile, *pinnate*, leaflets oblong-lanceolate, acuminate, serrulate, pinnately nerved, minutely glandular below; stipules small, obliquely ovate-cuspidate, deciduous; panicles axillary and terminal, the whip-like branches loosely spike-like and simple; flowers 3 in each cluster, subtended by a bract and 2 bracteoles; middle flower *bisexual*, shortly pedicellate, fertile, lateral flowers *female* but sterile, sessile; sepals 4, free, obovate-orbicular, imbricate, persistent in fruit; *petals and disk absent*; stamens in the bisexual flowers 6, erect in bud; anthers oblong, rounded at each end, emarginate, basifixed, the connective minutely glandular on both sides; ovary superior, 2-locular, *one loculus empty*, the other 1-ovuled; stigmas 2, free; ovule attached to the septum, ascending, with 2 integuments; nut formed only in the bisexual flowers, woody, tuberculate, *2-winged like that of an elm*, wings compressed, forming a circle of 5–8 mm diameter with a rectangular sinus at

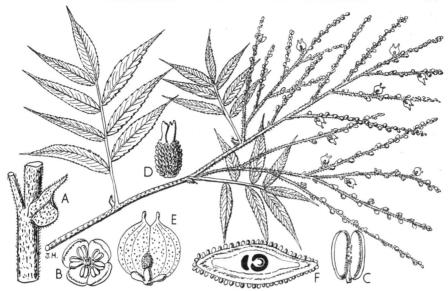

FIG. 64. Rhoiptelea chiliantha *Diels & Hand.-Mazz.* (Rhoipteleaceae). A, stipule. B, bisexual flower. C, anther. D, ovary. E, fruit. F, transverse section of fruit. (Orig.)

the top, chartaceous, greenish, at length purplish, minutely glandular; seed ovoid, *without endosperm*; embryo straight, radicle slender and with collateral ellipsoidal thick cotyledons. Indo-China.—RHOIPTELEA.

An interesting monotypic family probably representing a primitive type leading up to the more advanced *Juglandaceae*; remarkable in having fertile bisexual and sterile female flowers.

65. JUGLANDACEAE

Trees, often resinous and aromatic, with handsome durable dark-coloured wood; leaves deciduous, alternate, rarely opposite, *imparipinnate*; stipules

FIG. 65. Engelhardtia nudiflora *Hook. f.* (Juglandaceae). A, leaf and male inflorescence. B, portion of inflorescence. C, female flower and transverse section of ovary. D, vertical section of ovary. E, fruit with enlarged female bract.

absent; flowers ♂♀, *monoecious,* the male often in catkin-like pendulous spikes, rarely erect, the female spikes erect; calyx of the male flower adnate to the bract, 3–6-lobed and imbricate or absent; stamens 3–40, attached to the torus in 2 or more series; filaments short; anthers erect, 2-locular, opening lengthwise; rudimentary ovary rarely developed; female flowers sessile on the axis, variously bracteate and often 2-bracteolate; calyx adnate to the ovary, free at the apex, 4-toothed or shortly 4-lobed; ovary *inferior,* 1-locular; style short, with two short or elongated branches, often *plumose;* ovule 1, erect from the base, orthotropous; fruit a drupe or rarely a nut, often adnate to the enlarged bracts or bracteoles; exocarp succulent, endocarp mostly hard, bony, intrusive at the base, imperfectly dividing the fruit into 2–4 loculi; seed solitary, without endosperm; cotyledons often much contorted. B.H. **3**, 397; E.P. **3**, 1, 19. N. Temperate Hemisphere and mountains of N. Tropics.

USEFUL PRODUCTS: *Hickory nuts* (Carya alba *Nutt.,* C. tomentosa *Nutt.*), N. Amer.; *Peccan nuts* (C. olivaeformis *Nutt.*); *Walnut wood* and *nuts* (Juglans regia *L.*); *Butternut* (Juglans cinerea *L.*), N. Amer.

A. Leaves alternate: B. Catkins of the male flowers pendulous; female flowers spicate or subsolitary, very rarely paniculate: C. Fruit a large drupe without wings, solitary or in pendulous racemes: D. Husk of fruit splitting; nut smooth, often angled—CARYA (*Annamocarya, Rhamphocarya*) (N. Amer.). DD. Husk of fruit indehiscent; nut sculptured or rugose—JUGLANS (Temp. and Subtrop. N. Hemisph., West Indies). CC. Fruit a winged nutlet: E. Bract unchanged in fruit; bracteoles forming a wing to the fruit—PTEROCARYA (Temp. Asia from Caucasus to Japan). EE. Bracts 3-lobed and forming a wing to the fruit, veiny and spreading: F. Fruits divided by 2 dissepiments; wings small to medium-sized—ENGELHARDTIA (India to S. China). FF. Fruits divided by 4 dissepiments; wings very large and rigid (about 10 cm)— OREOMUNNEA (Cent. Amer.). BB. Spikes of both sexes erect, covered by imbricate bracts; fruit a winged nutlet—PLATYCARYA (N. China). AA. Leaves opposite, glandular below; fruits ellipsoidal, softly hispid, not winged; flowers monoecious, spicate, spikes terminal, males few, sessile at the base of the spike, females numerous above—ALFAROA (Costa Rica).

66. PICRODENDRACEAE

Trees with bark peeling off in long strips; leaves deciduous, alternate, longpetiolate, *trifoliolate,* leaflets oblong-elliptic, entire, pinnately nerved, petiolulate, petiolules jointed at the base; stipules very minute and setiform, persistent; flowers *unisexual,* males in slender interrupted simple or slightly branched *catkins* from the axils of fallen leaves of previous season's shoots, female flowers *solitary* in the axils of the leaves of the current year's shoots; male flowers subtended by 3 abaxial bracts, the middle bract a little larger and overlapping the edges of the lateral ones; sepals and petals absent; stamens *numerous* (20 or more), loosely clustered and forming a globose head and borne on a hemispherical receptacle; filaments free, short; anthers ellipsoidal, minutely pubescent, 2-locular, slightly extrorse, dehiscing by slits; no rudimentary ovary; female flowers on slender pedicels; sepals 4, narrowly lanceolate, unequal, remotely toothed; no disk; ovary superior, 2-locular, gradually narrowed into a stout deeply 2-lobed style; stigmas revolute on the margin; ovules 2 in each loculus, pendulous from a hemispherical placenta at the top of the loculi; fruit globose, *indehiscent*; seed 1 by abortion, occupying most

FIG. 66. Picrodendron baccatum (*Linn.*) *Krug & Urban* (Picrodendraceae). A, flowering shoot of male plant. B, male flower from the side. C, the same from below. D, stamen. E, flowering shoot of female plant. F, pistil. G, vertical section of ovary. H, fruit. J, embryo.

of the fruit, globular; cotyledons much *corrugated*, reflexed; no endosperm. West Indies.—PICRODENDRON.

ORDER 18. CASUARINALES

Trees or shrubs with jointed branches and much reduced connate leaves; flowers ♂♀, male spicate, female in heads; calyx and petals absent; stamen solitary; ovary superior, 1-locular; ovules 2, inserted above the base of the ovary; fruits in cone-like heads; seeds without endosperm.

67. CASUARINACEAE

Trees or shrubs with *jointed branches*; leaves *reduced* to many-toothed sheaths surrounding the nodes of the branches; flowers monoecious or dioecious, the ♂ spicate, ♀ in heads; ♂ flowers arranged in the *sheaths* towards the ends of the branchlets, each with 4 bracteoles; calyx absent; stamen *solitary*, central; filament lengthening during flowering; anther 2-locular, opening lengthwise; ♀ flowers *capitate* at the tips of the branchlets or lateral; calyx absent; ovary small, superior, 1-locular; style short, terminal, with elongated linear branches; ovules 2, collateral above the base of the ovary, ascending; fruits crowded into a *cone* with persistent bracts, the bracts opening like a capsule and exposing the samaroid indehiscent nut; seed solitary, without endosperm; embryo straight, with short radicle and large flat cotyledons. B.H. **3**, 401; E.P. **3**, 1, 16. Mascarene Islands through Malaya to New Caledonia and Australia.—CASUARINA.

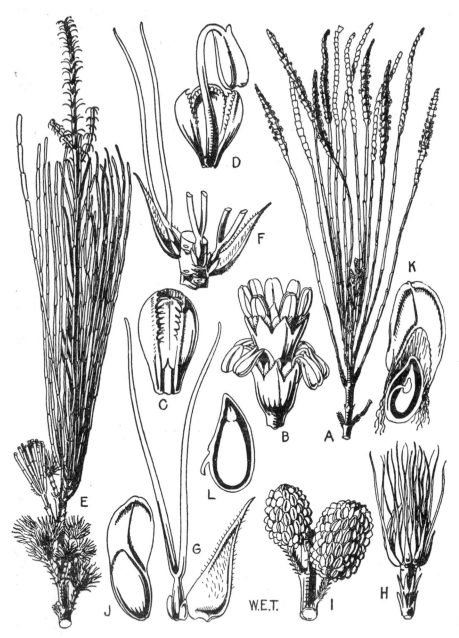

Fig. 67. Casuarina suberosa *R. Br.* (Casuarinaceae). A, male inflorescences. B, portion of same, enlarged. C, male flower, unopened. D, same, opened. E, female inflorescences. F, female flowers. G, single one enlarged. H, female inflorescence. I, fruit. J, seed. K, section of seed. (After Hook. f.)

USEFUL PRODUCTS: *Beefwood* or *Forest Oak* (Casuarina equisetifolia *Forst.*), India to Malaya, Austral., &c.; *She Oak* (C. stricta *Ait.*), Austral.

ORDER 19. URTICALES

Trees, shrubs, or herbs, sometimes epiphytic; leaves mostly alternate and usually stipulate; flowers ♀ or ♂♀; calyx small; no petals; stamens few, erect or inflexed in bud; ovary superior, 1–2-locular; ovule solitary, erect or pendulous; seeds with or without endosperm.

A. Calyx present, though sometimes much reduced; ovule 1:
  B. Leaves stipulate:
    C. Anthers erect in bud:
      D. Trees or shrubs with hard wood; leaves alternate, often unequal-sided at the base; seed without endosperm, embryo straight
                                          Ulmaceae
      DD. Erect or climbing herbs with often fibrous stems; leaves alternate or opposite, sometimes lobed; seed with fleshy endosperm and curved or spirally coiled embryo   *Cannabiaceae*
    CC. Anthers usually inflexed in bud:
      E. Trees, shrubs, rarely herbs, with milky juice; ovules mostly pendulous
                                          Moraceae
      EE. Herbs, undershrubs, or rarely soft-wooded trees, rarely climbing; leaf-epidermis mostly with prominent cystoliths; ovule erect
                                        Urticaceae
  BB. Leaves not stipulate, opposite; anthers erect in bud; female calyx enlarged and venose in fruit; ovule pendulous; seed without endo sperm embryo straight   *Barbeyaceae*
AA. Calyx absent; ovules 2, collateral, pendulous; leaves without stipules; seed with endosperm and straight embryo   *Eucommiaceae*

68. ULMACEAE

Trees or shrubs; leaves alternate, simple, often *unequal-sided*; stipules *paired*, caducous; flowers fasciculate, arising from the one-year-old branchlets, ♀ or ♂♀; calyx herbaceous, subcampanulate, 4–8-lobed, lobes imbricate, persistent; stamens inserted at the bottom of the calyx, *erect* in bud, the same number as the calyx-lobes and *opposite* to them, or a few more; filaments separate; anthers 2-locular, opening lengthwise; ovary composed of 2 *connate carpels*, 1–2-locular; styles 2, divergent, stigmatose on their inner face; ovules solitary, *pendulous* from near the top; fruit compressed, membranous, dry or thinly fleshy, often winged or appendiculate; seed without endosperm; embryo straight; cotyledons flat, sinuous or conduplicate. B.H. **3,** 351 (under *Urticaceae*); E.P. **3,** 1, 59. Mostly N. Temperate Zone.—ULMUS, HOLO-PTELEA, PHYLLOSTYLON, PLANERA, CELTIS, TREMA (Fig. 68), &c.

USEFUL PRODUCTS: Valuable timber trees are the common *Elm* (Ulmus spp.); *Keyaki* (Zelkova acuminata *Planch.*), Japan.

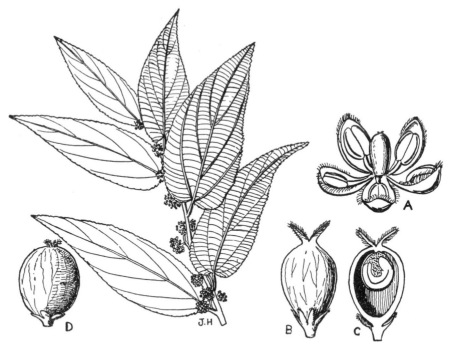

FIG. 68. Trema commersonii *Baill.* (Ulmaceae). A, flower. B, ovary. C, vertical section of same. D, fruit. (After Baill.)

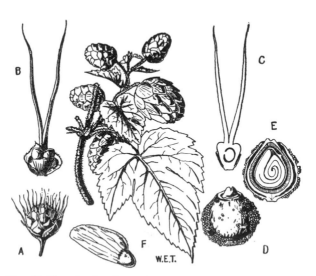

FIG. 69. Humulus lupulus *L.* (Cannabiaceae). A, female inflorescence. B, female flower. C, vertical section of same. D, fruit. E, vertical section of same. F, seed. (After Baill.)

69. CANNABIACEAE

Erect or scandent herbs; leaves alternate or opposite, simple, undivided or palmately lobed; stipules present; flowers dioecious, axillary, male paniculate, female sessile, crowded or strobilate, the female with large conspicuous persistent bracts; male flower: calyx 5-partite, segments imbricate; stamens 5; anthers erect in bud, 2-locular, opening lengthwise; rudimentary ovary absent; female flower: calyx closely enveloping the ovary, membranous, entire; ovary sessile, 1-locular; style central, 2-partite; ovule solitary, pendulous; fruit an achene, covered by the persistent perianth; seed with fleshy endosperm; embryo curved or spirally involute. B.H. **3**, 356 (under *Urticaceae*); E.P. **3**, 1, 96 (under *Moraceae*). N. Temperate Zone and much cultivated.

USEFUL PRODUCTS: *Hops* and *Lupulin* (Humulus lupulus *L.*, Fig. 68), Eur., &c.; *Hemp* fibre and drug (Cannabis sativa *L.*).

A. Erect annual herb; leaves alternate or the lower opposite—CANNABIS.
AA. Climbing perennial herbs; leaves opposite—HUMULUS.

70. MORACEAE

Trees or shrubs, rarely herbs, with *milky juice*; leaves alternate, rarely opposite, simple, penninerved or palminerved; stipules 2, often caducous and

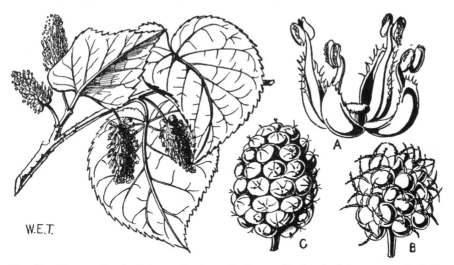

FIG. 70. Morus alba *L.* (Moraceae). A, male flower. B, female inflorescence. C, fruit. (After Baill.)

leaving a scar; flowers much reduced, often in heads, disks, or hollow receptacles; ♂♀, monoecious or dioecious, actinomorphic; calyx-lobes usually 4, sometimes reduced or absent, imbricate or valvate; stamens usually equal in number and *opposite* to the sepals; filaments *inflexed* or straight in bud; anthers 2-locular, opening lengthwise; rudimentary ovary present or not; female flower: ovary superior to inferior, of 2 carpels, one often not developed, usually 1-locular; ovule solitary, *pendulous* from the apex, rarely basal and erect; styles mostly 2, filiform; fruit a small achene, nut, or drupe; seed with or without endosperm, with often curved embryo. B.H. **3,** 357 (under *Urticaceae*); E.P. **3,** 1, 66. Mainly Tropics.—PSEUDOSTREBLUS, MORUS, TROPHIS, MACLURA, CHLOROPHORA, BROUSSONETIA, STREBLUS, DORSTENIA, MESOGYNE, CUDRANIA, TRECULIA, ARTOCARPUS, PEREBEA, CASTILLOA, ANTIARIS, BROSIMUM, FICUS, CONOCEPHALUS, MUSANGA, MYRIANTHUS, COUSSAPOA, POUROUMA, CECROPIA, &c.

USEFUL PRODUCTS: *Mulberry* (Morus nigra *L.*); *White Mulberry* (M. alba *L.*); *Paper Mulberry* (Broussonetia papyrifera *Vent.*), E. Trop.; *Fustic* (Chlorophora tinctoria *Gaud.*), Trop. Amer.; *Iroko Tree* (Chlorophora excelsa *Benth.*), W. Afr.; *Osage Orange* (Maclura aurantiaca *Nutt.*), N. Amer.; *Contrayerva Root* (Dorstenia brasiliensis *Lamb.*), Brazil; *Fig* (Ficus carica *L.*); *Sycamore Fig* (F. sycomorus *L.*), Trop. Afr., &c.; *Indiarubber Fig* (F. elastica *Roxb.*), E. Trop.; *Cow Tree* (Brosimum utile (*H. B. & K.*) *Pittier*), S. Amer.; *Castilloa Rubber* (Castilloa elastica *Cerv.*), Cent. and S. Amer.; *Affon* or *African Bread-fruit* (Treculia africana *Decne*); *Bread Fruit* (Artocarpus altilis (*Park.*) *Fosberg* (A. communis *Forst.*)), cultivated in Trop.; *Jack-fruit* (A. heterophyllus *Lam.*).

71. URTICACEAE

Herbs, undershrubs, or rarely soft-wooded trees, very rarely climbing, often armed with *stinging hairs*; epidermal cells mostly with prominent *cystoliths*; stems often *fibrous*; leaves alternate or opposite, simple; stipules present, very

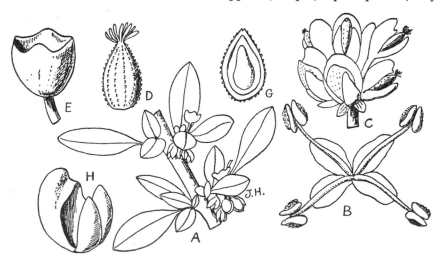

FIG. 71. Pilea microphylla (*L.*) *Liebm.* (Urticaceae). A, male flowers. B, single male flower. C, female flowers. D, ovary. E, calyx. G, section of fruit. H, fruiting calyx.

rarely absent; flowers very small, unisexual, usually cymose, sometimes crowded on a common enlarged receptacle; male flowers: calyx mostly 4–5-lobed, lobes imbricate or valvate; stamens the same number as and opposite to the calyx-lobes; filaments *inflexed in bud*; anthers 2-locular, opening lengthwise; rudimentary ovary usually present; female flowers: calyx as in the male, often enlarged in fruit, rarely absent; staminodes scale-like, opposite the calyx-lobes, or absent; ovary free or adnate to the calyx, sessile or shortly stipitate, 1-locular; style simple; ovule solitary, erect; fruit a dry achene or fleshy drupe; seed mostly with endosperm; embryo straight. B.H. **3**, 341, partly; E.P. **3**, 1, 98. Generally distributed.—URTICA, URERA, LAPORTEA, FLEURYA, PILEA, ELATOSTEMA, PROCRIS, BOEHMERIA, POUZOLZIA, PIPTURUS, PARIETARIA, HELXINE, FORSKOHLEA, &c.

USEFUL PRODUCTS: Stems fibrous in many. *Ramie fibre* (Boehmeria nivea *Gaud.*). Some noxious weeds.

72. BARBEYACEAE

Trees; leaves opposite, simple, entire, tomentose below with crooked hairs; stipules absent; flowers dioecious, shortly cymose, actinomorphic; male calyx 3–4-fid, lobes *valvate*; petals absent; stamens 6 9; filaments very short;

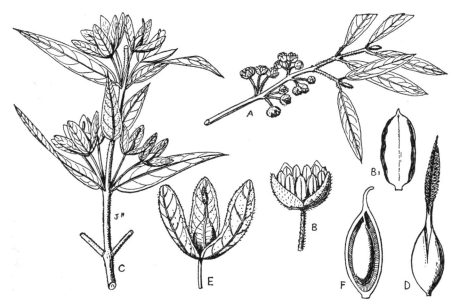

FIG. 72. Barbeya oleoides *Schweinf.* (Barbeyaceae). A, male flowers, B, male flower. B₁, stamen. C, female flowers. D, ovary. E, female flower. F, vertical section of ovary. (Orig.)

anthers *erect* in bud, 2-locular, opening lengthwise, connective *apiculate*; female calyx divided to the base into 3 or 4 segments which *enlarge* and become sub-membranous and venose in fruit; no staminodes; ovary superior, subsessile, 1-locular; style linear, *simple*, stigmatose all round; ovule solitary from near the apex of the loculus, anatropous; fruit dry, indehiscent, ellipsoidal, pericarp thin, nervose; seed without endosperm; embryo straight. Arabia and NE. Tropical Africa.—BARBEYA.

73. EUCOMMIACEAE

Trees; leaves deciduous, alternate, simple, *exstipulate*, petiolate, serrate, pinnately nerved; flowers *dioecious*, *without a perianth*, appearing with the leaves from *perulate buds*; male flowers in loose bracteate clusters, shortly stalked, composed only of about 10 linear apiculate stamens dehiscing longitudinally; female flowers solitary in the axil of each bract or bract-like leaf on the lower

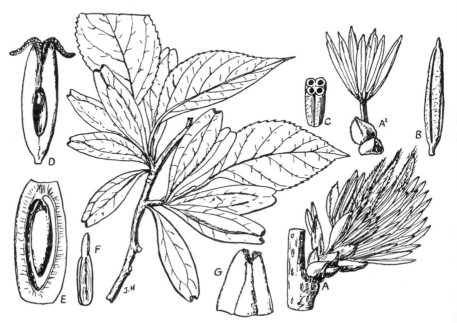

FIG. 73. Eucommia ulmoides *Oliv.* (Eucommiaceae). A, inflorescence. A¹, male flower. B, anther. C, cross-section of same. D, vertical section of ovary. E, same enlarged. F, embryo. G, apex of fruit. (After Hook. *Ic. Pl.*)

part of each shoot, shortly stalked; ovary syncarpous, flattened, stigmatose within the V-shaped apex; ovules 2, collateral, pendulous, anatropous; fruit samaroid, indehiscent, 1-seeded, thinly coriaceous, stipitate, oblong-oblanceolate, bifid at the apex; seed solitary, pendulous from the apex of the loculus, elongate-oblong; endosperm copious; testa membranous; raphe dorsal; embryo central, straight, as long as the endosperm, with a superior more or less compressed radicle; cotyledons flat, fleshy, oblong-linear, longer than the radicle. Hook. *Ic. Pl.* t. 1950. China.—EUCOMMIA.

USEFUL PRODUCTS: Bark of Eucommia ulmoides *Oliv.* contains caoutchouc, and is a valued medicine of the Chinese.

ORDER 20. BIXALES

Trees or shrubs; flowers hypogynous to rarely perigynous, ♀ to ♂♀, actinomorphic; sepals imbricate to valvate; petals present or absent; stamens numerous to few, mostly free; ovary superior with parietal placentation, rarely basal; seeds with copious endosperm and small embryo. Leaves mostly alternate and stipulate, simple.

A. Petals present:
  B. Petals free:
    C. Anthers narrowly horseshoe-shaped   *Bixaceae*
    CC. Anthers not horseshoe-shaped:
      D. Sepals contorted; anthers opening by slits lengthwise; leaves usually opposite; petals mostly contorted   *Cistaceae*
      DD. Sepals imbricate or open in bud; leaves alternate:
        E. Anthers opening by slits lengthwise; leaves alternate; petals imbricate
                      Flacourtiaceae
        EE. Anthers opening by terminal short pore-like slits; petals contorted
                      Cochlospermaceae
  BB. Petals united; leaves alternate:
    F. Flowers bisexual; ovary with parietal forked placentas.
                      Hoplestigmataceae
    FF. Flowers unisexual; ovary with basal placenta   *Scyphostegiaceae*[1]
AA. Petals absent; stipules absent:
  G. Flowers unisexual; embryo annular   *Achatocarpaceae*
  GG. Flowers bisexual; embryo straight   *Lacistemaceae*

74. BIXACEAE

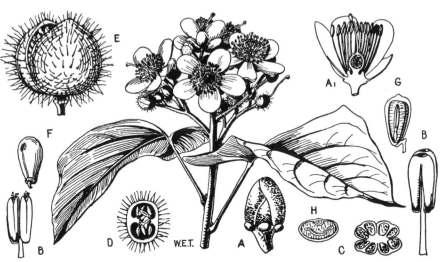

FIG. 74. Bixa orellana *L.* (Bixaceae). A, flower-bud and glands. A₁, vertical section of flower. B, anthers. C, section of same. D, cross-section of ovary. E, fruit. F, seed. G, section of seed. H, cross-section. (After Le Maout & Decne.)

Shrubs or small trees with *coloured juice*; leaves alternate, simple, *palminerved*, stipulate; flowers ⚥, medium-sized, showy, paniculate; sepals 5, *imbricate*, deciduous; petals 5, large, imbricate, without a *scale* at the base; disk

[1] Inserted here because of its possible affinity with this group of families.

none; stamens numerous, hypogynous; filaments free; anthers *horseshoe-shaped*, opening by short slits at the top; ovary superior, 1-locular, with 2 *parietal* placentas; ovules numerous; style slender, recurved in bud; stigma 2-lobed; fruit a densely echinate-setose or smooth capsule, 2-valved, valves thick with the placentas in the middle; seeds obovoid; testa rather fleshy, red; endosperm copious; embryo large; cotyledons broad, incurved at the apex. B.H. **1**, 122, partly; E.P. **3**, 6, 307. Widely distributed in the Tropics.—BIXA.

USEFUL PRODUCT: *Annatto dye* (seeds of Bixa orellana *L.*), Tropics generally.

75. CISTACEAE

Herbs or shrubs, often with *stellate* indumentum; leaves *opposite* or rarely alternate, simple; stipules present or adnate to the petiole; flowers ☿, actino-

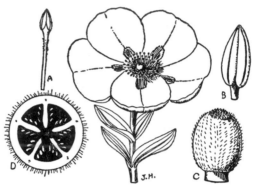

FIG. 75. Cistus loretii *Rouy & Fouc.* (Cistaceae). A, stamen. B, anther. C, ovary. D, cross-section of same. (After *Bot. Mag.*)

morphic, solitary to cymose, showy; sepals 3–5, *contorted*; petals 5 to 0, *contorted* or imbricate, usually caducous; stamens *numerous*, hypogynous; filaments free; anthers 2-locular, introrse, opening lengthwise; ovary superior, 1-locular with *parietal* placentas or incompletely septate towards the base; ovules 2 or more to each placenta; style simple with 3–5 free or united stigmas, sometimes almost absent; fruit a capsule opening by valves from the top downwards; seeds with endosperm, and bent, coiled, or folded embryo. B.H. **1**, 112; E.P. **3**, 6, 299. Mainly Mediterranean and N. Amer.

USEFUL PRODUCTS: *Labdanum* (Cistus polymorphus *Willk.*), SW. Eur. Many handsome garden shrubs.

A. Petals 5, contorted (very rarely absent): **B.** Capsule 10- or 5-valved; stamens all fertile—CISTUS (Mediterr. Reg.). **BB.** Capsule 3-valved: **C.** Stigma large, discoid or hemispherical; leaves mostly opposite: **D.** Style very short, straight; sepals 3 or 5—CROCANTHEMUM (S. Amer.). **DD.** Style elongated, curved or bent at the base; sepals 5: **E.** All the stamens fertile; ovules ortho-tropous—HELIANTHEMUM (Old World). **EE.** Outer stamens sterile, articulated; ovules anatropous—FUMANA (Eur., W. Asia). **CC.** Stigma minute, tridentate on a filiform style; embryo curved; habit ericoid, leaves alternate—HUDSONIA (Atlantic N. Amer.). **AA.** Petals 3, imbricate, persistent;

upper leaves alternate; embryo straight or slightly spiral—LECHEA (N. Amer., West Indies).

76. FLACOURTIACEAE
(including *Samydaceae*)

Trees or shrubs; leaves simple, alternate, sometimes *pellucid-dotted or lined*; stipules often soon falling off; flowers often *dioecious or polygamous*, variously arranged; sepals sometimes *not distinguishable from the petals*, imbricate or open in bud; petals sometimes not arranged regularly in relation to the sepals, large, small, or absent, with or without an opposite scale inside the base,

FIG. 76. Casearia lasiophylla *Eichl.* (Flacourtiaceae). A, section of flower. B, stamens and staminodes. C, stamen. D, ovary. E, fruits. F, seed. G, section of same. H, cross-section of ovary. (After Martius.)

imbricate; stamens numerous, rarely few, hypogynous, *free or in bundles opposite the petals*; anthers 2-locular, often short, opening lengthwise by slits; staminodes sometimes present; ovary 1-locular, with 1 or more *parietal* placentas or rarely the placentas meeting in the middle; ovules 2 or more on each placenta; styles or stigmas as many as the placentas; fruit *indehiscent*, mostly a berry or drupe, rarely a capsule, sometimes large; seeds with fleshy endosperm and medium-sized embryo; cotyledons often broad. B.H. **1**, 122 (under *Bixaceae*); E.P. **3**, 6a, 1; edn. **2**, 21, 377 (1925). Mainly Tropics.—ONCOBA, AZARA, SCOLOPIA, FLACOURTIA, XYLOSMA, HYDNOCARPUS, KIGGELARIA, CASEARIA, SAMYDA, RYANIA, BANARA, HOMALIUM, DIONCOPHYLLUM,[1] NEO-PRINGLEA (*Llavea*)(?), &c.

[1] In the *Kew Bull.* 1951, 327, pls. 1–4 the genus *Dioncophyllum* Baill. was divided by Airy-Shaw into three genera, *Dioncophyllum*, *Habropetalum* Airy-Shaw, and *Triphyophyllum* Airy-Shaw, and these proposed as a new family *Dioncophyllaceae* Airy-Shaw. I consider the characters given are no more than specific, and that *Dioncophyllum* should remain in the *Flacourtiaceae*.

USEFUL PRODUCTS: *Kei Apple* (Aberia caffra), S. Afr.; *Chaulmugra oil* (seeds of Taraktogenos kurzii *King*), E. India; *Lukrabo* or *Ta-Fung-Tsze seeds* (Hydnocarpus anthelminthicus *Pierre*), Indo-China.

77. COCHLOSPERMACEAE

Trees, shrubs, or rhizomatous subshrubs with *coloured juice*; leaves alternate, palmatilobed, *stipulate*; flowers ⚥, showy, paniculate or racemose; sepals 5, imbricate, deciduous; petals 5, imbricate or subcontorted; stamens numerous,

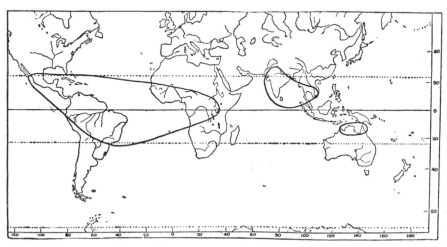

Range of Cochlospermum (Cochlospermaceae).

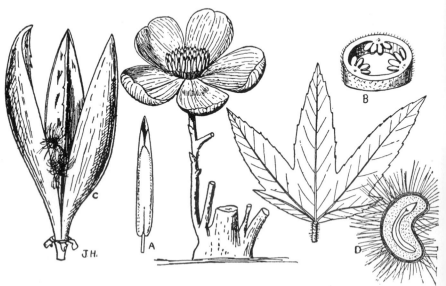

FIG. 77. Cochlospermum tinctorium *Rich.* (Cochlospermaceae). A, stamen. B, cross-section of ovary. C, fruit. D, section of seed. (Orig.)

the filaments free, equal or some longer than others; anthers 2-locular, linear, opening by terminal short, often confluent, *pore-like slits*; ovary 1-locular with *parietal placentas* projecting into the loculus, or perfectly 3-locular; ovules numerous; style simple with minutely denticulate stigma; fruit a 3–5-valved capsule; seeds glabrous or covered with *woolly hairs*, straight or *cochleate-reniform*; endosperm copious; embryo conforming to the shape of the seed, large; cotyledons broad. B.H. **1**, 122 (under *Bixaceae*); E.P.N. 251. Tropics.

USEFUL PRODUCTS: *Kuteera gum* (Cochlospermum religiosum (*L.*) *Alston*), India.

A. Ovary 1-locular or partly more-locular at the apex or base; seeds covered with woolly hairs—COCHLOSPERMUM (*Lachnocistus*) (Trop.). **AA.** Ovary completely 3-locular; placentas axile; seeds glabrous or slightly pilose —AMOREUXIA (Cent. Amer.).

78. HOPLESTIGMATACEAE

Trees; leaves alternate, undivided, large and obovate, pinnately nerved; *stipules absent*; flowers bisexual, fairly large, arranged in terminal cymes with

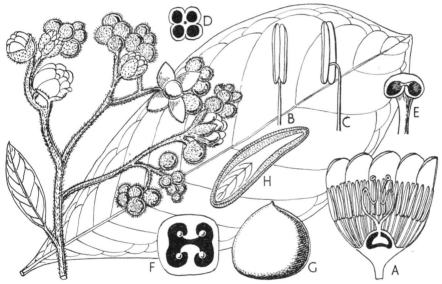

FIG. 78. Hoplestigma pierreanum *Gilg* (Hoplestigmataceae). A, vertical section of flower. B & C, anthers. D, cross-section of anthers. E, stigma. F, cross-section of ovary. G, fruit. H, vertical section of seed.

subscorpioid branches without bracts; calyx globose in bud, splitting irregularly into lobes; petals 14–11, *united into a short tube*, rounded, imbricate in 3–4 *irregular series*; stamens about 30–20 in about 3 irregular series *free from the corolla*; filaments filiform; anthers 2–locular, elongate-oblong, opening lengthwise by lateral slits, attached above the base; ovary superior, broadly ovoid, composed of 2 united carpels, *1-locular* with 2 *parietal* protruded forked placentas, each placenta with 2 pendulous anatropous ovules; style short and thick, divided into 2 long branches bent in the middle and each with a disk-like horseshoe-shaped stigma; fruit a drupe surrounded at the base by the calyx, with leathery mesocarp and hard endocarp; seed with scanty endosperm and large, nearly straight embryo with oblong cotyledons. Gilg, *Engl. Bot. Jahrb.* **40,** Beibl. 93, 76, with fig. (1908). W. Tropical Africa.—HOPLE-STIGMA.

A genus of two species endemic to W. Tropical Africa, ranging from the Cameroons to Gabon. Pierre assigned it to the *Bixaceae* (*sensu lato*), but Gilg when describing the family considered it to be related to *Sapotaceae*. Pierre's position for the genus is probably the better one.

79. ACHATOCARPACEAE

Small trees or shrubs, branchlets sometimes spiny; leaves alternate, spathulate to elliptic, entire, pinnately nerved; *stipules absent*; flowers *dioecious*, in axillary racemes or short panicles, or these fasciculate on the leafless older

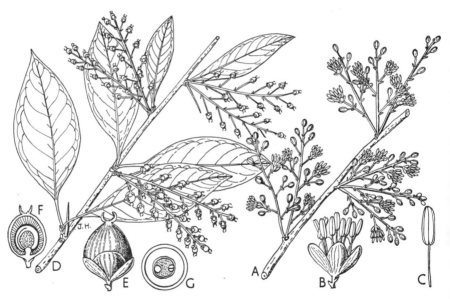

FIG. 79. Achatocarpus mexicanus *H. Walt.* (Achatocarpaceae). A, male flowering shoot. B, male flower. C, stamen. D, female flowering shoot and leaves. E, fruit. F, vertical section of fruit. G, cross-section of fruit. (Orig.)

branchlets; bracts and bracteoles small; calyx herbaceous, 5–4-partite, segments imbricate, *persistent in fruit*; petals absent; male flowers: stamens 20–10, filaments filiform, connate at the base; anthers exserted, oblong, basi-fixed, 2-lobed at the base, 2-locular, extrorsely dehiscent; rudimentary ovary absent; female flowers: staminodes absent; ovary compressed, *1-locular*; stigmas 2, subulate-filiform, incurved, papillous or fimbriate within the base; ovule 1, *erect on a short funicle*; fruit a globose slightly compressed *berry* crowned by the widely separated bases of the simple stigmas; seed solitary, erect, lenticular, without an aril; embryo *annular*, surrounding the mealy endosperm; cotyledons linear.—Central America to Temperate S. America.

A. Calyx always 5-partite; pedicels with bracteoles—ACHATOCARPUS.
AA. Calyx 4-partite or only the terminal flower 5-partite; pedicels without bracteoles—PHAULOTHAMNUS.

80. LACISTEMACEAE

Shrubs or small trees; leaves alternate, simple; stipules absent; flowers ♂, very small, crowded in axillary clustered spikes or racemes; bracts imbricate, concave; bracteoles 2 at the base of the flower; sepals 4–6, unequal, or absent;

Range of Lacistemaceae.

FIG. 80. Lacistema robustum *Schnitz*. (Lacistemaceae). A, inflorescence. B, male flower. C, female flower. D, stamen. E, ovary. (After Martius.)

petals absent; stamen solitary, inserted on or within a fleshy sometimes cupular disk; anther-loculi 2, *separate*, sometimes stipitate, ovoid, opening lengthwise; ovary sessile or subsessile, superior, 1-locular, with 2–3 *parietal placentas*; stigmas 2–3; ovules 1–2 on each placenta, pendulous, anatropous; fruit a capsule, dehiscing by valves, often 3-sided; seeds 1–3 in each capsule, pendulous; embryo straight in the middle of and slightly shorter than the copious fleshy endosperm; cotyledons foliaceous. B.H. **3**, 412; E.P. **3**, 1, 14. Tropical America (see map).

A. Bracts imbricate, conspicuous; leaves entire; flowers spicate—LACISTEMA. **AA.** Bracts minute; leaves dentate; flowers racemose—LOZANIA (*Monandrodendron, Lacistemopsis*).

ORDER 21. THYMELAEALES

Mostly woody and usually apetalous; calyx often corolline; mostly mono-carpellary; ovules few to solitary; seeds with or without endosperm and usually straight embryo. Leaves alternate or opposite; stipules absent or minute and glandular. Flowers often in heads surrounded by an involucre of leafy bracts.

A. Ovary more than 1-locular; ovules mostly pendulous:
  B. Fruit a capsule:
    C. Leaves alternate, scattered; ovule solitary in each loculus:
      D. Petals numerous, linear, sometimes divided nearly to the base; nerves of the leaves numerous, pinnate; stamens numerous; style thread-like, stigma small   *Gonystylaceae*
      DD. Petals represented by scales; stamens 10 or 5; style usually very short or absent, with a large stigma   *Aquilariaceae*
    CC. Leaves opposite, decussate, mostly sessile and overlapping; ovules 2–4 in each loculus:
      E. Calyx-lobes imbricate; stamens 8; styles 4, loosely united at the apex   *Geissolomataceae*
      EE. Calyx-lobes valvate; stamens 4; style 1; stigma capitate, 4-lobed   *Penaeaceae*
  BB. Fruit indehiscent; ovule solitary in each loculus or ovary; calyx-lobes (perianth) imbricate; petals present or absent   *Thymelaeaceae*
AA. Ovary 1-locular; ovule 1, erect; fruit indehiscent; petals absent; calyx often petaloid, lobes valvate or plicate in bud   *Nyctaginaceae*

81. GONYSTYLACEAE

Fig. 81. Gonystylus miquelianus *T. & B.* (Gonystylaceae). A, vertical section of flower. B, bud. C, anther. D, ovary. E, young fruit. F, fruit. (Orig.)

Trees; leaves alternate, leathery, nerves numerous; stipules absent; flowers ☿, paniculate, actinomorphic; calyx 5-lobed, imbricate; *petals numerous, linear*, sometimes *divided nearly to the base*; stamens *numerous*; filaments free; anthers basifixed, 2-locular, opening by longitudinal slits; ovary 3–5-locular, with hump-like or thread-like processes at the top; *style thread-like, bent*; stigma small; ovule solitary in each loculus, pendulous from near the top; fruit woody, at length opening into the loculi; seeds large, without endosperm. B.H. **3**, 201; E.P.N. 231 (under *Thymelaeaceae*). Malaya.—GONYSTYLUS (*Amyxa, Aetoxylon*).

82. AQUILARIACEAE

Trees; leaves alternate, closely pinnately nerved, often shining; *stipules absent*; flowers ♀ or ♂♀, arranged in subsessile axillary and terminal *umbels* or fascicles, sometimes these subpaniculate; bracts absent; calyx campanulate or

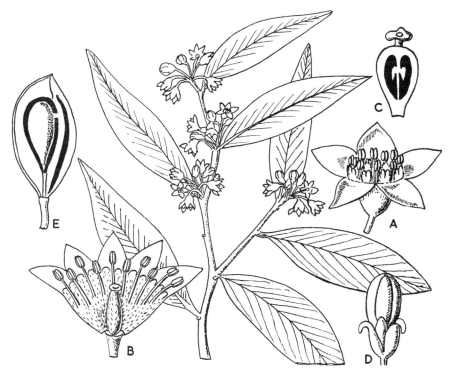

FIG. 82. Aquilaria agallocha *Roxb.* (Aquilariaceae). A, flower. B, the same opened out. C, vertical section of ovary. D, fruit. E, vertical section of fruit. (After Hook. *Ic. Pl.*)

slender, 5–4-lobed, lobes spreading, imbricate; petals present, often scale-like; scales 5 at the mouth of the calyx-tube, sometimes bilobed, *connate at the base into a ring*, pubescent or glabrous; stamens 10–8, or 5–4 and inserted below the scales; filaments very short; anthers 2-locular, oblong; no hypogynous disk; ovary subsessile to long-stipitate, completely or incompletely 2-locular; style usually very short or absent; *stigma large*; ovule solitary in each loculus or section, *pendulous*; capsule loculicidally dehiscent; seeds solitary on each placenta, with endosperm; cotyledons thick and fleshy. B.H. **3**, 200; E.P. **3**, 6a, 222 (in *Thymelaeaceae*).—Tropical Africa through E. Tropics to New Caledonia.

A. Stamens numerous, more than twice as many as the calyx-lobes, free or united into groups—MICROSEMMA (New Caled.). **AA.** Stamens up to twice as many as the calyx-lobes: **B.** Petals present, often scale-like; flowers bisexual: **C.** Flowers in axillary fascicles: **D.** Calyx-lobes 5—GYRINOPSIS (Indo-Malaya). **DD.** Calyx-lobes 4, mostly free—OCTOLEPIS (Trop. Afr.). **CC.** Flowers in umbels or panicles of umbels: **E.** Calyx-tube campanulate, lobes spreading, as long as the tube—AQUILARIA (E. Asia, Malay Archip.). **EE.** Calyx-tube cylindrical, slender—GYRINOPS (Ceylon, Malay Archip.). **BB.** Petals absent; flowers dioecious; calyx-tube subcampanulate—SOLMSIA (New Caled.).

83. GEISSOLOMATACEAE

Low shrub; leaves *opposite*, decussate, sessile, entire; stipules absent; flowers ♀, actinomorphic, in short much reduced bracteate axillary racemes; bracts 6, decussate, persistent; calyx hypogynous, persistent, shortly tubular, 4-*partite*

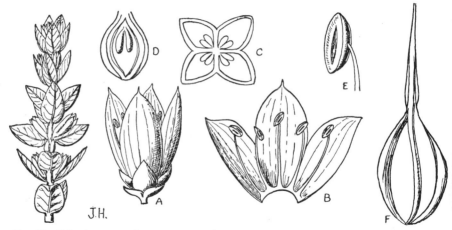

FIG. 83. Geissoloma marginatum *Juss.* (Geissolomataceae). A, flower. B, calyx and stamens. C, cross-section of ovary. D, vertical section of same. E, anther. F, fruit. (Orig.)

nearly to the base, segments petaloid, obovate, imbricate; stamens 8, inserted at the base of the calyx, opposite and alternate with the calyx-segments; filaments slender, free; anthers 2-locular, opening lengthwise; ovary superior, sessile, *4-locular*, loculi narrowly winged; styles 4, loosely united at the *apex*; ovules 2 in each loculus, pendulous from the apex; fruit a 4-locular capsule; seeds often solitary with scanty endosperm and straight central embryo; cotyledons long and linear. B.H. **3**, 203 (under *Penaeaceae*); E.P. **3**, 6a, 205. S. Africa.—GEISSOLOMA.

84. PENAEACEAE

Small shrubs of ericoid habit; leaves *opposite*, decussate, often *imbricate*, entire, mostly sessile; stipules when present very minute or glandular: flowers

♀, actinomorphic, solitary in the upper leaf-axils, often crowded; bracts leafy or coloured; bracteoles opposite, in one or more pairs; calyx hypogynous, tubular; lobes 4, *valvate*; petals absent; stamens 4, inserted in the throat of the calyx and *alternate* with its lobes; filaments short; anthers 2-locular, introrse, opening lengthwise; disk absent; ovary superior, sessile, 4-locular; style terminal, with a 4-lobed capitate stigma; ovules 2–4 in each loculus, anatropous, ascending or pendulous; fruit a *loculicidal capsule* included in the persistent calyx; seeds often solitary in each loculus; endosperm none; embryo thick, with large hypocotyl and 2 minute cotyledons. B.H. **3**, 202; E.P. **3**, 6*a*. 208. Entirely S. African.

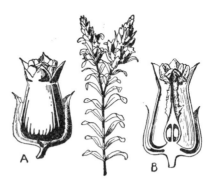

FIG. 84. Penaea myrtifolia *Endl.* (Penaeaceae). A, flower. B, dissection of same. (After Baill.)

A. Style winged or angular—PENAEA.
AA. Style terete: **B.** Bracts around the flowers becoming very sticky—SALTERA (*Sarcocolla*). **BB.** Bracts not sticky: **C.** Ovary-loculi with 2–4 ovules, all basal and erect—BRACHYSIPHON. **CC.** Ovary-loculi with 4 ovules, 2 erect and 2 pendulous: **D.** Perianth-tube long-cylindrical—ENDONEMA. **DD.** Perianth-tube oblong—GLISCHROCOLLA.

85. THYMELAEACEAE

Trees, shrubs, or rarely herbs; leaves opposite or alternate, *simple*, mostly small; *stipules absent*; flowers often in terminal bracteate or ebracteate heads, spikes, or racemes, rarely solitary, ♀ or dioecious, actinomorphic or slightly

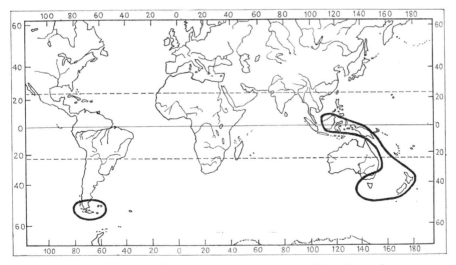

Range of the natural (homogeneous) genus Drapetes (Thymelaeaceae).

zygomorphic; calyx hypogynous, tubular, sometimes *petaloid*, often swollen below; lobes 4–5, *imbricate*; petals or staminodes 4–12, or absent, scale-like, inserted at the mouth or within the calyx-tube; stamens 2 to many, mostly the same number as the calyx-lobes and opposite to them or a second series alternate with them; anthers 2-locular, introrse, opening lengthwise; hypo-

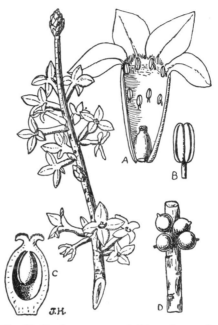

FIG. 85. Daphne mezereum *L.* (Thymelaeaceae). A, dissection of flower. B, anther. C, vertical section of ovary. D, fruits. (Orig.)

gynous *disk* annular, cupular, or of separate scales, or absent; ovary superior, 1–2-locular, entire; style in the 1-locular ovary often *excentric*; stigma more or less capitate: ovule *solitary* in each ovary or loculus, pendulous from near the apex, anatropous; fruit indehiscent; seed with copious to no endosperm, and straight embryo. B.H. **3**, 186; E.P. **3**, 6*a*, 216; Domke, *Bibliotheca Bot.* **27** (111), 1–151 (1934). Mainly S. Africa, Australia, and Mediterranean; rarer in the Tropics.—PIMELEA, DAPHNE, DIRCA, THYMELAEA, DAPHNOPSIS, WIKSTROEMIA, STELLERA, ARTHROSOLEN, PASSERINA, LACHNAEA, STRUTHIOLA, GNIDIA, LASIOSIPHON, PHALERIA, DRAPETES, &c.

USEFUL PRODUCTS: *Mezereon bark* (Daphne mezereum *L.*). Several beautiful sweet-scented garden plants.

86. NYCTAGINACEAE

Herbs, shrubs, or trees; leaves alternate or opposite, simple; stipules absent; flowers ☿ or ♂♀, usually cymose, sometimes surrounded by brightly *coloured bracts*, the latter occasionally *simulating a calyx*; calyx tubular, often *petaloid*, *valvate* or *plicate* in bud; petals absent; stamens 1 to many, hypogynous, free or connate at the base, *involute in bud*; anthers 2-locular, opening lengthwise; ovary superior, 1-locular; style slender; ovule solitary, erect and inverted; fruit indehiscent, sometimes enclosed in the persistent base of the calyx, often glandular; seeds with copious or scanty endosperm and straight or curved embryo. B.H. **3**, 1; E.P. **3**, 1*b*, 14. Mainly Tropical and Temperate America.—

FIG. 86. Abronia fragrans *Nutt*. (Nyctaginaceae). A, flower. B, stamens and ovary. C, ovary. D, fruit. (After *Bot. Mag.*)

MIRABILIS, OXYBAPHUS, NYCTAGINIA, BOERHAAVIA, BOUGAINVILLEA, ABRONIA, PISONIA, NEEA, &c.

USEFUL PRODUCTS: A few cultivated plants; *Marvel of Peru* (Mirabilis jalapa *L.*); *Bougainvillaea*, &c.

ORDER 22. PROTEALES

Trees or shrubs, rarely subherbaceous; flowers perigynous; calyx valvate, tubular, often coloured; stamens 4, opposite the calyx-lobes; ovary 1-locular; seeds without endosperm. Leaves alternate or rarely opposite, without stipules.

87. PROTEACEAE

Trees or shrubs, rarely subherbaceous; leaves alternate, rarely verticillate or opposite, simple or variously divided; *stipules absent*; flowers ♀ or ♂♀, sometimes dioecious, racemose to capitate, the latter often involucrate; *calyx corolla-like, coloured, tetramerous, valvate*, usually tubular in bud, variously *split when open*; stamens 4, *opposite* the calyx-lobes; filaments *adnate* to the lobes, rarely free; anthers free, 2-locular, opening lengthwise; ovary sessile or stipitate, with or without hypogynous scales or disk at the base, 1-locular; style simple; ovules 1 or more, pendulous or laterally attached; fruit a nut,

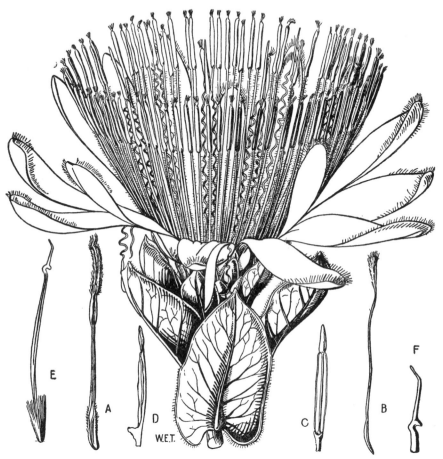

FIG. 87. Protea latifolia *R. Br.* (Proteaceae). A, larger perianth-segment. B, smaller perianth-segment. C, front view of anther. D, side view of same. E, ovary and style. F, stigma. (After *Bot. Mag.*)

drupe, follicle, or capsule; seeds often winged; endosperm 0. B.H. **3,** 165; E.P. **3,** 1, 119. Mostly S. Africa and Australia; a few in the Tropics and in Central and S. America.—LEUCADENDRON, PROTEA, LEUCOSPERMUM, FAUREA, SERRURIA, MIMETES, PETROPHILA, ISOPOGON, CONOSPERMUM, PERSOONIA, PANOPSIS, EUPLASSA, ROUPALA, HELICIA, GREVILLEA, HAKEA, STENOCARPUS, LOMATIA, EMBOTHRIUM, TELOPEA, BANKSIA, DRYANDRA, &c.

USEFUL PRODUCTS: *Terblanz wood* (Faurea macnaughtonii *Phillips*), Trop. and S. Afr.; *Silky Oak wood* (Grevillea robusta *A. Cunn.*), Austral.; *Silver Tree* (Leucadendron argenteum *R. Br.*), Cape of Good Hope. Many

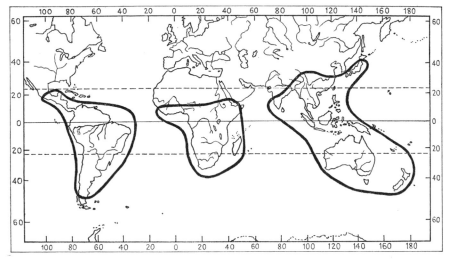

Range of the mainly austral family Proteaceae; no genus is common to Africa and to Indo-Malaya-Australasia.

beautiful ornamental trees and shrubs, including the Australian *Waratah* (Telopea speciosissima *R. Br.*), the S. African *Sugar Bush* (Protea mellifera *Thunb.*), and the *Fire Bush* (Embothrium coccineum *Forst.*), Chile.

ORDER 23. PITTOSPORALES

Trees, shrubs, or climbers; flowers hypogynous, mostly ♀, actinomorphic; sepals and petals imbricate or valvate; stamens the same as or double the number of the petals, free; anthers opening lengthwise or by pores; syncarpous with parietal to axile placentation; seeds with copious endosperm and minute embryo. Leaves alternate to verticillate, simple, exstipulate.

A. Sepals imbricate:
 B. Petals longer than the sepals, contorted or imbricate; stamens 5; anthers opening lengthwise or by pores:
  C. Trees, shrubs, or climbers; leaves not glandular *Pittosporaceae*
  CC. Herbs or undershrubs with linear, glandular-pilose leaves *Byblidaceae*
 BB. Petals shorter than the sepals, imbricate; stamens 10; anthers opening lengthwise *Stegnospermaceae*
AA. Sepals or calyx-lobes valvate:
 D. Leaves opposite; petals contorted; embryo much curved or circinate *Vivianiaceae*
 DD. Leaves alternate, opposite or verticillate; petals induplicate-valvate; embryo small or minute and straight *Tremandraceae*

88. PITTOSPORACEAE

Trees, shrubs, or climbers, sometimes spiny; leaves alternate or whorled, simple; *stipules absent*; flowers ♀, rarely ♂♀, actinomorphic, from solitary to corymbose; sepals 5, free or connate below, *imbricate*; petals 5, *imbricate*, with erect claws, the claws sometimes more or less *connivent*; stamens 5, alternate with the petals, hypogynous, free or somewhat connivent; anthers 2-locular, introrse, opening lengthwise or by *pores*; ovary superior, completely or incompletely 2–5-locular with *parietal* or *axile* placentas; style simple; ovules numerous; fruit a capsule or berry; seeds mostly immersed in a viscid pulp, rarely winged; embryo very minute with copious endosperm. B.H. **1**, 130; E.P. **3**, 2*a*, 106. Warmer regions of the Old World; absent from America.

USEFUL PRODUCTS: *Pittosporum* furnishes useful close-grained timber in W. Austral.; some ornamental plants.

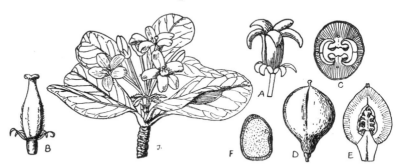

FIG. 88. Pittosporum viridiflorum *Sims* (Pittosporaceae); branch with flowers (P. phillyraeoides). A, flower. B, ovary. C, cross-section of same. D, fruit. E, section of same. F, vertical section of seed. (After Le Maout & Decne.)

A. Fruit a capsule; mainly trees or erect shrubs: **B.** Seeds not winged: **C.** Capsule more or less thick and leathery; seeds numerous; erect trees or shrubs—PITTOSPORUM (Afr., Asia, Australasia, Polynesia). **CC.** Capsule more or less membranous and compressed; seeds numerous; twining or procumbent undershrubs—MARIANTHUS (Austral.). **CCC.** Capsule thinly leathery, compressed; seeds 1–2; shrubs, usually spiny; ovary on a gynophore—BURSARIA (Austral.). **BB.** Seeds compressed and winged; inflorescence pedunculate, terminal, laxly corymbose; flowers large, yellow—HYMENOSPORUM (E. Austral.). **AA.** Fruit a berry (rarely at length dehiscent); mainly twiners, rarely spiny shrubs: **D.** Ovary 1-locular with parietal placentas: **E.** Erect spiny shrubs; anther-loculi not revolute; fruit globose—CITRIOBATUS (SW. Austral.). **EE.** Twiners; anther-loculi at length revolute; fruit oblong-ellipsoidal— PRONAYA (W. Austral.). **DD.** Ovary completely or rarely incompletely 2-locular: **F.** Anthers opening by longitudinal slits, straight; fruit ovoid or oblong; twiners: **G.** Anthers not connivent, shorter than the filaments— BILLARDIERA (Austral.). **GG.** Anthers connivent around the style, longer than the filaments—SOLLYA (W. Austral.). **FF.** Anthers opening by terminal pores, subdeclinate, longer than the filaments; branches flexuous or twining; flowers solitary or cymose; fruit oblong—CHEIRANTHERA (Austral.).

89. BYBLIDACEAE
(Roridulaceae)

Herbs or undershrubs with rather crowded linear *glandular-pilose* alternate leaves; stipules absent; flowers ⚥, actinomorphic, solitary or few in racemes:

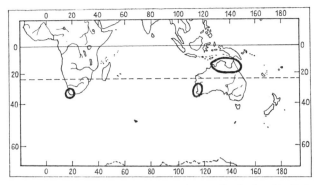

Byblidaceae, a small family with discontinuous distribution, Roridula in S. Africa, Byblis in Australia.

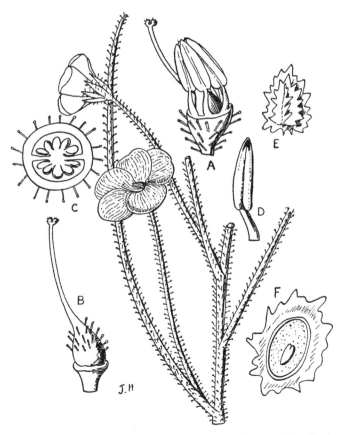

Fig. 89. Byblis gigantea *Lindl.* (Byblidaceae). A, flower with perianth removed. B, ovary. C, cross-section of same. D, stamen. E, seed. F, section of same. (After *Bot. Mag.*)

sepals 5, free, *imbricate*; petals 5, very shortly united at the base, *imbricate* or *contorted*; stamens 5, hypogynous or slightly united to the base of the petals; anthers 2-locular, erect or *inflexed* in bud, opening by *apical pores* or very short pore-like slits; ovary superior, 2–3-locular, with 1–2 ovules pendulous from the apex, or numerous and axile; style simple, with a *capitate* stigma; fruit a *loculicidal capsule*; seeds with endosperm and straight embryo. B.H. **1**, 664; E.P. **3**, 2, 272 (under *Droseraceae*). Australia, S. Africa.

A small group, raised to family rank by Domin, with whom I agree in placing it near *Pittosporaceae*. There is also a close general similarity with *Tremandraceae*. The supposed affinity with *Droseraceae* was based on superficial characters.

A. Ovary 3-locular; ovules 2–1, pendulous; shrublets; anthers opening by terminal pores; leaves short and crowded on short lateral branchlets—RORI-DULA (S. Afr.). **AA.** Ovary 2-locular; ovules numerous, axile; herbs; anthers opening by pore-like slits; leaves elongated—BYBLIS (Austral.).

90. STEGNOSPERMACEAE

Shrub; leaves alternate, obovate or elliptic, entire, pinnately nerved, fleshy, with translucent margins; *stipules absent*; flowers bisexual, in terminal

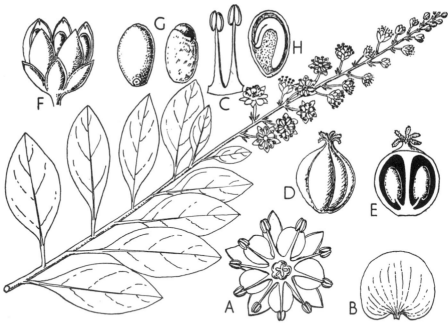

FIG. 90. Stegnosperma halimifolium *Benth.* (Stegnospermaceae). A, flower spread out. B, petal. C, two stamens. D, ovary and stigmas. E, vertical section of ovary. F, capsule. G, seeds back and front. H, vertical section of seed showing curved embryo.

racemes; pedicels bracteate and 2-bracteolate at the base; sepals 5, imbricate, *persistent in fruit*; petals 5, free, imbricate, shorter than the sepals; stamens 10; filaments *connate at the base*, subequal; anthers dorsifixed, cordate, introrsely dehiscent; ovary superior, sessile, ovoid-globose, 1-locular but with a *free central column*; stigmas 5–3, short, subulate, recurved, papillous inside, connate at the base; ovules as many as the stigmas, basal, erect, amphitropous; fruit a globose capsule, coriaceous, 1-locular, 5-valved to the base, 5–1-seeded, valves opposite the sepals; seeds erect, nearly covered by a *large fleshy aril*, obovoid; testa shining; embryo bent around the mealy endosperm; cotyledons oblong. California, Central America, West Indies —STEGNOSPERMA.

Formerly placed in the *Phytolaccaceae*, but probably more closely related to *Pittosporaceae* or even *Tamaricaceae*; striking features are the 1-locular ovary with a central column, basal ovules, 5-valved capsule, the seeds nearly covered by a large fleshy white aril, and embryo bent around the mealy endosperm.

91. VIVIANIACEAE

Shrublets or herbs woody at base, much branched and spreading; leaves *opposite*, entire, crenate to coarsely dentate, more or less white-tomentose below, connected by a *transverse line* but otherwise not stipulate; flowers in the upper axils, subfasciculate to cymose-paniculate, actinomorphic; calyx campanulate or tubular, 5–4-fid, lobes *valvate*; petals 5, rarely 4, hypogynous, free, *contorted*; glands the same number as the petals and alternate with them, entire or 2-partite; stamens 10, rarely 8, free, all fertile; ovary superior, 3–2-locular, not beaked; style central, divided into 3–2 stigmas sometimes nearly to the base; ovules 2 in each loculus, superposed on the inner angle; capsule 3–2-lobed, loculicidally 3–2-valved, valves persistent; seeds with fleshy endosperm and linear *much curved or circinate embryo*. B.H. **1**, 275 (in *Geraniaceae*). Chile and S. Brazil —VIVIANIA.

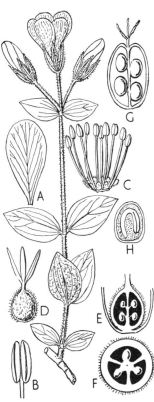

FIG. 91. Viviania rosea *Hook.* (Vivianiaceae). A, petal. B, anther. C, stamens and glands. D, ovary and stigmas. E, vertical section of ovary. F, cross-section of ovary. G, vertical section of fruit. H, vertical section of seed.

92 TREMANDRACEAE

Slender *heath-like* shrublets, sometimes with winged stems and *reduced* foliage; indumentum often *glandular* or rarely stellate; leaves alternate, opposite or verticillate, simple; flowers axillary, solitary, ♀, actinomorphic; sepals 4–5 (rarely 3) free, *valvate*; petals the same number, hypogynous, *induplicate-valvate*; stamens double the number of petals, hypogynous, free; anthers 2–4-locular, opening by a single *apical pore*; torus sometimes enlarged and glandular-lobulate between the petals and stamens; ovary sessile, 2-locular; style slender; ovules 1–2 (rarely 3), pendulous, anatropous; fruit a *compressed capsule*, 2-locular, dehiscing by the margins; seed with a conspicuous appendage to the chalaza, glabrous or pilose; endosperm copious, with rather small or minute straight embryo. B.H. **1**, 133; E.P. **3**, 4, 320. Extratropical Australia. Some graceful greenhouse plants.

A. Leaves alternate or whorled, glabrous or glandular-hairy; anthers continuous with the filament: **B.** Anthers 4-locular with the loculi in the same plane; seeds without an appendage—PLATYTHECA. **BB.** Anthers 2-locular, or

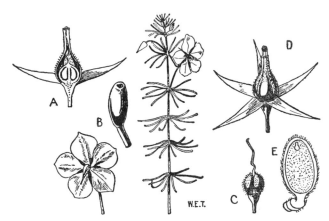

FIG. 92. Platytheca verticillata *Baill.* (Tremandraceae). A, vertical section of flower with corolla removed. B, stamen. C, pistil. D, pistil and calyx. E, section of seed. (After Baill.)

if with 4 loculi 2 in front of the others; seeds with an appendage to the chalaza —TETRATHECA. **AA.** Leaves opposite, clothed with stellate hairs; anthers articulated with the filament; seeds appendaged—TREMANDRA.

ORDER 24. CAPPARIDALES

Woody to herbaceous; flowers hypogynous or subperigynous, often somewhat zygomorphic; petals present or absent; stamens numerous to few, usually free; syncarpous with mostly parietal placentation; ovary often stipitate, often of two carpels; seeds without or with very little endosperm; embryo curved or variously folded. Leaves mostly alternate, simple or digitate, rarely stipulate.—Mainly Tropics.

A. Leaves simple or digitately 3–7-foliolate; ovary usually stipitate, mostly 1-locular; embryo more or less curved; anthers 2-locular   *Capparidaceae*
AA. Leaves 2–3-times pinnate; ovary stipitate, 1-locular; embryo straight; style slender, terminal; anthers 1-locular   *Moringaceae*
AAA. Leaves trifoliolate; ovary subsessile, 6–8-locular; embryo curved; anthers 2-locular   *Tovariaceae*

93. CAPPARIDACEAE

Trees, shrubs, or more rarely herbs, sometimes scandent; leaves alternate or rarely opposite, simple or digitately 3–7-foliolate; stipules when present minute or spiny; flowers mostly bisexual, actinomorphic or rarely zygomorphic, hypogynous, axillary or terminal, variously arranged; sepals free or partially united, imbricate or valvate, usually 4; petals 4 to many or absent; torus elongated or short, rarely with an appendix; stamens few to many, sometimes some of them without anthers; filaments sometimes partially adnate to the torus; anthers 2-locular, longitudinally dehiscent; ovary sessile or

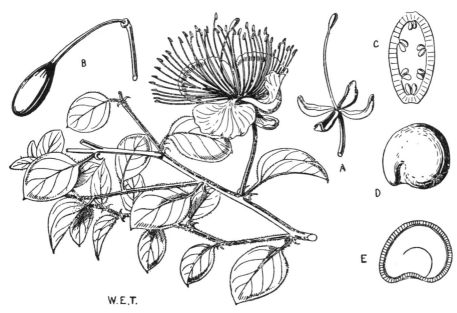

W.E.T.

FIG. 93. Capparis spinosa *L.* (Capparidaceae). A, calyx with stipitate ovary. B, fruit. C, ovary in section. D, seed. E, seed in section. (Orig.)

more usually supported on a *long or short gynophore*, 1-locular with parietal placentas or divided into 2 or more loculi by spurious dissepiments; ovules few to many; fruit a capsule or a berry, sometimes the latter elongate or torulose; seeds usually reniform or angular; *endosperm none or scanty*; embryo *arcuate* or *incurved*. B.H. **1**, 103; E.P. **3**, 2, 209. Tropics mainly.—CAPPARIS, CLEOME, POLANISIA, GYNANDROPSIS, MAERUA, CADABA, BOSCIA, OCEANO-PAPAVER, &c.

USEFUL PRODUCTS: *Capers* (flower buds of Capparis spinosa *L.*), Mediterr. Reg.

94. MORINGACEAE

Trees with gummy bark; leaves deciduous, alternate, 2–3 times *pinnate*, pinnae opposite; stipules 0, or represented by stipitate glands at the base of the petioles and pinnae; flowers in axillary panicles, white or red, ☿, zygomorphic; calyx-tube short, with 5 unequal spreading or reflexed imbricate lobes, the fifth posticous; petals 5, the upper two smaller, the lateral ones ascending, the anticous larger; disk lining the calyx-tube, with a short free margin;

stamens inserted on the margin of the disk, declinate, 5 perfect alternating with the same number antherless or reduced to setae; filaments free; anthers dorsifixed, 1-locular, opening lengthwise by a slit; ovary stipitate, terete, villous, curved, 1-locular, with 3 *parietal placentas*; style terminal, slender,

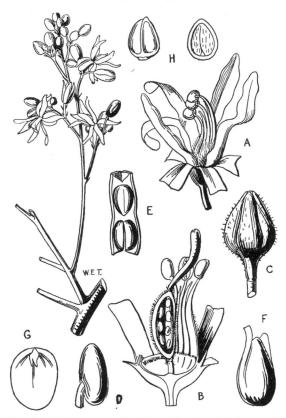

Fig. 94. Moringa peregrina (*Forrsk.*) *Fiori* (Moringaceae).
A, flower. B, flower in vertical section. C, flower-bud. D,
anther. E, part of fruit in longitudinal section showing seeds.
F, seed. G, embryo cut vertically. H, seed entire and cut
vertically. (After Le Maout & Decne.)

tubular, truncate at the apex; ovules numerous, in 2 series on each placenta, pendulous, anatropous; capsule long, beaked, 3–6-angled, torulose, 1-locular, 3-valved; seeds 3-winged or not, the chalaza and wings hardened or membranous; embryo without endosperm, straight. B.H. **1**, 429; E.P. **3**, 2, 242. N. Africa to India; also widely cultivated as an ornamental tree.—MORINGA. USEFUL PRODUCTS: *Horse Radish Tree* (Moringa pterygosperma *Gaertn.*).

95. TOVARIACEAE

Annual herbs with a strong odour; leaves alternate, *trifoliolate*, membranous; stipules 0; flowers ☿, hypogynous, nodding in terminal many-flowered racemes, 8-*merous*; sepals 8, lanceolate-subulate, imbricate, deciduous; petals 8, *sessile*;

stamens 8, free; filaments pilose; anthers 2-locular, opening lengthwise; ovary subglobose, 6–8-locular, slightly stipitate; septa membranous; ovules numerous on spongy *axile placentas*; stigma sessile, 8-rayed; fruit a small globose berry; pericarp membranous; seeds very numérous, small, shining;

FIG. 95. Tovaria pendula *R. & P.* (Tovariaceae). A, flower. B, stamen. C, flower with petals and stamens removed. D, fruit. E, ovary in cross-section. F, seed in section. (After Hk. *Ic. Pl.*)

embryo curved, enclosed in a *thick layer of endosperm*. B.H. **1**, 110 (under *Capparidaceae*); E.P. **3**, 2, 207. Tropical America, West Indies.—Tovaria.

ORDER 25. TAMARICALES

Trees or shrubs; flowers hypogynous, usually ⚥, actinomorphic; sepals imbricate or valvate; petals free to connate; stamens mostly definite; syncarpous with parietal or basal placentation; seeds with or with outendosperm, often hairy. Leaves alternate or opposite, often very small; no stipules.

A. Sepals connate, induplicate-valvate; petals free, with a claw-like appendage on the inside; stamens usually 6, free or shortly connate at the base; flowers solitary or cymose   *Frankeniaceae*

AA. Sepals free, imbricate; seeds hairy or winged:
B. Petals free; leaves small and scale-like   *Tamaricaceae*
BB. Petals united into a tube; leaves fleshy   *Fouquieriaceae*

96. FRANKENIACEAE

Herbs or shrublets; leaves *opposite*, exstipulate, often small and ericoid; flowers actinomorphic, usually bisexual, solitary or cymose; sepals 4–6, persistent, connate, induplicate-valvate; petals as many as the sepals, clawed, with a *scale-like appendage* on the inside, imbricate; stamens usually 6, hypo-

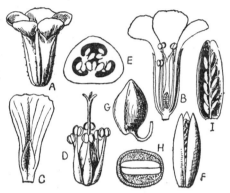

FIG. 96. Frankenia pulverulenta *L.* (Frankenia-
ceae). A, flower. B, section of same. C, petal.
D, stamens and ovary. E, cross-section of ovary.
F, fruit. G, seed. H, section of same. (After Le
Maout & Decne.)

gynous, free or shortly connate at the base; anthers 2-locular, didymous, dehiscing longitudinally; ovary superior, sessile, 1-locular, with 2–4 *parietal* placentas; ovules numerous; style simple, filiform; capsule enclosed in the persistent calyx, opening by valves; seeds with endosperm; embryo straight, axile. B.H. **1**, 140; E.P. **3**, 6, 283. Mostly maritime shores.

A. Flowers bisexual; usually all the placentas of the fruits bearing seeds:
B. Stamens 24–20; leaves ovate; flowers red—HYPERICOPSIS (S. Persia). **BB.**
Stamens 6–3: **C.** Petals free from one another: **D.** Low undershrubs; stigmas
3–2; fruit 3-angled—FRANKENIA (Warm dry regions). **DD.** Shrub 2–3 m;
stigmas 2—BEATSONIA (St. Helena). **CC.** Petals united—ANTHOBRYUM (W.
S. Amer.). **AA.** Flowers polygamous-monoecious; only 1 of the placentas of
the fruits bearing seeds—NIEDERLEINIA (Patagonia).

97. TAMARICACEAE

Shrubs or trees with slender branches, and small *scale-like* alternate leaves;
stipules absent; flowers very small, actinomorphic, usually bisexual, in slender
catkin-like spikes or racemes; sepals 4–6, imbricate, free; petals as many,
free; disk present; stamens hypogynous, 5–10, free coor nnate at the base;

anthers 2-locular, opening by longitudinal slits; ovary superior, 1-locular, with *parietal* or *basal* placentas; styles 3–4, free or united at the base; ovules numerous, ascending; fruit a capsule; seeds with or without endosperm, with a tuft of *hairs* at the apex or all around; embryo straight. B.H. **1**, 159; E.P. **3**, 6, 289. Mainly N. Hemisphere.

A. Seeds long-pilose all over, with endosperm; flowers solitary, axillary, or terminal: **B.** Stamens numerous; styles 5—REAUMURIA (Mediterr. Reg., Cent. Asia). **BB.** Stamens 10–5; styles 4–2—HOLOLACHNE (Cent. Asia). **AA.** Seeds

FIG. 97. Tamarix orientalis *Forssk*. (Tamaricaceae). A, ovary and stamens. B, flower. C, fruit. D, seed. E, portion of inflorescence. (Orig.)

comose at the apex, without endosperm; flowers racemose or spicate: **C.** Stamens free or slightly united at the base—TAMARIX (S. Eur. to India). **CC.** Stamens more or less monadelphous—MYRICARIA (Eur., east to China).

98. FOUQUIERIACEAE

Spiny trees or shrubs with soft wood; leaves fasciculate or solitary, small, fleshy; flowers showy, paniculate, ♂, actinomorphic; sepals 5, free, *much imbricate*; petals 5, hypogynous, *connate into a tube*, imbricate; stamens 10 or more, 1–2-seriate, *hypogynous*, the filaments free or slightly coherent; disk annular, small; ovary 1-locular, with 3 *parietal* septiform placentas reaching to the top of the ovary, each about 6-ovulate; fruit a capsule; seeds oblong, compressed, with broad wings, the wings finally breaking up into long filaments; endosperm thin; embryo straight; cotyledons flat, rather thick. B.H. **1**, 161 (under *Tamaricaceae*); E.P. **3**, 6, 298; see Nash, 'Revision of Fouquieriaceae', *Bull. Torr. Club*, **30**, 449 (1903). Mexico and nearby U.S.A.

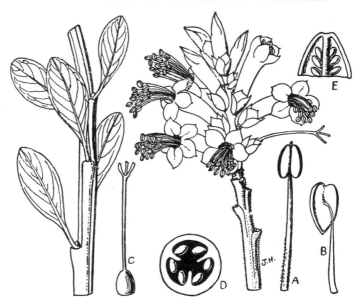

FIG. 98. Fouquieria formosa *H. B. & K.* (Fouquieriaceae). A, B, stamens. C, ovary. D, cross-section of same. E, vertical section of same. (Orig.)

A. Style branched at the apex, exserted, slender; shrubs or trees with branched stem; corolla red—FOUQUIERIA. **AA.** Style entire, stout, short, included, 3-angled; tree with a columnar normally undivided stem; corolla yellow—IDRIA.

ORDER 26. VIOLALES

Herbaceous to woody; flowers hypogynous to perigynous, mostly zygomorphic; petals present, sometimes divided; stamens several to few, mostly free; ovary syncarpous with parietal placentation; seeds with or without endosperm; embryo straight or curved. Leaves alternate, rarely opposite, stipulate.—Tropics and Temperate Regions.

99. VIOLACEAE

Herbaceous perennials or shrubs, rarely annuals; leaves alternate, rarely opposite, simple; *stipules leafy or small*; flowers solitary to paniculate, actinomorphic or zygomorphic, ⚥, rarely polygamous, sometimes cleistogamous; sepals 5, persistent, imbricate; petals 5, mostly unequal, the lowermost often *larger and spurred*, imbricate or contorted; stamens 5, mostly hypogynous; anthers erect, more or less *connivent in a ring around the ovary*, introrse, opening lengthwise, the abaxial stamen often *spurred at the base*; ovary free, sessile, 1-locular with 3–5 *parietal placentas*; style simple, rarely split; ovules numerous, or 1–2 on each placenta, anatropous; fruit an elastic capsule or baccate; seeds sometimes winged or tomentose; endosperm fleshy; embryo straight.

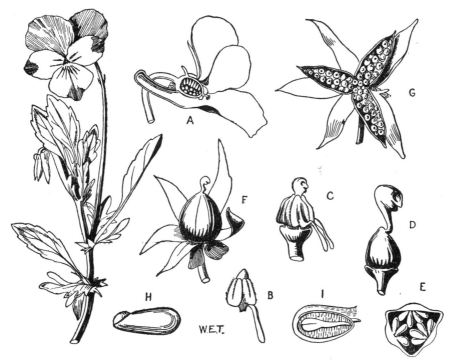

FIG. 99. Viola tricolor *L.* (Violaceae). A, flower cut lengthwise. B, stamen with spurred anther. C, ovary with 2 stamens. D, ovary with style and stigma. E, ovary in cross-section. F, fruit. G, fruit-capsule splitting into 3 valves. H, seed. I, seed in section. (After Le Maout & Decne.)

B.H. **1**, 114, partly; E.P. **3**, 6, 322. Temperate and Tropics.—VIOLA, HYBANTHUS, RINOREA (*Alsodeia*), &c.

USEFUL PRODUCTS: *False Ipecacuanha* (Hybanthus ipecacuanha *Baill.*). Many beautiful garden plants used for bedding, &c.

ORDER 27. POLYGALALES

Woody to herbaceous; flowers hypogynous to subperigynous, zygomorphic; petals present, sometimes some partially united; stamens definite, free or monadelphous, sometimes some infertile; syncarpous with axile or apical placentation; seeds with or without endosperm, pilose or with cottony hairs or winged; embryo straight. Leaves alternate, rarely opposite; stipules mostly absent.—Temperate and Tropical Regions.

A. Stipules absent; anthers mostly opening by apical pores; fertile stamens 8–4; seeds often pilose, with a conspicuous strophiole; lower sepal not spurred:

  B. Ovary 2- or more locular; fruits not bristly   *Polygalaceae*

  BB. Ovary 1-locular; fruits bristly   *Krameriaceae*

AA. Stipules usually present, though often small and caducous; anthers opening by slits; lower sepal more or less spurred:

C. Fertile stamens more than 2, unilateral; embryo transverse to the length
of the seed   *Trigoniaceae*
CC. Fertile stamens 2–1; embryo not transverse   *Vochysiaceae*

100. POLYGALACEAE

Herbs, shrubs, climbers, or rarely small trees; leaves alternate, rarely opposite, simple; stipules 0; flowers ☿, zygomorphic; pedicels often articulated;

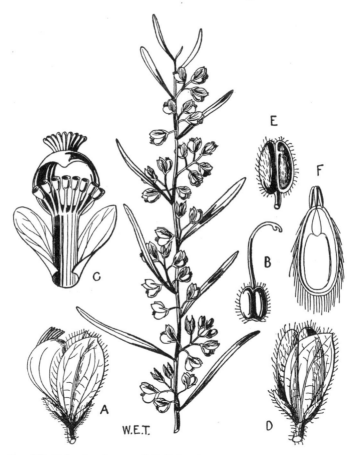

Fig. 100. Polygala eriocarpa *DC.* (Polygalaceae). A, flower. B, ovary with
style. C, part of flower showing 2 sepals, crested keel petal and staminal
tube. D, fruit with membranous inner sepals. E, fruit capsule showing one
half cut vertically. F, seed cut lengthwise. (After Deless.)

sepals 5, free, imbricate, the two inner larger *often petaloid*, wing-like; petals
3–5, hypogynous, declinate, outer 2 free or united with the lowermost; upper
2 free, or minute and scale-like or 0; stamens 8, rarely 5 or 4, *monadelphous
beyond the middle* or rarely free, the sheath split above, often adnate to the
petals; anthers erect, 1–2-locular, opening by an *apical pore*, rarely 2-valved

or opening nearly to the base; torus small or rarely expanded into an annular disk within the stamens; ovary free, 2-locular or rarely 1-locular or 3–5-locular; style simple; ovules solitary in each loculus, rarely more, pendulous; fruit a capsule or drupaceous; *seeds often pilose*, with a *conspicuous strophiole*; endosperm mostly present; embryo straight. B.H. **1**, 134; E.P. **3**, 4, 323, Temperate and Tropics.—POLYGALA, MURALTIA, SECURIDACA, MONNINA, COMESPERMA, CARPOLOBIA, DICLIDANTHERA.

USEFUL PRODUCTS: *Senega* or *Snake Root* (Polygala senega *L.*), U.S.A.

101. KRAMERIACEAE

Shrubs or perennial herbs with a woody rootstock, mostly pubescent or silky all over; leaves alternate, simple and entire, very rarely 3-foliolate; *stipules*

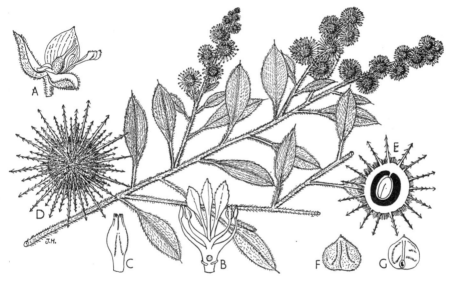

FIG. 101. Krameria tomentosa *A. St. Hil.* (Krameriaceae). A, open flower. B, 3 upper petals with stamens. C, anther. D, fruit. E, section of fruit. F, and G, seeds. Taxonomic botanists have sometimes been deceived by superficial resemblances. *Krameria* is an example, having been transferred from the *Polygalaceae* to the *Leguminosae* in the Englerian system; anatomical evidence supports affinity with *Polygalaceae*, in which family it was included as an anomalous member in Bentham and Hooker's *Genera Plantarum*.

absent; flowers axillary or in terminal racemes; pedicels with 2 opposite bracteoles about the middle, sometimes with stipitate glands; pedicels remaining as pegs; sepals 5 or 4, unequal, free, imbricate; petals 5, the 3 upper long-clawed, free or partly united, *the 2 others usually much smaller and heteromorphous*, sometimes broad, thick and sessile; stamens 4 or 3, free or the filaments partly adnate to the partly united claws of the upper petals; anthers 2-locular, opening by *terminal pores*; ovary superior, 1-*locular*; ovules 2, collateral, *pendulous* from the top of the ovary, anatropous; style cylindrical, stigma discoid; fruit globose, *indehiscent*, very bristly, bristles usually with *retrorse barbs*, rarely smooth, 1-seeded; seed with thick cotyledons and *no endosperm*; embryo straight. N. L. Britton, *N. Amer. Fl.* **23**, 195 (1930). N. to Temperate S. America, West Indies.—KRAMERIA.

USEFUL PRODUCTS: *Rhatany Root* (Krameria triandra *R. & P.*, &c.), S. Amer.

102. TRIGONIACEAE

Trees or scandent shrubs; leaves alternate or opposite, simple; stipules small and caducous; flowers ⚥, racemose or paniculate; sepals 5, imbricate, free or

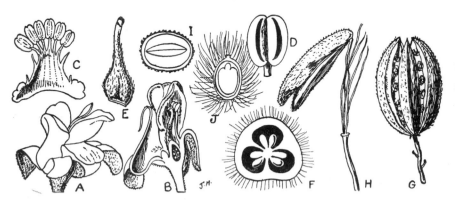

FIG. 102. Trigonia pubescens *Camb.* (Trigoniaceae). A, flower. B, flower cut vertically. C, staminal sheath. D, anther. E, ovary with style. F, ovary in cross-section. G, fruit-capsule opening loculicidally. H, old fruit. I, J, seed. (After Martius.)

connate at the base, unequal; petals 5 or 3, contorted, hypogynous or sub-perigynous, unequal, the posterior one often the largest and *gibbous at the base*; stamens 3–12, sometimes *some infertile, unilateral*, opposite the anterior petal; *filaments connate at the base*; anthers 2-locular, opening lengthwise; gland or a crenate crest often present opposite the posterior petal; ovary superior, 3-locular, woolly; style 1, truncate; ovules 2 to many in each loculus, axile; fruit a capsule, septicidally 3-valved; seeds compressed, enveloped in cottony hairs; endosperm absent; embryo straight, *transverse to the length of the seed.* B.H. **1**, 977 (under *Vochysiaceae*); E.P. **3**, 4, 309; E.P.N. 209 (1897). Tropical S. America and Malaya.

A. Petals 5, very dissimilar, one spurred; stamens up to 12, mostly only 6 fertile: **B.** Ovary with many ovules; leaves opposite; fruits not winged—TRIGONIA (Trop. Amer.). **BB.** Ovary with a single pendulous ovule; leaves alternate; fruits 3-winged—TRIGONIASTRUM (Malay Penin.). **AA.** Petals 3, a little unequal; stamens 3–5; ovary-loculi with 2 ovules; leaves alternate; fruits not winged—EUPHRONIA (*Lightia*) (Trop. Amer.).

103. VOCHYSIACEAE

Large trees full of resinous juice, shrubs, or climbers; leaves opposite or verti-cillate, rarely alternate, simple; stipules small or absent, or reduced to glands;

flowers ⚥, zygomorphic, racemose or paniculate; sepals 5, imbricate, the posticous often the largest and gibbous or spurred at the base; petals 1–5, contorted; stamens hypogynous or perigynous, *only* 1 *fertile*; *filaments free*;

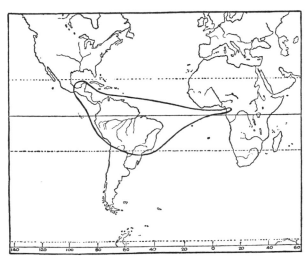

Range of Vochysiaceae. Entirely American except Erismadelphus in primeval forest in the Cameroons and S. Nigeria.

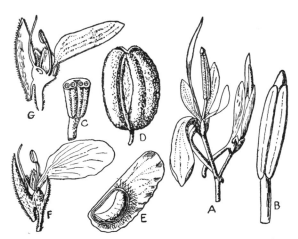

Fig. 103. A-D, Vochysia guianensis. F-G, Callisthene minor *Aubl.* (Vochysiaceae).

anthers 2-locular, opening lengthwise; ovary superior or rarely adnate to the calyx, often oblique, 1–3-locular; style 1; ovules 2–many in each loculus, rarely 1, axile; fruit capsular or samaroid, 3-valved; seeds one or more, often winged, sometimes pilose; endosperm absent or rarely present; embryo straight. B.H. **1,** 975; E.P. **3,** 4, 312. Tropical America, one genus in W. Tropical Africa.

A. Ovary superior, 3-locular; fruit a 3-locular capsule; seeds winged;

indumentum of simple hairs: **B.** Petals 5 or 3 (rarely 1 or absent), imbricate; ovary-loculi 2-ovuled: **C.** Petals 5, subequal; style very clavate with a unilateral stigma—SALVERTIA. **CC.** Petals 3–0, unequal; style with terminal stigma— VOCHYSIA. **BB.** Petal 1, folded in bud; ovary many-ovuled: **D.** Axis of capsule thick, persistent—CALLISTHENE. **DD.** Axis of capsule absent or imperfect— QUALEA. **AA.** Ovary inferior, 1-locular; fruit indehiscent, winged by the enlarged sepals: **E.** Ovules 2; indumentum stellate; petal 1; style filiform— ERISMA. **EE.** Ovule 1; indumentum not stellate; petals 5; style very short, thick—ERISMADELPHUS (W. Trop. Afr.).

ORDER 28. LOASALES

Woody or herbaceous; stipules absent; flowers hypogynous to epigynous, actinomorphic; petals present, contorted or valvate; stamens numerous to few, sometimes in bundles; syncarpous with parietal placentation; seeds with copious endosperm, often arillate; embryo straight. Leaves alternate, simple to much divided, exstipulate.—Mostly Tropical and Temperate America.

A. Ovary superior; petals contorted in bud; filaments free; styles 3; seeds
    arillate *Turneraceae*
AA. Ovary inferior or nearly completely so; petals induplicate-valvate;
    filaments free or connate into bundles opposite the petals; style 1; seeds
    not arillate *Loasaceae*

104. TURNERACEAE

Shrubs or herbs; leaves entire or lobed, alternate; stipules 0; flowers ☿, actinomorphic, red or yellow; *calyx tubular*, 5-toothed, teeth imbricate; petals 5, inserted on the calyx-tube, free, clawed, contorted in bud; stamens 5, inserted at the base of the calyx-tube; filaments free; anthers 2-locular, opening lengthwise; ovary superior, 1-locular, with 3 *parietal* placentas; styles 3, terminal, slender; stigmas fringed; ovules numerous; fruit a capsule opening *loculicidally* into 3 valves with the placenta in the middle of each; seeds *arillate*, pitted; endosperm horny or fleshy; embryo straight, large. B.H. **1**, 806; E.P. **3**, 6a, 57. Mainly Tropical America.

    A. Flowers pendulous, 1–3 in the leaf-axils; peduncle with a pair of large leafy bracts about the middle; leaves linear to oblanceolate, crenate; aril of seeds with long thread-like hairs—MATHURINA (Rodriguez Is.). **AA.** Flowers erect or suberect, rarely nodding; aril of seeds not long-pilose, at most lacerate: **B.** Corona absent from within the calyx: **C.** Sepals united only half way; petals and stamens inserted at the base of the tube—HYALOCALYX (Madag.). **CC.** Sepals more or less united into a tube; petals inserted towards the top of the tube: **D.** Flowers solitary; shrubs: **E.** Styles flabellately divided at the apex, multipartite, multilobulate, or very obscurely trilobed; leaves never with secretory glands; peduncle sometimes adnate to the petiole— TURNERA (Tropics). **EE.** Styles slightly thickened and concave at the apex, with subentire margins; leaves with the lower surface either covered with

resin secreting glands, or less manifestly glandular and with stellate hairs—
LOWEIA (Trop. Afr.). **DD.** Flowers racemose; annual herbs: **F.** Fruits short;
petals inserted at the throat of the calyx-tube—STREPTOPETALUM (Trop. Afr.).
FF. Fruits elongated, moniliform; petals inserted in the calyx-tube—WORMS-
KIOLDIA (Trop. Afr.). **BB.** Corona present, membranous, inserted below the
throat of the calyx or at the base of the sepals; peduncles free from the petiole:

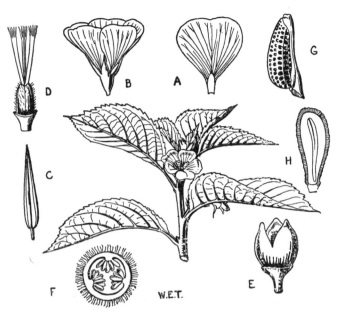

FIG. 104. Turnera salicifolia *Camb.* (Turneraceae). A, petal with scale.
B, flower. C, stamen. D, ovary with styles. E, capsule bursting from
above downwards. F, ovary in cross-section. G, seed with aril. H, seed
in longitudinal section. (After Le Maout & Decne.)

G. Indumentum of the leaves simple; sepals free; leaves minutely stipulate—
ERBLICHIA (S. Afr., Madag., Cent. Amer.). **GG.** Indumentum of the leaves
stellate; sepals united in the lower part; leaves not stipulate—PIRIQUETA
(Tropics).

105. LOASACEAE

Herbs or rarely woody, mostly *clothed with rough bristly hairs*; leaves alternate or opposite, entire or variously divided; stipules absent; flowers ☿, solitary to cymose or capitate, often leaf-opposed, actinomorphic; calyx-tube
adnate to the ovary, often ribbed, the ribs sometimes spirally twisted; lobes
4–5, contorted or imbricate, persistent; petals 4–5, inserted on the calyx,
sessile or clawed, *induplicate-valvate*; sometimes petaloid scales between the
petals; stamens numerous, rarely few; filaments free or collected into bundles
opposite the petals; staminodes present or absent; *ovary inferior* or nearly
completely so, 1–3-locular; style 1; ovules solitary or many, parietal or from

the top of the ovary; capsule often ribbed; seeds often minute, with or without endosperm; embryo straight, linear. B.H. **1,** 801; E.P. **3,** 6*a*, 100; see Urban, *Monographia Loasacearum* (1898). Tropical and Temperate America; Subtropical SW. Africa, Somaliland, and Arabia.

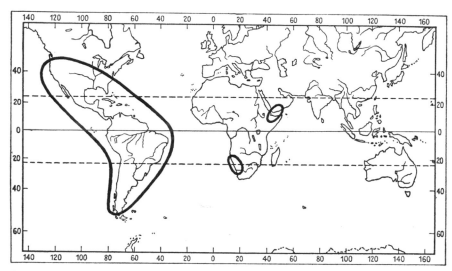

Loasaceae are confined to America except one genus, Kissenia, in Southwestern Africa, Somaliland, and Southern Arabia.

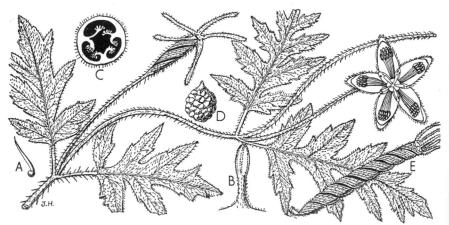

FIG. 105. Cajophora lateritia (Loasaceae). A, hair from stem. B, style. C, transverse section of ovary. D, seed. E, fruit.

All genera American except KISSENIA

A. Stamens 10 or more; endosperm usually present: **B.** Stamens not collected into fertile and sterile groups, the outermost often staminodal and sometimes petaloid; nectariferous scales absent; petals imbricate, often more or less connate: **C.** Ovary semi-inferior; inflorescence a terminal cyme; petals connate at the base; stamens 10, all fertile, unequal; placentas 5; herb with tuberous rootstock—SCHISMOCARPUS. **CC.** Ovary quite inferior: **D.** Ovules 1–2-seriate on each placenta; placentas if 5 then opposite the sepals; petals free or connate at the base; stamens all fertile or the outermost staminodial and often petaloid; trees, shrubs, or herbs—MENTZELIA. **DD.** Ovules more than 2-seriate on each placenta; placentas 5, alternating with the sepals (rarely 4); stamens all fertile; annual or biennial herbs: **E.** Petals connate only at the base; anthers 2-locular—EUCNIDE. **EE.** Petals connate into a tube; anthers 1-locular—SYMPETALEIA. **BB.** Stamens collected into fertile and sterile groups, the fertile opposite the petals, the sterile opposite the sepals and usually modified into nectariferous scales; petals usually valvate, free: **F.** Staminodes not united into nectariferous scales; flowers 4-merous; leaves opposite: **G.** Capsule not twisted; petals imbricate—KLAPROTHIA. **GG.** Capsule twisted; petals valvate or almost so—SCLEROTHRIX. **FF.** Staminodes united into nectariferous scales; flowers 5–6–7-merous: **H.** Ovary 1-locular; ovules numerous, parietal; fruit dehiscent, not woody or winged; endosperm present: **J.** Capsule not twisted, dehiscing at the apex within the sepals: **K.** Capsule claviform or turbinate or rarely almost globose, dehiscing only at the apex; petals usually valvate—LOASA. **KK.** Capsule linear or narrowly cylindrical, dehiscing at the apex and also along the commissures from the base upwards; petals imbricate; leaves opposite—SCYPHANTHUS. **JJ.** Capsule twisted (rarely not so), remaining closed at the apex but dehiscing along the commisures; leaves opposite: **L.** Stems terete; flowers in terminal (or rarely axillary) cymes, rarely solitary and axillary; capsules with a thin pericarp; placentas 2–3-furcate—CAJOPHORA. **LL.** Stems tetragonous; flowers solitary, axillary; capsule with a thick fleshy pericarp, the pericarp at length chartaceous; placentas undivided—BLUMBACHIA. **HH.** Ovary finally 2-locular; ovules 3, subapical; fruit indehiscent, woody, winged with the accrescent sepals; endosperm absent; leaves alternate; sole African genus—KISSENIA. **AA.** Stamens 5, alternating with the petals; endosperm absent; leaves alternate; sepals valvate; fruit indehiscent: **M.** Petals persistent; stamens all fertile; inflorescence cymose or capitate: **N.** Connective unappendaged; inflorescence not capitate; filaments filiform; climbers: **O.** Petals entire; annual herbs—GRONOVIA. **OO.** Petals divided; woody—FUERTESIA. **NN.** Connective with a long appendage; inflorescence capitate; filaments very short; erect herb—CEVALLIA. **MM.** Petals deciduous; stamens all or only 2 fertile; small shrubs or shrublets; inflorescence racemose, subcapitate, or subspicate—PETALONYX.

ORDER 29. PASSIFLORALES

More or less as in *Bixales* (p. 204); seeds with pitted testa; corona often present; fruits often stipitate; habit often more herbaceous and frequently climbing by tendrils; stipules present or absent.

A. Stipules absent; calyx-tube long, lobes valvate; petals free, valvate
Malesherbiaceae

AA. Stipules present, usually small and deciduous; calyx-lobes or free sepals imbricate; petals free or shortly united *Passifloraceae*
AAA. Stipules absent; sepals free; petals united into a tube *Achariaceae*

106. MALESHERBIACEAE

Undershrubs or herbs; leaves alternate, simple; stipules absent; flowers ☿, actinomorphic; *calyx-tube long*, straight or curved; lobes 5, *valvate*; petals 5,

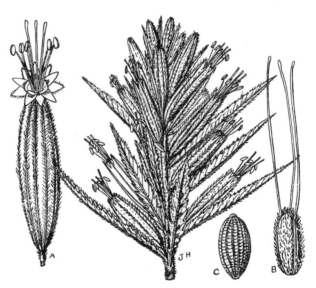

FIG. 106. Malesherbia thyrsiflora *Ruiz & Pav.* (Malesherbiaceae). A, flower. B, ovary. C, seed. (Orig.)

valvate; corona membranous, denticulate; stamens 5, inserted on the villous lobed *gynophore*; anthers 2-locular, opening lengthwise; ovary *stipitate*, 1-locular, with 3–4 *parietal* placentas; styles 3–4, *separated at the base*, filiform; ovules numerous; fruit a capsule enclosed by the persistent calyx, stipitate; seeds pitted, with fleshy endosperm and straight medium-sized embryo with orbicular cotyledons. B.H. **1**, 809 (under *Passifloraceae*); E.P. **3**, 6a, 65. Western S. America.

    A. Calyx tubular; flowers in bracteate racemes; petals smaller than the calyx-lobes—MALESHERBIA. **AA.** Calyx turbinate or campanulate; flowers paniculate or fasciculate; petals larger than the calyx-lobes—GYNOPLEURA.

107. PASSIFLORACEAE

Erect trees and shrubs or herbaceous climbers with tendrils; leaves alternate, entire or lobed, often with *glands on the petiole*; stipules usually small and deciduous; flowers ☿ or ♂♀; sepals 5, imbricate, persistent, free or partially united; petals 5, rarely absent, free or shortly united, imbricate; *corona* of one or more rows of thread-like filaments or scales or annular; stamens 5 or more, hypogynous to perigynous, shortly united or in bundles, sometimes springing from the gynophore; anthers 2-locular, opening lengthwise; ovary superior, sometimes on a *gynophore*, 1-locular, with 3 or rarely 4–5 *parietal* rarely apical *placentas*; ovules usually numerous; styles free or united, stigmas often capitate; fruit a capsule or berry, indehiscent or loculicidally 3-valved; seeds with pitted testa surrounded by a pulpy aril; endosperm fleshy; embryo large, straight. B.H. **1**, 807; E.P. **3**, 6*a*, 69. Tropics and Subtropics.—PASSI-

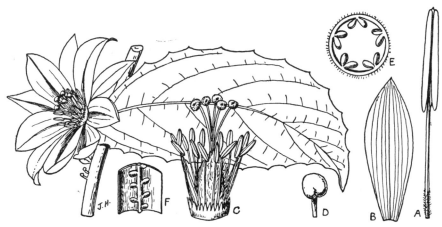

FIG. 107. Smeathmannia pubescens *Soland.* ex *R. Br.* (Passifloraceae). A, stamen. B, sepal. C, stamens and ovary. D, stigma. E, cross-section of ovary. F, placenta with ovules. (Orig.)

FLORA, TACSONIA, TRYPHOSTEMMA, PAROPSIA, SMEATHMANNIA, SOYAUXIA,[1] MODECCA, &c.

USEFUL PRODUCTS: *Granadillas fruits* (Passiflora quadrangularis *L.*, and P. macrocarpa *Mast.*); *Sweet Cup* or *Pomme d'Or* (P. maliformis *L.*); *Belle Apple* (P. laurifolia *L.*), Trop. Amer. and West Indies.

108. ACHARIACEAE

Slender or acaulescent herbs or shrublets; leaves alternate, palmately lobed; stipules absent; flowers ♂♀, *monoecious*, solitary or racemose, actinomorphic; male flower: sepals 3–4, free to the base; *petals united into a campanulate 3–5-lobed tube*; stamens 3–5 inserted at the base of or the filaments adnate to the corolla; anthers 2-locular, opening lengthwise, with broad connectives, introrse; no rudimentary ovary; female flower: calyx and corolla more or less as in the ♂; no staminodes; ovary subsessile or stipitate, 1-locular, with 3–5 *parietal* placentas; stigmas 2-lobed; ovules few or many; fruit a stipitate capsule, 3–5-valved; seeds with copious endosperm and small straight embryo. B.H. **1**, 814 (under *Passifloraceae*); E.P.N. 256. S. Africa.

A. Woody shrublet; stamens adnate to the corolla-tube; fruit a short capsule; corolla persistent—ACHARIA. AA. Slender scandent herb; stamens at the base of the corolla-tube; fruit elongated, with nerved valves; corolla

[1] See note under *Medusandraceae*, p. 335.

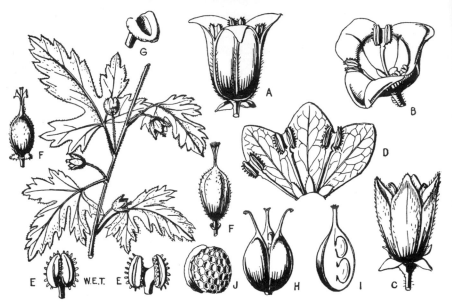

FIG. 108. Acharia tragodes *Thunb.* (Achariaceae). A, male flower, side view. B, same from above. C, female flower. D, male flower showing stamens. E, anther before and after dehiscence. F, pistil. G, stigma. H, fruit. I, section of pistil.

deciduous—CERATOSICYOS. **AAA.** Acaulescent herb with radical, cordate-ovate leaves; stamens at the mouth of the corolla-tube; fruit a short capsule; corolla persistent—GUTHRIEA.

ORDER 30. CUCURBITALES

Mostly herbaceous, often climbing by tendrils; flowers epigynous; mostly ♂ ♀; calyx-lobes imbricate or valvate; petals free or united, rarely absent; stamens numerous to few, free or united; anther-loculi straight or often flexuous; ovary inferior with parietal or axile placentation; seeds with scanty or no endosperm.

A. Stamens mostly 3, rarely 1–5, one anther always 1-locular, the others 2-locular; anther-loculi often flexuous or conduplicate   *Curcurbitaceae*

AA. Stamens numerous; anthers all 2-locular; leaves stipulate; petals free or absent, often only 2; anther-loculi straight   *Begoniaceae*

AAA. Stamens numerous to few; petals free, small or absent; anthers 2-locular, loculi straight; leaves not stipulate, simple or pinnate   *Datiscaceae*

AAAA. Stamens 10, inserted on the long corolla-tube; anthers 2-locular, loculi straight; leaves not stipulate, digitately lobed   *Caricaceae*

109. CUCURBITACEAE

Herbs or rarely undershrubs with watery juice, often scabrid; stems scandent or prostrate; *tendrils mostly present*, spirally coiled; flowers ♂♀, monoecious or dioecious, very rarely ☿, actinomorphic; male flower: calyx tubular, lobes

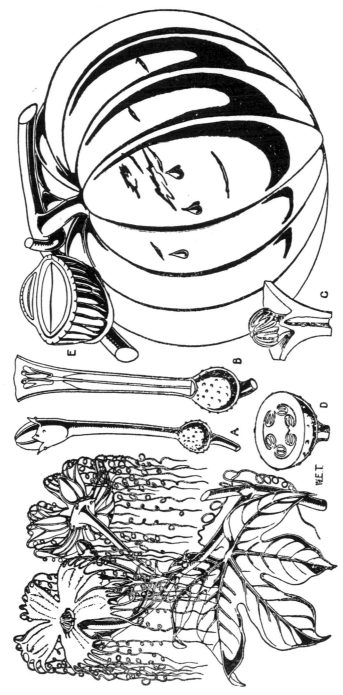

Fig. 109. Hodgsonia heteroclita *H. f. & Thoms.* (Cucurbitaceae) and fruit. A, flower. B, longitudinal section of same. C, stamens. D, cross-section of ovary. E, the same of the two united seeds. (After Hook. f.)

imbricate or open; corolla polypetalous or sympetalous, lobes imbricate or induplicate-valvate; stamens free or variously united, mostly 3, rarely 1–5, *one anther always 1-locular,* the others 2-locular, loculi straight or often curved, flexuous or conduplicate; connective often produced; female flower: calyx-tube adnate to the ovary and often produced beyond; staminodes usually not present; *ovary inferior* or very rarely free; placentas often 3, *parietal* but often meeting in the middle; ovules numerous, rarely few, arranged towards the walls of the ovary; style simple or rarely 3 free styles; stigmas thick; seeds various, often flattened, *without endosperm.* B.H. **1**, 816; E.P. **4,** 5, 1. Mainly Tropics and Subtropics.—TRICHOSANTHES, TROCHOMERIA, PEPONIA, LUFFA, MOMORDICA, CUCUMIS, CITRULLUS, CEPHALANDRA, CUCURBITA, BRYONIA, ZEHNERIA, MELOTHRIA, ANGURIA, TRIANOSPERMA, ECHINOCYSTIS, CYCLANTHERA, SICYOS, SECHIUM, HODGSONIA, &c.

USEFUL PRODUCTS: Many kinds of *Gourds* and *Calabashes. Cucumber* (Cucumis sativus *L.*); *Melon* (Cucumis melo *L.*); *Water Melon* (Citrullus vulgaris *Schrad.*); *Naras* (Acanthosicyos horrida *Welw.*), S. Afr.; *Bryony* (Bryonia dioica *Jacq.*), Eur., &c.; *Bitter Apple* or *Colocynth* (Citrullus colocynthis *Schrad.*), N. Afr. to India.

110. BEGONIACEAE

Undershrubs or herbs, mostly succulent; stems jointed, leaves alternate, simple, often *unequal-sided* or oblique; stipules free, deciduous; flowers *monoecious,* actinomorphic or zygomorphic, mostly in axillary cymes, showy; male flower: sepals 2, rarely 5, opposite, *valvate*; petals 5–2, imbricate, or absent; stamens numerous; filaments free or connate; anthers 2-locular, continuous with the filament, opening lengthwise; female flower: perianth more or less as in the male; stami-

FIG. 110. Begonia cathcartii *Hook f. & Thoms.* (Begoniaceae). A, anther. B, ovary. C, cross-section of same. (After Hook. f.)

nodes absent or very small; ovary *inferior,* or free at the apex (*Hillebrandia*), 2–4- (rarely 1-) locular, mostly *angled* or *winged*; styles 2–5, free or connate, stigmas often *twisted,* papillose nearly all over; ovules very *numerous,* on

axile projecting simple or lobed placentas; fruit a capsule or berry; seeds
minute and very numerous, with reticulate testa and scanty or no endosperm
and straight embryo. B.H. **1**, 841; E.P. **3**, 6*a*, 121. Tropics mainly.

USEFUL PRODUCTS: Valuable ornamental garden plants.

A. Sepals and petals of both sexes free: **B.** Sepals and petals together 10,
the latter very small; ovary not fully inferior; fruit opening between the
styles—HILLEBRANDIA (Hawaii Is.). **BB.** Sepals and petals together less than
10; ovary fully inferior; fruit loculicidal, rarely remaining closed—BEGONIA
(*Semibegoniella*) 'Tropics and Subtropics). **AA.** Sepals and petals of the male
flowers free, those of the female united high up; stamens numerous—SYM-
BEGONIA (New Guin.). **AAA.** Sepals and petals of both male and female
flowers united in one or two series; stamens few—BEGONIELLA (Trop. S.
Amer.).

111. DATISCACEAE

Trees or herbs, sometimes lepidote; leaves alternate, simple or pinnate;
stipules absent; flowers ♂♀, dioecious or rarely ☿, actinomorphic, spicate or
racemose; male flower: calyx-lobes 3–9, short; petals 8 or absent, small;

FIG. 111. Datisca cannabina *L.* (Datiscaceae). A, male flower.
B, C, fruit.

stamens 4–25, opposite the calyx-lobes; anthers 2-locular, opening lengthwise; rudimentary ovary small or absent; female and bisexual flowers: calyx-
tube *adnate to the ovary*; stamens similar to the ♂ or reduced to staminodes;
ovary 1-locular, open or closed at the apex; placentas *parietal*; styles free,
simple or branched; ovules very numerous, anatropous; capsule opening
amongst the styles, many-seeded; seeds very numerous, minute, with scanty
endosperm and cylindrical straight embryo. B.H. **1**, 844; E.P. **3**, 6*a*, 150.
N. Tropics and Subtropics.

A. Petals 8 in the male flowers; anthers recurved on long filaments; styles
8, with capitate stigmas; trees with simple leaves—OCTOMELES (Malaya). **AA.**
Petals absent: **B.** Anthers short; filaments elongated; styles 4, short; trees

with simple leaves—TETRAMELES (Indo-Malaya). **BB.** Anthers elongated; filaments short; styles filiform, 2-partite; herbs with trisected or pinnate leaves—DATISCA (Asia, Calif., Mexico).

112. CARICACEAE

Small trees or shrubs with a terminal cluster of leaves, or rarely herbs with scattered leaves, and *milky juice*; leaves alternate, often variously digitately lobed or foliolate; stipules absent; flowers ♀ and ♂♀, racemose; male flower:

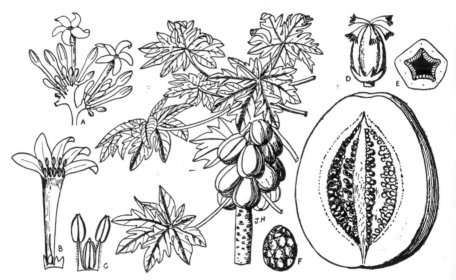

FIG. 112. Carica papaya *L.* (Caricaceae) and fruit in section. A, inflorescence. B, longitudinal section of flower. C, stamens. D, ovary. E, cross-section of same. F, seed. (Orig.)

calyx 5-lobed or toothed, small; *petals united into a slender tube*; lobes contorted or valvate; *stamens 10, inserted on the corolla*; filaments free or connate at the base; anthers 2-locular, opening lengthwise; rudimentary ovary present or absent; female flower: calyx of the male; petals at first connivent, at length free; no staminodes; ovary superior, sessile, 1-locular or spuriously 5-locular, with *parietal placentas*; ovules numerous; style short or absent; fruit a pulpy berry; seeds with *fleshy endosperm* and straight embryo. B.H. **1**, 815 (under *Passifloraceae*); E.P. **3**, 6*a*, 94. Tropical America and Africa.

USEFUL PRODUCTS: *Papaw* (fruit of Carica papaya *L.*), Tropics.

A. Filaments free from one another; leaves simple but sometimes deeply lobed or partite; stems not prickly—CARICA (Trop. and Subtrop. Amer.). **AA.** Filaments connate into a tube: **B.** Leaves simple, palmately lobed or incised; corolla-lobes alternate with the calyx-teeth: **C.** Trees with prickly stems—CYLICOMORPHA (Trop. Afr.). **CC.** Herbs with smooth stems—JARILLA (*Mocinna*) (Mexico). **BB.** Leaves digitately 7–9-foliolate; corolla-lobes opposite the calyx-teeth—JACARATIA (*Leucopremna*) (Trop. Amer.).

ORDER 31. CACTALES

Succulent or woody, often very spiny; sepals, petals, and stamens mostly numerous and in several series on a tubular axis; ovary inferior, 1-locular, with parietal placentas; fruit a berry; seeds usually without endosperm and with straight or semicircular embryo.—Mostly desert regions of America.

113. CACTACEAE

Succulent herbs and shrubs of diverse habit, often very spiny, and usually with much *reduced leaves*; flowers ☿, solitary, actinomorphic; calyx generally *petaloid*, superior; petals epigynous, in *several series*, the innermost largest,

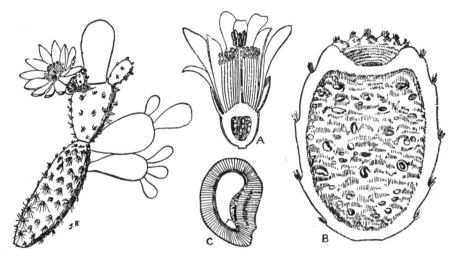

FIG. 113. Opuntia vulgaris *L.* (Cactaceae). A, longitudinal section of flower. B, fruit. C, section of seed.

sometimes coherent at the base; stamens ∞, inserted at and free or adnate to the base of the petals; anthers 2-locular, opening lengthwise; *ovary inferior*, 1-locular, with 3 or more many-ovuled *parietal placentas*; stigmas spreading or close; fruit a berry, often spiny or bristly, many-seeded; seeds numerous, immersed in the pulp, testa often black; endosperm usually absent; embryo straight to semicircular. B.H. **1**, 845; E.P. **3**, 6a, 156; see Britten and Rose, *The Cactaceae*, vols. i–iv (1919–23). America, naturalized in other warm countries.—PERESKIA, OPUNTIA, CEREUS, MAMILLARIA, EPIPHYLLUM, ECHINO-CACTUS, RHIPSALIS, &c.

USEFUL PRODUCTS: *Cochineal dye* (derived from small insects living upon spp. of *Cactaceae*: Opuntia and Nopalea. *Spineless Cactus* (Opuntia spp.) grown as emergency fodder in some dry regions; spines of others used as gramophone needles.

ORDER 32. TILIALES

Trees or shrubs; indumentum mostly stellate; leaves simple to compound, mostly alternate, usually stipulate; flowers hypogynous, actinomorphic, ♂ or ♂♀; calyx usually valvate; stamens free to monadelphous; anthers 2–1-locular; ovary superior, with axile placentation; seeds with copious endosperm.—Mostly Tropics (except some *Tiliaceae*).

A. Anthers 2-locular:
  B. Ovary 8-locular, very deeply laterally lobed; stamens 8, free, opposite the petals   *Dirachmaceae*
  BB. Ovary and other characters above not associated, if stamens few then not opposite the petals, often united into bundles:
    C. Calyx cupular, very short, entire or only toothed; petals valvate; anthers opening by a pore or pore-like slit; stipules absent
                                                                 Scytopetalaceae
    CC. Calyx deeply lobed or sepals free:
      D. Disk absent; ovules axile; loculi usually more than 1:
        E. Stamens numerous, free or very shortly connate at the base; stipules usually small and deciduous, rarely large or absent   *Tiliaceae*
        EE. Stamens more or less monadelphous or few and alternate with the petals; stipules various   *Sterculiaceae*
      DD. Disk present, multilobulate; ovules pendulous in the 1-locular ovary   *Peridiscaceae*
AA. Anthers 1-locular; stamens free or united into a single tube; seeds often embedded in hairs from the wall of the fruit, with little or no endosperm and with flat or contorted or plicate cotyledons; leaves simple or digitate
                                                                 Bombacaceae

114. DIRACHMACEAE[1]

Shrub; branches composed of *long and short shoots*; leaves alternate on the new long shoots, clustered on the short shoots, oblong-oblanceolate, serrate; stipules subulate, persistent; flowers white, actinomorphic, axillary towards the top of the long shoots; *epicalyx of 4 bracteoles*; sepals 8, *valvate*; petals 8, free, perigynous, *contorted*; stamens 8, free, *opposite the petals*, all fertile; anthers large, oblong-ellipsoidal, introrse, opening by slits lengthwise; ovary

---

[1] **Dirachmaceae** Hutch., fam. nov.; frutex; rami longi et breves; folia in ramis longis alterna, in ramulis brevibus fasciculata; flores albi, actinomorphi, solitarii, apicem versus ramorum longorum axillares; epicalyx bracteolis 4; sepala 8, valvata; petala 8, libera, perigyna, contorta; stamina 8, libera, petalis opposita, omnia fertilia; antherae magnae, oblongo-ellipsoideae, introrsae, longitudinaliter dehiscentes; ovarium superum, 8-loculare, profunde 8-lobatum, in stylum satis longum sensim angustatum, stigmatibus 8 linearibus; ovulum in loculis unicum, ex angulo interiore adscendens; capsula in segmentis 8 ventraliter dehiscentibus soluta, intra floccosa; semina compressa, testa nitida; endospermium tenue.—Typus: DIRACHMA Schweif. ex Balf. f.

superior, *8-locular*, laterally deeply 8-lobed, gradually narrowed into a longish style, stigmas 8, linear; ovule solitary in each loculus, *basal*, ascending from the inner angle; capsule separating into 8 ventrally dehiscent segments, woolly inside; seeds compressed, with shining testa; endosperm scanty. Schweinf. ex

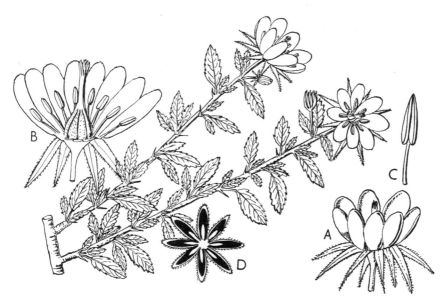

FIG. 114. Dirachma socotrana *Schweinf.* (Dirachmaceae). A, flower. B, flower spread out with some sepals removed. C, stamen. D, cross-section of fruit.

Balf. f. *Proc. Roy. Soc. Edinb.* **12**, 403 (1882–4), and *Trans. Roy. Soc. Edinb.* **31**, 45, t. 8 (1888); Knuth, Engl. *Pflanzenr. Geraniac.* 574, fig. 77; E.P., edn. 2, **19a**, 66, fig. 34 (1931). Socotra.—DIRACHMA.

115. SCYTOPETALACEAE

Trees; leaves alternate, simple; stipules absent; flowers ⚥, actinomorphic, in terminal panicles or axillary racemes, or fasciculate on the old wood; calyx cupular, entire or toothed; petals 3–10, free or connate at base, *valvate*; stamens *numerous*, in *several series* on the margin of or on the disk, free or united towards the base; anthers 2-locular, opening by a *pore* or slit at the side or towards the top; ovary superior, 3–6-locular, ovules 2–several in each loculus, axile or pendulous; fruit woody; seed with ruminate or uniform copious endosperm and linear embryo. B.H. **1**, 995; E.P.N. 242. W. Tropcal Africa.

A. Flowers in long lax panicles; branchlets sometimes winged; stamens connate at the base—OUBANGUIA (*Egassea*). AA. Flowers in fascicles or in very short axillary racemes: B. Flowers in the axils of the leaves: C. Petals several to many, connate at the base; pedicels flattened, twisted; stamens unequal in length—SCYTOPETALUM (*Pierrina*). CC. Petals 3; pedicels terete,

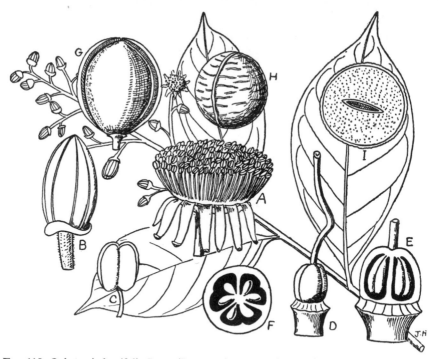

Fig. 115. Oubanguia laurifolia *Pierre* (Scytopetalaceae). A, flower. B, bud. C, anther. D, ovary E, vertical section of same. F, cross-section of same. G, fruit. H, seed. I, cross-section of same (Orig. partly.)

persistent; stamens equal in length—RHAPTOPETALUM. **BB.** Flowers in fascicles on the main stem or branches remote from the leaves—BRAZZEIA (*Pseudobrazzeia*).

116. TILIACEAE

Trees or shrubs, rarely herbs; leaves alternate, rarely opposite, simple; stipules paired or absent; flowers cymose, actinomorphic, ☿, rarely ♂♀; sepals mostly 5 and *valvate*; petals free, present or absent, sometimes like the sepals, contorted, imbricate or valvate; stamens mostly numerous, *free* or *shortly connate* at the base or in 5–10 bundles; *anthers* 2-locular, opening by a slit lengthwise or by an apical pore; ovary superior, sessile, 2–10-locular; style usually simple and divided at the apex, rarely the stigmas sessile; ovules on axile placentas; fruit 2–10-locular, rarely 1–locular by abortion, sometimes pluri-locular by transverse dissepiments, baccate or drupaceous or variously dehiscent; seeds solitary to many in each loculus, not arillate, sometimes pilose, mostly with copious or thin endosperm; embryo usually straight; incl. *Elaeocarpaceae*. B.H. **1**, 228; E.P. **3**, 6, 8. Throughout the world.— BROWNLOWIA, GREWIA, TRIUMFETTA, SPARRMANIA, CORCHORUS, LUHEA, TILIA, GLYPHAEA, PROCKIA, SLOANEA, ARISTOTELIA, ELAEOCARPUS, TRICUSPIDARIA, &c.

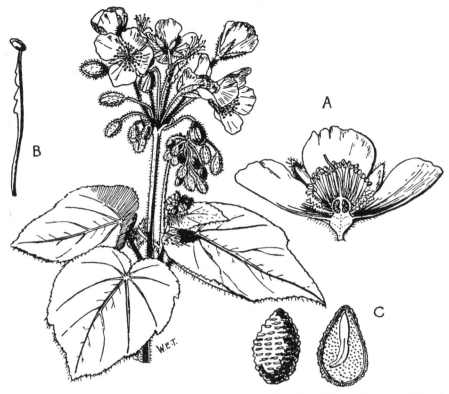

Fig. 116. Sparrmania africana *L. f.* (Tiliaceae). A, vertical section of flower. B, stamen. C, seed and vertical section of same. (After Baill.)

USEFUL PRODUCTS: Several valuable fibres from *Corchorus, Grewia,* and *Triumfetta. Common Lime* (Tilia europaea *L.*); *Basswood* (Tilia americana *L.*), N. Amer.; *Macqui berries* (Aristotelia maqui *L'Hérit.*), Chile.

117. STERCULIACEAE

Trees or shrubs with mostly soft wood, or rarely herbs; indumentum often *stellate*; leaves alternate or very rarely subopposite, simple or digitately compound; stipules usually present; flowers variously arranged, but inflorescence rarely terminal, ♀ or ♀♂, actinomorphic; sepals 3–5, more or less partially united, *valvate*; petals 5 or absent, hypogynous, free or adnate at the base to the staminal tube, *contorted-imbricate*; stamens often *connate into a tube* with as many staminodes, sometimes in more than one series, or the stamens quite free; *anthers 2-locular*, very rarely the loculi subconfluent at the apex; ovary free, of 2–5 or rarely 10–12 more or less united carpels or reduced to one carpel; ovules 2 or more in each loculus, rarely 1, inserted on the inner angle, ascending or horizontal; style simple or divided into lobes or rarely the styles free from the base; fruit dry or rarely baccate, indehiscent or variously dehiscent; seed with fleshy or thin or no endosperm; embryo straight or

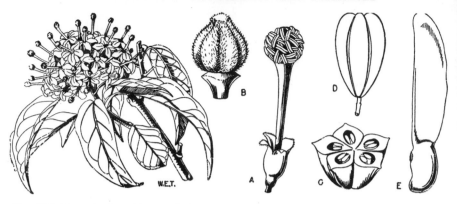

FIG. 117. Reevesia thyrsoidea *Lindl.* (Sterculiaceae). A, androgynoecium. B, ovary. C, cross-section of same. D, fruit. E, seed. (Orig.)

curved. B.H. **1,** 214; E.P. **3,** 6, 69. Mainly Tropics and Subtropics.—STER-CULIA, COLA, HELICTERES, PTEROSPERMUM, DOMBEYA, MELHANIA, HER-MANNIA, MAHERNIA, MELOCHIA, WALTHERIA, ABROMA, THEOBROMA, GUA-ZUMA, BUETTNERIA, RULINGIA, COMMERSONIA, THOMASIA, LASIOPETALUM, &c.

USEFUL PRODUCTS: Various fibrous barks. *Cola* or *Kola nuts* (Cola nitida (*Vent.*) *A. Chev.*), W. Trop. Afr.; *Cocoa* and *Chocolate* (Theobroma cacao *L.*), Trop. Amer., now chief industry in Ghana.

118. PERIDISCACEAE

Tree; leaves alternate, petiolate, subobliquely elliptic, acuminate, entire, shining above, strongly 3-nerved from the base with a *large pit in the axil* of

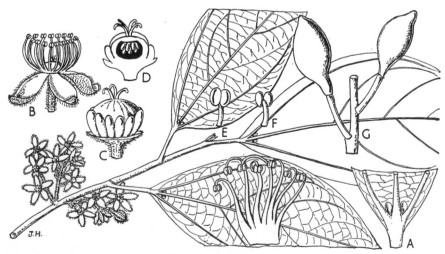

FIG. 118. Peridiscus lucidus *Benth.* (Peridiscaceae). A, base of leaf from below showing the two large pits in the axils of the basal nerves. B, flower. C, disk and ovary. D, vertical section of ovary. E, inner face of anther; F, outer face. G, fruits. Unlettered, part of stamens. (Orig.)

each basal nerve below, pinnately nerved above and reticulate; stipules *intra-petiolar*, early deciduous and leaving a narrow oblique scar; inflorescence an axillary cluster of very short racemes covered with short branched hairs; bracts fairly large, persistent; pedicels short; sepals usually 5, *valvate*, very hairy; *petals absent*; stamens numerous, inserted outside a large *cupular multi-lobulate fleshy disk*; filaments partially and rather irregularly united in the lower half; anthers small, 2-locular, didymous, opening lengthwise, introrse; ovary sessile and *half-immersed in the disk*, depressed, 1-locular, with *several ovules hanging from the top*; styles 4–3, short, free, spreading; fruit becoming stipitate, ovoid, umbonate, 1-locular and 1-seeded; seed without endosperm and with bent embryo. B.H. **1**, 127 (in *Bixaceae*); E.P., edn. 2, 21, 457 (excluded by Gilg from the *Flacourtiaceae*). Brazil.—PERIDISCUS.

This monotypic genus from the Brazilian forests shares a peculiar combination of characters which makes it difficult to classify, and it is included here for want of a better place.

119. BOMBACACEAE

Trees with sometimes bulging stems through excess of water storage; leaves simple or digitate, alternate, often lepidote; stipules deciduous; flowers ♀,

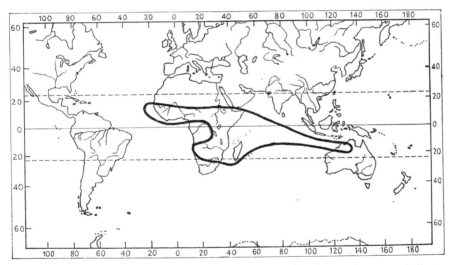

The distribution of the giant-stemmed tree genus Adansonia (Bombacaceae) seems to indicate that the land masses of Africa, Madagascar, and Australia were formerly in closer contact.

large and showy; calyx closed and *valvate* in bud or rarely deeply 5-lobed with slightly imbricate lobes, often subtended by an epicalyx; petals often elongated, sometimes absent; stamens free or *united into a tube*; anthers reniform to linear, *1-locular*; pollen smooth; ovary superior, 2–5-locular; style simple, capitate, or lobed; ovules 2 or more on the inner angle of each loculus; capsule loculicidally dehiscent or not dehiscent, the valves rarely falling away; seeds often embedded in hairs from the wall of the fruit, with little or no endosperm and flat or contorted or plicate cotyledons. B.H. **1**,

209 (under *Malvaceae*); E.P. **3**, 6. 53. Tropics.—ADANSONIA, PACHIRA, BOMBAX, CEIBA, FREMONTIA, DURIO, &c.

USEFUL PRODUCTS: *Baobab, Monkey Bread,* or *Monkey Tamarind* (Adansonia digitata *L.*), Trop. Afr.; *Silk Cotton* or *Semul* (Bombax malabaricum

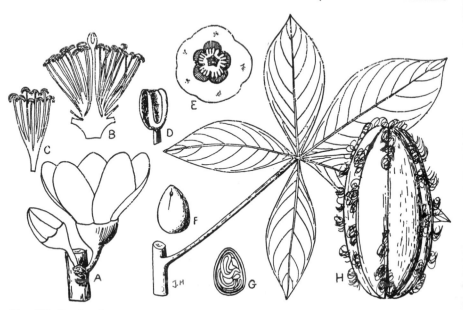

FIG. 119. Bombax buonopozense *P. Beauv.* (Bombacaceae). A, flowers. B, stamens and ovary. C, single bundle of stamens. D, anther. E, cross-section of ovary. F, seed. G, vertical section of same. H, fruit. (After Engler, partly.)

DC.), Trop. Asia, yields also *Mucherus gum*; *Kapok Tree* (Ceiba pentandra *Gaertn.*), Tropics; *Durian fruits* (Durio zibethinus *Murr.*), Malaya.

ORDER 33. MALVALES

More or less as in *Tiliales,* but herbaceous to softly woody, often fibrous; stamens more perfectly monadelphous and anthers 1-locular.—Temperate Regions and Tropics.

120. MALVACEAE

Herbs or shrubs, rarely small trees, often with fibrous stems; indumentum usually stellate or lepidote; leaves alternate, entire or variously lobed, mostly palmately nerved; stipules present; flowers actinomorphic, ☿, or rarely dioecious or polygamous; sepals 3–5, more or less united, *valvate,* sometimes subtended by an *involucre* of *bracteoles* (epicalyx); petals 5, free from each other, but often adnate at the base to the staminal-column, contorted or imbricate; stamens numerous, hypogynous, *monadelphous,* the staminal-column divided at the apex and bearing 1-*locular anthers* (by the division of the filaments), opening lengthwise; pollen muricate; ovary 2- or pluri-locular, often 5-locular, rarely of 1 carpel, or rarely the carpels in vertical rows; style branched above, rarely clavate; ovules 1 or more from the inner angle of each loculus; fruit dry, rarely baccate, breaking into cocci, or capsular; seeds with usually

FIG. 120. Hoheria lyallii *Hook*. (Malvaceae). A and B, flowers. C, anther. C₁, ovary. D, fruit. E, vertical section of carpel. F, seed. G, section of fruiting carpel. H, stellate hair. (After *Bot. Mag.*)

some endosperm and straight or curved embryo; cotyledons often plicate or contortuplicate. B.H. **1**, 200, partly; E.P. **3**, 6, 30. Throughout the world except very cold regions.—MALOPE, ALTHAEA, LAVATERA, MALVA, SIDALCEA, MALVASTRUM, PLAGIANTHUS, CRISTARIA, SIDA, WISSADULA, ABUTILON, SPHAERALCEA, URENA, PAVONIA, HIBISCUS, THESPESIA, GOSSYPIUM, &c.

USEFUL PRODUCTS: *Cotton* (Gossypium spp.); *Oil-cake* from seeds. Many fibre plants.

ORDER 34. MALPIGHIALES

Mostly climbers with alternate or opposite leaves; flowers actinomorphic to subzygomorphic; sepals often bearing a pair of large glands; stamens usually definite, often connate at the base; anthers usually 2-locular, rarely 4-locellate; ovary superior, syncarpous with subapical or sub-basal placentation; ovules few; seeds usually without endosperm.—Tropics.

A. Leaves simple, never unifoliolate (therefore petiole not pulvinate):
  B. Sepals contorted; petals contorted; fruit a septicidal capsule; seeds with
    endosperm   *Ixonanthaceae*

BB. Sepals imbricate or rarely valvate:
  C. Leaves alternate:
    D. Carpels usually 3, often free from one another but sometimes connate; ovule ascending from a broad pendulous funicle; fruit indehiscent, often winged; seeds without endosperm; indumentum often of medifixed hairs   *Malpighiaceae*
    DD. Ovary 5–7-locular; ovules 1–3, pendulous from the apex of the axis; fruit a drupe; seeds with copious endosperm   *Humiriaceae*
    DDD. Ovary 3–5-locular, loculi often again partially subdivided; ovules 2 in each loculus, axile; fruit a septicidal capsule; seeds with or without endosperm   *Linaceae*
    DDDD. Ovary 2-locular with 1 pendulous ovule from near the top of the axis in each loculus; stipules large and folded around the terminal bud, intrapetiolar   *Irvingiaceae*
    DDDDD. Ovary 1-locular, with 1 basal ovule; anthers 4-locellate
        Huaceae
  CC. Leaves opposite:
    E. Fruit a capsule:
      F. Stamens 4–5; styles filiform; ovules 2 in each loculus, axile
        Linaceae
      FF. Stamens 10; style very short or stigmas sessile; ovules numerous or 2 collateral and pendulous   *Ledocarpaceae*
    EE. Fruit a drupe or nut:
      G. Seeds with endosperm; hairs when present not branched
        Erythroxylaceae
      GG. Seeds without endosperm; hairs when present medifixed:
        H. Leaves often with glands on the petiole or lower surface; sepals often biglandular outside   *Malpighiaceae*
        HH. Leaves without glands; sepals without glands *Ctenolophonaceae*
AA. Leaves compound or unifoliolate:
  J. Leaves alternate:
    K. Stipules and stipels caducous   *Lepidobotryaceae*
    KK. Stipules absent   *Balanitaceae*
  JJ. Leaves opposite or alternate; stipules paired, persistent, often spinescent   *Zygophyllaceae*

121. IXONANTHACEAE

Trees or shrubs; leaves alternate, entire or serrate, pinnately nerved; stipules small or minute; flowers small, bisexual, arranged in cymes, racemes, or panicles; pedicels sometimes fasciculate; sepals 5, *contorted*, free or connate at the base; petals 5, *contorted*, free, persistent and often becoming *indurated*; stamens 20, 10, or 5, filaments connate at the base; anthers 2-locular, short, opening lengthwise; ovary free, 5–3-locular, with axile placentas; ovules 2 or 1 in each loculus, pendulous; style simple, or 5 and free almost to the base; fruit a *septicidally dehiscent capsule*, the loculi sometimes *spuriously septate*; seed with fleshy endosperm and often oblique or lateral embryo. B.H. **1**, 245 (in *Linaceae*); E.P. **3**, 4, 34.—Tropics.

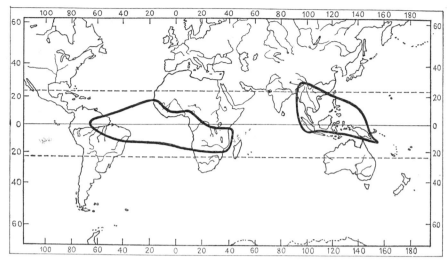

Range of the family Ixonanthaceae; Ochthocosmus common to S. America and Tropical Africa; Ixonanthes in Indo-Malaya, China, and New Guinea.

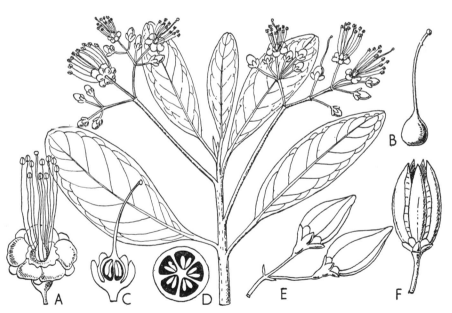

FIG. 121. Ixonanthes chinensis *Champ.* (Ixonanthaceae). A, flower. B, ovary and style. C, vertical section of ovary. D, cross-section of ovary. E, fruits. F, open capsule. (Partly after Champion.)

A. Flowers hypogynous; stamens 10–5; inflorescence racemose or paniculate—OCHTHOCOSMUS (*Phyllocosmus*) (Trop. S. Amer., Trop. Afr.). **AA.** Flowers perigynous; stamens 20–10; inflorescence long-stalked and cymose—IXONANTHES (Indo-Malaya, China, New Guin.).

122. MALPIGHIACEAE

Trees, shrubs, or climbers, with often *appressed medifixed hairs*; leaves mostly opposite, simple; *glands* often present either on the petiole or on the lower surface of the leaves; stipules present or absent, sometimes large and connate; flowers ☿, rarely polygamous, mostly actinomorphic; sepals 5, imbricate or

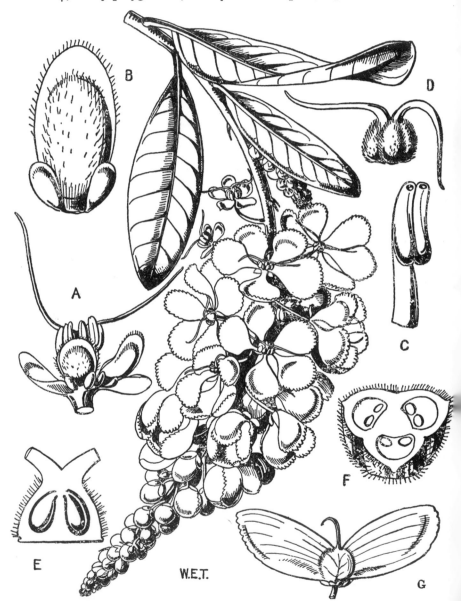

FIG. 122. Acridocarpus natalitius *A. Juss.* (Malpighiaceae). A, flower (less petals). B, sepal with glands C, anther. D, ovary. E, vertical section of same. F, cross-section of same. G, fruit. (After *Bot. Mag.*)

very rarely valvate, often *biglandular* outside; petals 5, clawed, convolute; disk small; stamens mostly 10, hypogynous or nearly so, sometimes some without anthers; filaments often connate at the base; anthers short, 2-locular, sometimes winged, opening lengthwise or by a pore-like slit; carpels 3, rarely 2 or 4, free or more or less connate into a 3-locular ovary; loculi 1-ovuled; styles usually distinct; ovule ascending from a broad pendulous funicle; fruiting carpels often winged, or carpels connate into a fleshy or woody drupe; seeds without endosperm and with straight, curved or uncinate, rarely circinate, embryo. B.H. **1**, 247; E.P. **3**, 4, 41. Mainly Tropics, rare in Subtropics.— BYRSONIMA, MALPIGHIA, HETEROPTERYS, ACRIDOCARPUS, STIGMAPHYLLON, BANISTERIA, TRISTELLATEIA, ASPIDOPTERYS, TETRAPTERYS, HIRAEA, GAUDI-CHAUDIA, &c.

USEFUL PRODUCT: *Shoemakers' bark* (Byrsonima spicata *Rich.*), West Indies.

123. HUMIRIACEAE

Trees or shrubs; leaves alternate, simple; *stipules absent*; flowers ♀, actinomorphic; sepals 5, imbricate, shortly or wholly connate; petals 5, free, soon

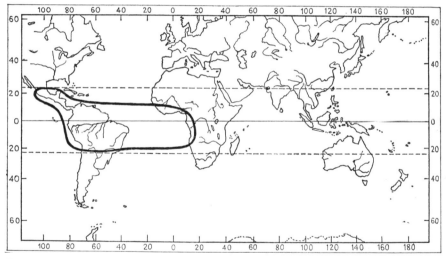

Range of Humiriaceae, which occur only in Tropical America and W. Africa, the genus Saccoglottis being found on both sides of the mid-Atlantic.

falling away, slightly imbricate-contorted; stamens 10 or more, hypogynous, more or less *connate* in the lower part; anthers versatile, 2–4-locular, opening lengthwise; disk *annular* and often toothed or of separate glands, surrounding the base of the ovary; ovary free, sessile, 5–7-locular; style simple; ovules 1–3, pendulous from the apex, anatropous; fruit a drupe with rather thin fleshy pericarp and hard endocarp, sometimes with numerous resin-filled cavities; seeds 1–2 in each loculus; embryo straight in the middle of copious endosperm; cotyledons short. B.H. **1**, 246; E.P. **3**, 4, 35. Tropical America and Africa.

A. Stamens very numerous (50 or more); anthers 4-locular—VANTANEA (Trop. S. Amer.). **AA.** Stamens 20–10; anthers 2-locular: **B.** Anthers barbate;

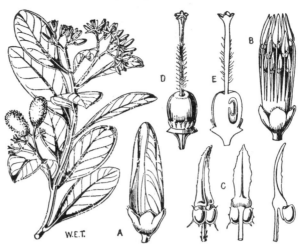

FIG. 123. Humiria arenaria *Guill.* (Humiriaceae). A, flower-bud. B, stamens. C, views of anther. D, ovary. E, vertical section of same. (After Baill.)

ovary-loculi with 2 ovules—HUMIRIA (Trop. Amer.). **BB.** Anthers glabrous; ovary-loculi with 1 ovule—SACCOGLOTTIS (Trop. Amer., W. Trop. Afr.).

124. LINACEAE

Trees, shrubs, or herbs; leaves simple, alternate or opposite; stipules present or absent, sometimes gland-like; flowers ♀, actinomorphic; sepals 4–5, free

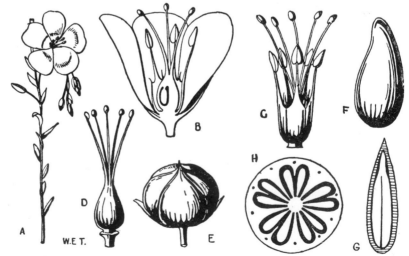

FIG. 124. Linum usitatissimum *L.* (Linaceae). A, shoot with flower. B, vertical section of flower. C, stamens and ovary. D, ovary. E, fruit. F, seed. G, section of same. H, cross-section of ovary. (After Le Maout & Decne.)

or partially united, imbricate; petals contorted, fugacious, free, often clawed, claw naked or crested; stamens the same number as the petals and alternate with them, sometimes alternating with *small staminodes*; filaments *connate at the base*; anthers introrse, 2-locular, opening lengthwise; ovary superior, 3–5-locular, loculi often again *subdivided nearly to the placentas*; ovules 2 in each loculus; styles 3–5, filiform, *free* or united, with simple subcapitate stigmas; fruit a capsule, *septicidally dehiscent*; seeds compressed, shining; endosperm copious, scanty or absent; embryo straight, with flat cotyledons. B.H. **1**, 241 (partly); E.P. **3**, 4, 27. Tropical and Temperate Regions.—LINUM, RADIOLA, REINWARDTIA, HUGONIA, DURANDEA, HEBEPETALUM, PHILBORNEA, INDO-ROUCHERA, ROUCHERIA, ANISADENIA, &c.

USEFUL PRODUCTS: *Flax* (Linum usitatissimum *L.*), generally cultivated. *Linseed* (seeds of same) from which *linseed oil* is obtained, and *oil-cake* for cattle.

125. IRVINGIACEAE

Trees; leaves alternate, elliptic to ovate-elliptic, entire, pinnately nerved, coriaceous; stipules present, large or very long, *embracing the terminal bud*

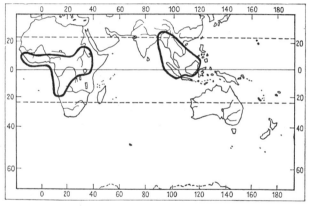

Range of the small family Irvingiaceae consisting of three closely related genera formerly included in the Simaroubaceae.

and intrapetiolar, folded, early caducous; inflorescence paniculate, axillary and terminal; bracts very small; flowers bisexual, small; sepals 5, small, imbricate; petals 5, free, imbricate; stamens 10 (–9), filaments free, inserted below the conspicuous fleshy sometimes lobulate *cupular disk*; anthers sub-basi-fixed, 2-locular, short, opening by slits lengthwise; ovary superior, seated within the base of the disk, 5–4- or 2-locular; style 1, *undivided*, short; ovule 1, more or less pendulous in the upper half of each loculus; fruit a *drupe* or broadly *winged samara*; seeds with thin or no endosperm; cotyledons flat face to face. Simaroubaceae subfamily *Irvingioideae* Engl., E.P. edn. 2, 19a, 396, figs. 184–9 (1931).—Tropical Africa, Tropical E. Asia.

USEFUL PRODUCT: *Dika bread* (Irvingia barteri *Hook. f.*), W. Trop. Afr.

FIG. 125. Desbordesia glaucescens (*Engl.*) *van Tiegh.* (Irvingiaceae). A, young shoot show-ing stipules. B, flower. C, vertical section of flower. D, stamen. E, disk and ovary. F, fruit. G, cross-section of fruit. H, vertical section of fruit-body showing section of seeds. J, cross-section of seed.

A. Ovary 5–4-locular; fruit composed of 5–4 drupes—KLAINEDOXA (Trop. Afr.). **AA.** Ovary 2-locular: **B.** Fruit a 1-locular drupe, not winged—IRVINGIA (Trop. Afr. and Trop. E. Asia). **BB.** Fruit 2-locular and 2-seeded, broadly winged all around—DESBORDESIA (W. Trop. Afr.).

126. HUACEAE

Tree; leaves alternate, shortly petiolate, oblong-elliptic, acuminate, entire, pinnately nerved; stipules small, *extra-axillary*, deciduous; flowers very small,

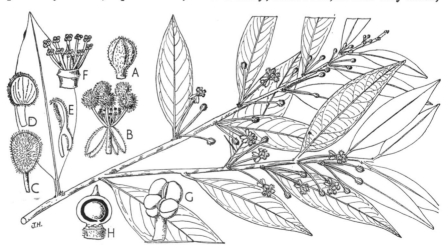

FIG. 126. Hua gabonii *Pierre* (Huaceae). A, flower-bud. B, open flower. C, petal, front view. D, petal, back view. E, side view. F, stamens and ovary. G, anther. H, vertical section of ovary.

bisexual, few in axillary fascicles; pedicels filiform; sepals 5–3, *valvate*; petals 5–4, free, long-clawed, *induplicate-valvate*, lamina villous; stamens 10, hypogynous, free, 1-seriate, equal, all fertile; filaments flattened; anthers *4-locular, peltate*, rounded, basifixed, the lower 2 loculi smaller than the upper; staminodes and disk absent; ovary superior, 1-locular; style simple; stigma small; ovule 1 on a *basal placenta*, erect, anatropous; fruit oblong-ellipsoidal, dehiscent from the apex into 5 segments; endocarp thin; seed 1, large, with a basal hilum; endosperm copious, smelling like an onion; embryo large, central, straight; cotyledons large, ovate, flattened face to face; radicle short. Tropical Africa.—HUA.

A generically and specifically monotypic family found in Gabon and the Belgian Congo, Tropical Africa. I cannot find a better place for it than near *Erythroxylaceae*. Chevalier included *Afrostyrax* in this family, but the genus differs widely and should be retained in the *Styracaceae* as originally placed by its author.

127. LEDOCARPACEAE

Small shrubs or shrublets; leaves mostly *opposite*, entire to deeply dissected, connected by a *transverse line* at the base but with no true stipules; flowers bisexual, actinomorphic, solitary or in terminal fascicles with or without an involucre of bracteoles; sepals 5, free, *imbricate*; petals 5, or absent, *contorted or imbricate*, free; disk or disk-glands absent; stamens 10, free, hypogynous; anthers 2-locular, opening by slits lengthwise; ovary 5- or 3-locular, superior; style very short or stigmas sessile, 5 or 3; ovules numerous in each loculus and *2-seriate on the inner angle*, or 2 collateral and pendulous; capsule loculicidally 5-valved or septifragally dehiscent, sometimes beaked; seeds numerous or 2–1 in each loculus, with thin fleshy endosperm and flat or folded cotyledons. B.H. **1**, 276 (in *Geraniaceae*); E.P. edn. 2, 19a, 65, figs. 31 A–C, D–F, and 32 (in *Geraniaceae*). Western S. America. (Fig. 127.)

A. Calyx with an epicalyx of bracteoles; petals 5; fruit not beaked: **B.** Ovules numerous in each loculus; petals contorted—BALBISIA (*Ledocarpon*). **BB.** Ovules 1–2 in each loculus; petals imbricate—WENDTIA. **AA.** Calyx without an epicalyx; petals absent; fruit beaked; ovules 2–1 in each loculus—RHYNCHOTHECA.

128. ERYTHROXYLACEAE

Trees or shrubs; leaves alternate, rarely opposite, simple, entire; *stipules intrapetiolar*, rarely extrapetiolar, often caducous; flowers fasciculate, ♀, rarely subdioecious, actinomorphic; calyx persistent, campanulate, lobes 5, imbricate; petals 5, free, deciduous, imbricate, mostly ligulate on the inside; stamens 10, 2-seriate, more or less connate at the base; anthers ellipsoidal, 2-locular, opening lengthwise; ovary tricarpellary, 3-locular, mostly two of the loculi sterile, fertile loculi 1–2-ovuled; ovules pendulous, anatropous; styles 3, free or more or less connate; stigmas oblique, depressed-capitate or clavate; fruit drupaceous; seeds with endosperm;

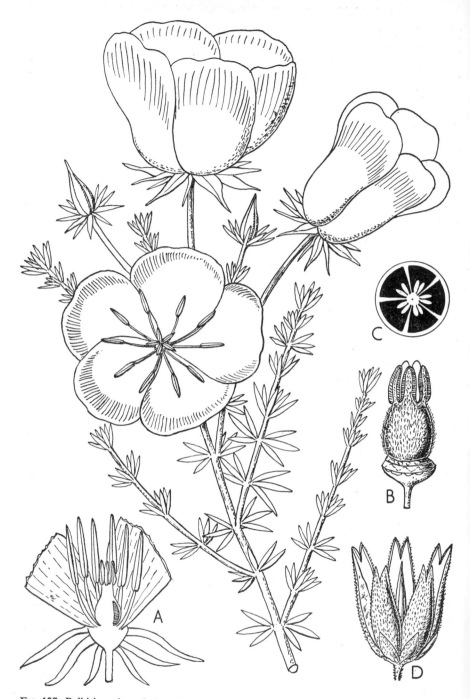

FIG. 127. Balbisia peduncularis *D. Don* (Ledocarpaceae). A, vertical section of flower. B, ovary and stigmas. C, cross-section of ovary. D, fruit.

embryo straight. B.H. **1**, 244 (under *Linaceae*); E.P. **3**, 4, 37. Tropics and Subtropics.

USEFUL PRODUCT: *Cocaine* (Erythroxylum coca *Lamk.*), S. Amer.

A. Leaves alternate: B. Filaments free except at the very base: C. Flowers fasciculate in the leaf-axils, not on a common peduncle—NECTAROPETALUM (*Peglera*) (S. Afr.). CC. Flowers on a common peduncle in the leaf-axils—PINACOPODIUM (*Morelodendron*) (Angola). BB. Filaments connate into a tube;

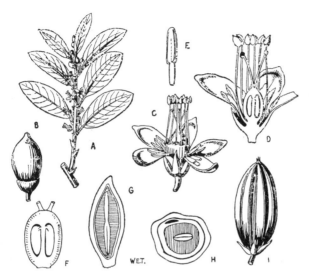

FIG. 128. Erythroxylum coca *L.* (Erythroxylaceae). A, shoot with flowers. B, flower-bud. C, flower. D, vertical section of same. E, anther. F, vertical section of ovary. G, vertical section of seed. H, cross-section of same. I, fruit. (After Le Maout & Decne.)

ovary with one fertile loculus—ERYTHROXYLUM (Tropics and Subtropics). AA. Leaves opposite; filaments connate only at the base—ANEULOPHUS (Trop. Afr.).

129. CTENOLOPHONACEAE

Trees, with *branched hairs* on the young shoots, stipules, and on the outsides of the sepals and petals; leaves *opposite*, petiolate, coriaceous, entire, pinnately nerved; stipules *united in pairs*, shorter than or as long as the petioles, thick, linear-lanceolate, very caducous; flowers small, yellow, in terminal and lateral cyme-like racemes; sepals 5, persistent, thick, imbricate; petals 5, imbricate, deciduous, thick, linear, *spoon-shaped at the base*; stamens 10; filaments attached to the inside of a *cup-like disk*; anthers introrse, ovoid, apiculate; ovary 2-locular, with 2 pendulous ovules in each loculus; styles 2, partly connate or free in the upper part; stigmas *disk-like*; fruit a woody 1-seeded indehiscent nut; seed pendulous from a *long funicle* and with a fibrous *aril*. Linaceae, subfamily *Ctenolophonoideae*, H. Winkl., Engl. and

Prantl, *Pflanzenfam.* edn. 2, 19a, 122, fig. 56, F–O. Malacca, Malay Archipelago, Philippines, and Tropical Africa—CTENOLOPHON.

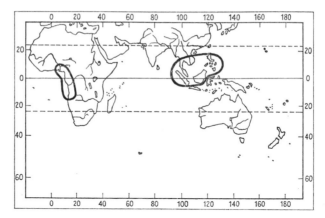

Range of the genus Ctenolophon, the sole member of the family Ctenolophonaceae; a striking example of discontinuous distribution.

FIG. 129. Ctenolophon parvifolius *Oliv.* (Ctenolophonaceae). A, flower-bud. B, vertical section of flower. C, ovary and style. D, young seed and abortive ovules attached to placenta. E, fruit. F, seed with part of pericarp.

130. LEPIDOBOTRYACEAE[1]

Trees, shrubs, or climbers; leaves alternate, *pinnately trifoliolate or unifoliolate with a jointed petiole*, leaflets entire, pinnately nerved; stipules and stipels caducous; flowers bisexual or unisexual, in axillary or terminal panicles or slender or short catkin-like racemes; sepals 5, imbricate, united in the lower part; petals 5, free, imbricate; stamens 10, inserted on the margin of a *fleshy disk*; filaments more or less connate at the base or into a *short tube*, sterile in

[1] *Sarcotheca* and *Dapania* are added here for the first time.

female flowers; anthers 2-locular, dorsifixed, opening by slits lengthwise; ovary superior, 5- or 3-locular; styles 5 or 3, free or shortly connate at the base; ovules 2 in each loculus, on axile placentas, collateral or superposed; fruit berry-like, indehiscent or a septicidally dehiscent capsule; seeds covered by a fleshy, sometimes laciniate *aril*, with endosperm; embryo straight or oblique, with 2 fleshy foliaceous cotyledons.—Tropical Asia and Tropical Africa.

A. Flowers bisexual; styles 5; ovules superposed; trop. Asia: **B.** Leaves trifoliolate or unifoliolate; fruit septicidally dehiscent at the apex; flowers in

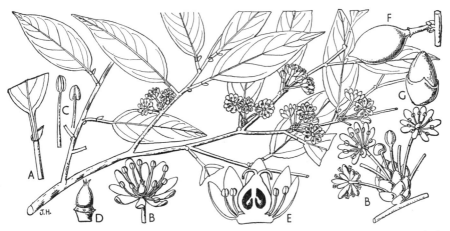

FIG. 130. Lepidobotrys staudtii *Engl.* (Lepidobotryaceae). A, petiole showing the joint and stipel. B, male flowers. C, stamens. D, rudimentary ovary of male flower. E, vertical section of female flower. F, fruit. G, seed with aril. (Orig. except for E, after Léonard.)

axillary and terminal panicles—SARCOTHECA (Malay Archip.). **BB.** Leaves unifoliolate; fruit deeply lobed, opening stellately; flowers in slender fasciculate racemes—DAPANIA (Malay Archip.). **AA.** Flowers unisexual, dioecious, in short racemes strobiliform when young; styles 3; ovules collateral; leaves unifoliolate—LEPIDOBOTRYS (Trop. Afr.).

131. BALANITACEAE

Shrubs or small trees with *axillary simple or forked spines*; *bark bitter*; leaves alternate, *2-foliolate*, leaflets coriaceous, entire, not punctate; *stipules absent*; flowers bisexual, axillary, greenish, scented; sepals 5, free, slightly imbricate, deciduous; petals 5, narrowly oblong, spreading, imbricate; stamens 10, inserted in the grooves below the outside of the disk; filaments free, filiform; anthers dorsifixed; disk thick, shortly cupular or cushion-shaped, 10-grooved; ovary globose, *semi-immersed in the disk*, 5-locular; style very short, subulate, stigmas minute; ovule 1 in each loculus, pendulous from the axis below the apex of the loculi; fruit a fleshy oily drupe, stone bony, 5-angled, 1-locular, and 1-seeded; seed pendulous, ovoid, testa subfibrous; *endosperm none*; embryo green, ovoid, cotyledons thick, oblong, plano-convex, *corrugated or*

2-lobed. See Sprague, *Kew Bull.* 1913, 131. Tropical Africa to India and Burma.—BALANITES.

Placed by Bentham and Hooker f. in the *Simaroubaceae* and by Engler in the *Zygophyllaceae*, it is perhaps better regarded as belonging to neither family. Hooker, in the *Gen. Pl.* **1**, 315, said of it: 'Genus anomalum, nulli arcte affine, *Meliaceis*, fide Planchonii proximum ob flores *Cedrelae* similes. Folia 2-juga, epunctata, stigmata simplicia, et flores herma-

FIG. 131. Balanites aegyptiaca *Del.* (Balanitaceae). A, pair of leaflets and a spine. B, flower. C, vertical section of flower. D, disk. E, cross-section of ovary. F, fruit.

phroditi *Zygophylleis* accedunt, a quibus *Balanites* differt foliis alternis, staminibus esquamatis, ovulis solitariis fructuque drupaceo. A *Rutaceis* plerisque differt foliis epunctatis, antheris non glandulosis, carpellis omnino coalitis et fructu drupaceo. A *Simarubeis* nullo charactere valido distinguitur.'

132. ZYGOPHYLLACEAE

Shrubs or herbs woody at the base, rarely trees; branches often jointed at the nodes; leaves opposite or alternate, *2-foliolate or pinnate*, rarely 3-foliolate, not gland-dotted; *stipules paired*, persistent, often spinescent; flowers rarely blue, ⚥, actinomorphic or zygomorphic; sepals 5, rarely 4, free or rarely connate at the base, imbricate, rarely valvate; petals 5–4, rarely absent, hypogynous, free, imbricate or contorted, rarely valvate; *disk mostly present*; stamens the same number as, to triple the number of, the petals, often unequal in length; filaments free, often *with a scale inside*; anthers 2-locular, opening lengthwise; ovary superior, sessile or rarely stipitate, usually 4–5-locular, loculi rarely transversely locellate; style simple, short, or stigmas sessile; ovules 2 or more in each loculus, axile; fruit various but *never baccate*; seeds mostly with some endosperm; embryo as long as the seed, straight or slightly curved. B.H. **1**, 262; E.P. **3**, 4, 74; edn. 2, 19a, 144 (1931). Mainly Tropical

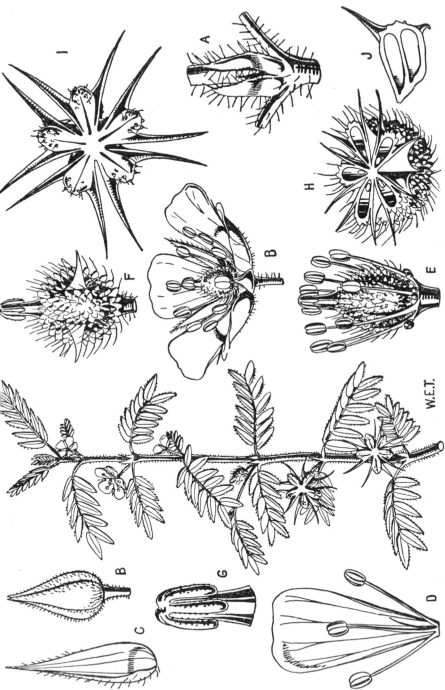

W.E.I.

Fig. 132. Tribulus terrestris L. (Zygophyllaceae). A, stipules. B, flower. C, sepal. D, petal and stamens. E, stamens and ovary. F, young fruit. G, stigma. H, same from above. I, same from side. J, segment of fruit. (After Hutch. & Dalz. *Fl. West. Trop. Afr.*)

and Subtropical Regions, often in dry or desert places.—TRIBULUS, ZYGO-PHYLLUM, FAGONIA, PEGANUM, SERICODES, TETRADICLIS, AUGEA, GUAIACUM, SISYNDITE, NITRARIA, &c.

USEFUL PRODUCTS: *Guaiacum wood* or *Lignum Vitae* (Guaiacum offici-nale *L.* and G. sanctum *L.*), Amer. and West Indies.

ORDER 35. EUPHORBIALES

Trees, shrubs, or rarely annual herbs; indumentum simple, stellate, or lepi-dote; leaves simple or rarely compound; stipules mostly present; flowers hypogynous, ♂ ♀, actinomorphic; calyx rarely absent, imbricate or valvate; petals rarely present; stamens very numerous to solitary, free or monadel-phous; ovary superior, with axile placentation; seeds with copious endosperm.

133. EUPHORBIACEAE

Herbs, shrubs, or trees, occasionally with milky juice; leaves alternate or rarely opposite, simple or compound, sometimes reduced, mostly stipulate;

FIG. 133. A–G, Ricinus communis *L.* (Euphorbiaceae). H–J, Euphorbia lathyris *L.* (After Baill.)

flowers ♂ ♀, mostly monoecious; sepals valvate or imbricate or in very specialized inflorescences sometimes much reduced or absent (*Euphorbia*); petals absent or rarely present and sometimes united (*Iatropha*); stamens from 1000 to 1, free or connate; anthers 2- (3–4-) locular, erect or inflexed in bud, opening lengthwise, rarely by pores; rudimentary ovary often present in the male flowers; ovary mostly 3-locular; styles free or united at the base; ovules solitary or paired, pendulous; funicle often thickened; disk often present in both sexes, annular or of separate glands; fruit a capsule or drupe; seeds often with a conspicuous *caruncle*; endosperm mostly copious, fleshy; embryo straight. B.H. **3**, 239 (excl. *Buxaceae*); E.P. **3**, 5, 1. Tropics and Temperate Regions.—EUPHORBIA, BRIDELIA, PHYLLANTHUS, APOROSA, ANTIDESMA, BACCAUREA, HYMENOCARDIA, HEVEA, IATROPHA, ALEURITES, CROTON, CODIAEUM, CLUYTIA, ARGITHAMNIA, MANIHOT, ACALYPHA, ALCHORNEA, MACARANGA, MALLOTUS, RICINUS, TRAGIA, DALECHAMPIA, SAPIUM, HURA, PERA, &c.

USEFUL PRODUCTS: This family furnishes very many valuable commodi-ties, amongst which the most important are *Hevea Rubber* (Hevea brasiliensis

Müll. Arg.), native of Brazil, much cultivated in E. Tropics; *Ceara Rubber* (Manihot glaziovii *Müll. Arg.*), S. Amer.; *Castor Oil* (Ricinus communis *L.*), widely cultivated; *Tung Oil* (Aleurites fordii *Hemsl.*); *Tapioca* (Manihot); *Kamala* (Mallotus philippinensis *Müll. Arg.*), India to Austral.; *Cascarilla bark* (Croton eluteria *Benn.*); *Physic nut* (Iatropha curcas *L.*), Trop. Amer.; *Cassava* (Manihot utilissima *L.*); *Garden Croton* (Codiaeum spp. and vars.).

ORDER 36. THEALES

Trees, shrubs, or rarely woody climbers, sometimes epiphytic; leaves simple, alternate, *without stipules*; flowers hypogynous to rarely subperigynous, mostly ♀; sepals imbricate, rarely contorted; petals contorted or imbricate; stamens numerous or few, free or shortly connate; ovary superior, with axile placentation; seeds with scanty or no endosperm.

A. Leaves alternate:
  B. Petals contorted; capsule septicidal; flowers in terminal panicles or racemes   *Bonnetiaceae*
  BB. Petals imbricate:
    C. Leaves simple:
      D. Bracts not modified into pitcher-like or spurred bodies; terrestrial trees, shrubs, or climbers:
        E. Stamens usually numerous:
          F. Pedicels with a pair of bracts below the calyx   *Theaceae*
          FF. Pedicels without a pair of bracts below the calyx:
            G. Anthers not inflexed in bud   *Saurauiaceae*
            GG. Anthers inflexed in bud   *Actinidiaceae*
        EE. Stamens 5:
          H. Anthers much elongated, opening by slits lengthwise; no leaf-bud scales; ovule 1 in each loculus   *Pellicieraceae*
          HH. Anthers short and rounded, opening by a short pore at the apex; buds perulate; ovules 2 in each loculus   *Pentaphylacaceae*
        EEE. Stamens 4; ovary 1-locular with 1 basal ovule   *Tetrameristaceae*
      DD. Bracts variously modified into pitcher-like saccate or spurred bodies; mostly epiphytic scramblers   *Marcgraviaceae*
    CC. Leaves compound; radicle very large with small inflexed cotyledons; stamens connate at the base   *Caryocaraceae*
AA. Leaves opposite; styles in a ring on the shoulders of the carpels
                                Medusagynaceae

134. BONNETIACEAE

Trees or rarely shrubs, sometimes resinous; leaves alternate, entire; *stipules absent*; flowers bisexual, in terminal panicles or racemes; bracts sometimes subfoliaceous; sepals 5, imbricate, unequal; petals 5, *contorted*, free, sometimes more or less *unequal-sided*; stamens numerous, filaments free or *connate at the base or into 5 bundles*; anthers short, more or less versatile, opening by slits lengthwise; connective sometimes with a *gland at the apex*; ovary

5–3-locular; style entire or shortly 3-fid; ovules usually numerous in each loculus, spreading from the axis or rarely pendulous; fruit a *septicidal capsule*, with a persistent columella; seeds linear to reniform, with or without endosperm, sometimes winged; embryo straight, with often large cotyledons. B.H. **1**, 187 (in *Ternstroemiaceae*). E.P. **3**, 6, 180 (in *Theaceae*). For revision of *Bonnetia* see Kobuski, *J. Arnold Arbor.* **29**, 393 (1948). Tropics of S. America and Malay Archipelago.

    A. Stamens free or slightly connate (not in bundles); styles more or less

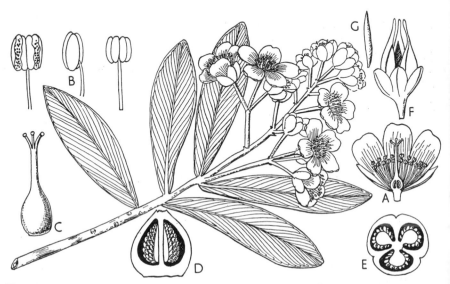

Fig. 134. Bonnetia paniculata *Spruce* (Bonnetiaceae). A, vertical section of flower. B, stamens. C, ovary and style. D, vertical section of ovary. E, cross-section of ovary. F, fruit. G, seed. (Orig.)

united: **B.** Ovules numerous in each loculus: **C.** Anthers oblong, sub-basifixed, glandular at the apex—MAHUREA (Trop. Amer.). **CC.** Anthers small and short and more or less versatile: **D.** Seeds winged—KIELMEYERA (Trop. Amer.). **DD.** Seeds not winged—BONNETIA (Trop. Amer.). **BB.** Ovules 2–4 in each loculus; anther-connective glandular at the apex; seeds not winged—CARAIPA (Trop. Amer.). **AA.** Stamens united into 5 bundles; capsule dehiscing from the base upwards: **E.** Styles free; flowers solitary within each pair of bracts; leaves without a conspicuous marginal nerve; fruits rather long—PLOIARIUM (Asia). **EE.** Styles united; flowers 3 in each pair of bracts; leaves with a double marginal nerve; fruits very short—ARCHYTAEA (S. Amer.).

135. THEACEAE
(Ternstroemiaceae)

Trees or shrubs; leaves alternate, simple, mostly evergreen; *stipules* 0; flowers mostly solitary, rarely paniculate or racemose, often showy, actinomorphic, ☿ rarely ♂ ♀; bracteoles often paired below the calyx; sepals 5, free or shortly connate, *much imbricate*; petals 5, hypogynous, free or slightly connate,

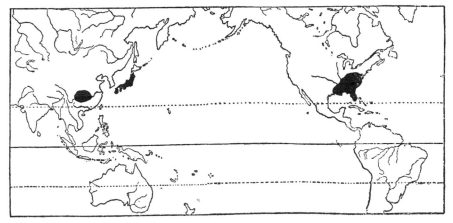

Distribution of Stuartia (Theaceae).

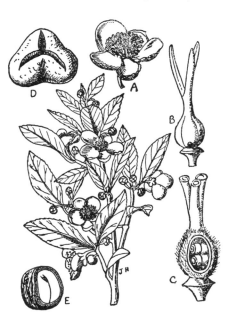

FIG. 135. Camellia sinensis (*L.*) *O. Ktze.* (Theaceae). A, flower. B, ovary. C, longitudinal section of same. D, fruit. E, seed. (After Baill.)

imbricate; stamens *numerous* in several series, rarely definite, hypogynous, free or shortly connate, sometimes adnate to the base of the petals; anthers 2-locular, opening lengthwise, very rarely by *terminal pores*; ovary superior, sessile, 3–5-locular; styles free or connate; ovules 2 or more in each loculus, rarely 1, axile; fruit dehiscent or not, loculicidal or septicidal, often leaving a central column; seeds with usually scanty endosperm and straight or curved embryo variously *folded* or *spirally twisted*. B.H. **1**, 177, partly; E.P. **3**, 6,

175; edn. 2, **21,** 109 (1925). Mainly Tropics and Temperate E. Asia.—
VISNEA, TERNSTROEMIA, CLEYERA, EURYA, STUARTIA, GORDONIA, LAPLACEA,
CAMELLIA (Thea), KIELMEYERA, FICALHOA, &c.

USEFUL PRODUCTS: *Tea plant* (Camellia sinensis (*L.*) *O. Ktze.*), E. Asia;
Mura Piranga wood (Haploclathra paniculata *Benth.*), Brazil. Many beautiful
garden plants.

136. SAURAUIACEAE

Trees or shrubs; leaves alternate, simple, mostly serrate with *strong parallel
nerves* diverging from the midrib as in *Dilleniaceae*, often roughly hairy or

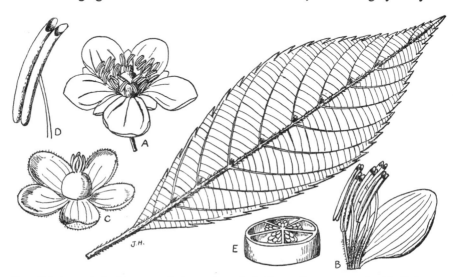

FIG. 136. Saurauia barbigera *Hook.* (Saurauiaceae). A, flower. B, stamens and petal. C, flower,
to show ovary. D, stamen. E, cross-section of ovary. (After Hook. *Ic. Pl.*)

scaly; stipules 0; flowers hypogynous, mostly ⚥, small to medium-sized, in
small axillary or lateral panicles; bracts small, remote from the calyx; sepals 5,
much imbricated; petals 5, imbricate, free or connate into a *short tube* at the
base; stamens numerous, adnate to the base of the petals; anthers small,
versatile, opening by an *apical pore or short slit*; ovary superior, 3–5-locular;
styles 3–5, free or variously united, sometimes completely so; ovules numerous
in each loculus, on axile placentas, anatropous; fruit a berry, 3–5-locular,
rarely somewhat dry and slightly dehiscent; seeds small, immersed in pulp;
endosperm rather plentiful; embryo straight or slightly curved; cotyledons
short. B.H. **1,** 184 (under *Ternstroemiaceae*); E.P. **3,** 6, 126 (under *Dilleniaceae*). Tropical and Subtropical America and Asia.—SAURAUIA.

137. ACTINIDIACEAE

Trailing or climbing shrubs; leaves alternate, *simple*, rounded, glabrous, or
with strigose, simple or *stellate* hairs; stipules 0; flowers small, in axillary

cymes or fascicles, rarely subsolitary, ☿, polygamous or dioecious; sepals 5, *imbricate*; petals 5, imbricate or subcontorted, deciduous; stamens hypogynous, 10 or more; anthers versatile, *inflexed in bud*, opening lengthwise or by pores; ovary 3- or more-locular, sometimes the carpellary walls scarcely reaching the central axis; loculi 2- or more-ovuled; ovules spreading from the central axis, anatropous; styles 5 and united to the apex, or many and spreading, usually persistent; fruit a berry or dry capsule; seeds small, with copious endosperm and straight embryo with short cotyledons. B.H. **1**, 184 (under *Ternstroemiaceae*). E. Asia.

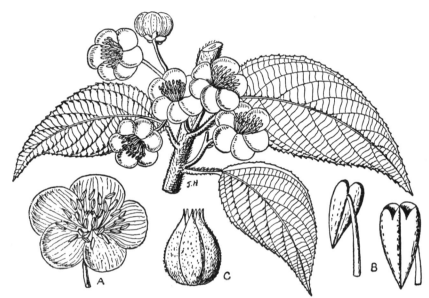

Fig. 137. Actinidia strigosa *Hk. f. & Thoms.* (Actinidiaceae). A, flower. B, stamens. C, ovary. (Orig.)

A. Styles free, radiating from the base; ovary several-locular; stamens numerous; flowers polygamous or dioecious; fruit a berry—Actinidia (E. Asia, Java). **AA.** Styles united to the apex; fruit a dry capsule; flowers bisexual: **B.** Ovary 5-locular; stamens 10, in two series; ovules 10–8 in each loculus—Clematoclethra (China). **BB.** Ovary 3-locular; stamens 13–11, 1-seriate; ovules 2 in each loculus—Sladenia (Burma and W. China).

138. Pellicieraceae

Glabrous tree, with the habit of *Rhizophora*; leaves alternate, *involute in bud*, leathery; *stipules absent*; flowers axillary, sessile, solitary, included for a time by 2 *long bracteoles*; flower-buds long-acuminate; sepals at first white, at length, like the petals, rose, 5, much shorter than the bracteoles and petals, much imbricate; petals 5, elongated, imbricate, free; stamens 5, filaments free; anthers elongated, *adherent to the style* and opening subextrorsely;

FIG. 138. Pelliciera rhizophorae *Planch. & Triana* (Pellicieraceae). A, flower with bracts removed. B, stamens and pistil. C, pistil and remains of filaments. D, vertical section of ovary. E, transverse section of ovary. F, ripe fruit. G, vertical section of flower. (Mainly after Hemsley.)

ovary 10-grooved, 2-locular; ovules solitary in each loculus, axile, pendulous; fruit ovoid, 10-grooved, long-acuminate, leathery, *indehiscent*, 1-locular; seed pendulous, *without endosperm*; cotyledons broad, thick and fleshy; radicle short, plumule long. B.H. **1**, 186 (in *Ternstroemiaceae*); E.P. **3**, 6, 192 (in *Theaceae*). Mangroves of Panama and Colombia.—PELLICIERA.

139. PENTAPHYLACACEAE

Evergreen shrubs or trees; buds perulate; leaves simple, alternate, entire, pinnately nerved; *stipules absent*; flowers bisexual, actinomorphic, small, racemose or subspicate; *bracteoles 2*, appressed to the calyx, persistent; sepals 5, free, imbricate, persistent; petals 5, free, imbricate; stamens 5, alternate with the petals, free, *inflexed in bud*, later erect; filaments loosely connivent towards the base; anther-loculi 2, separate, rounded, opening by a very small pore at the apex; disk absent; ovary superior, 5-locular; ovules 2 in each loculus, collateral and pendulous from the inner angle, with 2 integuments; style 1, long-persistent, stout; stigmas 5, very small; capsule ellipsoidal, loculicidally dehiscent half-way down or right to the base; valves long-

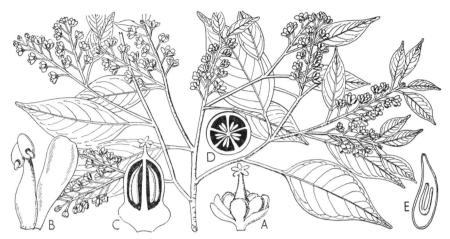

Fig. 139. Pentaphylax euryoides *Gardn. & Champ.* (Pentaphylacaceae). A, flower without stamens. B, stamen and petal. C, vertical section of ovary. D, cross-section of ovary. E, vertical section of seed.

persistent, with a median septum; axis persistent; seeds more or less *winged*, with scanty endosperm and *horseshoe-shaped embryo*. See van Steenis, *Flora Malesiana*, ser. 1, **5**, 2. 121, fig. 1, with map (1956); Mattfeld, E.P., edn. 2, **20**b, 232 (1942). S.E. Asia, Malaya.—PENTAPHYLAX.

140. TETRAMERISTACEAE[1]

Trees; leaves alternate, undivided, sessile, leathery, *punctate with black glands* below and with two longitudinal rows of glands; no stipules; flowers small in axillary pedunculate umbel-like racemes with sub-foliaceous bracts; pedicels subverticillate, 2-bracteolate; sepals 4, *imbricate in two series*, persistent, the outer pair larger; petals 4, imbricate, persistent; stamens 4; filaments flattened at the base; anthers *oblong-sagittate*, loculi separate, *glandular at the base*, opening by slits lengthwise; ovary 4-angled, 4-locular with thin septa; style subulate, with a 4-toothed stigma; ovule solitary in each loculus, *basal*; fruit a *globose berry*, surrounded at the base by the persistent bracteoles, sepals

[1] **Tetrameristaceae**, Hutch., fam. nov.; arbores; folia alterna, integra, sessilia, infra glandulis nigris punctata et glandularum lineis longitudinalibus duabus ornata; stipulae nullae; flores bisexuales, in racemis umbelliformibus pedunculatis axillaribus dispositi; bracteae subfoliaceae; sepala 4, biseriata, persistentia; petala 4, imbricata, persistentia; stamina 4, libera; antherae oblongo-sagittatae, loculis discretis basi glandulosis longitudinaliter dehiscentibus; ovarium 4-loculare, septis tenuibus; stylus subulatus, 4-dentatus; ovulum pro loculo 1, basale; bacca globosa, basi bracteolis sepalis et petalis persistentibus circumdata, exocarpio coriaceo, mesocarpio carnoso; semina 4, oblonga.—Typus *Tetra-merista* Miq.

FIG. 140. Tetramerista glabra *Miq.* (Tetrameristaceae). A, flower-bud. B, vertical section of flower. C, anthers. D, fruit. E, vertical section of fruit. (Orig.)

and petals; exocarp leathery, mesocarp fleshy; seeds 4, oblong. B.H. **1**, 318 (in *Ochnaceae*); E.P., edn. 2, **21**, 152 (in *Theaceae*). Malay Peninsula, Borneo, Sumatra.—TETRAMERISTA.

141. MARCGRAVIACEAE

Climbing and mostly *epiphytic* shrubs, rarely arborescent; leaves simple, alternate, sometimes *dimorphic*; stipules 0; flowers ☿, hypogynous, in terminal racemes or racemose umbels, the *bracts* of the *sterile* flowers variously modified into *pitcher-like*, *saccate*, or *spurred bodies* adnate to or free from the pedicel; sepals 5, much imbricate; petals 5, free or connate into a deciduous calyptra; stamens 3 to numerous, free or slightly connate; anthers 2-locular, opening lengthwise; ovary 2- or more-locular; stigmas sessile, radiate; ovules numerous in several rows on thick placentas; fruit thick and fleshy, globose, indehiscent or slightly dehiscent into the loculi at the base; seeds numerous, small, without endosperm; embryo slightly curved, with large radicle and two small cotyledons. B.H. **1**, 178 (under *Ternstroemiaceae*). E.P. **3**, 6, 157. Tropical America.

A. Leaves all of one kind; inflorescences mostly elongate-racemose or spicate, all the flowers fertile; bracts not adnate to the pedicels: **B.** Stamens numerous; bracts saccate—NORANTEA. **BB.** Stamens 5–3: **C.** Ovary 5-locular; bracts 3-lobed, one lobe spur-like—SOUROUBEA. **CC.** Ovary 2-locular; bracts not lobed, urn-shaped: **D.** Stamens 5; petals and filaments united at the base—RUYSCHIA. **DD.** Stamens 3; petals and filaments free —CARACASIA. **AA.** Leaves of two kinds, the lowermost much smaller and

Fig. 141. Marcgravia umbellata *L.* (Marcgraviaceae). A, flower. B, stamen. C, cross-section of ovary. D, young shoot. (Orig.)

very different from the others; bracts of the central flowers of the umbelliform inflorescence completely adnate to the pedicels and often pitcherlike and indurated; petals connate into a calyptra; stamens numerous —MARCGRAVIA.

142. CARYOCARACEAE

Erect trees or shrubs: leaves opposite or alternate, *digitately 3–5-foliolate*; flowers ⚥, in terminal ebracteate racemes; calyx 5–6-lobed, imbricate or truncate; petals 5–6, free or cohering above, imbricate; stamens subperigynous, numerous, in 5–6 series or shortly connate at the base; filaments variously bent in bud, sometimes the inner ones *without anthers*; anthers small, 2-locular, opening lengthwise; ovary 4–20-locular; styles the same number, filiform; ovule solitary in each loculus, ascending; fruit rather drupaceous with a woody muricate endocarp breaking up into 1-seeded parts; seeds kidney-shaped, with scanty thin endosperm; embryo with a large spirally twisted radicle; cotyledons small, hooked-inflexed. B.H. **1,** 178 (under *Ternstroemiaceae*); E.P. **3,** 6, 153. Tropical America.

USEFUL PRODUCTS: *Souari nuts* (Caryocar nuciferum *L.,* and C. tomentosum *Willd.*), S. Amer.

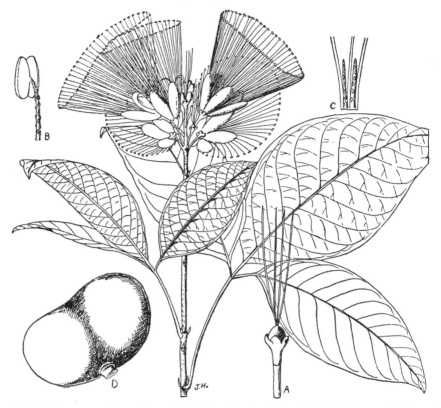

Fig. 142. Caryocar glabrum *Pers.* (Caryocaraceae). A, calyx and pistil. B, stamen. C, base of filaments. D, fruit. (After Martius.) *Note*: Alternate leaves have been removed for clarity (following Martius) the leaves being strictly opposite.

A. Leaves opposite; petals free; styles 4–6, very long and filiform—CARYOCAR. **AA.** Leaves alternate; petals connate into a calyptra; styles 8–20, short—ANTHODISCUS.

143. MEDUSAGYNACEAE

Shrubs; leaves *opposite*, simple; stipules absent; flowers in terminal panicles, red, actinomorphic, bisexual; sepals 5, *imbricate*, deciduous; petals 5, *imbricate*, free; stamens *very numerous*, hypogynous, shorter than the ovary; filaments free, very slender; anthers 2-locular, basifixed, opening lengthwise; ovary superior, 20–25-locular, the carpels nearly free to the central axis; styles stout, *in a ring on the shoulders* of the carpels; stigmas capitate; ovules 2 in each loculus, and attached about the middle of the inner angle, one *ascending*, the other *descending*; fruit capsular, the carpels septicidally dehiscent from the base and diverging like an umbrella; seeds winged. Hemsl., Hook. *Ic. Pl.* t. 2790; E.P., edn. 2, **21.** 50. Seychelles Is.—MEDUSAGYNE.

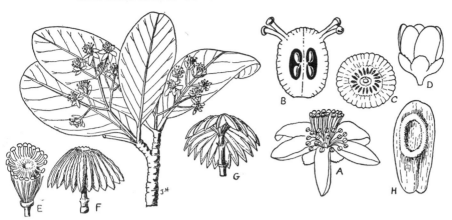

Fig. 143. Medusagyne oppositifolia *Baker* (Medusagynaceae). A, flower, open. B, longitudinal section of ovary. C, cross-section of same. D, flower, side view. E, styles and stigmas from above. F, fruit, side view. G, same from below. H, seed. (After Hook. *Ic. Pl.*)

Order 37. OCHNALES

Mainly as in *Theales*, but leaves with stipules, intra- or extra-petiolar; calyx-lobes often enlarged and wing-like in fruit or involucrate by bracts.—Tropics.

A. Erect trees and shrubs:
  B. Anther-connective not produced at the apex:
    C. Stipules intrapetiolar; stamens free among themselves; anthers sub-sagittate, versatile; no staminodes; ovules 2 in each loculus, axile
                                                                    Strasburgeriaceae
    CC. Stipules extrapetiolar:
      D. Stamens free among themselves; ovules axile:
        E. Sepals 10–5, not involucrate by bracts   *Ochnaceae*
        EE. Sepals 3, usually involucrate at the base   *Sarcolaenaceae*
      DD. Stamens irregularly connate at the base; ovules erect from the base
        of the loculi   *Sphaerosepalaceae*
  BB. Anther-connective produced at the apex; calyx-lobes usually enlarged
    and wing-like in fruit; ovary 3-locular; ovules 2 in each loculus
                                                                    Dipterocarpaceae
AA. Climbing shrubs with hooked branches; petals contorted; calyx enlarged
    and wing-like in fruit; ovary 1-locular; ovule 1   *Ancistrocladaceae*

144. Strasburgeriaceae

Tree; leaves alternate, large, simple, obovate, remotely toothed; stipules *intrapetiolar*, two together and connate into a short subentire or 2-toothed scale; flowers bisexual, solitary, axillary; pedicels thick, short; calyx coriaceous, lobes 10–8, very unequal, closely imbricate, gradually larger from the outer to the inner, persistent below the fruit; petals 5, free, longer than the calyx, imbricate, venose and rather fleshy; stamens 10; filaments free; anthers introrse, *subsagittate*, *versatile*; disk hypogynous, thick and annular at the

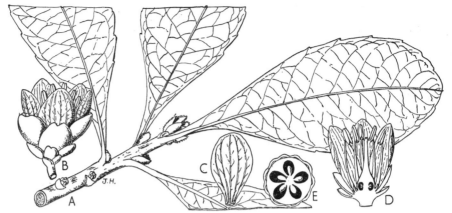

FIG. 144. Strasburgeria robusta (*Pancher & Sebert*) *Guillaumin* (Strasburgeriaceae). A, leafy shoot drawn from specimen in the Kew Herbarium showing the intrapetiolar stipules. B, flower. C, petal. D, vertical section of flower. E, cross-section of ovary surrounded by the disk. B–D adapted from Engler.

base, *10-lobed above*, lobes alternating with the stamens; ovary free, pyramidately 10-ribbed, narrowed into a subulate style, 5-locular; ovules 2 in each loculus, superposed, descending from the axis; fruit subglobose, baccate, corky-woody when dry, *indehiscent* (5–6 cm long and broad), apiculate with the base of the style; seeds 2–1 in each loculus, unequally trigonous-compressed, testa shining, with a *wing-like broad opaque hilum*; endosperm fleshy; embryo axile; cotyledons subelliptic. New Caledonia.—STRASBURGERIA.

145. OCHNACEAE

Trees or shrubs with watery juice, rarely herbs; leaves alternate, simple, very rarely pinnate, often with *numerous pinnate nerves*; stipules present,

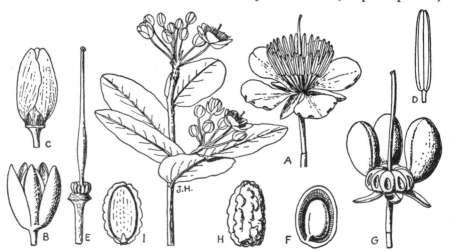

FIG. 145. Ochna andravinensis *Baill.* (Ochnaceae). A, flower. B, sepals. C, petals. D, anther. E, ovary. F, seed. G, fruit. H, seed. I, longitudinal section of seed. (After Baill.)

sometimes *laciniate*; flowers ☿, actinomorphic, mostly racemose or paniculate; sepals 4–5, rarely 10, free, imbricate or rarely contorted; petals free, 4–10, subsessile, contorted or imbricate; stamens few to many, free; *staminodes* sometimes present, subulate or petaloid, sometimes connate into a tube; filaments persistent; anthers linear, basifixed, opening lengthwise or by a *terminal pore*; ovary entire to *deeply lobed*, 1–10-locular; ovules 1 to many, axile or parietal or attached to the intrusive placentas; style simple or fid at the apex; fruiting carpels often becoming *quite separate* on the *enlarged torus* and drupaceous, or elongated, capsular and septicidal; seeds 1 to many, with or without endosperm; embryo usually straight (*incl.* Sauvagesieae). B.H. **1**, 316; E.P. **3**, 6, 131. Tropics.—OCHNA, OURATEA (*Gomphia*), EUTHEMIS, LUXEMBURGIA, GODOYA, SAUVAGESIA, LAVRADIA, NECKIA, &c.

USEFUL PRODUCTS: *Meni Oil* (from kernels of Lophira alata *Banks*); wood known as *African Oak*.

146. SARCOLAENACEAE

Shrubs or trees; leaves alternate, entire; stipules caducous; flowers ☿, actinomorphic, cymose or paniculate; *sepals 3, imbricate*, usually involucrate or bracteolate at the base; petals 5–6, *contorted*, free; stamens 10 or more, inserted inside an entire or toothed cupular ring of staminodes; anthers

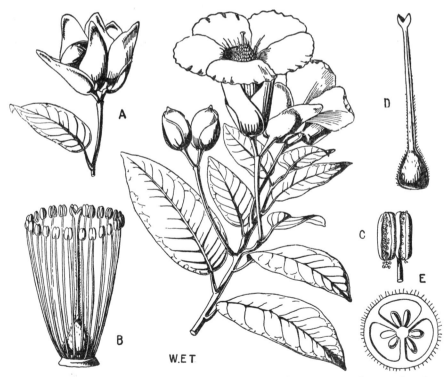

FIG. 146. Rhodolaena altivola *Baill.* (Sarcolaenaceae). A, bud. B, stamens and ovary. C, anther. D, ovary. E, cross-section of ovary. (After Baill.)

2-locular, opening lengthwise; ovary 3-locular; style simple, elongated; stigma 3-lobed; ovules 2 or more in each loculus, mostly pendulous, anatropous; capsule opening loculicidally, 3-valved or by suppression 1-locular and 1-seeded; seeds with fleshy or horny endosperm and straight embryo; cotyledons flat or plaited. B.H. **1**, 194; E.P. **3**, 6, 168. Madagascar.

An interesting family of beautiful trees and shrubs, remarkable in being confined to Madagascar, where numerous other unusual types of plants are found.

A. Stamens numerous (12 or more): **B.** Involucre absent from below the calyx—EREMOLAENA. **BB.** Involucre present below the calyx and sometimes resembling it: **C.** Sepals 5—XYLOLAENA. **CC.** Sepals 3: **D.** Involucre not a closed calyx-like organ: **E.** Involucre small, not enlarged after flowering—RHODOLAENA. **EE.** Involucre enlarged after flowering—SCHIZOLAENA. **DD.** Involucre a closed calyx-like organ: **F.** Involucre dry, a simple tube—XEROCHLAMYS. **FF.** Involucre of numerous spathulate bracts—SARCOLAENA. **AA.** Stamens 10; involucre a closed calyx-like organ; ovules 2 in each loculus of the ovary, collateral—LEPTOLAENA.

147. SPHAEROSEPALACEAE

Trees or shrubs; leaves alternate, petiolate, elliptic or ovate, pinnately nerved or trinerved, nerves rather prominent on both sides, looped and branched towards the entire margin; stipules present but very soon falling off and leaving a transverse semi-amplexicaul scar; flowers bisexual, in axillary and terminal *subumbelliform cymules*; bracts early caducous and leaving an annular

FIG. 147. Rhopalocarpus alternifolius (*Baker*) R. *Capuron* (Sphaerosepalum alternifolium *Baker*) (Sphaerosepalaceae). A, flower-bud. B, petal. C, stamen. D, anther from the back. E, disk and ovary. F, vertical section of ovary, G, fruit of R. lucidus *Bojer*. H, seed of R. lucidus. (Orig.)

rim; bracteoles absent; pedicels stout; sepals 4, free, very imbricate, the innermost the largest and folded closely over the petals, coriaceous; petals 4, unequal, free, imbricate, broadly obovate and slightly clawed, densely streaked *with short resinous lines*, thinner at the margin; stamens numerous, hypogynous, inserted below a large thick *cupular wrinkled disk*; filaments irregularly connate at the base, slender, dotted with resin; anthers 2-locular, loculi short and separated by a broad *glanaular connective*, dehiscing lengthwise; ovary superior but partly immersed in the disk, vertically deeply 2-lobed and 2-locular; *style undivided*, inserted between the lobes, stigma entire, spoon-shaped; ovules about 3 in each loculus, anatropous, erect from the base of the loculi; fruit globose or kidney-shaped with 2 rounded lobes, *densely muricate*, 1-seeded; seed large, conforming to the fruit in shape. Madagascar.—RHOPALOCARPUS (*Sphaerosepalum*).[1]

A small and very interesting family with a single genus of about 5 known species which I have tried without success to fit into some larger established family. Under the name *Sphaerosepalum* it was originally assigned to the *Clusiaceae* (*Guttiferae*) by Baker, and later transferred to *Flacourtiaceae* by Warburg, and later to the segregate family *Cochlospermaceae* by Pilger (E.P., edn. 2, **21**, 320 (1925).

van Tieghem pointed out that it did not belong to any of these families, and I have followed him in maintaining it as a separate family near to the *Sarcolaenaceae* and *Theaceae*, but more especially to the *Ochnaceae*. The basal placenta and the partly connate filaments of the stamens are an unusual combination of characters. See also Dangy, *Bull. Mus. Hist. Nat. Paris*, **31**, 203 (1925).

148. DIPTEROCARPACEAE

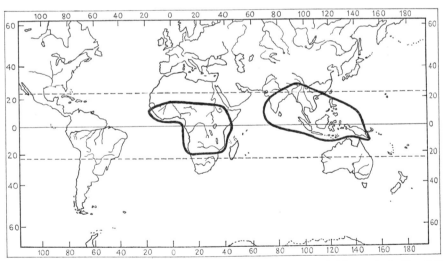

Range of Dipterocarpaceae, all Indo-Malayan except Monotes and Marquesia in Tropical Africa.

Trees with *resinous wood*; leaves alternate, simple; indumentum of *stellate hairs* or of *peltate scales*; stipules small or large, deciduous; flowers ☿, actino-

---

[1] The identity of these two genera was first indicated by R. Capuron, inspector of 'Eaux & Forêts de Madagascar', according to labels in the Kew Herbarium.

morphic, fragrant, in axillary panicles; bracts usually absent; calyx-tube short or long, free or adnate to the ovary; lobes 5, imbricate or valvate, usually *enlarged and wing-like* in fruit; petals 5, much *twisted*, free or slightly connate, often hairy; stamens usually numerous, hypogynous or subperigynous; anthers 2-locular, opening lengthwise, with *produced connective*; ovary 3-locular; style entire or 3-lobed; ovules 2 in each loculus, pendulous or patent, anatropous; fruit indehiscent, mostly 1-seeded; seeds *without endosperm*; cotyledons often twisted, enclosing the radicle. B.H. **1**, 189; E.P. **3**, 6, 243.

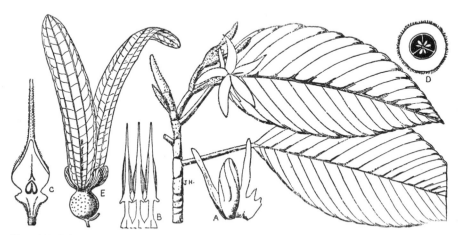

FIG. 148. Dipterocarpus trinervis *Roxb.* (Dipterocarpaceae). A, calyx and corolla. B, stamens. C, longitudinal section of ovary. D, cross-section of same. E, fruit. (After Blume.)

Tropical Old World, rare in Africa.—DIPTEROCARPUS, VATICA, SHOREA, HOPEA, DOONA, VATERIA, MONOTES, MARQUESIA, &c.

USEFUL PRODUCTS: Numerous valuable timbers from SHOREA, HOPEA, &c.; *Sal or Saul Tree* (Shorea robusta *Gaertn.*), India; *Piny Resin, Indian Copal*, or *White Dammar* (from Vateria indica *L.*), S. India; *Sumatra Camphor Tree* (Dryobalanops aromatica *Gaertn.*); *Garjan* or *Kanyin Oil* (Dipterocarpus turbinatus *Gaertn.*), E. India and Malay Penin.; *In* or *Eng Oil* (D. tuberculatus *Roxb.*), E. India.

149. ANCISTROCLADACEAE

Scandent shrubs; *branches hooked*; leaves alternate, simple; stipules small, caducous; flowers ♀, actinomorphic, small, paniculate with recurved branches; calyx-tube short, at length *adnate to the base of the ovary*; lobes imbricate, becoming unequally *enlarged and wing-like* in fruit; petals 5, *contorted*, slightly connate; stamens 5 or 10; anthers 2-locular, opening lengthwise; ovary 1-locular; ovule solitary, ascending; style thick, with 3 stigmas; fruit a nut, surrounded by the wing-like calyx-lobes; seeds with the *testa intruding* between the folds of the embryo; cotyledons remarkably *folded* and enclosing the radicle. B.H. **1**, 191 (under *Dipterocarpaceae*); E.P. **3**, 6, 274. Tropical Asia, W. Tropical Africa (see map).—ANCISTROCLADUS.

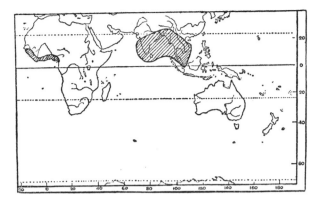

Distribution of Ancistrocladus.

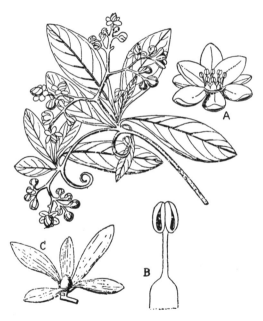

FIG. 149. Ancistrocladus heyneanus *Wall.* (Ancistrocladaceae). A, flower. B, stamen. C, fruit. (Orig.)

ORDER 38. ERICALES

Shrubs, rarely herbs or trees, sometimes parasitic or epiphytic; leaves simple, sometimes scaly, alternate to rarely opposite; stipules absent; flowers ☿, rarely ♂ ♀, actinomorphic; petals united (rarely free); stamens hypogynous or epigynous, very rarely epipetalous, usually double the number of the corolla-lobes; anthers often opening by terminal pores; ovary superior to inferior, with axile placentation; seeds with copious endosperm and small embryo.—Mainly Temperate Regions, and Mountainous Regions of the Tropics.

A. Petals free or nearly so; anthers opening by terminal pores; fruit a capsule:
  B. Shrubs or small trees; flowers racemose or paniculate; pollen not united
  in tetrads   *Clethraceae*
  BB. Herbs with mostly radical leaves; pollen united in tetrads   *Pyrolaceae*
AA. Petals free or absent; anthers opening lengthwise   *Monotropaceae*
AAA. Petals united into a tube:
  C. Ovary superior:
    D. Leafy plants, shrubs, trees, or herbs (sometimes epiphytic):
      E. Stamens hypogynous:
        F. Anthers 2-locular, opening by terminal pores or pore-like slits
                                                                  Ericaceae
        FF. Anthers 1-locular, opening by a single slit   *Epacridaceae*
      EE. Stamens epipetalous; anthers opening by slits lengthwise or trans-
        versely   *Diapensiaceae*
    DD. Leafless parasitic herbs devoid of green colouring:
      G. Ovary 6–1-locular; ovules very numerous on axile or parietal placentas
                                                                  Monotropaceae
      GG. Ovary 15–10-locular; ovules paired in each loculus on axile placen-
        tas   *Lennoaceae*
  CC. Ovary inferior; fruit indehiscent (very rarely dehiscent), fleshy, juicy, or
    drupaceous   *Vacciniaceae*

150. CLETHRACEAE

Shrubs or trees; leaves alternate, simple; stipules 0; flowers ☿, fragrant, in racemes or panicles; calyx deeply 5-lobed, lobes *imbricate, persistent* around the fruit; corolla of 5 *free* imbricate petals; stamens 10–12, *hypogynous*, free; filaments hairy or glabrous; anthers *inflexed in bud*, sagittate, opening by *apical pores*; pollen not united in tetrads; disk obsolete; ovary superior, hairy, 3-locular, 3-lobed; style 1, 3-lobed at the apex; ovules numerous on axile placentas; fruit a subglobose 3-lobed loculicidally 3-valved capsule; seeds numerous, compressed or trigonous, often winged; endosperm fleshy, with a cylindrical embryo. B.H. **2**, 603 (under *Ericaceae*); E.P. **4**, 1, 2. Subtropical and Tropical E. Asia, Madeira, Southeastern U.S.A., Central and Tropical S. America.

USEFUL PRODUCTS: Evergreen and deciduous garden shrubs.

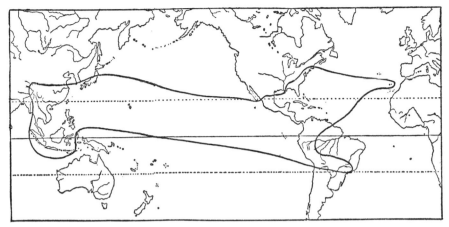

The distribution of the genus Clethra, the most primitive of the Ericales alliance, seems to lend support to the hypothesis of continental drift. One outlying endemic species, *Clethra arborea L.*, is a dominant tree in parts of the island of Madeira.

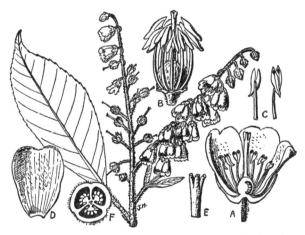

FIG. 150. Clethra arborea *L.* (Clethraceae). A, vertical section of flower. B, flower with sepals and petals removed. C, stamens. D, petal. E, style. F, transverse section of ovary. (Orig.)

A. Inflorescence terminal; sepals not accrescent in fruit or only slightly so— CLETHRA (Subtrop. and Trop. E. Asia, Madeira, Southeastern U.S.A., Cent. and Trop. S. Amer.). **AA.** Inflorescence axillary; sepals laciniate and accrescent in fruit—SCHIZOCARDIA (British Honduras).

151. PYROLACEAE

Perennial herbs, caulescent or acaulescent, leaves radical or alternate or subverticillate, evergreen, rarely reduced, entire or toothed; stipules absent; flowers in racemes, umbels, or corymbs, or scapose and solitary, bracteate, nodding, white, rose, or purplish; calyx 5–4-partite, persistent; petals 5 or rarely 4, *free or very shortly united*, imbricate, more or less orbicular and sessile, entire or toothed; stamens 10, rarely 8, hypogynous, free; anthers at

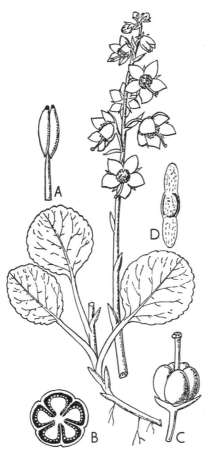

first *inverted*, at length erect, 4–2-locular, opening by *terminal pores*; *pollen united in tetrads*; disk present, often small; ovary superior, partially 5-locular; style straight or declinate, stigma 5-lobed or orbicular and crenate; ovules numerous, crowded on thick fleshy axile placentas; fruit a more or less globose capsule, 5-locular, loculicidally 5-valved at the base or apex; seeds small, testa loose, *produced at each end*, reticulate; endosperm fleshy; embryo very minute. N. Temperate Zone south to Mexico and the West Indies.—See Copeland, 'Observations on the Structure and Classification of Pyrolaceae', *Madrono*, 9, 65 (1947).

A. Flowers solitary; petals spreading— MONESES (*Bryophthalmum, Monanthium*) (Temp. N. Hemisph.). AA. Flowers in racemes—PYROLA (*Ramischia, Erxlebenia, Braxilia*). (Temp. N. Hemisph.). AAA. Flowers in umbels or corymbs— CHIMAPHILA (Temp. N. Hemisph., south to Mexico and the West Indies).

FIG. 151. Pyrola rotundifolia *L.* (Pyrolaceae). A, stamen. B, cross-section of ovary. C, ovary and style. D, seed.

152. ERICACEAE

Shrubs or undershrubs, rarely trees; leaves mostly alternate, simple, mostly evergreen; stipules absent; flowers ☿, actinomorphic or slightly zygomorphic; calyx persistent; corolla hypogynous, mostly *sympetalous*, inserted below a fleshy disk, lobes contorted or imbricate; stamens mostly *double the number of the corolla-lobes*, rarely the same number and then alternate, *hypogynous*, inserted on the disk; filaments free or rarely somewhat connate; anthers 2-locular, often with tails, *opening by pores*; ovary *superior*, several-locular, with numerous ovules on axile placentas which often protrude into the loculi, rarely ovule 1; style simple; fruit a capsule, berry, or drupe; seeds with fleshy endosperm and straight embryo, sometimes winged. B.H. 2, 577; E.P. 4, 1, 15. Generally distributed; great concentration of species in S. Africa (*Erica*) and W. China (*Rhododendron*).—ARBUTUS, ARCTOSTAPHYLOS, PERNETTYA, GAULTHERIA, CASSIOPE, LEUCOTHOE, AGARISTA, ANDROMEDA, PIERIS, ENKIANTHUS, CALLUNA, ERICA, PHILIPPIA, BLAERIA, GRISEBACHIA,

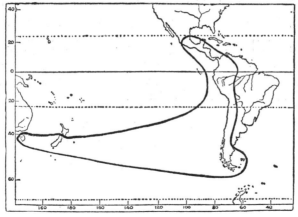

Range of Pernettya (Ericaceae) emphasizing the close relationship of the floras of New Zealand and Western S. America.

W.E.T.

FIG. 152. Rhododendron cinnamomeum *Wall.* (Ericaceae). A, anther. B, section of ovary. (After Hook. f.)

SIMOCHEILUS, SCYPHOGYNE, LOISELEURIA, BRYANTHUS, DABEOCIA (*Daboecia*), KALMIA, ELLIOTTIA, LEDUM, RHODODENDRON (*Azalea*), &c.

USEFUL PRODUCTS: Many beautiful outdoor shrubs and rock-garden plants; *Rhododendron, Erica*, &c. *Bear-Berry* (Arctostaphylos uva-ursi *Spreng.*), N. cool Temp. Zone; *Heather* (Calluna vulgaris *Salisb.*); *Briar Root wood* (Erica arborea *L.*), S. Eur., &c.; *Labrador Tea* (Ledum latifolium *Jacq.*), N. Amer.

153. EPACRIDACEAE

Shrubs or small trees; leaves alternate, rarely opposite, often crowded; stipules

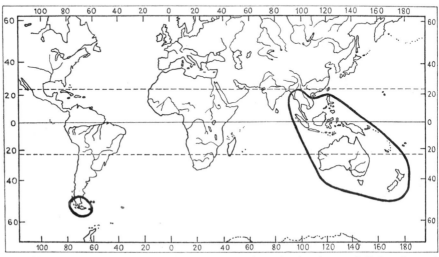

Epacridaceae are nearly all Australasian, except for Lebetanthus in subantarctic S. America, and Leucopogon, which reaches into the northern hemisphere as far as Indo-China and the Philippines.

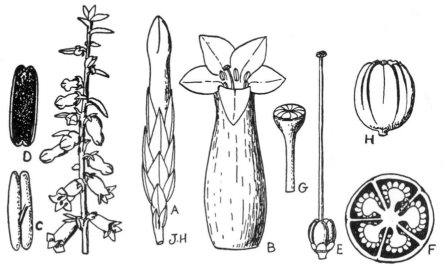

FIG. 153. Epacris nivalis *Lodd.* (Epacridaceae). A, flower in bud. B, open flower. C and D, anthers. E, pistil. F, section of ovary. G, stigma. H, fruit. (After Le Maout & Decne.)

absent; flowers ☿, rarely ♂ ♀, bracteate; calyx 4–5-lobed, persistent; corolla sympetalous, hypogynous, lobes imbricate or valvate, rarely the lobes coherent and then the tube opening transversely near the persistent base; stamens usually 4–5, *hypogynous* or *epipetalous*, alternate with the corolla-lobes, sometimes alternating with bunches of *hairs* or *glands*; *anthers 1-locular*, opening lengthwise; ovary superior, often surrounded at the base by hypogynous disk-glands, 1–10-locular; style simple; ovules 1 to many, on axile or apical placentas, rarely erect; fruit a capsule or drupe; seeds with straight embryo in the middle of fleshy endosperm. B.H. **2**, 608; E.P. **4**, 1, 66. Mainly extratropical Australia, New Caledonia, New Zealand, a few in subantarctic S. America (see map).—Astroloma, Leucopogon, Epacris, Andersonia, Richea, Dracophyllum, &c.

Useful Products: Ornamental greenhouse shrubs.

154. Diapensiaceae

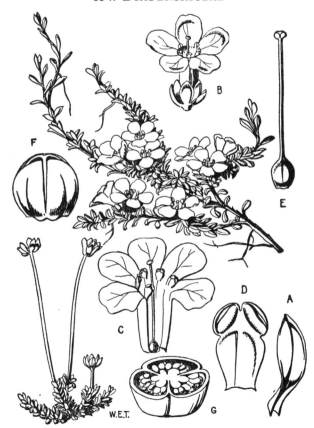

Fig. 154. Diapensia himalaica *Hk. f. & Thoms.* A, leaf. B, flower. C, same opened. D, stamen. E, ovary. F, fruit. G, same in transverse section. (After Hook. f.)

Small shrublets; leaves simple, small and imbricate or few and larger; flowers ☿, actinomorphic, solitary to subcapitate, white, rose, or purple; calyx

5-lobed, persistent, lobes imbricate; corolla sympetalous, 5-lobed, lobes imbricate; stamens 5, *inserted on the corolla* and *alternate* with the lobes, free, or connate into a ring with as many *staminodes*; anthers 1–2-locular, mostly *opening lengthwise*; staminodes when present either scale-like or spathulate; disk none; ovary superior, 3-locular; ovules few to numerous on *axile placentas*; fruit a capsule, loculicidally 3-valved; seeds minute with copious fleshy endosperm and cylindrical central embryo. B.H. **2**, 618; E.P. **4**, 1, 80. Temperate and cold N. Hemisphere.

A. Staminodes absent; flowers solitary; leaves narrow and imbricate, entire: **B.** Anther-loculi transversely dehiscent, cuspidate below; flowers sessile —PYXIDANTHERA (Eastern U.S.A.). **BB.** Anther-loculi dehiscent lengthwise; flowers pedicellate—DIAPENSIA (Circumpolar, south to Himal.). **AA.** Staminodes 5, opposite the petals, separate or united with the filaments into a ring; leaves orbicular to obovate or spathulate, long-petiolate: **C.** Corolla-lobes toothed or fringed: **D.** Corolla campanulate; lobes crenate; staminodes small and scale-like—SHORTIA (*Sherwoodia, Shortiopsis*) (E. Asia, Eastern U.S.A.). **DD.** Corolla funnel-shaped, lobes fringed; staminodes linear—SCHIZOCODON (E. Asia). **CC.** Corolla-lobes entire: **E.** Anthers 2-locular; style elongated— BERNEUXIA (Tibet, W. China, Upper Burma). **EE.** Anthers 1-locular; style very short—GALAX (Eastern U.S.A.).

155. MONOTROPACEAE

Leafless herbs *parasitic* on the roots of trees, never green; stem scaly, scales alternate, the upper ones becoming bracteate or involucrate; flowers ☿,

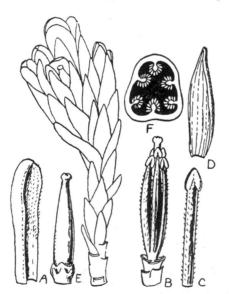

actinomorphic, solitary to capitate, often dull-coloured; sepals 2–6, erect, imbricate, often not distinguishable from the bracts; petals 3–6, free or united into a lobed corolla, subcontorted or imbricate, very rarely absent; stamens 6–12, *hypogynous*; filaments free or connate at the base; anthers 2-locular, *opening lengthwise*; pollen mostly in a *mass*; disk present or absent; ovary superior, 1–6-locular; style various, with a mostly *capitate, indusiate* stigma; ovules very numerous, minute, in the 1-locular ovaries on *parietal* placentas, axile in the ovaries with more loculi; capsule often membranous, loculicidally 4–6-valved; seeds minute, with copious endosperm and minute undivided embryo. B.H. **2**, 604; E.P. **4**, 1, 9 (under *Pyrolaceae*). Northern Hemisphere.

FIG. 155. Cheilotheca malayana *Scort.* (Monotropaceae). A, sepal. B, flower with perianth removed. C, stamen. D, petal. E, ovary. F, transverse section of same. (After Hook. *Ic. Pl.*)

A. Petals free or absent: **B.** Ovary and capsule 5–4-locular with a central column and axile placentas; disk present: **C.** Petals present: **D.** Flowers solitary, terminal; anthers opening by 2 equal chinks—MONOTROPA (Asia, N. and Cent. Amer.). **DD.** Flowers racemose; anthers opening by a continuous line into two very unequal halves—HYPOPITYS (Eur. to E. Asia, N. Amer.). **CC.** Petals absent; anthers extrorse in bud, introrse in the open flower—ALLOTROPA (N. Amer.). **BB.** Ovary and capsule 1-locular with parietal placentas but no central column: **E.** Anthers ovoid or elongated: **F.** Flowers few; stamens 6; disk absent—CHEILOTHECA (Himal., Malay Penin.). **FF.** Flowers numerous; stamens 10 or 8; disk present—PLEURICOSPORA (Calif.). **EE.** Anthers rounded-reniform; disk absent: **G.** Flowers solitary, terminal—MONOTROPASTRUM (E. Asia). **GG.** Flowers racemose—PITYOPUS (N. Amer.). **AA.** Petals united into a tube; placentas usually axile: **H.** Disk absent; ovary and capsule 6–4-locular, with a central column: **J.** Sepals 5: **K.** Anthers erect in bud, not spurred at the base—SARCODES (Calif.). **KK.** Anthers introrsely pendulous in bud, 2-spurred at the back—PTEROSPORA (N. Amer.). **JJ.** Sepals 2; ovary and capsule 1-locular, without a central column—NEWBERRYA (N. Amer.). **HH.** Disk present: **L.** Disk 10-crenate; anthers globular or didymous —MONOTROPSIS (N. Amer.). **LL.** Disk distinctly 5-lobed—CRYPTOPHILA (U.S.A.).

156. LENNOACEAE

Parasitic leafless herbs destitute of chlorophyll; flowers ⚥, actinomorphic, spicate, cymose or capitate; calyx 6–10-lobed, lobes linear or subulate; corolla

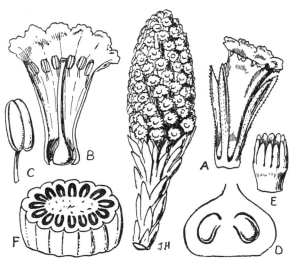

FIG. 156. Pholisma arenarium *Nutt.* (Lennoaceae). A, flower. B, same opened. C, stamen. D, vertical section of ovary. E, stigmas. F, transverse section of ovary.

sympetalous, 5–8-lobed, lobes imbricate; stamens inserted *below the apex* of the tube, 1–2-seriate, the same number as the corolla-lobes and *alternate* with them; filaments short; anthers 2-locular, *opening lengthwise*; disk absent;

ovary superior, *10–15-locular,* loculi surrounding the *thick central axis,* each loculus *spuriously divided*; style simple; stigma subcapitate; ovules paired in each loculus, axile; fruit at length irregularly circumscissile; seeds small, with copious endosperm and small subglobose undivided embryo. B.H. **2,** 621; E.P. **4,** 1. 12. Mexico and California.

A. Stamens 2-seriate; anther-loculi divergent—LENNOA (Mexico). **AA.** Stamens 1-seriate; anther-loculi parallel: **B.** Calyx-segments as long as or longer than the corolla, filiform, plumose; flowers in a saucer-shaped head—AMMOBROMA (Colorado to Mexico). **BB.** Calyx-segments shorter than the corolla, linear, glandular-hairy, not plumose; flowers spicate—PHOLISMA (Calif.).

157. VACCINIACEAE

Shrubs; leaves alternate, simple; stipules absent; flowers ☿; calyx deciduous or persistent; corolla sympetalous, *epigynous,* lobes *imbricate*; stamens

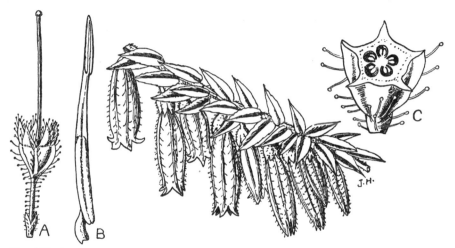

FIG. 157. Agapetes serpens (*Wight*) *Sleumer* (Vacciniaceae). A, flower with corolla and stamens removed. B, stamen. C, ovary in transverse section. (After Hook. f.)

twice as many as the corolla-lobes, epigynous; anthers 2-locular, opening by *terminal pores*; ovary *inferior,* 4–10-locular; ovules usually many, on axile placentas; fruit a berry or drupe, rarely dehiscent; seeds with copious fleshy endosperm and straight embryo. B.H. **2,** 564; E.P. **4,** 1, 15 (under *Ericaceae*). Mountainous regions of Tropical America and Asia; very rare in Tropical Africa, rare in Temperate Regions.—PSAMMISIA, CERATOSTEMMA, CAVENDISHIA, AGAPETES (*Pentapterygium*), GAYLUSSACIA, VACCINIUM, OXYCOCCUS, WITTSTEINIA, &c.

USEFUL PRODUCTS: *Cranberry* (Oxycoccus palustris *Pers.*); *Whortle-berry* or *Bilberry* (Vaccinium myrtillus *L.*); *Cowberry* (V. vitis-idaea *L.*); *Broussa Tea* (V. arctostaphylos *L.*). Many garden shrubs.

ORDER 39. GUTTIFERALES

Advanced hypogynous types derived from the *Theales* (p. 272), with opposite leaves as in *Myrtales* and frequently gland-dotted or resinous-lined;
some herbs; stipules rare; stamens often united into separate bundles
(phalanges); usually no endosperm; sepals always imbricate; flowers bisexual
or unisexual.

A. Stipules absent; seeds without endosperm; stamens often in bundles;
trees, shrubs, or herbs with resinous juice:
  B. Flowers bisexual; leaves often gland-dotted; seeds not arillate; indumen-
tum when present often stellate   *Hypericaceae*
  BB. Flowers mostly unisexual; seeds often arillate   *Clusiaceae*
AA. Stipules present; stamens free; trees, shrubs, or climbers, not resi-
nous:
  C. Seeds with endosperm, winged; stipules intrapetiolar   *Eucryphiaceae*
  CC. Seeds without endosperm, tomentose; stipules interpetiolar
                                      Quiinaceae

158. HYPERICACEAE

Trees to herbs, rarely climbers; *juice resinous*; leaves *opposite* or *verticillate*,
simple, often *gland-dotted*; stipules absent; indumentum when present often

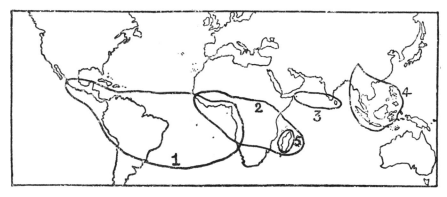

1, Distribution of Vismia; 2, Haronga; 3, Hypericum mysorense; 4, Cratoxylon; 5, Eliaea.

stellate; flowers showy, mostly terminal, solitary to cymose-paniculate, yellow
or white, ☿, actinomorphic; sepals *imbricate*; petals imbricate or contorted;
stamens *numerous*, hypogynous, often *united into bundles*; anthers 2-locular,
opening lengthwise; ovary 1-locular or variously 3–5-locular; styles mostly
free; ovules numerous, axile or pendulous, anatropous; fruit a capsule or
berry, rarely a drupe; seeds with straight or arcuate embryo, but no endosperm. B.H. **1**, 163; E.P. **3**, 6, 205 (under *Guttiferae*).—HYPERICUM, CRATO-
XYLON, ENDODESMIA, VISMIA, PSOROSPERMUM, HARONGA, &c.
    USEFUL PRODUCTS: A few ornamental garden plants.

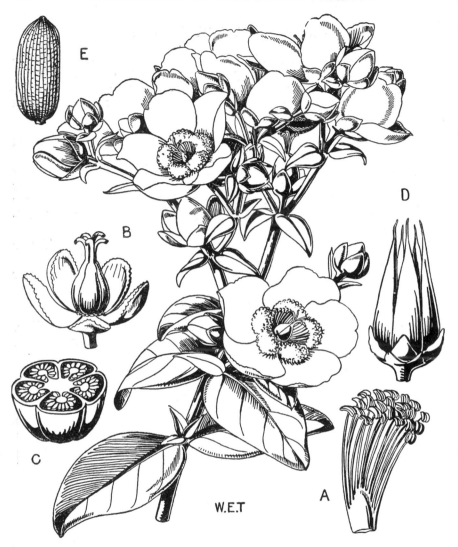

FIG. 158. Hypericum hookerianum *Wight & Arn.* (Hypericaceae). A, bundle of stamens. B, ovary. C, cross-section of same. D, fruit. E, seed. (After *Bot. Mag.*)

159. CLUSIACEAE
(Guttiferae)

Trees or shrubs with *resinous juice*; leaves *opposite*, simple; stipules absent; flowers actinomorphic, ♂ ♀ and polygamous or dioecious, rarely ⚥; sepals 6–2, rarely more, imbricate; petals the same number, hypogynous, contorted or imbricate, very rarely subvalvate; stamens mostly numerous, hypogynous, free or *variously connate* in the lower part or into bundles *opposite the petals*; anthers 2-locular, opening lengthwise; rudimentary ovary sometimes present in the ♂

flower; staminodes often present in the ♀ flower; ovary sessile, superior, 1- to many-locular; ovules 1 to many, on the inner angle or erect from the base of the loculi, rarely parietal; stigmas various, sometimes radiating; fruit dehiscent or not, sometimes large and globose; seeds often arillate, without endosperm; embryo large; cotyledons often minute. B.H. **1**, 167; partly; E.P. **3**, 6, 194 (excl. *Hypericaceae*). Tropics. —CLUSIA, TOVOMITA, SYMPHONIA (see map), PENTADESMA, GARCINIA, XANTHOCHYMUS, RHEEDIA, CALOPHYLLUM, MAMMEA, &c.

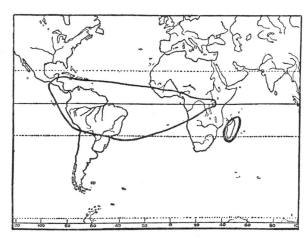

Range of Symphonia (Clusiaceae).

USEFUL PRODUCTS: *Mangosteen fruits* (Garcinia mangostana *L.*), cultivated, Tropics; *Butter* or *Tallow Tree* (Pentadesma butyracea *Sabine*), W. Afr.; *Gamboge Tree* (Garcinia hanburyi *Hk. f.*), Siam; *Bitter Kola* (Garcinia kola *Heckel*), W. Afr.; *Alexandrian Laurel* (Calophyllum inophyllum *L.*),

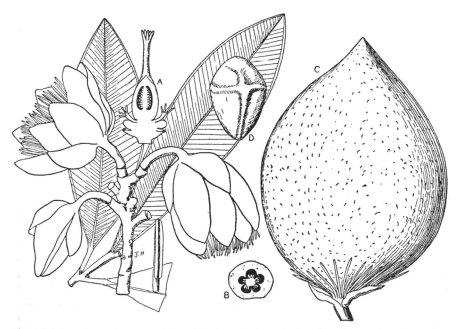

FIG. 159. Pentadesma butyracea *Sabine* (Clusiaceae). A, vertical section of ovary. B, cross-section of same. C, fruit. D, seed. (After Hook. *Ic. Pl.*)

India, &c., giving *Pinnay* or *Domba Oil*; *Mammee Apple* (Mammea americana *L.*), Trop. Amer.

160. EUCRYPHIACEAE

Resinous, glabrous or tomentose trees; leaves *opposite*, *simple* or *pinnate*, evergreen; stipules small, *intrapetiolar*; flowers bisexual, axillary, solitary,

FIG. 160. Eucryphia glutinosa (*Poepp. & Endl.*) *Baill.* (Eucryphiaceae). A, stamen. B, ovary. C, vertical section of same. D, fruit. E, segment of fruit. F, seed. G, cross-section of same. (After Gay.)

actinomorphic, large, white; sepals 4, rigid, imbricate, cohering at the apex and somewhat calyptrately deciduous; petals 4, large, imbricate; stamens numerous, in many series on a thin disk; filaments filiform; anthers small, *orbicular*; ovary 5–12-locular, sulcate, narrowed into 5–12 slender styles; ovules few in each loculus, pendulous from the inner angle of each loculus; fruit a leathery or woody capsule, oblong, *septicidally* 5–12-*valved*, valves boat-shaped, beaked by the persistent styles and separating from the axis; seeds pendulous, oblong, compressed, imbricate, *winged*; embryo in the

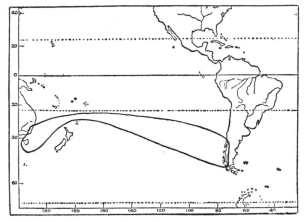

The distribution of Eucryphia (Eucryphiaceae) conjures up a former closer connexion between Australasia and S. America.

middle of the endosperm; cotyledons leafy; radicle short. B.H. **1,** 616 (under *Rosaceae*); E.P. **3,** 6, 129. Australia, Tasmania, Chile.—EUCRYPHIA. Ornamental trees with showy flowers.

161. QUIINACEAE

Trees, shrubs, or climbers; leaves *opposite* or *whorled*, simple or pinnately lobed; *lateral nerves numerous*, tertiary nerves *feather-veined*; stipules paired,

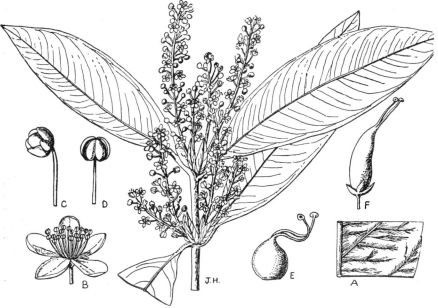

FIG. 161. Quiina longifolia *Spruce* (Quiinaceae). A, portion of under-surface of leaf to show veins. B, flower. C, bud. D, stamen. E, ovary. F, young fruit. (Orig.)

interpetiolar, rigid or foliaceous; flowers ♂ or ♂ ♀, paniculate or racemose; sepals 4–5, imbricate in pairs, small, unequal; petals 4–8, imbricate; stamens 15–30 or more, free or nearly so; anthers 2-locular, opening lengthwise; ovary 2–11-locular; styles 2–3, free, with disk-like stigmas; ovules paired, ascending; fruit a 1–4-seeded berry; *seed tomentose*; embryo straight; endosperm 0. B.H. **1,** 176 (under *Guttiferae*); E.P. **3,** 6, 165. Tropical America.—QUIINA.

ORDER 40. MYRTALES

More or less as in *Theales* (No. 36), but leaves mostly opposite and often gland-dotted; ovary inferior; calyx becoming valvate, and ovules reduced in number in the higher types; stamens show tendency to grouping in bundles as in *Hypericaceae*, sometimes dimorphous and then opening by terminal pores.

A. Anthers opening by slits lengthwise; leaves rarely with parallel nerves lengthwise:
  B. Ovules spreading on axile or rarely parietal placentas:
    C. Leaves glandular-punctate; calyx-lobes mostly imbricate   *Myrtaceae*
    CC. Leaves not punctate but sometimes with glands on the margins; calyx-lobes valvate:
      D. Ovary-loculi not superposed; placentation axile
      E. Leaves alternate   *Lecythidaceae*
      EE. Leaves mostly opposite:
        F. Ovary inferior or semi-inferior; leaves stipulate   *Rhizophoraceae*
        FF. Ovary superior; leaves exstipulate   *Sonneratiaceae*
    DD. Ovary-loculi superposed in 2 series, the lower with axile, the upper with parietal placentas; leaves not glandular   *Punicaceae*
  BB. Ovules suspended from the apex of the 1-locular ovary by slender funicles; leaves not glandular-punctate   *Combretaceae*
AA. Anthers mostly opening by a terminal pore, filaments often geniculate and inflexed, the connective often produced at the base and mostly appendaged; leaves usually with 3 or more longitudinal nerves parallel with the margins   *Melastomataceae*

162. MYRTACEAE

Trees or shrubs; leaves simple, mostly entire, opposite or rarely alternate, *glandular-punctate*; stipules 0 or rarely very small; flowers mostly actinomorphic, ♂ or polygamous by abortion; calyx-tube more or less adnate to the ovary; lobes 3 or more, imbricate or valvate or irregularly split; petals 4–5, rarely 6 or 0, inserted on the margin of the disk lining the calyx-tube, imbricate or connivent in a mass; stamens *numerous*, rarely few, inserted on the margin of the disk, 1- or more-seriate, inflexed in bud or twice folded or straight; filaments free or connate at the base into a short tube or in bundles opposite the petals; anthers small, 2-locular, opening lengthwise by slits or rarely by apical pores, the connective often tipped by a *gland*; *ovary inferior*, syncarpous, 1- to many-locular, with mostly axile, rarely parietal, placentation; ovules rarely solitary or few; fruit inferior, loculicidally dehiscent or indehiscent; seeds with no (or very little) endosperm; embryo straight, incurved, circular or spiral. B.H. **1**, 690, partly; E.P. **3**, 7, 57. Mainly Tropics and Australia.— Darwinia. Verticordia, Calythrix, Baeckea, Leptospermum, Calli-stemon, Melaleuca, Calothamnus, Eucalyptus, Metrosideros, Feijoa, Campomanesia, Psidium, Myrtus, Myrcia, Calyptranthes, Pimenta, Eugenia, Syzygium, &c.

Useful Products: *Eucalyptus Oil* (Eucalyptus globulus *Labill.*), Austral.; *Cajaput Oil* (Melaleuca leucadendron *L.*), Trop. Asia; *Citron Gum*

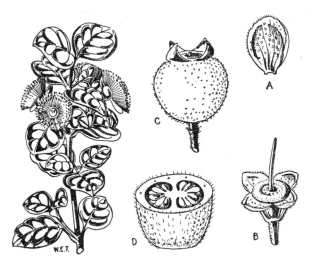

Fig. 162. Myrtus bullata *Banks* (Myrtaceae). A, petal. B, pistil. C, fruit. D, section of ovary. (After *Bot. Mag.*)

(Eucalyptus maculata *Hook.*), Queensland; *Red Gum* (E. rostrata *Schlech-tend.*), Austral.; *Blue Gum* (E. globulus *Labill.*), S.E. Austral.; *Iron Bark Tree* (E. leucoxylon *F. Muell.*), W. Austral.; *Karri timber* (E. diversicolor *F. Muell.*), and *Jarrah* (E. marginata *Sm.*), Austral.; *Guava fruit* (Psidium guajava *L.*), Tropics (cultivated); *Pimenta* or *Allspice* (Pimenta officinalis *Lindl.*), Jamaica; *Cloves* (flower buds of Eugenia caryophyllus *Bullock & Harrison*), cultivated Tropics; *Rose Apple* (Eugenia jambos *L.*), India, &c.; *Jambolana fruit* (E. jambolana *Lam.*), E. Tropics.

163. Lecythidaceae

Trees or shrubs; leaves simple, *alternate, not gland-dotted*, but sometimes with *large glands* on the *margin*; stipules absent; flowers usually rather large and showy, actinomorphic or zygomorphic, bisexual; calyx 4–6-lobed, lobes *valvate* or slightly imbricate; petals 4–6, free or united into a *campanulate tube* and then with many ribs; stamens *numerous*, in several series, sometimes the outer ones modified into staminodes and *resembling a corona*; filaments mostly united and often *arranged to one side* of the flower; anthers basifixed or rarely adnate, opening at the side by a slit; staminal disk sometimes lobed;

ovary inferior or semi-inferior, 2- or more-locular; ovules 1 to many on axile placentas, sometimes towards the apex of the loculi; style mostly simple; fruit woody, fibrous or fleshy, indehiscent or operculate at the apex; seeds without endosperm; embryo divided or entire. B.H. **1**, 720 (under *Myrtaceae*); E.P. **3**, 7, 26, incl. *Asteranthaceae*. Tropics.—BARRINGTONIA, PETERSIA, CAREYA, PLANCHONIA, GRIAS, GUSTAVIA, COURATARI, COUROUPITA, LECYTHOPSIS, LECYTHIS, NAPOLEONA, ASTERANTHOS, BERTHOLLETIA.

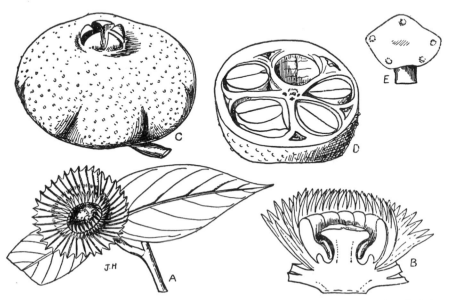

FIG. 163. Napoleona vogelii *Hk. f.* (Lecythidaceae). A, flower. B, same, vertical section. C, fruit. D, same, cross-section. E, stigma. (After Hook. *Ic. Pl.*)

USEFUL PRODUCTS: *Couratari fibre* (Couratari sp.); *Wadadura wood* (Lecythis grandiflora *Aubl.*), British Guiana; *Kakaralli wood* (L. ollaria *L.*), British Guiana; *Sapucaia nuts* (L. usitata *Miers* and L. ollaria *L.*); *Brazil nuts* (Bertholletia excelsa *H. B. & K.*), Brazil; *Anchovy Pear* (Grias cauliflora *L.*), West Indies.

164. RHIZOPHORACEAE

Trees or shrubs, frequently on maritime shores; branches swollen at the nodes; leaves opposite and stipulate, rarely alternate and exstipulate, leathery, simple; stipules interpetiolar, caducous; flowers ☿, in axillary inflorescences; *calyx-tube adnate to the ovary* or free; lobes 3–14, persistent, *valvate*; petals usually small, often notched, bifid, or lacerate, *convolute or inflexed in bud*; stamens equal or usually more than the petals, often in *pairs opposite the petals* on the edge or at the base of a perigynous disk; anthers 2- or many-locular; ovary mostly inferior, 2–6-locular or 1-locular by the suppression of the septa; style simple or rarely styles several; ovules 2, rarely more, inserted towards the apex on the inner angle of each loculus; fruit mostly indehiscent, usually 1-seeded or loculi 1-seeded; seeds with or without fleshy endosperm; cotyledons terete or connate. B.H. **1**, 677; E.P. **3**, 7, 42. Mainly mangrove trees of the

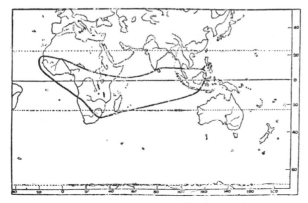

Range of Anisophyllea (Rhizophoraceae).

FIG. 164. Anisophyllea laurina *R. Br.* (Rhizophoraceae). A, male flower. B, female flower. C, petal. D, stamen. (After Baill.)

Tropics.—RHIZOPHORA, BRUGUIERA, CARALLIA, CASSIPOUREA (*Weihea*), ANISOPHYLLEA, ANOPYXIS, POGA, &c.

USEFUL PRODUCTS: *Poga nuts* (Poga oleosa *Pierre*).

Besides the position assigned to this family here there is also strong affinity with the *Tiliales*.

165. Sonneratiaceae

(Blattiaceae)

Trees; leaves *opposite*, simple, entire; *stipules absent*; flowers solitary or 3 together, axillary or terminal, ⚥, actinomorphic; calyx-tube campanulate, thick and leathery; lobes 4–8, *valvate*; petals 4–8, small, or absent; *stamens numerous*, inserted on the calyx in several series; filaments free, at length reflexed; anthers reniform, versatile, opening lengthwise; ovary free or adnate

FIG. 165. Sonneratia acida *Roxb.* (Sonneratiaceae). A, perianth and stamens. B, young fruit. C, vertical section of ovary. D, fruit. E, ovary. (Orig.)

at the base to the calyx-tube, *many–4-locular*; septa thin; style long, simple; ovules numerous, on thick axile placentas; fruit with numerous to 4 loculi and seeds; seeds *without endosperm*; embryo with short leafy cotyledons. B.H. **1,** 784 (under *Lythraceae*); E.P. **3,** 7, 17. Tropical coasts from E. Africa to Australia and Polynesia.

A. Fruit a capsule; ovary 8–4-locular; calyx spreading, partite—Duabanga (Indo-Malaya, New Guin.). **AA.** Fruit a berry; ovary 20–10-locular; calyx campanulate, 8–4-lobed—Sonneratia (E. Afr., Indo-Malaya, New Guin., Austral., Polynesia).

166. Punicaceae

(Granataceae)

Woody and sometimes spiny; leaves mostly *opposite*, subopposite, or fascicled, simple, not glandular; stipules absent; flowers ⚥, terminal, solitary or clustered; calyx coloured, tubular, *adnate to the ovary*, 5–7-lobed, lobes *valvate*; petals 5–7, imbricate and *crumpled* in bud; stamens numerous, epigynous; filaments slender, free; anthers 2-locular, dorsifixed, opening lengthwise; ovary *inferior*, many-locular, loculi *superposed in two series*, the lower with *axile*, the upper with *parietal* placentation; style slender, simple; ovules numerous on each placenta; fruit a spherical berry crowned by the calyx-limb; seeds numerous, covered with pulp; endosperm absent; cotyledons convolute. B.H. **1**, 784

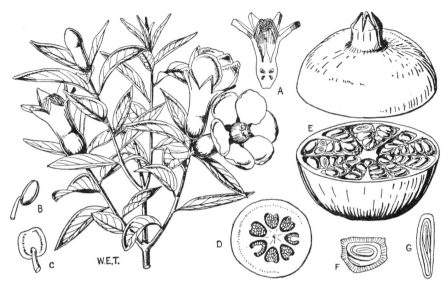

Fig. 166. Punica granatum *L.* (Punicaceae). A, vertical section of flower. B and C, views of anther. D, cross-section of ovary. E, fruit to show seeds. F and G, sections of seed.

(under *Lythraceae*); E.P. **3**, 7, 22. Orient to NW. India; widely cultivated.— PUNICA.

USEFUL PRODUCTS: *Pomegranate* (Punica granatum *L.*), Tropics and Sub-tropics, cultivated.

167. COMBRETACEAE

Trees or shrubs, often scandent; leaves *opposite*, alternate, or rarely verticillate, simple; *stipules 0*; flowers spicate or racemose, mostly small, ⚥, rarely ♂ ♀; calyx-tube *adnate to the ovary*; limb 4–8-fid or lobed, *lobes valvate*; petals 4–5 or 0, rarely many, small, imbricate or valvate; stamens 4–10, rarely more; filaments *inflexed in bud*; anthers versatile, didymous, opening lengthwise by slits; disk epigynous; ovary inferior, rarely half inferior, 1-locular; style simple; ovules 2–6, *suspended from the apex of the ovary* by slender funicles; fruit often *winged*, rarely dehiscent; seeds pendulous, without endosperm; embryo with convolute, plicate, or contorted cotyledons and small radicle. B.H. **1**, 683; E.P. **3**, 7, 106. For key to genera see Exell, *J. Bot.* **69**, 113 (1931). Tropics, rare in Subtropics.—COMBRETUM, PTELEOPSIS, TERMINALIA, ANOGEISSUS, GUIERA, LUMNITZERA, LAGUNCULARIA, QUISQUALIS, &c.

USEFUL PRODUCTS: *Bahera Tree* (Terminalia belerica *Roxb.*); *Asan wood* (T. tomentosa *W. & A.*), India; *Myrobalans or Hirda fruits* (T. chebula *Retz.*),

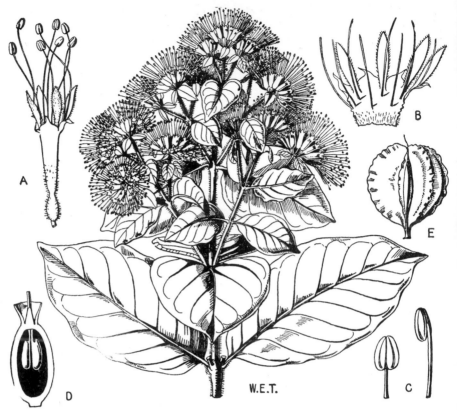

FIG. 167. Combretum racemosum *Guill. & Perr.* (Combretaceae). A, flower. B, to show insertion of stamens. C, stamens. D, vertical section of ovary. E, fruit. (After Guill. & Perr.)

India; *Bois Benzoin* (T. angustifolia *Jacq.*), Mauritius; *Indian Almond* (T. catappa *L.*), India. Some beautiful climbers and shade trees.

168. MELASTOMATACEAE

Herbs, shrubs, or trees, rarely scandent; branches opposite; leaves simple, *opposite* or *verticillate*, mostly with 3 to 9 *longitudinal nerves*, rarely pinnately nerved; stipules absent; flowers ♀, mostly very showy, actinomorphic; calyx tubular, free or adnate to the ovary sometimes by septa-like connexions; lobes imbricate or rarely valvate; petals *imbricate*, free, rarely united at the base; corona usually present between the petals and stamens; stamens the same as to double the number of the petals: filaments free, often *geniculate and inflexed*; anthers 2-locular, basifixed, opening by a single *pore*, (rarely 2) rarely by 2 slits; *connective often thickened at the base and produced, often appendaged*; ovary mostly *inferior*, 2- to many-locular, rarely 1-locular; style simple; ovules numerous, axile, rarely basal or parietal; fruit capsular or baccate; seeds often minute, without endosperm; embryo straight or conforming to the shape of the seed when large. B.H. **1**, 725; E.P. **3**, 7, 130.

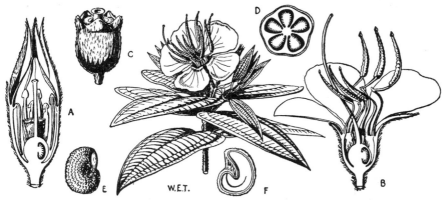

Fig. 168. Melastoma malabathricum *L.* (Melastomataceae). A, flower, vertical section, closed. B, the same open. C, fruit. D, ovary cross-section. E, seed. F, ditto, vertical section. (After Baill.)

Mainly Tropics, rare in Subtropics.—Microlicia, Pterolepis, Pleroma, Osbeckia, Tristemma, Melastoma, Dissotis, Monochaetum, Rhexia, Oxyspora, Blastus, Sonerila, Amphiblemma, Medinilla, Oxymeris, Miconia, Clidemia, Ossaea, Astronia, Mourira, Memecylon, Leandra, Tibouchina, &c.

Useful Products: Many beautiful flowering plants, a few cultivated.

ORDER 41. CELASTRALES

Trees, shrubs, or climbers; leaves alternate or opposite, simple, not glandular; stipules absent or very small; flowers actinomorphic, mostly ♂̦, often small; calyx imbricate or valvate; petals usually present, imbricate, free to partially connate; stamens definite, alternate with the petals; disk often present; ovary superior or partially immersed in the disk; ovules 1–2, erect or pendulous from the inner angles; seeds with endosperm.—Generally distributed, but mostly tropical.

The following key to the *Celastrales* should be regarded as not more than *tentative*. The group contains a remarkable range of combinations of morphological and floral features which are extremely difficult to separate on a family basis in a key of this kind.

Striking features of the most advanced members are the enclosure of the fruit by the enlarged calyx in the *Erythropalaceae*, and by the greatly enlarged disk in the *Capusiaceae* and *Scyphostegiaceae*. The last named is included in this order for the first time, having been previously placed in *Monimiaceae*, *Moraceae*, and *Flacourtiaceae*.

A. Carpels or ovary not enclosed by the disk, the latter often absent, rarely the fruit enclosed by the enlarged calyx:
B. Disk absent:
  C. Stipules present though sometimes very small:
    D. Leaves alternate, not prickly on the margin; petals imbricate, free; flowers dioecious, borne on the old wood; stamens 10; seed with endosperm and cordate cotyledons *Pandaceae*
    DD. Leaves alternate, often prickly on the margin; flowers bisexual or unisexual; stamens usually 5–4; petals often connate *Aquifoliaceae*

DDD. Leaves opposite; petals imbricate, free or partly connate; stamens 4; flowers in dense axillary fascicles or panicles, bisexual or dioecious   *Salvadoraceae*

CC. Stipules absent:

E. Petals imbricate or rarely contorted:

F. Sepals imbricate:

G. Erect trees, shrubs, or shrublets, never climbing:

H. Ovules spreading from the central axis; petals free to the base; fruit a capsule with winged seeds or a berry   *Koeberliniaceae*

HH. Ovules pendulous from the apex of the loculi; petals free or shortly connate:

J. Peduncle not adnate to the petiole; petals often united at the base; embryo straight   *Aquifoliaceae*

JJ. Peduncle adnate to the petiole; petals free; embryo hook-like   *Cneoraceae*

GG. Climbing herbs with milky juice and cordate leaves 3–5-nerved from the base; stigmas very unequal   *Cardiopteridaceae*

FF. Sepals valvate; petals shortly connate; shrubs; stigmas equal   *Cyrillaceae*

EE. Petals valvate, often united into a tube; ovules pendulous from near the top of the ovary   *Icacinaceae*

EEE. Petals absent:

K. Shrublets with small ericoid leaves; temperate and cold regions of both hemispheres   *Empetraceae*

KK. Trees or shrubs with larger not ericoid leaves; tropics and subtropics   *Icacinaceae*

BB. Disk present, annular or of separate glands:

L. Leaves and inflorescence lepidote; stipules absent; flowers dioecious, in axillary racemes, in bud completely enclosed by the bracteole   *Aextoxicaceae*

LL. Leaves not lepidote; flowers not enclosed by the bracteole:

M. Petals imbricate:

N. Trees, shrubs, or climbers:

O. Staminodes absent; disk more or less cupular or annular:

P. Stamens 10; petals with a scale at the base   *Pentadiplandraceae*

PP. Stamens 4 or 5; seeds with copious endosperm   *Celastraceae*

PPP. Stamens 4; seeds without endosperm   *Salvadoraceae*

PPPP. Stamens 3; seeds without endosperm   *Hippocrateaceae*

OO. Staminodes present; leaves alternate; stamens opposite to the petals alternating with as many petaloid staminodes; disk of separate large glands   *Corynocarpaceae*

NN. Herbs with fleshy leaves; petals connivent; disk thin, lining the calyx-tube   *Stackhousiaceae*

MM. Petals valvate:

Q. Ovary 5-locular; ovules ascending from the inner angle of the loculi; calyx not enlarged; racemes umbel-like on axillary peduncles; stipules present   *Goupiaceae*

QQ. Ovary 3-locular; ovules axile, spreading from the inner angle; calyx not enlarged; seeds compressed and often winged; stipules small or absent   *Hippocrateaceae*

QQQ. Ovary 1-locular; ovules pendulous from the top of the loculus; calyx much enlarged and completely enclosing the fruit; stipules absent   *Erythropalaceae*

AA. Carpels enclosed by the enlarged disk which becomes a false fruit:

  R. Carpels completely immersed in the swollen disk, with 5 styles and stigmas adnate to its inner side; stipules present, minute, caducous; flowers bisexual; bracts not tubular; stamens 5, free   *Capusiaceae*

  RR. Carpels free within the swollen disk; stipules absent; flowers unisexual, dioecious; bracts tubular; stamens 3, connate   *Scyphostegiaceae*

169. PANDACEAE

Small trees; leaves alternate, simple; stipules present; flowers ♂ ♀, dioecious; male flowers racemose; racemes fasciculate from the older wood; calyx

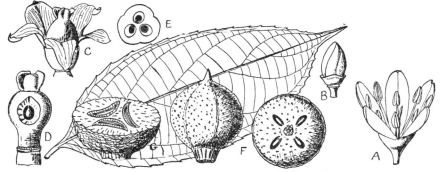

Fig. 169. Panda oleosa *Pierre* (Pandaceae). A, male flower. B, flower-bud. C, female flower. D, ovary showing ovule. E, cross-section of same. F, fruit. G, cross-section of same. (After Pierre.)

cupular, open in bud; petals 5, weakly imbricate; stamens 10, alternately long and short; anthers 2-locular, opening lengthwise; rudimentary ovary linear-subulate; female flowers racemose, fasciculate on the main trunk; calyx cupular, truncate or toothed; petals 5, imbricate; staminodes and disk absent; ovary subsessile, 3–4-locular; style 3–4-branched, reflexed; ovule solitary, pendulous from near the apex of the axis; fruit drupaceous; seed with copious oily endosperm; cotyledons cordate. Pierre, *Bull. Soc. Linn. Paris*, **2**, 1255 (1896). W. Tropical Africa.—PANDA.

170. AQUIFOLIACEAE

(Ilicaceae)

Trees or shrubs, mostly evergreen; leaves alternate, simple; *stipules absent or very small*; flowers actinomorphic, ♂ or ♂♀, cymose, fasciculate or rarely solitary; calyx imbricate; petals 4–5, free or connate at the base, imbricate or valvate; stamens hypogynous, 4–5, rarely more, free; anthers 2-locular, opening lengthwise; *disk absent*; ovary 3- or more-locular; style terminal or absent; ovules 1–2 in each loculus, pendulous from the apex; fruit drupaceous, of 3 or more 1-seeded pyrenes; seed with copious fleshy endosperm and small straight embryo. B.H. **1**, 356; E.P. **3**, 5, 183; edn. 2, **20***b*, 36. Generally distributed, but rare in Africa and Australia.

USEFUL PRODUCTS: *Common Holly* (Ilex aquifolium *L.*), useful timber;

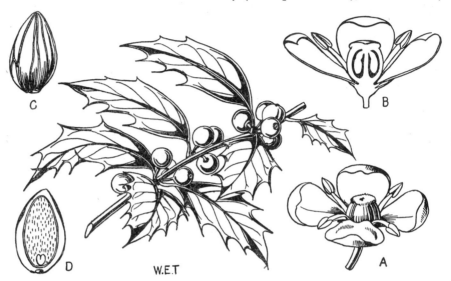

FIG. 170. Ilex aquifolium *L.* (Aquifoliaceae). A, flower. B, vertical section of same. C, seed. D, vertical section of same.

Bird-lime (from holly bark); *Yerba de Mate* or *Paraguay Tea* (Ilex paraguensis *St. Hil.*), S. Amer.

A. Petals imbricate: **B.** Petals free, linear; pedicels axillary, solitary; branches with long and short shoots—NEMOPANTHUS (N. Amer.). **BB.** Petals connate at the base; flowers more or less cymose: **C.** Stamens often more numerous than the corolla-lobes; ovary 18–10-locular—BYRONIA (Austral., Polynesia). **CC.** Stamens as many as corolla-lobes; ovary 5–4- rarely 8–7-locular—ILEX (Widely distrib.). **AA.** Petals valvate, 6–4, free, with inflexed apex; stamens as many as petals—PHELLINE (New Caled.). For ONCOTHECA, formerly placed in this family, see *Ebenaceae*.

171. SALVADORACEAE

Trees or shrubs, unarmed or with axillary spines; leaves opposite, simple; rudimentary stipules often present; flowers in dense axillary fascicles or panicles, ⚥ or dioecious, actinomorphic; calyx 3–4-toothed; petals 4, free or partially connate, *imbricate*; *stamens* 4, inserted at or near the base of the petals and alternate with them; filaments free or connate at the base; anthers 2-locular, *loculi back to back*, opening lengthwise; disk absent or of separate glands between the filaments; ovary superior, 1–2-locular; style short; ovules 1–2, erect; fruit a berry or drupe; seed erect, without endosperm; embryo with thick cordate cotyledons. B.H. **2**, 680; E.P. **4**, 2, 17; edn. 2, **20***b*, 232 (1942). Tropical Africa and Mascarene Islands, Arabia, Indo-Malaya.

USEFUL PRODUCTS: *Tooth-brush Tree* (Salvadora persica *L.*), E. Tropics.

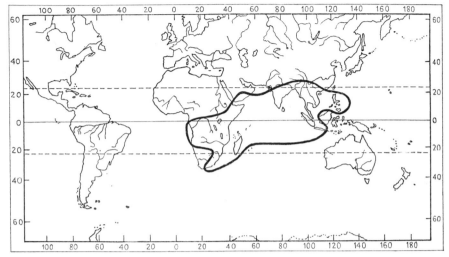

Range of the genus Azima (Salvadoraceae).

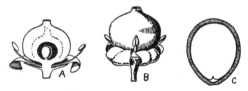

FIG. 171. Salvadora persica *L.* (Salvadoraceae). A, vertical section of flower. B, flower. C, seed. (After Le Maout & Decne.)

A. Thorny shrubs; ovary 2-locular; petals and stamens free—AZIMA (Indo-Malaya, Arabia, Mascar., Trop. and S. Afr.). **AA.** Spineless trees and shrubs; ovary 1-locular: **B.** Petals free; stamens hypogynous, united into a tube at the base—DOBERA (Trop. Afr., Arabia, and India). **BB.** Petals shortly united at the base; stamens united at the base with the corolla-tube—SALVADORA (Afr., W. Asia, India).

172. KOEBERLINIACEAE

Trees or shrubs, almost leafless; branches stiff, *spine-tipped*; leaves alternate, *minute*, scale-like, early deciduous; stipules absent; flowers in very short axillary racemes, bisexual; bracts minute; sepals 5 or 4, small, imbricate; petals 5 or 4, hypogynous, free, imbricate, slightly clawed, deciduous, whitish; stamens *twice as many* or as many as the petals; anthers introrse, apiculate, 2-locular, opening lengthwise; disk absent; ovary superior, 5–2-locular, *shortly stipitate*; ovules numerous to several in each loculus, axile, anatropous; style subulate, persistent; fruit a capsule or berry, few-seeded; seeds with very *scanty endosperm*; embryo straight or much curved. See Barnhart, *N. Amer. Fl.* **25,** 101 (1910). N. and Central America.

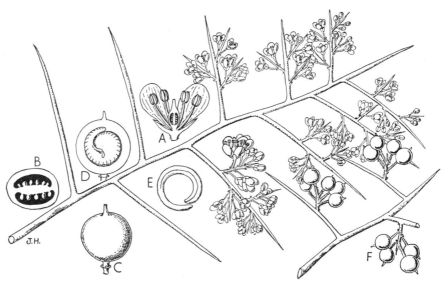

FIG. 172. Koeberlinia spinosa *Zucc.* (Koeberliniaceae). A, vertical section of flower. B, cross-section of ovary. C, fruit. D, vertical section of fruit. E, embryo. F, fruits.

A. Sepals, petals, and stamens 5; fruit a 5-locular capsule; seeds winged— CANOTIA. AA. Sepals 4, petals 4, stamens 8; fruit a 2-locular berry; seeds not winged—KOEBERLINIA.

173. CNEORACEAE

Small shrublets, glabrous or clothed with medifixed hairs; flowers ⚥, axillary, cymose, the *peduncle adnate* to the petiole; sepals 3–4, persistent; petals 3–4, elongated, imbricate; *torus elongated*, columnar, 3–4-grooved; stamens 3–4, inserted on the middle of the torus; filaments free; anthers 2-locular, opening lengthwise; ovary sessile on the gynophore, 3–4-locular, loculi 1–2-ovuled; ovules pendulous; style 3–4-lobed; fruit of 1–4 cocci, cocci drupaceous, globose, sometimes spuriously septate; seeds uncinately conduplicate, with fleshy endosperm and uncinate embryo. B.H. **1,** 311 (under *Simaroubaceae*); E.P. **3,** 4, 93. Mediterranean and Canary Is.—CNEORUM.

174. CARDIOPTERIDACEAE

(Peripterygiaceae)

Glabrous climbing herbs with *milky juice*; leaves alternate, petiolate, broadly cordate, entire or lobed, 3–7-nerved from the base, thinly membranous; *stipules absent*; flowers bisexual, very small, secund in axillary branched cymes; bracts absent; calyx 5-partite, segments imbricate; petals hypogynous, *connate into a 5-lobed corolla*, lobes spreading, thin, imbricate; stamens 5,

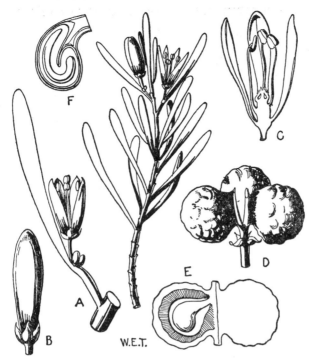

FIG. 173. Cneorum pulverulentum *Vent.* (Cneoraceae). A, flower.
B, bud. C, vertical section of flower. D, fruit. E, vertical section
of same. F, section of seed. (Orig.)

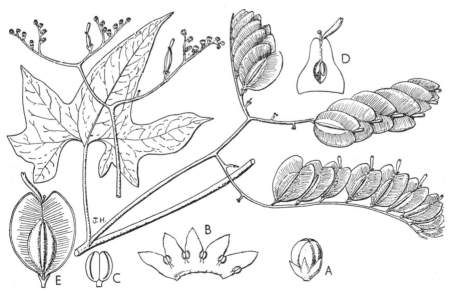

FIG. 174. Peripterygium quinquelobum *Hassk.* (Cardiopteridaceae). A, flower-bud. B, corolla
opened out. C, anther. D, vertical section of ovary with the peculiar unequal styles. E, fruit.

inserted *on the corolla-tube* and alternate with the lobes; filaments as long as the oblong, longitudinally dehiscent anthers; disk absent; ovary superior, *1-locular*; stigmas 2, one *elongated* and columnar and persistent in fruit, the other *short*, capitate and stipitate; ovules 2, pendulous from the apex of the loculus; fruit obovate-oblong, emarginate at the apex, indehiscent, *2-winged lengthwise*, wings broad, transversely striolate; seeds pendulous, linear, grooved; embryo *very minute* at the apex of very densely granular-fleshy endosperm. B.H. **1**, 355; E.P. **3**, 5. 257; Beccari, *Nuovo G. bot. ital.* **9**, 100, t. 8 (1877). Indo-Malaya.—PERIPTERYGIUM (*Cardiopteris, Cardiopteryx*).

175. CYRILLACEAE

Shrubs; leaves alternate, simple; stipules absent; flowers ⚥, actinomorphic, racemose; calyx 5-lobed, *valvate*; petals 5, *shortly connate* at the base, con-

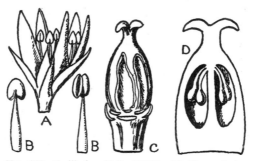

FIG. 175. Cyrilla brevifolia *N.E.Br.* (Cyrillaceae). A, flower. B, stamens. C, ovary. D, vertical section of same. (After N.E.Br.)

torted or imbricate; stamens 5 or 10, hypogynous, inserted on the receptacle; filaments free; anthers 2-locular, opening lengthwise; ovary superior, 2–4-locular; style short, with 3–1 acute stigmas or stigmas subsessile; ovules 1 or more in each loculus, pendulous; fruit a capsule or drupe, sometimes winged by the enlarged calyx; seeds with fleshy endosperm and straight cylindrical embryo. E.P. **3**, 5, 179; edn. 2, **20**b, 1. America.

A. Stamens 10: **B.** Calyx not enlarged after flowering, soon deciduous; sepals equal; stamens erect in bud; style very short and thick, divided into 3 stigmas—CLIFTONIA (Southeastern U.S.A.). **BB.** Calyx enlarged after flowering and coriaceous, embracing the fruit; sepals unequal; stamens bent in bud; style slender, undivided—PURDIAEA (*Costaea*) (West Indies and Trop. S. Amer.). **AA.** Stamens 5: **C.** Pedicels not articulated; style short, thick, shortly 2–3-lobed—CYRILLA (Eastern U.S.A., West Indies, Trop. S. Amer.). **CC.** Pedicels articulated above the bracteoles; style long and undivided—CYRILLOPSIS (Brazil).

176. ICACINACEAE

Trees or shrubs; leaves mostly *alternate*, simple; *stipules absent*; flowers ⚥ or rarely unisexual by abortion, actinomorphic; calyx small, inferior, 4–5-lobed; lobes imbricate or rarely valvate; petals 4–5, free or united, *valvate*, rarely

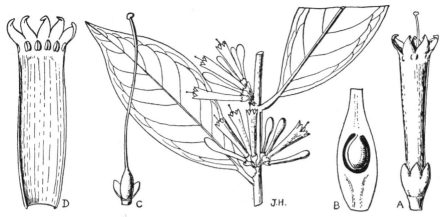

FIG. 176. Leptaulus daphnoides *Benth.* (Icacinaceae). A, flower. B, vertical section of ovary. C, ovary. D, corolla with stamens. (After Hook. *Ic. Pl.*)

absent; stamens the same number as the petals and alternate with them; anthers 2-locular (sometimes deeply 4-lobed); filaments often *hairy* below the anthers, free; disk rarely present; ovary 1-locular, rarely 3–5-locular; ovules pendulous from near the top of the ovary, usually 2; style usually short; fruit drupaceous, 1-locular, 1-seeded, rarely winged; seeds mostly with endosperm; embryo usually small, more or less straight. B.H. **1**, 350 (under *Olacaceae*); E.P. **3**, 5, 233; edn. 2, **20***b*, 322. Tropics.—LASIANTHERA, GOMPHANDRA, DESMOSTACHYS, APODYTES, PENNANTIA, MAPPIA, ICACINA, VILLARESIA, PHYTOCRENE, IODES, SARCOSTIGMA, &c.

177. EMPETRACEAE

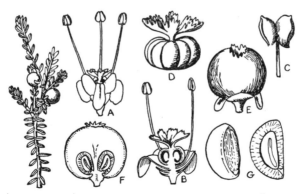

FIG. 177. Empetrum nigrum *L.* (Empetraceae). A, flower. B, vertical section of same. C, anther. D, ovary. E, fruit. F, section of same. G, seeds. (After Le Maout & Decne.)

Shrubs or shrublets with small *ericoid, crowded*, alternate leaves pulvinate at the base; stipules 0; flowers small, axillary or crowded into terminal heads, ♂ or rarely polygamous; sepals 4–6, somewhat petaloid, much overlapping

and sub-biseriate; petals absent; stamens 2–4, central or around the rudimentary ovary, hypogynous in the ♂ flower; filaments free; anthers 2-locular,
small, opening longitudinally; disk 0; ovary sessile, 2–9-locular, globose;
style short, variously divided; ovules solitary in each loculus, central, amphitropous; fruit subglobose, drupaceous, succulent, with 2 or more pyrenes

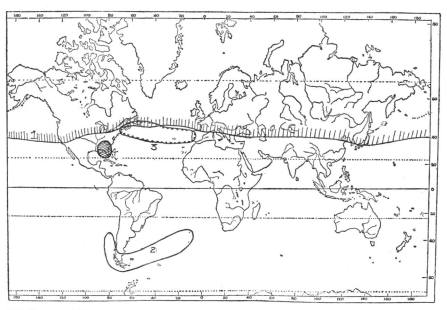

Distribution of Empetraceae. 1, Southern limit of Empetrum nigrum; 2, E. rubrum; 3, Corema;
4, Ceratiola.

each with 1 seed; seeds with copious fleshy endosperm and central straight
embryo nearly as long as the endosperm; cotyledons small. B.H. **3**, 413; E.P.
3, 5, 123. N. Temperate and Arctic, southernmost S. America and Tristan da
Cunha (see map).

  A. Flowers axillary, solitary; stamens 3; ovary 9–6-locular—EMPETRUM
(N. Temp. Zone, Antarct. S. Amer.). **AA.** Flowers 2–3 in the leaf-axils;
stamens 2; ovary 2-locular—CERATIOLA (Southeastern U.S.A.). **AAA.** Flowers
subcapitate at the apex of the shoots; stamens often 3; ovary 2–4-locular—
COREMA (Eastern U.S.A., Spain, Portugal).

178. AEXTOXICACEAE

Tree; branches, leaves (below), and inflorescence *lepidote all over*; leaves evergreen, alternate to subopposite, oblong, entire, pinnately nerved; stipules
absent; flowers *dioecious*, in axillary racemes; bracts very small, rounded;
bracteole calyptrate and *completely enclosing the flower-bud*, deciduous;
sepals 5, free, very imbricate, rounded-obovate, thin and striate, deciduous;
petals 5, free, incurved in bud, imbricate, broadly clawed, with a thick midrib,
at length spreading; stamens in the male 5, free, alternate with the petals and

between large fleshy reniform *disk-glands*; anthers 2-locular, opening by *pore-like slits* in the upper half at the side, introrse; filaments thick and fleshy; rudimentary ovary small in the male flowers; female flowers with 5 broadly linear fleshy *staminodes* and disk glands as in the male flowers; ovary superior, globose, *1-locular* with 2 pendulous ovules from near the top; style short,

FIG. 178. Aextoxicon punctatum *Ruiz & Pav.* (Aextoxicaceae). A, male flowering shoot. B, portion of leaf showing scales on the lower surface. C, flower-bud. D, sepal. E, bud with bracteole removed. F, open male flower. G, petal. H, stamens. J, ovary, showing staminodes and glands. K, vertical section of ovary. L, fruits.

appressed over the side of the ovary, shortly 2-fid; fruit ellipsoidal, black and smooth when dry, *indehiscent*; seed solitary, with *ruminate endosperm* and orbicular-cordate cotyledons. B.H. **3,** 285 (in *Euphorbiaceae*). Chile.—AEXTOXICON.

Although the family *Euphorbiaceae* is composed of many very different elements which have probably been evolved from several separate stocks, it can well dispense with *Aextoxicon*. The alternate, densely lepidote leaves and inflorescence, the racemose, unisexual flowers enclosed in bud by the bracteole, the well-developed petals, and especially the ruminate endosperm, form a combination of characters not found in other *Euphorbiaceae*. I agree with Miers that the relationship is closer with the *Aquifoliaceae* and *Celastraceae*. Baillon (*Hist. des Pl.* **2,** 497) referred it to the *Elaeagnaceae*.

179. PENTADIPLANDRACEAE

Arborescent shrubs or climbers; leaves alternate, simple, pinnately nerved; stipules absent; flowers *polygamous*, racemose, racemes axillary, short, several-flowered; bracts very small; sepals 5, free, *valvate*; petals 5, scale-like at the base and thicker and there loosely connivent, with a lanceolate free limb, *imbricate*; stamens 13–9 in the male and bisexual flowers, inserted within a thick broadly turbinate fleshy *disk*; filaments free, filiform; anthers basifixed,

2-locular, dehiscing at the side, connective rounded and *produced into a knob at the top*; rudimentary ovary present in the male flowers, short, ovoid, without any styles, 5–3-locular, with 2 series of abortive ovules in each loculus; female flowers with about 10 filiform *staminodes within the disk*; ovary superior, shortly stipitate, 5–4-locular, with several axile ovules in 2–3 series

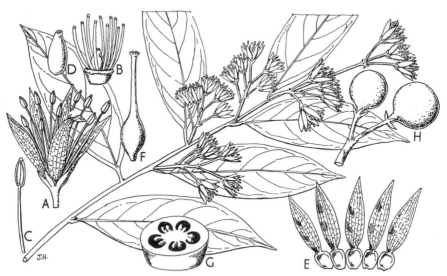

FIG. 179. Pentadiplandra brazzeana *Baill.* (Pentadiplandraceae). A, male flower. B, part of same showing the large disk and lower part of filaments. C, stamen. D, rudimentary ovary of male flower. E, petals. F, gynoecium of bisexual flower. G, cross-section of ovary. H, fruits.

in each loculus; style single, 5–4-fid at the apex; fruit a globose *berry*; seeds small, numerous, immersed in pulp. Hutch. and Dalz., *Fl. West Trop. Afr.* **1**, 461, fig. 162 (1928). Tropical Africa.—PENTADIPLANDRA.

180. CELASTRACEAE

Erect trees, shrubs, or climbers; leaves alternate or opposite, simple; stipules small and caducous or absent; flowers mostly *cymose* or *fasciculate*, often ⚥, actinomorphic, small; calyx 4–5-lobed, imbricate, very rarely valvate; petals 5, rarely 0, imbricate or rarely valvate; stamens 4–5, rarely more, alternate with the petals, inserted on or below the margin of the disk; anthers 2-locular, opening lengthwise; *disk usually present*, often fleshy and flat; ovary superior, free or adherent to the disk, 1–5-locular; style short, more or less 3-lobed; ovules mostly 2, from the inner angle of the loculi; fruit various; seeds mostly with copious fleshy endosperm and rather large straight embryo; cotyledons flat, foliaceous. B.H. **1**, 357; E.P. **3**, 5, 189; edn. 2, **20***b*, 87. Generally distributed.—EUONYMUS, CELASTRUS, MAYTENUS, GYMNOSPORIA, ELAEODENDRON, LOPHOPYXIS, MICROTROPIS (*Chingithamnus*), &c.

USEFUL PRODUCTS: *Arabia Tea* (Catha edulis *Forssk.*); *Spindle Tree* (Euonymus europaeus *L.*); *Paiche wood* (Euonymus europaeus, var. hamil-

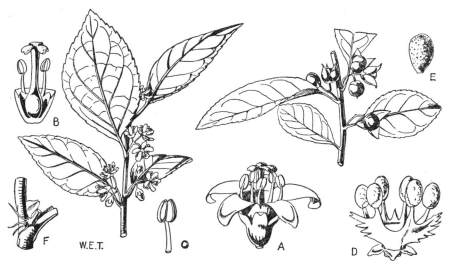

FIG. 180. Celastrus orbiculatus *Thunb*. (Celastraceae). A, flower. B, ovary. C, stamen. D, seeds. E, seed. F, stipule.

tonianus), India, &c.; *Kokoon Tree* (Kokoona zeylanica *Thw*.), Ceylon; *Euonymus bark* (Euonymus atropurpureus *Jacq*.), U.S.A.

181. CORYNOCARPACEAE

Trees; leaves alternate, simple, entire; stipules absent; flowers ⚥, actinomorphic; sepals 5, much imbricate, free; petals 5, adnate to the base of the sepals, imbricate; stamens perigynous, 5, inserted on the base of the petals and opposite to them, alternating with as many petaloid toothed bifid clawed

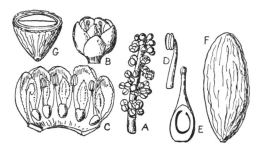

FIG. 181. Corynocarpus laevigata *Forst*. (Corynocarpaceae). A, flowers. B, single flower. C, flower opened to show stamens. D, stamen. E, vertical section of ovary. F, seed. G, cross-section of same. (After *Bot. Mag.*)

staminodes; anthers 2-locular, opening lengthwise; disk-glands large, within the base and opposite to the staminodes; ovary superior, 1–2-locular; styles 1–2, *free*; ovule solitary and pendulous; fruit a drupe; seed without endosperm; cotyledons plano-convex; radicle minute. E.P.N., 215; E.P., edn. 2,

20b, 22. Aru Is., New Guinea, Polynesia, New Caledonia, New Zealand, NE. Australia.—CORYNOCARPUS.

182. STACKHOUSIACEAE

Small herbs with a *woody branched rhizome*; leaves alternate, simple, fleshy or leathery; stipules absent; flowers ♀, racemose, spicate, or fasciculate; *calyx tubular,* lobes imbricate; petals 5, perigynous, linear or spathulate, long-clawed, free or *claws connate into a tube but free at the base,* imbricate; disk

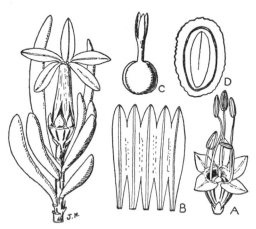

FIG. 182. Stackhousia pulvinaris *F. Muell.* (Stackhousi-aceae). A, flower with corolla removed. B, corolla. C, ovary. D, section of seed. (After F. Muell.)

lining the calyx-tube; stamens 5, erect, alternate with the petals; anthers 2-locular, opening lengthwise; ovary superior, 2–5-locular; styles 2–5, free or connate; ovules basal, solitary, erect in each loculus; fruit of 2–5 indehiscent 1-seeded cocci; seed with fleshy endosperm and equally large straight embryo. B.H. **1,** 371; E.P. **3,** 5, 231; edn. 2, **20b,** 240. Philippines to Australia and New Zealand.

A. Petals free, spathulate; stamens equal in length, with very short filaments; flowers without bracteoles—MACGREGORIA (Austral.). **AA.** Claws of the petals free, upper parts united into a tube; stamens unequal in length, with elongated filaments: **B.** Ovary and fruit lobed both laterally and vertically; style sunk between the lobes—STACKHOUSIA (New Zeal., Austral., New Guin., Philipp. Is.). **BB.** Ovary and fruit lobed only laterally; style terminal—TRIPTEROCOCCUS (Austral.).

183. GOUPIACEAE

Trees or shrubs; leaves alternate, coriaceous, shining, entire (seedlings with dentate leaves), subtriplinerved and transversely venose; stipules very narrow, rather long, caducous; peduncles axillary, solitary, slender, thickened towards the top and bearing an umbel-like cluster of very short bracteate racemes; pedicels slender; bracts short and triangular, hairy; calyx small, 5-lobed, lobes imbricate, ovate-triangular; petals 5, very long and linear-elongate-lanceolate, concave, *induplicate-valvate*, with a long *inflexed upper part* which becomes erect or at an angle in the open flower; stamens 5, inserted on the margin of the disk; filaments extremely short; anthers introrse, short, with a thickened connective *setose-pilose* with deflexed or spreading hairs; loculi ellipsoidal, separate; disk thin and cupular, sinuate on the margin; ovary *partly enclosed by the disk* but free, depressed-globose, 5-locular; styles 5,

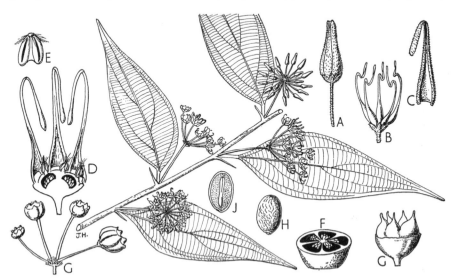

FIG. 183. Goupia glabra *Aubl.* (Goupiaceae). A, flower-bud. B, open flower. C, petal. D, vertical section of flower. E, anther. F, cross-section of ovary. G, fruits. H, seed. J, vertical section of seed.

free and very divergent, subulate; ovules several ascending from the inner angle at base of each loculus; fruit a small globose 3–2-locular hard *berry-like drupe*; seeds erect, obovoid, with axile straight embryo in fleshy endo-sperm; testa slightly reticulate, *pitted inside*; cotyledons oblong. B.H., 369; E.P., edn. 2, **20***b*, 193, fig. 60. Tropical S. America.—GOUPIA.

The family *Goupiaceae* was described so long ago as 1869 by that great British botanist, John Miers, F.R.S., who had many very original ideas about the classification of flowering plants, some of which have not received the attention they deserved.

In his account of this small and distinct family he recounted the history of the genus *Goupia*, its sole representative. Willdenow considered it to belong to *Araliaceae*. Jussieu placed it in *Rhamnaceae*, and he was followed by many other botanists. But Endlicher classed it among the dubious genera of *Celastraceae*, and he was followed by Lindley and later by Bentham. In the latest classification of *Celastraceae* by Loesener,[1] it has been retained as a subfamily in that family.

It seems deserving of family rank as advocated by Miers, and recently by Metcalfe and Chalk,[2] who drew attention to the peculiar structure of the petiole, which is unlike that of most *Celastraceae*.

The floral structure is very remarkable. The petals are valvate, with the upper portion sharply inflexed and connivent in bud, anthers subsessile on the margin of the disk, the

[1] Loesener, Engl. E.P., edn. 2, **20***b*, 193, fig. 60 (1942).
[2] Metcalfe and Chalk, *Anat. Dicots.* **1,** 397 (1950).

connective at the top and at the back clothed with deflexed or spreading bristly hairs, and the quite separate short styles of the 5-lobed ovary with several ovules ascending from the base of each of the 5 loculi. The flowers are not truly umbellate but are arranged in closely contracted bracteate racemes at the end of axillary peduncles.

184. HIPPOCRATEACEAE[1]

Mostly glabrous, small erect trees or shrubs or scandent; leaves mostly *opposite*, simple; stipules small or absent; flowers fasciculate or cymose, bisexual,

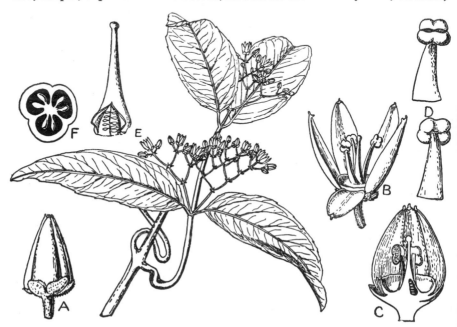

Fig. 184. Hippocratea cymosa *De Wild. & Th. Durand* (Hippocrateaceae). A, flower-bud. B, flower. C, vertical section of same. D, stamens. E, ovary. F, cross-section of same. (After De Wild.)

actinomorphic, mostly quite small; calyx small, 5-partite, imbricate; petals 5, imbricate or valvate; *disk present*, conical, cupular or expanded; *stamens mostly* 3, rarely 2–5, inserted on the disk, alternate with the petals; antherloculi distinct or confluent; ovary superior or more or less confluent with the disk, 3-locular; style subulate or short, mostly 3-fid; ovules 2–10 in each loculus, axile, 1–2-seriate; fruit capsular and compressed, or baccate; seeds compressed and often *winged* or angular, without endosperm; cotyledons large, connate, thick. B.H. **1**, 369 (under *Celastraceae*); E.P. **3**, 5, 222; edn. 2, **20b**, 198. Tropics generally.—HIPPOCRATEA, SALACIA, &c.

185. ERYTHROPALACEAE

Scandent shrubs; leaves alternate, entire, 3-nerved at the base, long-petiolate; stipules absent; flowers bisexual, very small, in lax axillary dichotomously

[1] For key to genera see Loesener, E.P., edn. 2, **20b**, 205 (1942).

branched cymes; bracts subulate; peduncles sometimes *modified into tendrils*; calyx-tube in flower very shortly adnate to the ovary, lobes 5, short, broad, subimbricate, the *tube becoming enlarged and enclosing the fruit*; petals 5, free, perigynous, *valvate*, smooth, spreading; stamens 5, *opposite to and adnate to the petals*; anthers ovoid, erect, connective rather thick; ovary half-immersed in the disk, 1-locular; style very short, conical; stigma 3-lobed; ovules 3–2, pendulous from the apex of the loculus; drupe pear-shaped, girt near the apex by the margin of the enlarged calyx which *resembles a stipitate fruit*; stone crustaceous; seed pendulous; embryo minute, within the apex of

FIG. 185. Erythropalum scandens *Blume* (Erythropalaceae). A, flower. B, vertical section of flower. C, fruit. D, vertical section of fruit.

fleshy endosperm. B.H. **1**, 347; E.P. **3**, 1, 236; E.P.N., 149; edn. 2, **20***b*, 401. Tropical Asia.—ERYTHROPALUM.

In every respect this is a very highly advanced member of the *Celastrales* amongst which it is outstanding on account of the remarkable fruit which is completely enclosed until ripe by the persistent enlarged calyx with its long stipe-like pedicel.

The family was first established as such by van Tieghem[1] and supported more recently by Sleumer.[2] There are three species of the genus in Tropical Asia. Curiously enough it keys out and shares several characters with *Vitaceae*.

186. CAPUSIACEAE

Trees or lianes; leaves alternate, petiolate, crenate-serrate or subentire; stipules minute, caducous; peduncles axillary, short, umbelliform, flowers 3–4; pedicels short, bracteate; sepals 5, very imbricate; petals 5, free, imbricate, erect-spreading; stamens 5, inserted below and *arcuate over the disk*;

[1] van Tieghem, *Bull. Soc. bot. Fr.* **43**, 128 (1900).
[2] Sleumer, E.P., edn. 2, **16***b*, 32 (1935) (in obs.).

anthers 2-locular, short, opening lengthwise; *disk very large and hemispherical, resembling an ovary*, entirely *covering the carpels* and leaving a small *ostiole-like opening at the top* through which protrudes the tip of the floral axis resembling a stigma; carpels *embedded in the disk*, the styles adnate to the inner wall of the disk-tube and showing as 5 penicillate stigmas; ovule 1 in each carpel; fruit 'false', i.e. composed of the much enlarged disk with a minute orifice at the top, pear-shaped to orbicular, crustaceous and in which the bony carpels radiate from the central axis; seeds with membranous testa

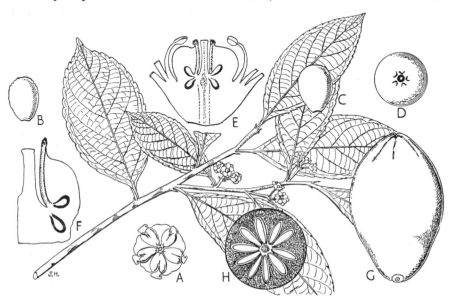

FIG. 186. Siphonodon celastroides *Griff.* (Capusiaceae). A, view of top of flower without the sepals showing the anthers appressed to the disk. B, sepal. C, petal. D, view of the disk from above showing the 'ostiole' and the 5 stigmas. E, vertical section of flower with sepals and petals cut off. F, portion of same. G, the false fruit composed of the greatly enlarged disk with the little 'ostiole' at the top. H, cross-section of 'fruit'. (Orig.)

and rather bony endosperm; cotyledons large, foliaceous, orbicular, sub-cordate at the base. Tropical Asia from Bengal and Little Cocos Island through Malaya to the Philippines and in E. Queensland, south to the Clarence River.—SIPHONODON (*Capusia*).

A very remarkable genus with probably a unique floral structure, but clearly related and very close to the *Hippocrateaceae*. See notes under *Scyphostegia*, p. 328.

187. SCYPHOSTEGIACEAE

Tree; leaves alternate, oblong-elliptic, rounded at the base, acuminate, serrulate-crenate, pinnately nerved, with numerous transverse nerves; stipules very small, caducous; flowers *dioecious*, in axillary and terminal racemes; these composed of *tiers of tubular bracts*, the male with 3–4 tiers, the female with 2 tiers, each bract embracing a single flower; male flowers pedicellate within the bracts, pedicel 2-nerved; calyx tubular, 6-lobed, lobes in *2 series, imbri-*

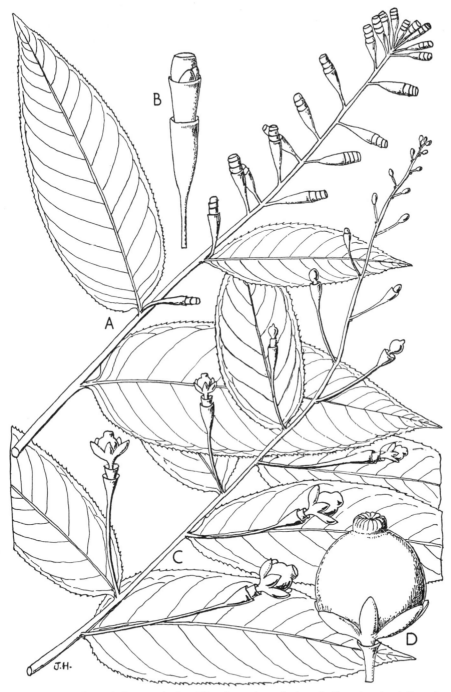

FIG. 187a. Scyphostegia borneensis *Stapf* (Scyphostegiaceae). A, male flowering shoot. B, male raceme. C, female flowering shoot. D, false fruit (enlarged swollen disk, according to the writer's interpretation). (Orig.)

cate; at the foot of the staminal column *3 large fleshy glands*; stamens 3, *united in a column* produced at the apex beyond the 3 extrorse 4-locular anthers, these dehiscing by slits lengthwise; female perianth of 6 free segments; within these a *large globular fleshy disk* with several *inflexed stigma-like rays* but no apparent stigmas, and with an aperture ('ostiole') in the middle; carpels numerous, *free on a wide basal receptacle*, stipitate, with 3 partly adnate hyaline lobules from the receptacle at the base and with a subterminal stigma; fruits a bunch of narrow achenes *enclosed by the greatly*

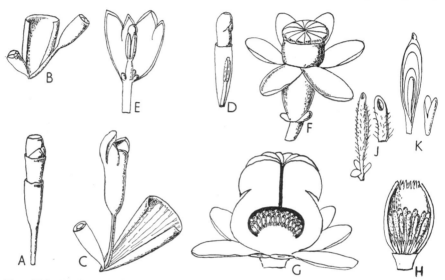

Fig. 187b. Scyphostegia borneensis *Stapf* (Scyphostegiaceae). A, male raceme. B, lower bract opened out. C, bracts and male flower. D, abortive stamen outside one of the bracts. E, vertical section of male flower. F, female flower. G, vertical section of female flower. H, vertical section of disk with free carpels. J, fruiting carpel. K, vertical section of same with embryo. (Orig.)

enlarged disk, hairy; ovule 1 in each achene, erect; embryo large; cotyledons 2, ovate; endosperm scanty. Borneo.—SCYPHOSTEGIA.

Stapf, *Trans. Linn. Soc.*, ser. 2, **4**, 217, t. 17 (1894); Baehni, 'Note sur les inflorescences mâle et femelle du *Scyphostegia borneensis* Stapf', *Ber. schweiz. bot. Ges.* **48**, 22 (1938); Swamy, 'On the floral structure of *Scyphostegia*', *Proc. Nat. Hist. Sci. India*, **19**, no. 2, 127 (1953).

As may be gathered from the description above, I am not now in any doubt as to the correct interpretation of the floral structure of this most interesting Bornean genus on which I ventured to found a separate family in my first edition of this work. At that time only female flowers were known, and I hazarded the opinion that when male flowers were available the genus might prove to belong to *Moraceae*. That surmise has proved very wide of the mark.

Since then excellent dried and spirit material has been collected, and a comprehensive account with excellent figures was published by Swamy (see above). I am not happy, however, about his interpretation of the structure of the female flower. He considers the large fleshy globose organ to be a 1-locular *ovary* containing a large number of ovules on a wide basal placenta.

An equally feasible view, however, is that it is a very large fleshy *disk*, as suspected by Stapf (not a fig-like receptacle as I suggested previously), enclosing a number of *free carpels*, each with a short stipe to which adhere lobules from the receptacle, with a subterminal stigma, and a solitary erect ovule. At Kew there is now a dried rather mutilated 'fruit' from which protrude a number of hairy achenes (scarcely seeds).

I have come to this more definite conclusion on comparing the female flower with the flowers of *Siphonodon* (*Capusia*) related to *Hippocratea* in the *Celastrales*, in which the disk completely encloses the carpels and forms a false fruit after the manner of a fig (*Ficus*) (see figure 186). But a fig, of course, is a modified inflorescence.

ORDER 42. OLACALES

More or less as in *Celastrales*; petals mostly valvate, sometimes more or less connate, rarely absent; ovules pendulous from the apex of the ovary or the top of a basal placenta.—Mainly Tropics.

A. Leaves without stipules:
  B. Stamens free, not united into a column:
    C. Ovary superior to semi-inferior; petals present; stamens opposite the petals:
      D. Disk annular, more or less adherent around the base of the ovary (perigynous); calyx small, lobed   *Olacaceae*
      DD. Disk of separate glands or parts only united at the base but not adherent to the ovary (hypogynous); calyx very small or almost absent   *Opiliaceae*
    CC. Ovary inferior; indumentum of stellate hairs or forked hairs; petals absent; stamens opposite the sepals, free; disk absent
        Octoknemaceae
  BB. Stamens united into a column; fruit a drupe more or less enclosed by the large accrescent calyx; disk-glands outside the stamens
        Aptandraceae
AA. Leaves with small and sometimes very caducous stipules:
  E. Sepals and petals indistinguishable from each other; disk-glands opposite to the valvate petals; flowers in globose umbels; ovary with a free basal placenta; staminodes absent   *Dipentodontaceae*
  EE. Sepals and petals distinct from each other; petals imbricate; flowers in slender catkin-like racemes; ovary with a slender free-central placenta; staminodes 5   *Medusandraceae*

188. OLACACEAE

Trees, shrubs, or climbers; leaves alternate, simple; *stipules absent*; flowers actinomorphic, usually ⚥ and small; calyx-lobes imbricate or open in bud; petals free or variously connate, *valvate*; disk various, often annular; stamens free, the same number as and *opposite* to or fewer or more numerous than the petals, some often without anthers; anthers 2-locular, opening lengthwise or by pore-like slits; ovary superior or slightly immersed in the annular disk, 1–3-locular, sometimes imperfectly so; style simple, with a 2–5-lobed stigma; ovules 1–5 from the apex of the central placenta of the 1-locular ovaries, or pendulous from the inner angle of the 2- or more-locular ovaries; fruit often drupaceous; seeds with copious endosperm and small or medium-sized straight embryo. B.H. **1,** 342, partly; E.P. **3,** 1, 231.

Tropics and Subtropics.—HEISTERIA, XIMENIA, OLAX, LIRIOSMA, STROMBOSIA, SCHOEPFIA, BRACHYNEMA, ANACOLOSA, &c.

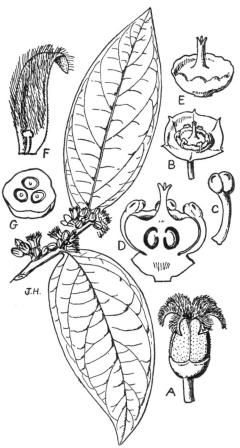

FIG. 188. Anacolosa densiflora *Bedd.* (Olacaceae). A, flower. B, same, petals removed. C, stamen. D, vertical section of ovary. E, ovary. F, petal. G, cross-section of ovary.

189. OPILIACEAE

Trees, shrubs, or woody climbers; leaves alternate, simple; stipules absent; flowers mostly ♀, actinomorphic; *calyx minute*; petals 4–5, free or more or less united; stamens as many as the petals and opposite to them, free or united to the base of the petals; anthers 2-locular, opening lengthwise by slits; disk-glands alternating with the stamens; ovary superior or semi-inferior, 1-*locular*; stigma sessile or style slender; ovule solitary, pendulous or erect; fruit *drupaceous*, often fleshy; seed with copious endosperm and rather small embryo. B.H. **1**, 349; E.P. **3**, 1, 240 (under *Olacaceae*). Tropical Asia and Africa; rare in Tropical America (Brazil).

A. Flowers racemose: **B.** Racemes not covered by large bracts when young and not caterpillar-like: **C.** Flowers bisexual: **D.** Petals free—UROBOTRYA (Trop. Afr.). **DD.** Petals united—CANSJERA (Trop. Asia, NE. Austral.). **CC.** Flowers dioecious; male petals free, female flowers without petals—AGO-NANDRA (Trop. S. Amer.). **BB.** Racemes covered by large imbricate bracts when young and resembling caterpillars; petals free: **E.** Filaments short and flattened; fruits ellipsoidal—LEPIONURUS (Trop. E. Asia). **EE.** Filaments filiform: **F.** Flowers bisexual; fruits ellipsoidal—OPILIA (Trop. Afr., Trop. Asia, NE. Austral.). **FF.** Flowers dioecious; fruits subglobose—GJELLERUPIA (New Guin.). **AA.** Flowers umbellate or subumbellate—RHOPALOPILIA (Trop. Afr.). **AAA.** Flowers paniculate: **G.** Petals present; filaments very short—MELIENTHA (Indo-China). **GG.** Petals absent; bracts minute; filaments filiform—CHAM-PEREIA (Malaya).

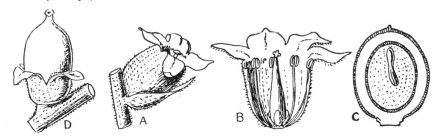

FIG. 189. Cansjera timorensis *Decne.* (Opiliaceae). A, flower. B, vertical section of same. C, section of seed. D, fruit.

190. OCTOKNEMACEAE

Trees or shrubs; leaves alternate, simple, with stellate hairs; stipules absent; flowers unisexual, in axillary racemes; petals absent; male flower: sepals 5,

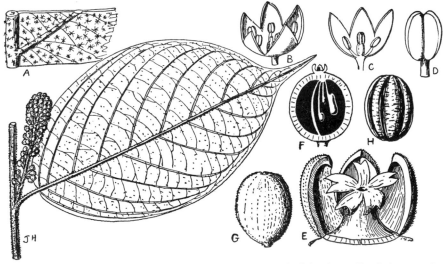

FIG. 190. Octoknema gabonensis *Pierre* (Octoknemaceae). A, leaf showing stellate hairs. B, male flower. C, vertical section of same. D, anther. E, female flower. F, vertical section of ovary. G, fruit. H, seed. (After Pierre, partly.)

valvate; stamens 5, opposite the sepals, free; rudimentary ovary present; female flower: sepals 5, valvate; no staminodes or disk; ovary inferior, 1-locular; style very short, 3–5-lobed, lobes bifid; ovules 3, at the apex of a basal thread-like placenta which reaches and is adnate to the top of the ovary; fruit drupaceous, with a single seed; endosperm slightly ruminate, with small embryo, the radicle much longer than the cotyledons. Engl. and Gilg, *Syllabus*, edns. 9 and 10, 187 (1924). W. Tropical Africa.

A. Inflorescence mostly unbranched, usually axillary; indumentum stellate; drupes small (up to 3 cm long)—OCTOKNEMA. **AA.** Inflorescence paniculate; on the older part of the branches; hairs simple, forked, or stellate; drupes larger (9–15 cm)—OKOUBAKA.

191. APTANDRACEAE

Trees; leaves alternate, entire, pinnately nerved; stipules absent; flowers bisexual or unisexual, in short axillary racemes or clustered in short axillary

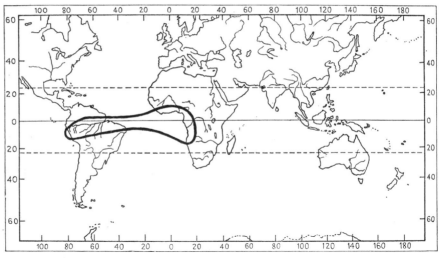

The presence on both sides of the mid-Atlantic of the small and homogeneous genus Aptandra (Aptandraceae) lends strong support to the Wegener theory of continental drift.

panicles; calyx very small, at most denticulate, becoming much *enlarged and persistent in fruit*; petals 5–4 in the bisexual flowers, or 8–6 in the female flowers, free, *valvate*, glabrous inside; *disk present* between the petals and stamens, annular or divided into lobes between the petals; stamens 5–4, within the disk; filaments *united into a column around the style*, with as many sessile anthers in a whorl at the top; anthers extrorsely reflexed, 2-locular; ovary superior, sessile within the staminal column, 2–1-locular; ovules *pendulous from the free top of the central placenta*; style elongated within the staminal column and subentire or stigmas sessile on the ovary; fruit a drupe, more or less enclosed by the *large accrescent calyx*; exocarp fleshy, endocarp woody; seed spuriously erect, with oily endosperm and very small embryo.—Tropics.

A. Disk lobed between the petals; style elongated within the staminal column; flowers in panicles: **B.** Calyx in fruit not splitting into segments; ovary 2-locular to nearly the apex—APTANDRA (Trop. Amer., W. Trop. A fr.)

FIG. 191. Ongokea kamerunensis *Engl.* (Aptandraceae). A, flower-bud. B, vertical section of flower. C, calyx and staminal column. D, fruit enclosed by the enlarged calyx. E, vertical section of fruit.

BB. Calyx in fruit splitting into segments; ovary 1-locular—ONGOKEA (Trop. Afr.). **AA.** Disk annular; stigmas sessile on the ovary; flowers dioecious, in short axillary racemes—HARMANDIA (Malaya, Indo-China).

192. DIPENTODONTACEAE

Small tree or shrub; leaves alternate, elliptic to ovate-elliptic, denticulate, pinnately nerved; stipules lanceolate, caducous; flowers small, bisexual, about 25–30 in axillary pedunculate globose umbels at first surrounded by an involucre of 4–5 small bracts; pedicels jointed in the middle; calyx cupular at the base; segments 7–5, free, linear, valvate; petals 7–5, indistinguishable from the calyx-segments; disk-glands 7–5 opposite the same number of petals;

stamens 7–5, alternate with the petals, free, erect; anthers ellipsoidal, 2-locular, opening by slits lengthwise; ovary superior, imperfectly 3-locular at the base, 1-locular above; ovules 2 in each loculus, axile at the top of a free

FIG. 192. Dipentodon sinicus Dunn (Dipentodontaceae). A, flowers. B, stamen. C, ovary and style. D, vertical section of ovary. E, fruit. F, seed with abortive ovules.

basal placenta; style straight, undivided; stigma small, subdiscoid; capsule 1-locular, obovoid, tardily dehiscent; seed 1, erect on the thickened columella; testa slightly reticulate, coriaceous. SE. Asia.—DIPENTODON.

Represented by a single genus and species, *Dipentodon sinicus* Dunn, distributed from SE. Tibet and Upper Burma through Yunnan and Kweichow to Kwangsi; doubtfully placed by Dunn in the *Celastraceae* (*Kew Bull.* 1911, 310), and later raised to family rank by Merrill. Merrill came to the conclusion that the genus could not be retained in the *Celastraceae* and placed the new family in the *Rosales* (of the Engler and Prantl system), between the *Hamamelidaceae* and the *Rosaceae*. At the same time he called attention to the similarity of the perianth to that of *Homalium* in the *Flacourtiaceae*, but said that 'the floral structure otherwise forbids this disposition of the genus'.

Metcalfe and Chalk (*Anat. Dicots.* **1**, 126) included the genus in the *Flacourtiaceae* as advocated by T. A. Sprague (ined.) and because of the wood anatomy. Merrill, however, stated that Record, to whom wood specimens were submitted, reported that its anatomical characters indicated the *Hamamelidaceae*, a view also confirmed by I. W. Bailey, though the latter pointed out that the floral structure was very different, whilst the internal structure of the leaves and the structure of the hairs are not typical for the *Hamamelidaceae*.

The sepals and petals of *Dipentodon* are very remarkable in that they are not distinguishable from each other, a feature, it is true, that is found in some genera of *Flacourtiaceae*. The sepals and petals in some of that family, however, are *spirally* arranged, whereas in

Dipentodon they are *valvate*. And, furthermore, a *free-basal* placenta is quite unknown in *Flacourtiaceae*. This type of placentation, however, is quite a common feature in *Olacales*, and *Dipentodon* is perhaps best regarded as an advanced member of that group.

193. MEDUSANDRACEAE[1]

Tree; leaves unifoliolate (?), alternate, remotely and minutely crenulate, pinnately nerved, the lower nerves subopposite, transverse nerves numerous and parallel; petiole tumid at the apex; stipules small and very caducous; flowers bisexual, in slender axillary *pendulous catkin-like racemes* on the young shoots or from the axils of fallen leaves; racemes solitary or paired, shortly tomentellous; bracts very small, soon caducous; sepals 5, *open in bud*, free or nearly so; petals 5, free, imbricate, small, with a single nerve in the middle; fertile stamens 5, *opposite the petals*, erect in bud, free from each other but filaments slightly adnate to the base of the petals; *anthers 4-locular*, introrse, the outer (abaxial) loculi by an outwardly recurved valve, the inner (adaxial) loculi by an inwardly recurved valve; staminodes 5, longer than the fertile stamens, opposite the sepals, the filaments tomentellous, inflexed at the apex, *much elongated in the open flower*, with an abortive 4-locular anther at the apex; ovary superior, 1-locular, composed of 3–4 carpels, with a slender *free central placenta*; ovules 8–6 *from the apex of the placenta*, pendulous, anatropous, micropyle superior; stigmas usually 3 (–4), widely separate; fruit subtended by the persistent reflexed sepals at the base, broadly ovoid-globose, umbonate, capsular, 4–3-valved or sometimes spuriously 2-valved through coalescence; seed solitary, pendulous, large, more or less rugose; endosperm copious, *slightly ruminate*; embryo small, straight, near the *edge of the endosperm*. Tropical W. Africa (British Cameroons).—MEDUSANDRA.

[1] I cannot agree that *Soyauxia* Oliv., hitherto included in *Passifloraceae*, should be associated with *Medusandra*, as suggested by Brenan (*Kew Bull.* 1952, 228, figs. 1–2, and loc. cit. 1953, 507, fig. 1). The following differences, in my opinion, far outweigh their resemblances, and are much more than generic:

	SOYAUXIA	MEDUSANDRA
Leaves	Simple, entire, with numerous nerves	Unifoliolate (?), crenate, long-petiolate (petiole with a pulvinus at the top, a common feature in unifoliolate leaves)
Inflorescence	Spicate	Racemose, pendulous, racemes in pairs
Sepals	Imbricate in bud	Open in bud
Stamens	Very numerous, all fertile; no staminodes	Five fertile opposite the petals; 5 staminodes opposite the sepals
Styles	Three, long and divergent	Three, very short
Disk	Present, annular	Absent
Wood anatomy	No secretory canals	Secretory canals present in the pith

Any one of these characters taken by itself would not necessarily amount to very much but in combination with the other differences seem to be of greater importance.

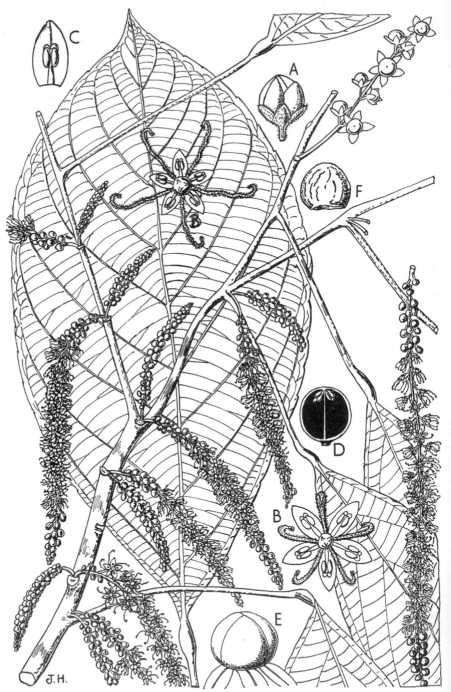

Fig. 193. Medusandra richardsiana *Brenan* (Medusandraceae). A, flower-bud. B, flowers young and older. C, stamen and petal. D, vertical section of ovary. E, fruit. F, young seed.

ORDER 43. SANTALALES

Trees, shrubs, or herbs, often parasitic; leaves mostly opposite, sometimes reduced to scales; stipules absent; flowers actinomorphic; calyx valvate or open, often reduced; petals present or absent; stamens definite, opposite the calyx-lobes, or opposite the petals when latter present; disk often present; ovary inferior; placentation axile or at the top of a basal placenta; ovules few; seeds with abundant endosperm and straight embryo.—Mainly Tropics.

A. Petals present, free or united into a tube often split down one side; stamens opposite the petals   *Loranthaceae*
AA. Petals absent:
  B. Stamens twice as many as the calyx-lobes   *Grubbiaceae*
  BB. Stamens the same number as the calyx-lobes and opposite to them or calyx absent:
    C. Not parasites, or if so then with chlorophyll; ovules 1–3, pendulous from a free basal placenta; seeds without testa   *Santalaceae*
    CC. Parasites destitute of chlorophyll:
      D. Ovules 3 from the apex of a central placenta; undershrubs parasitic on trees; flowers minute or in small catkins   *Myzodendraceae*
      DD. Ovule solitary, mostly pendulous from the apex of the ovary or loculus; fleshy herbs, parasitic on roots; flowers densely crowded into inflorescences   *Balanophoraceae*

194. LORANTHACEAE

Shrubs *parasitic* on trees or very rarely erect terrestrial trees or shrubs; leaves mostly *opposite* or whorled, simple, entire, sometimes reduced to scales;

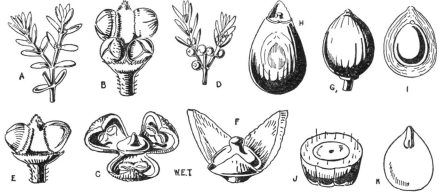

Fig. 194. Viscum bolleanum *Seem.* (Loranthaceae). A, shoot. B, male flowers. C, single male flower. D, fruits. E, female flowers. F, single female flower. G and H, fruit. I, vertical section of fruit. J, cross-section of same. K, embryo with one cotyledon removed. (After Seem.)

stipules absent; flowers actinomorphic, ☿ or ♂ ♀, often very brightly coloured; perianth double or apparently single by suppression of calyx-rim; calyx adnate to the ovary, annular or cupular or obscure; petals free or united into a tube often *split down one side*; stamens the *same number* as the petals and inserted

on them or at their base; anthers normally 2-locular, sometimes 1-locular
by the confluence of the loculi, opening lengthwise or by terminal pores or
transverse slits, sometimes transversely locellate; disk present or absent; rudimentary ovary often present in the male flowers, staminodes in the female;
ovary *inferior*; ovules mostly not distinct; style simple or absent; fruit a berry
or drupe; seed solitary, devoid of testa; endosperm mostly copious; embryo
large, sometimes up to 3 in one seed. B.H. **3**, 205; E.P. **3**, 1, 156. Mainly
Tropics.—LORANTHUS, VISCUM, DENDROPHTHORA, PHORADENDRON, &c.
    USEFUL PRODUCT: *Mistletoe* (Viscum album *L.*).

195. GRUBBIACEAE

Shrubs; leaves *opposite*, simple, linear; stipules absent; flowers ☿, small,
arranged in small axillary bracteate cones; calyx adnate to the ovary; segments 4, *valvate*; petals absent; stamens 8, 4 at the base of the lobes and 4
alternate and slightly shorter; anthers small, opening laterally; disk hairy;

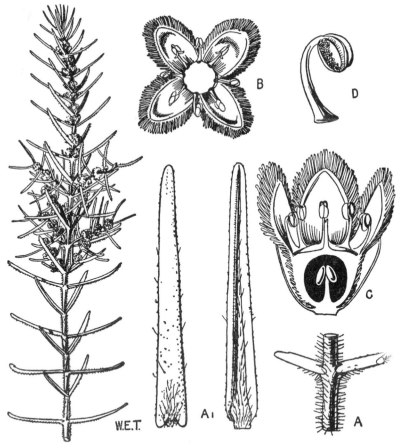

FIG. 195. Grubbia rosmarinifolia *Thunb.* (Grubbiaceae). A, node. A1, leaves. B, flower.
C, vertical section of same. D, stamen. (Orig.)

ovary *inferior*, at first 2-locular; style bifid at the apex; ovules 2, pendulous on a *central placenta* or the latter sometimes adnate to the ovary wall; fruit a drupe; seed 1, with a thin testa and fleshy endosperm; embryo linear, central, subterete, the radicle much longer than the cotyledons. B.H. **3**, 231 (under *Santalaceae*); E.P. **3**, 1, 228. S. Africa.—GRUBBIA.

196. SANTALACEAE

Trees, shrubs, or herbs, sometimes *parasitic* on trees or roots; leaves alternate or opposite, entire, sometimes reduced to scales; *stipules absent*; flowers often

FIG. 196. Santalum album *L.* (Santalaceae). A, section of flower. B, sepal and stamen. C, fruit. D, section of fruit.

greenish, ♀ or ♂ ♀, actinomorphic; calyx green or petaloid, often fleshy, adnate to the ovary; lobes 3–6, *valvate* or slightly imbricate; petals absent; stamens the same number as the calyx-lobes and opposite to them; anthers 2-locular, opening lengthwise; disk epigynous; ovary *inferior* or half inferior, 1-locular; style more or less simple; ovules 1–3, pendulous from a *basal placenta*; fruit indehiscent, nut-like or drupaceous; seed without a testa; endosperm copious, fleshy; embryo often oblique, straight; cotyledons mostly terete. B.H. **3**, 217; E.P. **3**, 1, 202. Widely distributed in Tropical and Temperate Regions.— THESIUM, COMANDRA, SANTALUM, COLPOON, BUCKLEYA, OSYRIS, LEPTOMERIA, EXOCARPUS, &c.[1]

USEFUL PRODUCTS: *Sandalwoods*: Sandwich Is. (Santalum freycinetianum *Gaud.*); Fiji (S. yasi *Seem.*); India and Malaya (S. album *L.*); Austral. (Eucarya spicata (*R. Br.*) *Sprague & Summerhayes*). *Bark Bosch* or *Cape Sumach* (Colpoon compressum *Berg.*).

197. MYZODENDRACEAE

Undershrubs parasitic on trees; leaves alternate, small or *reduced*; flowers dioecious, minute, ebracteate, or arranged in small catkins; male flower *with-*

---

[1] For *Champereia* see *Opiliaceae* (p. 331).

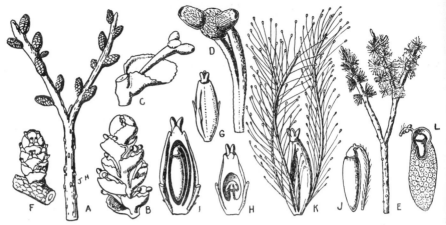

FIG. 197. Myzodendron punctulatum *Banks & Soland.* (Myzodendraceae). A, male shoot. B, male inflorescence. C, male flower and bract. D, male flower. E, female shoot. F, female inflorescence. G, ovary. H, vertical section of same. I, vertical section of fruit. J, seed with abortive ovules at top. K, fruit with ciliate setae. L, section of seed. (After Hook.)

out a calyx or corolla; stamens 2–4, around a small disk; filaments slender; anthers 1-*locular*, opening by 2 *valves*; female flower: calyx adnate to the ovary and free at the top; no petals or staminodes; ovary inferior, 1-locular, crowned by an obscure disk; style thick, with 3 stigmas; ovules 3, pendulous from the apex of a thick *central placenta*; fruit small, nut-like; seed with fleshy endosperm and fleshy central embryo. B.H. **3,** 229 (under *Santalaceae*); E.P. **3,** 1, 198. Temperate S. America.—MYZODENDRON.

198. BALANOPHORACEAE

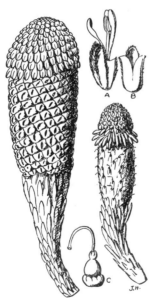

FIG. 198. Mystropetalon thomii *Harv.* (Balanophoraceae). A, male flower. B, calyx. C, female flower.

Fleshy herbs *parasitic* on roots, annual or perennial, *destitute of chlorophyll* and stomata; flowers ♂ ♀, very rarely ⚥, densely crowded into unisexual or androgynous inflorescences; ♂ flowers without or with a valvate 3–8-lobed perianth; stamens 1–2 in the achlamydeous flowers, in those with a perianth often equal in number to and *opposite* the lobes; filaments free or connate; anthers 2–4-locular or with many loculi, free or connate, opening by pores or slits; ovary 1–3-locular, adnate to the perianth when present; styles 1–2, terminal or rarely the stigma sessile and discoid; ovule solitary in each loculus, mostly pendulous, nude or with a single integument; fruit small, nut-like, 1-locular, 1-seeded; seeds with abundant endosperm, and very small embryo, incl. *Cynomoriaceae*. B.H. **3**, 232; E.P. **3**, 1, 243. Mainly Tropics and Subtropics.—CYNOMORIUM, SARCOPHYTE, BALANOPHORA, THONNINGIA, SCYBALIUM, HELOSIS, CORYNAEA, &c.

ORDER 44. RHAMNALES

Trees, shrubs, or climbers; leaves alternate or opposite, simple to compound, mostly stipulate; flowers more or less as in *Celastrales* (p. 309), but stamens opposite the petals or alternate with the sepals when petals absent; petals imbricate or valvate, rarely absent; seeds with copious or scanty endosperm, sometimes ruminate; embryo usually straight.—Tropics and Temperate Regions.

A. Calyx-lobes imbricate; leaves pellucid-punctate; ovules numerous on axile
placentas   *Heteropyxidaceae*
AA. Calyx-lobes valvate or calyx open in bud; ovules 1–2, erect:
  B. Leaves lepidote or stellate-pubescent   *Elaeagnaceae*
  BB. Leaves not as above and not pellucid-punctate; inflorescence axillary,
    not leaf-opposed; fruit mostly drupaceous   *Rhamnaceae*
  BBB. Leaves often pellucid-punctate; inflorescence leaf-opposed; peduncles
    often tendriliform; fruit baccate   *Vitaceae*

199. HETEROPYXIDACEAE

Trees; leaves alternate, *pellucid-punctate*; stipules absent; flowers paniculate, ☿, actinomorphic; calyx 5-lobed, lobes imbricate; petals 5, shortly clawed,

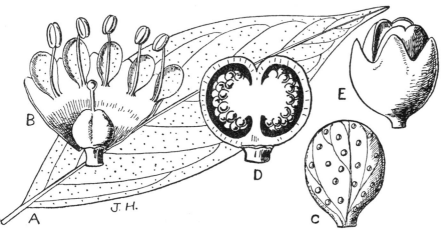

FIG. 199. Heteropyxis canescens *Oliv.* (Heteropyxidaceae). A, leaf. B, flower. C, petal. D, vertical section of ovary. E, fruit. (After Hook. *Ic. Pl.*)

gland-dotted; stamens 5, *opposite the petals*; anthers oblong, 2-locular, opening lengthwise; ovary superior, 2–3-locular, style single, with capitate stigma; ovules numerous, on axile placentas; fruit a small capsule, loculicidally 2–3-valved; seeds without endosperm; cotyledons flat, with stout straight radicle. B.H. **1**, 785 (under *Lythraceae*); E.P.N. 335. SE. and E. Tropical Africa.—HETEROPYXIS.

200. ELAEAGNACEAE

Trees or shrubs with *lepidote* or *stellate indumentum*; leaves alternate, rarely opposite, entire; flowers ☿ or ♂ ♀, often dioecious, solitary, fasciculate, spicate, or racemose; calyx tubular, hypogynous, constricted and persistent around the ovary, 2–4-lobed or rarely truncate, *valvate*; stamens inserted in the tube

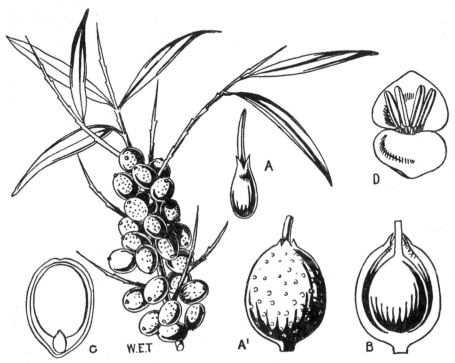

FIG. 200. Hippophaë rhamnoides *L.* (Elaeagnaceae). A, female flower. A¹, fruit. B, section of same. C, section of seed. D, male flower. (Orig.)

of the calyx or at the base in the ♂, 4 and *alternating* with the lobes or 8 alternate and opposite; filaments free; anthers 2-locular, opening lengthwise; no staminodes in the ♀ flower; ovary sessile at the base of the calyx, 1-locular; style terminal, linear, stigmatose on one side; ovule 1, basal, erect, anatropous; fruit enclosed by the persistent berry-like thickened calyx; seed erect, with scanty or no endosperm, straight embryo, and thick fleshy cotyledons. B.H. **3**, 203; E.P. **3**, 6*a*, 246. N. Temperate Zone, Tropical Asia to Australia.

USEFUL PRODUCTS: *Trebizonde Dates* (Elaeagnus angustifolia *L.*), Eur. to N. Asia; *Buffalo berries* (Shepherdia argentea *Nutt.*), N. Amer.

A. Leaves alternate; stamens 4: B. Flowers bisexual or polygamous; calyx-tube elongated much beyond the ovary, 4-lobed—ELAEAGNUS (Mediterr. Reg., Asia, NE. Austral., N. Amer.). BB. Flowers unisexual, mostly dioecious; calyx-tube short, 2-lobed—HIPPOPHAË (Eur., Asia). AA. Leaves opposite; stamens 8; flowers dioecious, with 4 sepals—SHEPHERDIA (N. Amer.).

201. RHAMNACEAE

Trees or shrubs, very rarely herbs, sometimes scandent; leaves simple, alternate or opposite; stipules mostly present; flowers mostly *cymose*, small, ⚥, rarely polygamous-dioecious; calyx tubular, 4–5-lobed, lobes *valvate*; petals 4 or 5, or absent, small; stamens 4–5, *opposite* to and often *embraced by the petals*; anthers 2-locular, opening lengthwise; disk mostly present, *perigynous*, sometimes *lining the calyx-tube*; ovary sessile, free or sunk in the disk, 2–4-

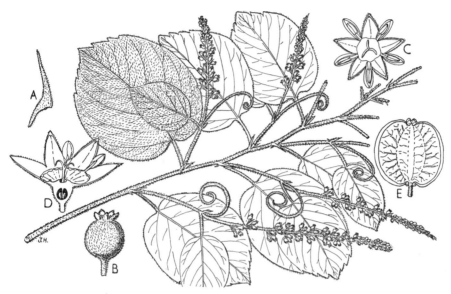

FIG. 201. Gouania corylifolia *Raddi* (Rhamnaceae). A, stipule. B, young flower. C, open flower from above. D, vertical section of flower. E, fruit.

locular; style shortly lobed; ovules solitary, rarely paired, erect from the base, anatropous; fruit various, often *drupaceous*; seed mostly with copious endosperm and large straight embryo. B.H. **1**, 371; E.P. **3**, 5, 393. Mostly Tropics and Temperate Regions.—VENTILAGO, PALIURUS, ZIZYPHUS, BERCHEMIA, RHAMNUS, HOVENIA, CEANOTHUS, SCUTIA, SAGERETIA, COLUBRINA, PHYLICA, ALPHITONIA, POMADERRIS, SPYRIDIUM, CRYPTANDRA, COLLETIA, DISCARIA, GOUANIA, &c.

USEFUL PRODUCTS: *Popli-chekké root bark* (Ventilago maderaspatana *Gaertn.*), India; *Lote fruit* (Zizyphus lotus *Lam.*), Mediterr.; *Indian Jujube* or *Chinese Date* (Z. jujuba *Lam.*); *Cascara Sagrada* (Rhamnus purshiana *DC.*), Pacific N. Amer.; *Alder Buckthorn* (Frangula alnus *Mill.*), Eur. to Siberia; *Sap Green* pigment from berries of *Buckthorn* (Rhamnus catharticus *L.*); *Coral Tree* (Hovenia dulcis *Thunb.*), E. Asia; *Mabee bark* (Ceanothus reclinatus *L'Hérit.*), Trop. Amer.; *Chew Stick* (Gouania domingensis *L.*), West Indies.

202. VITACEAE

(Ampelidaceae)

Mostly climbing shrubs (by tendrils) or small trees, *nodose* or *jointed*, often with watery juice; leaves alternate or the lower sometimes opposite, simple or variously compound, often pellucid-punctate; stipules petiolar or absent; flowers ♀ or ♂ ♀, actinomorphic, small, in *leaf-opposed* spikes, racemes,

FIG. 202. Cissus discolor *Planch.* (Vitaceae). A, branch showing tendril. B, flower. C, stamen. D, ovary. (After *Bot. Mag.*)

panicles, or cymes; peduncles often *cirrhose*; calyx small, entire or 4–5-toothed or lobed; petals 4–5, free or united, caducous, *valvate*; stamens 4–5, *opposite the petals*, inserted at the base of the disk; anthers free or connate, 2-locular, opening lengthwise; disk intra-staminal, mostly very distinct; ovary 2–6-locular, loculi 1–2-ovuled; style short; stigma capitate or discoid; fruit baccate, often watery, 1–6-locular; seed with copious sometimes ruminate endosperm and small embryo. B.H. **1,** 386; E.P. **3,** 5, 427. Tropics and Warm Temperate Regions.—VITIS, CISSUS, AMPELOCISSUS, PARTHENOCISSUS, PTERISANTHES, LEEA.

USEFUL PRODUCTS: *Grape Vine* (Vitis vinifera *L.*); various forms producing *Muscatels, Sultanas, Raisins, Currants, Wines, Grape Sugar,* &c. Ornamental climbers: *Virginia Creeper* (Parthenocissus tricuspidata *Planch.*), &c.

ORDER 45. MYRSINALES

Leaves mostly gland-dotted; stipules absent; flowers small; petals united, rarely free, usually contorted or imbricate; stamens the same number as and *opposite* the corolla-lobes, usually epipetalous; anthers opening lengthwise or by apical pores; ovary superior to half-inferior, with numerous ovules on a free-basal placenta.—Mostly Tropics.

A. Seeds with endosperm, short and with a short embryo; cotyledons not connate; anthers not transversely septate; fruit mostly indehiscent:
  B. Anthers introrse; staminodes absent; leaves punctate or with schizogenous lines *Myrsinaceae*
  BB. Anthers extrorse; staminodes alternate with the corolla-lobes *Theophrastaceae*
AA. Seeds without endosperm, very elongated; embryo long and arcuate, germinating within the pericarp of the fruit; cotyledons connate into a tube around the plumule; anthers introrse, loculi transversely septate; fruit a capsule *Aegicerataceae*

203. MYRSINACEAE

Trees, shrubs, rarely subherbaceous; leaves alternate, rarely subopposite or subverticillate, simple, *punctate* or with schizogenous lines; stipules absent;

FIG. 203. Ardisia humilis *Vahl* (Myrsinaceae). A, bud. B, vertical section of same. C, stamens. D, ovary. E, transverse section of same. (After De Wild.)

flowers small, ☿ or rarely dioecious, in racemes or panicles; sepals free or connate, often *punctate, valvate, imbricate,* or *contorted,* persistent; corolla rotate or tubular, rarely the petals free; lobes contorted, imbricate or rarely valvate; stamens *opposite the petals* and the same number; filaments adnate to the corolla or rarely almost free; anthers introrse, opening lengthwise or by *apical pores*; ovary *superior or half-inferior, 1-locular*, style simple, sometimes capitate; ovules numerous on a *free-basal placenta*; fruit a berry or drupe, rarely irregularly dehiscent; seeds with smooth or rarely ruminate endosperm with the embryo sometimes placed transversely, straight or arcuate. B.H. **2,** 639; E.P. **4,** 1, 84. Mainly Tropics.—MAESA, MYRSINE, CYBIANTHUS, EMBELIA, CONOMORPHA, ARDISIA, &c.

204. THEOPHRASTACEAE

Trees or shrubs; leaves alternate, in false whorls at the ends of the shoots, entire or spinose-serrate, sometimes very pungent at the apex, pinnately

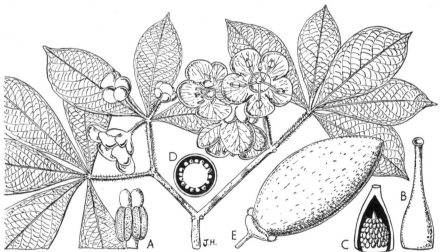

FIG. 204. Deherainia smaragdina (*Planch.*) *Decne.* (Theophrastaceae). A, anther. B, ovary and style. C, vertical view inside the ovary. D, cross-section of ovary. E, fruit. (Orig.)

nerved; *stipules absent*; inflorescence terminal or rarely lateral, racemose or fasciculate or rarely reduced to one flower; flowers bisexual or dioecious, fairly large, white, yellow, or rose; calyx below the ovary, segments 5–4, free or shortly connate, imbricate, persistent, like the corolla marked with *glandular dots or lines*; corolla *sympetalous*, fleshy; tube short; lobes 5–4, imbricate; stamens 5, inserted near the base of the tube, *opposite the corolla-lobes*; filaments free or connate into a tube; anthers bilocular, extrorse, dehiscing by slits lengthwise, mostly with a produced connective; *staminodes 5*, alternate with the corolla-lobes, either just above the fertile stamens or at the mouth between the lobes; ovary 1-locular, stigma discoid or conical; placenta basal, *sterile at the apex*, ovules numerous immersed in mucilage; fruit baccate or drupaceous, *indehiscent*; seeds many to 1; endosperm copious, not ruminate; embryo erect, cotyledons conspicuous. B.H. **2,** 641. 648; E.P.

4, 1, 88; Mez, Engl. *Pflanzenr.*, *Theophrastaceae*, 1–48, figs. 1–7 (1903). Tropical America, West Indies.

A. Staminodial tube short, much exceeded by the corolla-tube; flowers bisexual, in racemes; anthers apiculate—THEOPHRASTA (Trop. Amer.). **AA.** Staminodial tube about as long as and adnate to the corolla-tube: **B.** Staminodes gland-like or ligulate, not petaloid: **C.** Flowers solitary, bisexual; anthers free, apiculate—DEHERAINIA (Mexico, West Indies). **CC.** Flowers racemose, polygamo-dioecious; anthers of the male flowers connate, truncate, of the female free—CLAVIJA (Trop. Amer.). **BB.** Staminodes petaloid; flowers in racemes or corymbs; anthers mostly not apiculate—JACQUINIA (Trop. Amer.).

205. AEGICERATACEAE

Mangrove shrubs or small trees with the habit of *Rhizophora*; leaves alternate, coriaceous, entire, *minutely punctate*; *stipules absent*; flowers bisexual, in

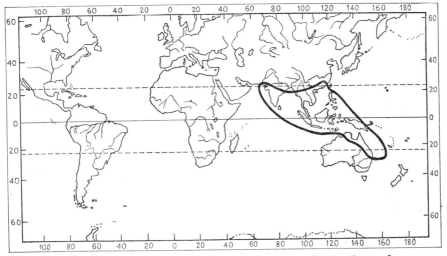

The genus Aegiceras, the only member of the family Aegicerataceae, is a constituent of mangroves of SE. Asia, Malaya, and NE. Australia.

sessile terminal or axillary umbels or very short branched racemes, white, fragrant; *bracts and bracteoles absent*; sepals 5, very strongly and *dextrorsely contorted*, very asymmetric, coriaceous; corolla *sympetalous*, shortly tubular; lobes 5, *dextrorsely contorted*, soon *reflexed*; stamens 5, *opposite the corolla-lobes*, inserted in the densely hairy tube of the corolla, filaments shortly connate, villous in the lower part; anthers 2-locular, the loculi *transversely septate* into numerous loculi, introrse, dehiscing by a slit lengthwise; ovary 1-locular, fusiform, narrowed into a subulate style, stigma acute; ovules numerous, *immersed in the ovoid-globose basal placenta*, the upper ones *ascending*, lower *spreading*; fruit cylindrical and arcuate, acute, coriaceous, striate, at length longitudinally split; seed 1, elongated, erect, *without endosperm*, embryo erect, arcuate, cylindrical, *germinating within the pericarp*, cotyledons *connate into a tube* enclosing the plumule. B.H. **2**, 648; E.P. **4**, 1, 97; Mez, Engl. *Pflanzenr.*, *Myrsinac.* 55, fig. 8 (all in *Myrsinaceae*). Tropical Asia, Malaya, Tropical and Subtropical Australia.—AEGICERAS.

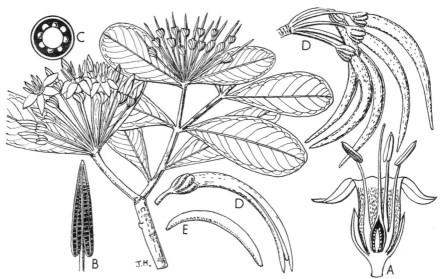

FIG. 205. Aegiceras corniculatum (*L.*) *Blanco* (Aegicerataceae). A, vertical section of flower. B, anther. C, cross-section of ovary. D, fruits. E, seed.

ORDER 46. EBENALES

Trees or shrubs; leaves mostly alternate; stipules absent; flowers ♀ or ♂ ♀, actinomorphic; petals united, imbricate; stamens epipetalous or rarely hypogynous, 1–4 usually 2 times as many as the corolla-lobes; petaloid staminodes often present; anthers opening lengthwise; ovary superior; loculi 1–2-ovuled; ovules axile; seeds with copious or thin endosperm.—Mainly Tropics.

A. Flowers mostly unisexual; stamens hypogynous or inserted at the bottom of the corolla; ovules pendulous from the inner angle; seeds with a small hilum   *Ebenaceae*

AA. Flowers bisexual; stamens epipetalous, the fertile ones opposite to the corolla-lobes; ovules ascending from the inner angle; seeds with a large broad basal or lateral hilum:

B. Flowers fasciculate in the leaf-axils or at the nodes; leaves alternate   *Sapotaceae*

BB. Flowers in axillary racemes or panicles; leaves opposite or subopposite   *Sarcospermaceae*

206. EBENACEAE

Trees or shrubs with often hard and black wood; leaves alternate, rarely opposite, entire; stipules absent; flowers mostly ♂ ♀, often *dioecious*, the ♂ with a rudimentary ovary, the ♀ with imperfect or no stamens; female flowers

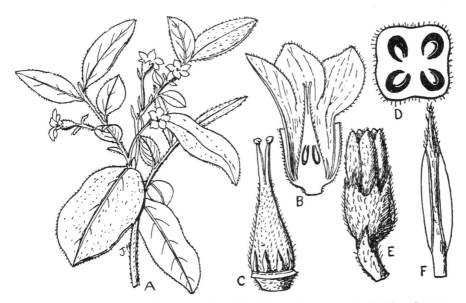

FIG. 206a. Royena lucida *L.* (Ebenaceae). A, habit. B, female flower in vertical section. C, ovary. D, transverse section of same. E, male flower. F, stamen.

FIG. 206b. Diospyros mespiliformis *Hochst.* (Ebenaceae). A, male flower. B, vertical section of same. C, a pair of stamens. D, vertical section of female flower. E, cross-section of ovary. F, fruiting shoot. (After Hutch. and Dalz., *Fl. W. Trop. Afr.*)

usually solitary; calyx 3–6-lobed, persistent and often accrescent in fruit; corolla 3–7-lobed, lobes imbricate; stamens *hypogynous* or on the bottom of the corolla, *2–4 times the number* of the corolla-lobes, rarely equal and alternate; filaments free or united in pairs; anthers 2-locular, introrse, opening lengthwise; ovary superior, 3- or more-locular; style often divided; ovules 1–2 in each loculus, pendulous from the inner angle; berry more or less succulent; seeds with a thin testa; embryo about half as long as the endosperm; cotyledons about equal to the radicle, foliaceous. B.H. **2**, 662; E.P. **4**, 1, 153. Tropics and Subtropics of the Old World and N. America.

USEFUL PRODUCTS: Heavy and valuable timbers, including *Calamander wood* (Diospyros quaesita *Thw.*), Ceylon; *Andaman Marble* or *Zebra wood* (Diospyros kurzii *Hiern*), Indian Archip.; *Ebony* (Diospyros ebenum *Koenig*), S. India, Ceylon; *Gaub fruits* (D. embryopteris *Pers.*), India to Malaya; *Date Plum* (D. lotus *L.*), Italy and Orient; *Persimmon* (Diospyros virginiana *L.*), U.S.A.; *Kaki Plum* (D. kaki *L. f.*), Japan.

A. Flowers bisexual: **B.** Stamens 10 or more—ROYENA (Trop. and S. Afr.). **BB.** Stamens 5; doubtfully placed here[1]—ONCOTHECA (New Caled.). **BBB.** Stamens 3–2—RHAPIDANTHE (W. Trop. Afr.). **AA.** Flowers unisexual or polygamous: **C.** Corolla-lobes contorted: **D.** Calyx not enlarged after flowering or scarcely so—EUCLEA (Afr., Arabia). **DD.** Calyx mostly much enlarged after flowering: **E.** Flowers 5–4-merous; ovary 4- or 8–16-locular—DIOSPYROS (*Brayodendron*) (Trop. and Temp. Reg.). **EE.** Flowers 3-merous; ovary 6- or 3-locular—MABA (Trop. and Subtrop. Reg.). **CC.** Corolla-lobes valvate; stamens numerous—TETRACLIS (Madag.).

207. SAPOTACEAE

Trees or shrubs with *milky juice*, often cauliflorous; leaves simple, alternate, entire, leathery; *stipules usually absent*; flowers ⚥, actinomorphic, usually rather small; calyx 4–8-lobed; corolla 4–8-lobed, lobes 1–2-seriate, imbricate; stamens *epipetalous*, the fertile ones equalling the corolla-lobes and *opposite to them*, or more numerous and 2- or more-seriate; *staminodes sometimes present*; anthers opening lengthwise; ovary several-locular, superior; style simple; ovules solitary in each loculus, ascending from the inner angle; fruit 1- to many-locular, often a rather hard berry, rarely a capsule; seeds with a bony, often shining, testa, and a large broad hilum; endosperm mostly scanty; embryo large, with small radicle and broad foliaceous cotyledons. Including *Boerlagellaceae*. B.H. **2**, 650; E.P. **4**, 1, 126. Mainly Tropics and Subtropics.—CHRYSOPHYLLUM, LUCUMA, SIDEROXYLON, ACHRAS, DICHOPSIS, BASSIA, BUMELIA, BUTYROSPERMUM, MIMUSOPS, IMBRICARIA, &c.

USEFUL PRODUCTS: *Shea Butter Tree* (Butyrospermum parkii *Kotschy*), N. Trop. Afr.; *Balata* or *Bully Tree* (Mimusops globosa *Gaertn.*); *Gutta Percha* (Palaquium gutta *Burck.*), Malay Penin.; *Mahwa* or *Mowa Tree* (Madhuca indica *Gmelin*) (Bassia latifolia *Roxb.*), India; *Sapodilla Plum* (Achras sapota *L.*), Trop. Amer. and cultivated; *Star Apple* (Chrysophyllum cainito *L.*), Trop. Amer., West Indies; *Mammee Sapote Plum* (Lucuma mammosa *Gaertn.*), S. Amer., West Indies.

[1] See Guillaumin, *Rev. gén. Bot.* **50**, 629 (1938).

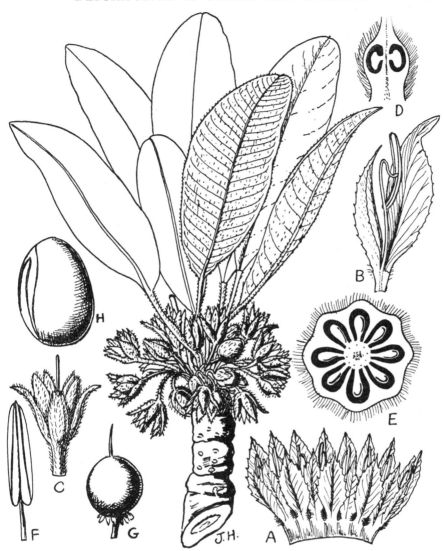

FIG. 207. Butyrospermum parkii *Kotschy* (Sapotaceae). A, flower opened. B, stamen and staminodes. C, calyx. D, vertical section of ovary. E, transverse section of same. F, stamen. G, fruit. H, seed. (After Kotschy.)

208. SARCOSPERMACEAE

Trees or shrubs, some with latex; leaves *opposite or subopposite*, rarely subverticillate, pinnately nerved, often with large *pits in the axils of the nerves*; stipules small, mostly caducous; petiole sometimes with a pair of *stipel-like appendages* at the top; flowers bisexual, in axillary *racemes or panicles*; bracts minute, deltoid; sepals 5, imbricate; corolla-tube short, lobes 5, imbricate; stamens 5, inserted on the corolla *opposite the lobes*; anthers basifixed, 2-locular, dehiscing lengthwise; *staminodes 5*, alternate with the corolla-lobes; ovary superior,

FIG. 208. Sarcosperma arboreum *Benth.* (Sarcospermaceae). A, flower-bud. B, flower. C, corolla opened out showing the 5 stamens and 5 staminodes. D, ovary. E, vertical section of ovary. F, fruits. G, seed. (Orig.)

2–1-locular, style short and stout; ovule 1 in each loculus, ascending from the base of the central axis; fruit a 1–2-seeded *drupe*, ovoid to oblong and slightly 2-lobed; pericarp thin; seeds conforming to the shape of the fruit, with a pale dull testa; hilum small, circular, basal; *no endosperm*; cotyledons thick. Lam, *Flora Malesiana*, **4**, 32, fig. 1 (1948). SE. Asia, Malaya.—SARCOSPERMA (*Bracea*).

A small family represented by a single genus of about 6 species in SE. Asia from India and S. China to the Malay Archipelago. It seems to provide a link between the *Myrsinaceae* and the *Sapotaceae*, in the latter of which it was formerly included.

ORDER 47. RUTALES

Trees, shrubs, or climbers, rarely herbs; leaves often gland-dotted, simple or compound; stipules very rarely present; flowers hypogynous to slightly perigynous, mostly ⚥; sepals mostly imbricate; petals contorted to valvate, free or connate near the base; disk mostly conspicuous; ovary superior, syncarpous or subapocarpous; styles free or connate; ovules 1–2 or numerous; seeds with or without endosperm and straight or curved embryo.—Mainly Tropics.

A. Leaves glandular-punctate, mostly opposite; disk almost invariably present between the stamens and ovary, from annular to tubular or produced into a gynophore or lining the calyx; ovary mostly lobed   *Rutaceae*
AA. Leaves not glandular-punctate or very rarely so, usually alternate; stipules absent or very rare:
  B. Disk present; petals imbricate or valvate:
    C. Ovary mostly deeply lobed or carpels free; stamens often with a scale at the base; ovule usually solitary in each loculus   *Simaroubaceae*
    CC. Ovary entire; stamens without a scale; ovules usually 2 in each loculus
Burseraceae
  BB. Disk absent; petals contorted; ovules numerous in each loculus
Averrhoaceae

209. RUTACEAE

Shrubs or trees, very rarely herbs; leaves simple or compound, mostly gland-dotted; stipules absent; flowers ⚥, rarely ♂ ♀, rarely zygomorphic; sepals 4–5, imbricate, free or connate; petals imbricate, rarely valvate, mostly free; stamens the same as or double the number of the petals, rarely many, free or rarely united; anthers 2-locular, introrse, opening lengthwise, the connective

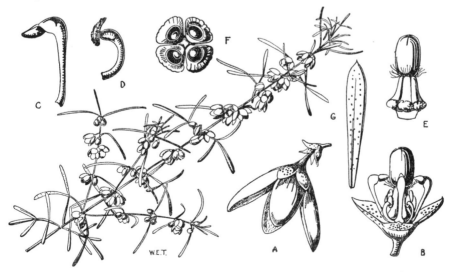

FIG. 209. Boronia heterophylla *F. Muell.* (Rutaceae). A, flower. B, same opened. C, stamen before dehiscence. D, same after dehiscence. E, ovary. F, fruit. G, leaf. (Orig.)

often glandular at the apex; disk usually present within the stamens; ovary superior, syncarpous and often 4–5-locular, or sometimes the carpels free towards the base, or rarely altogether free; styles free or connate; ovules often 2, superposed; fruit baccate, drupaceous, or coriaceous, rarely capsular; seeds with or without endosperm; embryo straight or curved. B.H. **1**, 278; E.P. **3**, 4, 95. Temperate and Warmer Regions; very numerous in S. Africa and Australia.—ALMEIDEA, GALIPEA, TICOREA, RUTA, DICTAMNUS, CALODENDRUM, DIOSMA, ACMADENIA, ADENANDRA, BAROSMA, AGATHOSMA, BORONIA, ERIOSTEMON, PHEBALIUM, CORREA, MELICOPE, EVODIA, CHOISYA, XANTHOXYLUM, ESENBECKIA, &c.

USEFUL PRODUCTS: *Lemons* (Citrus medica, var. limonum, *Brand.*); *Oranges* (C. aurantium *L.*); *Limes* (Citrus medica, var. acida, *Brand.*), India; *Cape Chestnut* (Calodendrum capensis *Thunb.*); *Buchu* (Barosma betulina *B. & W.*, &c.), S. Afr.; *Japan Pepper* (Zanthoxylum piperitum *DC.*); *Jaborandi* (Pilocarpus jaborandi *Holmes*), Brazil; *Bael Fruit* (Aegle marmelos *Corr.*), India; *Cusparia bark* (Galipea officinalis *Hancock*), Trop. S. Amer.

210. SIMAROUBACEAE

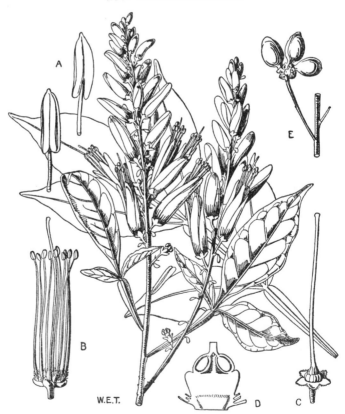

FIG. 210. Quassia amara *L.* (Simaroubaceae). A, stamens. B, stamens and ovary. C, ovary. D, section of lower portion of same. E, fruits. (After Kohler.)

Trees or shrubs, sometimes with a very *bitter bark*; leaves alternate or rarely opposite, *pinnate*, rarely simple or glandular; stipules absent or very rare; flowers small, unisexual or polygamous, rarely ♀, actinomorphic; calyx-lobes 3–5; petals 3–5, imbricate or valvate, rarely absent or united into a tube; *disk present*; stamens inserted at the base of the disk, equal to or double the number of the petals, rarely numerous, free, sometimes with a scale at the base; anthers 2-locular, opening lengthwise; ovary mostly 2–5-*lobed*, 1–5-locular, or carpels quite separate; styles 2–5; ovules usually solitary, rarely 2 or more, axile; fruit usually indehiscent, sometimes samaroid; seeds with or without endosperm; embryo straight or curved. B.H. **1**, 306; E.P. **3**, 4, 202; edn. 2, **19a**, 359 (1931). Mainly Tropics.—QUASSIA, SIMABA, HANNOA, SIMAROUBA, AILANTHUS, CASTELA, PICRASMA, SURIANA, &c.

USEFUL PRODUCTS: *Surinam Quassia wood* (Quassia amara *L.*), Surinam; *Cedron* (Simaba cedron *Planch.*), Cent. Amer.; *Simarouba bark* (Simarouba amara *Aubl.*), Trop. Amer.; *Quassia wood* (Picrasma excelsa *Lindl.*), West Indies; *Tree of Heaven* (Ailanthus altissima *Swingle*), China.

211. BURSERACEAE

Trees or shrubs, secreting *resin* or *oil*; leaves alternate, rarely opposite, *compound*, rarely 1-foliolate, usually not punctate; *stipules absent*; flowers ♀ or

FIG. 211. Boswellia carteri *Birdw.* (Burseraceae). A, flower. B, ovary and disk.
(After Birdw.)

♂ ♀, small; sepals 3–5, imbricate or valvate; petals 3–5, rarely absent, free or variously connate, imbricate or valvate; *disk present*; stamens equal or generally double the number of the petals; filaments free; anthers 2 locular, opening lengthwise; ovary superior, 2–5-locular; ovules 2 or rarely 1 in each loculus, axile; fruit a drupe or tardily dehiscent; seeds without endosperm and often contortuplicate cotyledons. B.H. **1**, 321; E.P. **3**, 4, 231. Tropics.— BOSWELLIA, GARUGA, BALSAMODENDRON, BURSERA, CANARIUM, AMYRIS, &c.

USEFUL PRODUCTS: Abounding in fragrant *balsams* and resins. *Gum Olibanum* or *Frankincense* (Boswellia carteri *Birdw.*), Somaliland, Arabia; *Myrrh* (Balsamodendron, &c.), S. Arabia, &c.; *Carana gum resin* (Protium carana *Marsh.*), S. Amer.

212. AVERRHOACEAE[1]

Small trees; leaves alternate, *imparipinnate*, leaflets opposite or alternate; *stipules absent*; flowers actinopmorphic, small, in small axillary panicles; sepals 5, free, imbricate; petals 5, free or loosely *connivent* only in the middle, *contorted*; disk absent; stamens 10, all perfect or only 5 bearing anthers; filaments shortly united at the base; anthers 2-locular, dehiscing by slits lengthwise; ovary somewhat 5-lobed, 5-locular; styles 5, free, stigmas capitate; ovules numerous in each loculus, axile; fruit a large oblong *berry*, 5-lobulate; seeds *nude or arillate*; endosperm fleshy, scanty; embryo straight. Tropical Asia; widely cultivated.—AVERRHOA.

USEFUL PRODUCTS: *Bilimbi fruit* (Averrhoa bilimbi *L.*); *Carambola fruit* (Averrhoa carambola *L.*), India and China.

ORDER 48. MELIALES

Very similar to preceding group, but stamens often completely connate into a tube with the anthers inside; leaves not gland-dotted.

213. MELIACEAE

Trees or shrubs, mostly with hard *scented* wood, very rarely subherbaceous; leaves alternate, *mostly pinnate*; stipules absent; flowers actinomorphic, mostly ♀; calyx often small, imbricate, rarely valvate; petals free or partially connate, contorted or imbricate, or adnate to the staminal-tube and valvate; stamens mostly 8 or 10, rarely numerous, mostly with connate filaments and the anthers often sessile in the tube; anthers 2-locular, opening lengthwise; disk various; ovary superior, often 3–5-locular; stigma often *disciform* or *capitate*; ovules mostly 2, rarely 1 or more; fruit baccate, capsular, or rarely a drupe, often with a large angular central axis; seeds with or without endosperm, sometimes winged. B.H. **1**, 327; E.P. **3**, 4, 258. Warm Regions.— TURRAEA, MELIA, AZADIRACHTA, DYSOXYLUM, AGLAIA, MILNEA, AMOORA,

---

[1] **Averrhoaceae** *Hutch.*, fam. nov.; arbores parvae; folia alterna, imparipinnata, foliolis oppositis vel alternis; stipulae nullae; flores actinomorphi, parvi, paniculis dispositi; sepala 5, libera, imbricata; petala 5, libera vel medio laxe conniventia, contorta; discus nullus; stamina 10, omnia fertilia vel 5 solum antherifera; filamenta basi breviter connata; antherae 2-loculares, longitudinaliter dehiscentes; ovarium leviter 5-lobum, 5-loculare; styli 5, liberi, stigmatibus capitatis; ovula in loculis numerosa, axilia; bacca magna, oblonga, 5-lobulata; semina nuda vel arillata, endospermio carnoso, embryo recto. Genus typicum AVERRHOA.

FIG. 212. Averrhoa carambola *L.* (Averrhoaceae). A, flower. B, same with petals removed. C, stamens and staminodes. D, anther. E, fruit. F, cross-section of fruit. (Orig.)

GUAREA, EKEBERGIA, TRICHILIA, CARAPA, SWIETENIA, KHAYA, CEDRELA, FLINDERSIA, &c.

USEFUL PRODUCTS: *Neem* or *Margosa* (Azadirachta indica *Juss.*), India; *Persian Lilac* (Melia azedarach *L.*), Tropics (generally cultivated); *Lansa* or *Langsat fruit* (Lansium domesticum *Jack*); *Mafureira Seeds* (Trichilia emetica *Vahl*), Trop. Afr.; *Mahogany wood* (Swietenia mahogani *L.*, &c.), Trop. Amer., West Indies; *Guiana Crab Tree* (Carapa guianensis *Aubl.*); *African Cedar* (Khaya senegalensis *Juss.*, &c.), W. Afr.; *Rohan Tree* or *Indian Redwood* (Soymida febrifuga *A. Juss.*), India; *Chittagong wood* (Chickrassia tabularis

FIG. 213. Pseudocedrela kotschyi (*Schweinf.*) *Harms* (Meliaceae). A, flower. B, same with corolla removed. C, portion of staminal ring. D, ovary. E, fruit. F, seed. (Orig.)

A. Juss.), India, Burma, &c.; *Toon wood* (Cedrela toona *Roxb.*), India, &c.; *Satin wood* (Chloroxylum swietenia *DC.*), India, &c.; *Yellow wood* (Flindersia oxleyana *F. Muell.*), E. Austral.

ORDER 49. SAPINDALES

Trees or shrubs; leaves mostly compound, usually pinnate, rarely digitate, not gland-dotted; stipules rare; flowers hypogynous or slightly perigynous, often polygamous or unisexual, sometimes zygomorphic; sepals imbricate; petals mostly present; disk usually present; ovary superior, with 1–2 very rarely numerous ovules in each loculus, axile; seeds mostly without endosperm; embryo curved or crumpled.—Mainly Tropics.

A. Sepals more than 2; spineless trees and shrubs:
  B. Disk present, sometimes unilateral:
    C. Leaves with large intrapetiolar persistent stipules, alternate; ovary 5–4-locular; disk unilateral; stamens 4   *Melianthaceae*

CC. Leaves without stipules or with extrapetiolar stipules, alternate or opposite:

D. Ovules few:

E. Leaves alternate:

F. Ovules axile:

G. Stamens usually 8, inserted within the disk or unilateral:

H. Seeds often arillate; embryo often plicate or twisted
Sapindaceae

HH. Seeds not arillate; embryo not twisted *Podoaceae*

GG. Stamens 5, 4, or 2, opposite the petals; cotyledons contorted
Sabiaceae

FF. Ovule 1, pendulous or adnate to the ovary or from a basal funicle; fruit mostly drupaceous *Anacardiaceae*

EE. Leaves opposite:

J. Fruit separating into 2 divergent winged indehiscent samaras; ovary 2-locular, compressed contrary to the septum; leaves simple or palmately lobed or pinnate *Aceraceae*

JJ. Fruit a 3-locular or by abortion 1–2-locular loculicidal capsule, not compressed contrary to the septum; leaves digitately 5–9-foliolate *Hippocastanaceae*

DD. Ovules numerous; leaves alternate or opposite, either trifoliolate or pinnate; carpels 3–2, more or less united *Staphyleaceae*

BB. Disk absent:

K. Petals 5, contorted; flowers bisexual *Akaniaceae*

KK. Petals absent; flowers dioecious *Julianiaceae*

AA. Sepals 2, decussate, petaloid, persistent; ovary 3-locular but with only 1 loculus fertile; very spiny trees; Madagascar *Didiereaceae*

214. MELIANTHACEAE

Shrubs or small trees; leaves alternate, *pinnate*, stipulate; stipules intra-petiolar, often large; flowers ⚥, rarely ♂ ♀, racemose, zygomorphic; calyx of 5

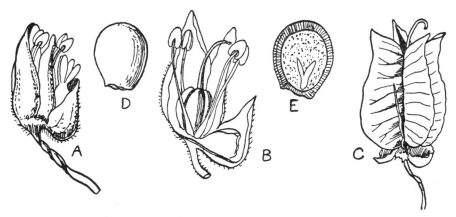

FIG. 214. Melianthus major *L.* (Melianthaceae). A, flower. B, vertical section of same. C, fruit. D, seed. E, vertical section of same. (Orig.)

unequal segments, imbricate; petals 5 free, subperigynous, clawed, unequal; disk unilateral, lining the inside of the calyx; stamens 4, inserted within the disk, free or variously connate, often declinate; anthers 2-locular, opening lengthwise; ovary 4–5-locular, superior; style central, dentate or truncate; ovules 1–4 in each loculus, axile; fruit a papery or woody capsule, loculicidally 4–5-valved or opening only at the apex; seeds with copious endosperm and straight embryo. B.H. **1,** 411 (under *Sapindaceae*); E.P. **3,** 5, 374. Tropical and Subtropical Africa.

A. Calyx very oblique at the base; ovules 4–2 in each loculus—MELIANTHUS (S. Afr.). **AA.** Calyx subequal at the base; ovule 1 in each loculus—BERSAMA (Trop. and S. Afr.).

215. SAPINDACEAE

Trees, shrubs, or climbers; leaves alternate or very rarely opposite, simple or *compound*; stipules rarely present; flowers actinomorphic or zygomorphic,

FIG. 215. Koelreuteria paniculata *Laxm.* (Sapindaceae). A and B, flower. C, vertical section of same. D, bract. E, sepal. F, petal. G, stamens. H, cross-section of ovary. I, carpel opened. J, bud. (After De Wild.)

often much reduced and usually *polygamo-dioecious*, variously arranged; sepals free or variously connate, imbricate or rarely valvate; petals 3–5 or rarely more, often absent, equal or unequal, imbricate; disk usually present, sometimes *unilateral*; stamens hypogynous, often 8, inserted *within the disk* or unilateral, filaments free, often hairy; anthers 2-locular; ovary superior, entire, lobed, or divided nearly to the base, 1–4- (often 3-) locular; style terminal or between the lobes, rarely styles 2–4, simple or divided; ovules 1–2 or rarely many in each loculus, inserted on the central axis and usually ascending, or rarely on parietal placentas; fruit various; seeds without endosperm, often arillate, with often plicate or twisted embryo; incl. *Bretschneideraceae*[1]. B.H. **1,** 388, partly; E.P. **3,** 5, 277. Mainly Tropical Regions.—URVILLEA, SER-JANIA, CARDIOSPERMUM, PAULLINIA, ERIOGLOSSUM, ALLOPHYLUS (*Schmidelia*), KOELREUTERIA, BRETSCHNEIDERA, CUPANIA, RATONIA, ERIOCOELUM, THOUINIA, TALISIA, SAPINDUS, DEINBOLLIA, NEPHELIUM, HARPULLIA, &c.

216. PODOACEAE

Shrubs or rhizomatous tuberous-rooted perennial herbs; leaves alternate or opposite, long-petiolate, serrate or palmately trilobed; *stipules absent*; flowers *unisexual*, in terminal panicles, very small; bracts linear or some of those of the male flowers *long-stalked*, large and *membranous-reticulate*, at length *coloured*, the female bracts suborbicular and membranous-reticulate; male flowers: calyx cupular, 4-toothed; petals 4, free, clawed, *valvate*, sometimes elongate-filiform; stamens 8, filaments free or adnate at the base to the rudi-mentary ovary or the latter absent; anthers short, extrorse; *disk absent*; female flowers: *pedicels adnate to the large veiny bract*; calyx and petals absent; disk annular; ovary sessile, 1-locular; style elongated, undivided; ovule 1, erect from the base; fruit lenticular, in one genus borne on the dilated flat reticulately veined bract, compressed, *indehiscent*; seed 1, erect; cotyledons flat, oval.—E. Asia.

A. Leaves pinnately nerved, not lobed; male bracts small and linear; female bracts adnate to the pedicel, persistent and membranous-reticulate in fruit, suborbicular; petals of the male flowers elliptic to oblanceolate; style very short—DOBINEA (*Podoon*) (India, China) (Fig. 216). **AA.** Leaves palmately 3-nerved and 3-lobed; some male bracts long-stalked, large and foliaceous, oblong, female bracts suborbicular; petals of the male flowers filiform; style elongate-filiform—CAMPYLOPETALUM (Thailand).

217. SABIACEAE

Trees or shrubs; leaves alternate, simple or pinnate; *stipules absent*; flowers ☿ or polygamo-dioecious, small, often paniculate; calyx 4–5-partite, imbri-cate; petals 4–5, imbricate, opposite or alternate with the sepals; disk small, annular; stamens 4–5, *opposite the petals*, free or adherent to the petals, sometimes only 2 with anthers; anthers 2-locular, with a thick connective; ovary sessile, 2–3-locular; styles more or less united; ovules 1–2 in each loculus, horizontal or pendulous; fruit dry or drupaceous; seed without or with very thin endosperm adhering to the testa, and large embryo; cotyledons

---

[1] I consider the genus *Bretschneidera* Hemsl., regarded by Radlkofer as related to *Morin-gaceae* and transferred to Engler's *Parietales*, to belong to *Sapindaceae* as defined in the present work, and where it was placed originally by Hemsley. This view is supported on anatomical grounds by Heimsch (*Lilloa* 8: 189 (1942)).

Fig. 216. Dobinea delavayi *H. Baill.* (Podoaceae). A, male flowering shoot. B, male flower and vertical section. C, petal. D, female flower. E, female in fruit. F, female flower and bract. G, vertical section of female flower. H, fruit and bract. J, seed. (Partly adapted from Franchet, *Plantae Delavayae.*)

contorted, with curved radicle. B.H. **1**, 413; E.P. **3**, 5, 367. Tropics and Subtropics, absent from Africa.

USEFUL PRODUCTS: Some ornamental shrubs (Meliosma).

A. Stamens 5 or 4, all fertile and opposite the petals; leaves simple—SABIA (Trop. Asia to Japan). **AA.** Stamens not all fertile; leaves simple or pinnate: **B.** Petals more or less equal in shape; style scarcely developed: **C.** Petals linear-lanceolate with long tails; stigmas wide apart—PHOXANTHUS (Trop.

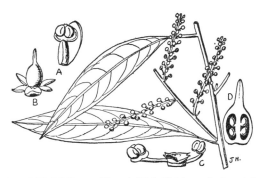

FIG. 217. Meliosma Henryi *Diels* (Sabiaceae). A, petal and stamen. B, pistil and calyx. C, stamens and disk. D, vertical section of ovary. (After Hook. *Ic. Pl.*)

S. Amer.). **CC.** Petals elliptic to orbicular, not tailed; stigmas contiguous— OPHIOCARYON (Trop. S. Amer.). **BB.** Inner petals different from the outer, much smaller; style well developed—MELIOSMA (Trop. and Subtrop. Asia, Mexico, West Indies to Brazil).

218. ANACARDIACEAE

Trees or shrubs, often with *resinous bark*; leaves alternate, very rarely opposite, simple or *compound*; stipules absent, very rarely present but obscure; flowers ⚥ or ♂ ♀, mostly actinomorphic; calyx variously divided, sometimes semisuperior in fruit; petals 3–7 or absent, free or rarely connate and adnate to the torus; disk present; stamens often double the number of the petals, rarely equal or numerous; filaments free among themselves; anthers 2-locular, opening lengthwise; ovary superior, *1-locular*, rarely 2–5-locular, or very rarely carpels free; styles 1–3, often *widely separated*; ovule solitary, pendulous from the apex or adnate to the ovary wall, or pendulous from a basal funicle; fruit mostly drupaceous; seed without or with very thin endosperm; cotyledons fleshy. B.H. **1**, 415; E.P. **3**, 5, 138. Mainly Tropics.—RHUS, PISTACIA, SORINDEIA, MANGIFERA, ANACARDIUM, BUCHANANIA, SCHINUS, ODINA, SEMECARPUS, SPONDIAS, DRACONTOMELON, SCLEROCARYA, BLEPHARO-CARYA, &c.

USEFUL PRODUCTS: *Lacquer Tree* (Rhus vernicifera *DC.*), Japan; *Poison Ivy* (Rhus toxicodendron *L.*); *Sumach* (Rhus coriaria *L.*), Mediterr.; *Chian Turpentine* (Pistacia terebinthus *L.*), Mediterr., etc.; *Pistachio nuts* (Pistacia vera *L.*), Mediterr., W. Asia; *Mastic* (Pistacia lentiscus *L.*),

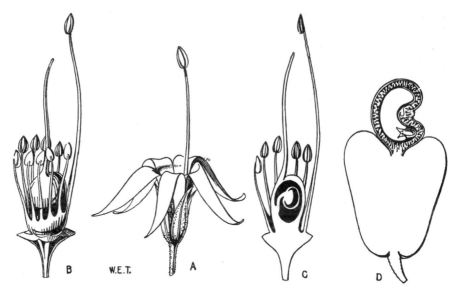

Fig. 218. Anacardium occidentale *L.* (Anacardiaceae). A, flower. B, same with petals removed. C, same in vertical section. D, fruit in vertical section. (After Baill.)

Greece; *Quebracho Colorado wood* (Quebrachia lorentzii *Griseb.*), Argentine; *Mango* (Mangifera indica *L.*), Tropics; *Cashew nut* (Anacardium occidentale *L.*), Tropics; *Burmese Lacquer Tree* (Melanorrhoea usitata *Wall.*); *Kaffir Date* (Harpephyllum caffrum *Bernh.*), S. Afr.; *Hog Plum* (Spondias mangifera *Willd.*), India, &c.

219. ACERACEAE

Trees or shrubs with *perulate* buds; leaves *opposite*, simple or palmately lobed or pinnately foliolate; flowers in fascicles, racemes, or corymbs, actinomorphic, andromonoecious or dioecious; sepals and petals 4–5, rarely without petals; disk annular or lobed, or reduced to teeth, rarely absent, either outside or within the stamens; stamens 4–10, often 8, hypogynous or perigynous, or in the ♀ flowers central; filaments free; rudimentary ovary often present in the ♂ flowers; ovary 2-locular, compressed contrary to the septum; styles 2, free or connate at the base; ovules 2 in each loculus, attached to the central axis; *fruit samaroid*, 2-winged, the carpels at length separating at the base, indehiscent; seeds often solitary, compressed, without endosperm; embryo with elongated radicle and flat or plicate cotyledons. B.H. **1**, 409 (under *Sapindaceae*); E.P. **3**, 5, 263. Temperate N. Hemisphere.

USEFUL PRODUCTS: *Sycamore* (Acer pseudoplatanus *Linn.*); *Maple* (Acer campestre *L.*); *Sugar Maple* (A. saccharum *Marsh*), N. Amer.

A. Fruit-lobes divergent, connate only at the base, completely surrounded by a broad wing with the seed near the middle; leaves pinnate—DIPTERONIA (China). AA. Fruit-lobes connate, with the wing only on the upper side; leaves

Fig. 219. Acer campestre *L.* (Aceraceae). A, male flower. B, ovary.
C, fruit. (Orig.)

simple or palmately foliolate—ACER (*Negundo, Argentacer, Rufacer, Saccharo-
dendron,* and *Sacchrosphendamnus*).

220. HIPPOCASTANACEAE

Trees and shrubs; winter buds often sticky; leaves *opposite, digitately 5–9-
foliolate,* leaflets serrate or entire, pinnately nerved; *stipules absent*; flowers
polygamous, somewhat *zygomorphic,* in terminal panicles or racemes, white,
red, or yellow; sepals 5, imbricate, or tubular and 5-fid; petals 5–4, unequal,
clawed, imbricate; disk entire, annular or unilateral; stamens 8–5, inserted
within the disk; filaments free; ovary sessile, 3-locular, or by abortion 2–1-
locular; style elongated *with a simple stigma*; ovules 2 in each loculus, superposed on the inner angle, or the lower ascending and the upper pendulous;
capsule coriaceous, smooth or echinate, 3-lobed or subglobose, loculicidally
3-locular, or by abortion 1–2-locular; seeds solitary by abortion, subglobose;
hilum large, testa coriaceous; cotyledons thick, often *adherent face to face.*
B.H. **1,** 398 (in *Sapindaceae*); E.P. **3,** 5, 273, fig. 150 (1895). N. and S. America,
Persia, Himalaya, Malay Peninsula.

USEFUL PRODUCTS: *Horsechestnut* (Aesculus hippocastanum *L.*), and
other beautiful species of trees and shrubs in cultivation.

A. Sepals free; disk excentric—BILLIA (Trop. S. Amer.). **AA.** Sepals united
in a tube—AESCULUS (Fig. 220) (N. Temp. Zone).

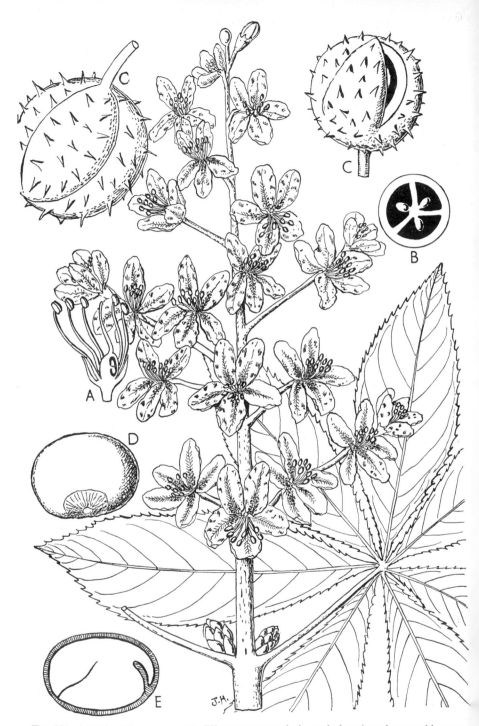

FIG. 220. Aesculus hippocastanum *L.* (Hippocastanaceae). A, vertical section of ovary with some stamens. B, cross-section of ovary. C, fruits. D, seed ('conker'). E, section of seed. (Orig.)

221. STAPHYLEACEAE

Trees or shrubs; leaves alternate or *opposite, trifoliolate* or *pinnate*; stipules paired; flowers ☿ or ♂ ♀, actinomorphic; sepals imbricate; petals imbricate, inserted on or below the hypogynous disk; stamens 5, inserted with the petals and alternate with them, free; anthers 2-locular, opening lengthwise; carpels 2–3, more or less united into a 2–3-locular and lobed ovary; styles free or coherent, at length free; ovules numerous, in 1–2 series on the ventral suture;

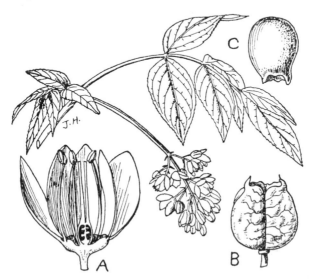

FIG. 221. Staphylea pinnata *L.* (Staphyleaceae). A, vertical section of flower. B, fruit. C, seed. (After Baill.)

fruit a membranous *inflated capsule* opening at the top, or a berry; seeds few, truncate at the base, with scanty endosperm and straight embryo; cotyledons flat. B.H. **1**, 412 (under *Sapindaceae*); E.P. **3**, 5, 258. N. Hemisphere, S. America.—Some garden shrubs.

A. Leaves alternate; leaflets 3–10 pairs; carpels completely united; fruit indehiscent, berry- or drupe-like: **B.** Sepals and petals 5 each: **C.** Stipules and stipels present; sepals united into a tube with 5 short teeth—TAPISCIA (China). **CC.** Stipules and stipels reduced to blackish glands or absent; sepals united in the lower third—HUERTEA (West Indies, Peru). **BB.** Sepals and petals 3 each—TRISCAPHIS (Indo-China). **AA.** Leaves opposite, sometimes unifoliolate; carpels free or only partly united: **D.** Carpels free from the base, bladdery, coriaceous or slightly fleshy in fruit, dehiscent; disk prominent—EUSCAPHIS (Japan). **DD.** Carpels united in the lower third; fruit with a thin skin, more or less bladdery, the ripe carpels united in their lower half and opening along the inner suture of the free part—STAPHYLEA (N. Temp. Reg.). **DDD.** Carpels completely united; disk large, collar- or cuff-like; fruit coriaceous, dry to softly fleshy, indehiscent—TURPINIA (Trop. and Temp. Asia and Amer.).

222. AKANIACEAE

Trees; leaves alternate, imparipinnate; flowers paniculate, ☿, actinomorphic; sepals 5, imbricate; petals 5, contorted; disk absent; stamens usually 8, the 5 outer opposite the sepals, the others around the base of the ovary; filaments free; anthers 2-locular, opening lengthwise; ovary 3-locular; style simple;

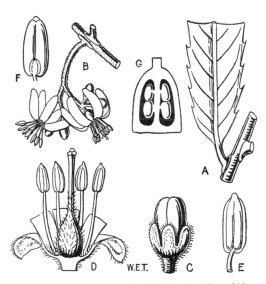

FIG. 222. Akania lucens (*F. Muell.*) *Airy-Shaw* (Akaniaceae). A, twig with leaf. B, flowers. C, flower bud. D, single flower enlarged. E and F, anthers. G, vertical section of ovary. (After *Bot. Mag.*)

stigma minute, 3-lobed; ovules 2 in each loculus, superposed, pendulous; fruit a capsule, loculicidally 3-valved; seeds not arillate, with fleshy copious endosperm; embryo straight. B.H. **1,** 409 (under *Sapindaceae*); Stapf in *Kew Bull.* 1912. 378. E. Australia.—AKANIA (*Apiocarpus*).

223. JULIANIACEAE

Trees or shrubs abounding in resin; leaves deciduous, alternate, pinnate; stipules absent; flowers dioecious, small, the male racemose-paniculate, the female crowded in an involucre; calyx of the male 3–9-lobed, thin; petals absent; stamens the same number as the calyx-lobes and alternate with them; anthers 2-locular, opening by a longitudinal slit, hairy; no rudimentary ovary; female flower: calyx and petals absent; no staminodes; ovary 1-locular, 1-ovuled; style 3-parted; ovule ascending from the base of the loculus, half anatropous; fruits enclosed in the enlarged involucre; seeds without endosperm. Mexico and Peru.

A. Male inflorescence pendulous; calyx 5–8-partite; fruiting pedicels much

FIG. 223. Juliania adstringens *Schl.* (Julianiaceae). A, male flower. B, female flowers. C, same in section. (After Hemsl.)

dilated, with tapering margins—JULIANIA (Cent. Amer.). **AA.** Male inflorescence erect; calyx 4-partite; fruiting pedicels little dilated, with parallel margins—ORTHOPTERYGIUM (Peru).

224. DIDIEREACEAE

Trees with the habit of *Euphorbia*, very spiny; leaves alternate; flowers unisexual, dioecious; male flower: sepals 2, decussate, petaloid, persistent; petals 4, imbricate; stamens 8–10, slightly united at the base, inserted outside an annular disk; female flower: sepals and petals as in the male; sterile anthers sometimes present; ovary superior, 3-locular, only 1 loculus fertile with 1 erect ovule; style single, with an expanded irregularly 3–4-lobed stigma; fruit 3-angled, not dehiscent; seed with folded embryo and fleshy cotyledons. Engl. and Gilg, *Syllabus*, edns. 9 and 10, 269 (1924). Madagascar.—DIDIEREA (Fig. 224).

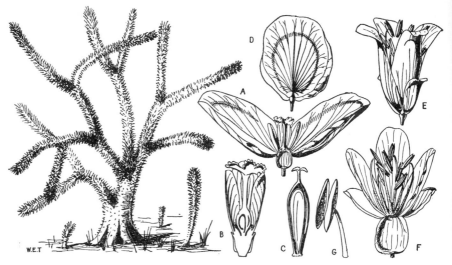

Fig. 224. Didierea mirabilis *Baill.* (Didiereaceae). A, female flower. B, vertical section of same. C, ovary in vertical section. D, fruit. E and F, male flower. G, stamen. (After Drake.)

Order 50. LOGANIALES

Mostly trees and shrubs with opposite, simple or rarely compound leaves; stipules present or absent; sepals mostly valvate; corolla sympetalous, rarely polypetalous, lobes contorted, imbricate, or valvate; stamens epipetalous, alternate with the corolla-lobes or fewer; ovary superior, 2–4-locular; ovules mostly numerous; seeds with endosperm and straight embryo.—Tropics and Temperate Regions.

A. Stamens 4 or more, rarely only 1 (*Usteria*); ovules usually numerous in each ovary or loculus; fruit when capsular usually septicidally dehiscent:
  B. Corolla-lobes contorted, 16–5; fruit a berry with the seeds often immersed in pulp; seeds never winged   *Potaliaceae*
  BB. Corolla-lobes imbricate, very rarely contorted; fruit usually a capsule; seeds often winged:
    C. Intraxylary phloem present; indumentum when present neither glandular, stellate, nor lepidote   *Loganiaceae*
    CC. Intraxylary phloem absent; indumentum when present glandular, stellate, or lepidote   *Buddleiaceae*
  BBB. Corolla-lobes valvate:
    D. Fruit a capsule; calyx with or without an epicalyx:
      E. Trees, shrubs, or climbing shrubs; stamens inserted in the throat of the corolla; seeds winged at each end   *Antoniaceae*
      EE. Herbs or rarely shrublets; stamens inserted in the corolla-tube; seeds not winged   *Spigeliaceae*
    DD. Fruit indehiscent, drupaceous or baccate; no epicalyx; seeds not winged   *Strychnaceae*

AA. Stamens usually 2, rarely 4; ovules 2 in each of the 2 ovary-loculi; fruit when capsular loculicidally dehiscent, often baccate or drupaceous; petals or corolla-lobes imbricate or valvate *Oleaceae*

225. POTALIACEAE

Shrubs or trees, wood with *intraxylary phloem*, sometimes climbing or epi-phytic; leaves large, opposite, mostly obovate, entire or very rarely spinose-

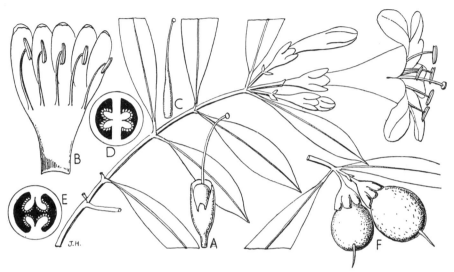

FIG. 225. Fagraea lanceolata *Blume* (Potaliaceae). A, calyx and young fruit. B, corolla laid open. C, ovary and style. D, cross-section of lower part of ovary. E, same of upper part. F, fruit.

dentate, connected at the base by a *transverse line or stipule-like sheath*, pinnately nerved, sometimes with a short axillary spine; flowers in terminal cymes, often with thick branches, or few or solitary and terminal; bracts often scale-like; calyx deeply 5–4-partite, segments broadly imbricate, often *opposite in pairs*; corolla tubular, tube short to long, sometimes widened upwards; lobes 16–5, *contorted*; stamens 16–5, inserted in the tube or throat, filaments free or connected by a ring; anthers 2-locular, loculi parallel, opening length-wise; ovary superior, usually 2- rarely 5–3-locular, sometimes 1-locular in the middle, *inserted on a fleshy disk*; style 1, with a more or less capitate stigma; ovules numerous on deeply 2-lobed placentas; fruit a *berry*; seeds sometimes immersed in pulp, embryo straight in endosperm.—Tropics and Subtropics.

A. Leaves not spinose-dentate, entire; flowers cymose: **B.** Corolla and androecium 10–8-merous; calyx 4-merous—POTALIA (Trop. S. Amer.). **BB.** Corolla and androecium 7–5-merous; calyx 5-merous—FAGRAEA (Indo-Malaya, Polynesia, Austral.). **BBB.** Corolla 16–10-merous; calyx 4-merous—ANTHOCLEISTA (Trop. Afr.). **AA.** Leaves spinose-dentate; flowers solitary to few together; calyx, corolla, androecium, and often the pistil 5-merous—DESFONTAINEA (S. Amer.).

226. LOGANIACEAE

Shrubs or trees, wood with *intraxylary phloem*, sometimes climbers or herbs; leaves opposite, entire, rarely linear, connected at the base by a *line or stipular*

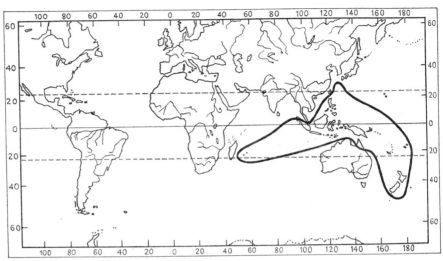

The island of Mauritius has a strong Malayan element in its flora, illustrated here by the range of the genus Geniostoma (Loganiaceae).

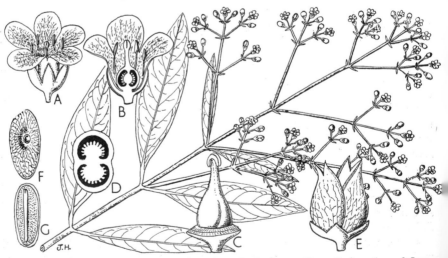

FIG. 226. Logania longifolia *R. Br.* (Loganiaceae). A, flower. B, vertical section of flower. C, ovary and style. D, cross-section of ovary. E, fruit. F, seed. G, vertical section of seed. (Orig.)

sheath, pinnately nerved; flowers in terminal cymes or rarely solitary; bracts small or rarely large and petaloid; calyx 5–4-lobed or partite, lobes imbricate; corolla tubular, lobes *imbricate* or rarely contorted; stamens 5–4, inserted on the corolla-tube, mostly not exserted; anthers 2-locular, opening lengthwise; ovary superior or *rarely semi-inferior,* 3–2-locular; style 2-lobed; ovules numerous to 1, axile; fruit a capsule, septicidally 3–2-valved, sometimes compressed *contrary to the septum* and loculicidally valved; seeds with more or less straight embryo in fleshy endosperm, *sometimes winged,* often enveloped in pulp on the placentas.—Tropical and Subtropical Regions, S. Temperate and N. America.

USEFUL PRODUCTS: *False Jasmine Root* (Gelsemium sempervirens *Ait.*), N. Amer.

A. Seeds not winged, often enveloped in pulp on the placentas: B. Shrubs or shrublets, rarely subherbaceous; flowers 5-merous; ovary superior: C. Corolla-lobes contorted or imbricate; seeds enveloped in pulp: D. Flowers axillary, mostly small with a short corolla-tube; seeds often verrucose— GENIOSTOMA (Mascar., Malay Archip. to N. Austral., New Zeal., New Caled.). DD. Flowers terminal, large, with a distinct corolla-tube; seed smooth— LABORDIA (Polynesia). CC. Corolla-lobes imbricate; seeds not enveloped in pulp—LOGANIA (Austral., New Zeal.). BB. Low herbs with the habit of some *Caryophyllaceae* (*Alsine,* &c.); flowers 4-merous, small, solitary and sub-sessile on the dichotomous branches; corolla shorter than the calyx; ovary semi-inferior—POLYPREMUM (N. to S. Amer., West Indies). AA. Seeds winged: E. Flowers not involucrate: F. Climbing shrubs; ovules numerous in each loculus on linear placentas; style once 2-lobed—GELSEMIUM (N. and Cent. Amer.). FF. Erect shrubs; ovules 2 in each loculus, collateral, erect from the base of the septum; style twice 2-lobed—MOSTUEA (Trop. Afr., Madag., S. Amer.). EE. Flowers involucrate with 2 face-to-face large petaloid bracts— COINOCHLAMYS (Trop. Afr.).

227. BUDDLEIACEAE

Trees, shrubs, or shrublets, very rarely herbs, indumentum when present *glandular, stellate, or lepidote; intraxylary phloem absent from the wood;* leaves

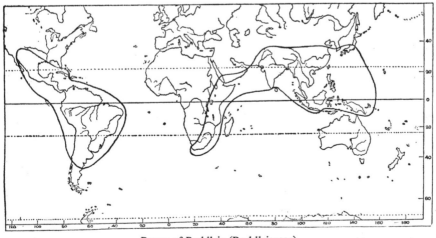

Range of Buddleia (Buddleiaceae).

opposite or verticillate, entire to coarsely dentate, often bullate, united at the base by a *stipular line*; flowers solitary to cymose, racemose, paniculate, or capitate; calyx 4-lobed; corolla tubular, tube short to fairly long, lobes 4, imbricate; stamens 4, inserted in the corolla-tube; filaments free or anthers sessile; anthers included or exserted, 2-locular, opening lengthwise; ovary 2-locular, very rarely 4-locular; ovules numerous on axile placentas; *style single*, stigma capitate, entire or shortly 2-lobed; fruit usually a capsule,

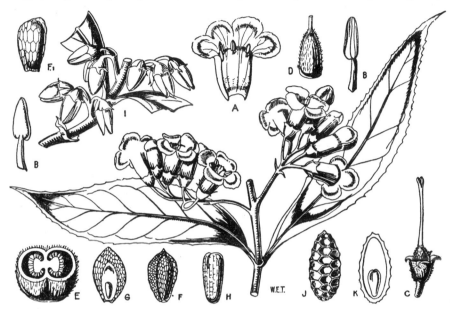

FIG. 227. Buddleia colvillei *Hk. f. & Thoms.* (Loganiaceae). A, flower opened. B, stamens. C, flower with corolla and stamens removed. D, ovary. E, transverse section of same. F and F₁, ovules. G, section of ovule. H, embryo. I, fruits. J, seed. K, same in vertical section. (After Hook. f.)

rarely a drupe or berry, capsule septicidally 2-valved; seeds *often winged or produced at each end*, embryo straight in often scanty endosperm.—Tropical and warm Temperate Regions.

USEFUL PRODUCTS: Many ornamental trees and shrubs (BUDDLEIA).

A. Fruit a capsule: B. Flowers racemose; leaves linear; anthers exserted—GOMPHOSTIGMA (Trop. and S. Afr.). BB. Flowers cymose or in heads: C. Corolla falling off right from the base: D. Anthers sessile or subsessile, inserted in or below the throat; indumentum often stellate or woolly; cymes mostly dense, globose, corymbose or paniculate—BUDDLEIA (Tropics and Sub-tropics and Temp. E. Asia and N. Amer.). DD. Anthers with distinct filaments, exserted: E. Trees or shrubs with stellate or lepidote indumentum; calyx-lobes short, imbricate—CHILIANTHUS (S. Afr.). EE. Shrubs with oblong subhastate sinuate-dentate leaves; calyx-lobes linear-subulate—EMORYA (Texas). CC. Corolla falling off by a circular slit above the base; leaves opposite or verticillate; calyx-lobes subvalvate; corolla-tube enclosed by the calyx; anthers often exserted—NUXIA (*Lachnopylis*) (Afr. and Mascar.).

AA. Fruit a berry or drupe; indumentum often stellate: **F.** Leaves entire, connected by a transverse line but not stipular; lower bracts foliaceous; ovary 4-locular—ADENOPLEA (Madag.). **FF.** Leaves minutely serrulate, connected by an interpetiolar foliaceous stipule; lower bracts not foliaceous; ovary 2-locular; panicles spike-like—ADENOPLUSIA (Madag.). **FFF.** Leaves entire or coarsely dentate, connected by a transverse line; bracts not foliaceous; ovary 2-locular; cymes capitate—NICODEMIA (Mascar.).

228. ANTONIACEAE[1]

Shrubs, small trees, or climbing shrubs, wood with *intraxylary phloem*; leaves opposite, pinnately nerved, entire or denticulate, connected at the base by

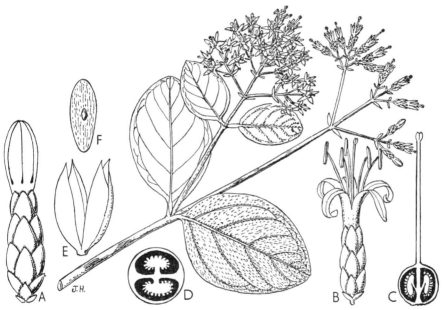

FIG. 228. Antonia ovata *Pohl* (Antoniaceae). A, flower-bud. B, flower. C, vertical section of ovary and style. D, cross-section of ovary. E, fruit. F, seed. (Orig.)

an *interpetiolar line, short sheath, or ciliolate rim*; flowers in cymes; bracts sometimes scale-like and numerous; calyx 5–4-lobed or partite, lobes or segments equal or *one lobe enlarged and petaloid*; corolla tubular, tube often slender; lobes 5 or 4, *valvate*; stamens 5, 4, or 1, inserted in the throat; anthers

[1] **Antoniaceae** Hutch., fam. nov.; frutices erecti vel scandentes vel arbusculae, ligno phloeointraxylari praedito; folia opposita, pinnatim nervosa, integra vel denticulata, basi linea interpetiolare vel vagina breve vel rima ciliolata conjuncta; flores bisexuales, cymosi; bracteae interdum squamiformes et numerosae; calyx 5–4-lobatus vel partitus, lobis aequalibus vel uno magno et petaloideo; corolla tubulosa, tubo saepe tenui; lobi 5 vel 4, valvata; stamina 5, 4, vel 1, fauce inserta; antherae 2-loculares, loculis parallelis vel divergentibus longitudinaliter dehiscentibus; stylus simplex, stigmate capitato vel breviter 2-lobato; ovula numerosa, axilia; capsula septicide 2-valvis; semina utrinque alata, embryone recto vel incurvo, endospermio carnoso. Genus typicum ANTONIA.

2-locular, loculi parallel or divergent, opening lengthwise; style single, stigma capitate or shortly 2-lobed; ovules numerous, axile; fruit a septicidally 2-valved capsule; seeds *winged at each end or all around*, embryo straight or incurved in fleshy endosperm.—Malaya, Tropical America, Tropical Africa.

A. Calyx 5-lobed; stamens more than 1: **B.** Anther-loculi not confluent and not peltate: **C.** Calyx not surrounded by imbricate bracts: **D.** Corolla-lobes short; calyx equally partite—NORRISIA (Malaya). **DD.** Corolla lobes linear; calyx unequally lobed—BONYUNIA (Trop. S. Amer.). **CC.** Calyx surrounded by many imbricate bracts—ANTONIA (Trop. S. Amer.). **BB.** Anther-loculi confluent, peltate when open; calyx equally partite—PELTANTHERA (Peru). **AA.** Calyx 4-lobed; stamen 1; outer calyx-lobe large and petaloid—USTERIA (W. Trop. Afr.).

229. SPIGELIACEAE

Perennial or annual *herbs*, rarely shrublets, indumentum sometimes *stellate*; *intraxylary phloem present*; leaves opposite, connected by an *interpetiolar line or small stipule*; flowers in cymes or unilateral spikes, rarely solitary or fasciculate or subumbellate; calyx 5–2-partite or lobed, sometimes *glandular within the base*; corolla tubular, tube short to elongated, sometimes ventricose; lobes 5 or 4, *valvate*; stamens 5 or 4, inserted in the corolla-tube; anthers usually included, loculi 2, parallel, dehiscing lengthwise; ovary superior, 2-locular; style bifid or deeply 2-lobed or partite, stigmas capitate; ovules numerous, densely arranged on *peltate axile placentas*; fruit a capsule, compressed more or less *contrary to the septum*, sometimes broadly 2-lobed at the apex, dehiscing septicidally or by a *transverse circular slit*; seeds with straight embryo in fleshy endosperm.—Widely distributed.

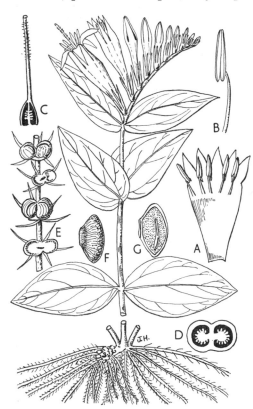

FIG. 229. Spigelia marilandica *L*. (Spigeliaceae). A, corolla opened out. B, stamen. C, vertical section of ovary with style. D, cross-section of ovary. E, fruits. F, seed. G, vertical section of seed.

USEFUL PRODUCTS: *Indian Pink Root* (Spigelia marilandica *L*.), Southern U.S.A.

A. Capsule not circumscissile at the base: **B.** Corolla 5-lobed; flowers in terminal or axillary dichotomous cymes—MITREOLA (N. Amer. to Brazil,

Indo-Malaya, N. Austral., Madag.). **BB.** Corolla 4-lobed: **C.** Flowers solitary or in fascicles or irregular umbels; styles 2, at first connate, at length free except below the capitate 2-lobed stigma—MITRASACME (Austral., New Zeal., Trop. Asia). **CC.** Flowers in axillary or terminal cymes; style bifid—MITRASACMOPSIS (Madag.). **AA.** Capsule circumscissile at the base; style articulated; spikes more or less unilateral; perennial or annual herbs—SPIGELIA (N. and S. Amer., elsewhere introduced).

230. STRYCHNACEAE

Trees or shrubs with *intraxylary phloem*, often climbing and branchlets sometimes armed with *spines or tendrils*; leaves opposite, sometimes large and

FIG. 230. Strychnos spinosa *Lam.* (Strychnaceae). A and B, spiny fruiting and flowering shoots. C, flower. D, vertical section of flower. E, stamen. F, cross-section of ovary. G, fruit. H, cross-section of fruit. (From Hutch. and Dalz., *Fl. W. Trop. Afr.*)

obovate, entire, pinnately nerved or 3–5-nerved from the base; flowers usually in cymes or corymbose-paniculate, rarely solitary; bracts small; calyx 5–4-lobed or partite; corolla-tube usually *very short*, lobes 5–4, *valvate*; stamens 5–4, inserted in the tube or throat; anthers oblong, 2–1-locular, free or connivent, opening lengthwise by slits; ovary superior, 2-locular; ovules numerous to 1 in each loculus; style usually short, stigma capitate or 2-lobed; fruit a *drupe or berry*, often globose, sometimes rather large and often with a hard or fibrous endocarp; seeds with straight embryo in fleshy endosperm.—World-wide distribution, mostly Tropics and Subtropics, very rare in Temperate Regions.

USEFUL PRODUCTS: *Nux-vomica* (Strychnos nux-vomica *L.*), Trop. Asia, also yielding *Strychnine*; *St. Ignatius' Beans* (Strychnos ignatii *Berg.*), Philipp. Is.; *Wourali Poison bark* (S. toxifera *Schomb.*), Guiana.

A. Fruit a drupe; leaves large, pinnately nerved; trees: **B.** Corolla very short, not twice as long as the calyx—COUTHOVIA (New Guin., Polynesia). **BB.** Corolla long-tubular, 2–3 times as long as the calyx—CRATERIPHYTUM (Moluccas). **AA.** Fruit a berry: **C.** Leaves pinnately nerved; climbing shrubs: **D.** Anthers connivent or subconnate, 1-locular—GARDNERIA (E. Asia). **DD.** Anthers free: **E.** Corolla-throat without a corona—PSEUDOGARDNERIA (E. Asia). **EE.** Corolla-throat with a corona—SCYPHOSTRYCHNOS (Trop. Afr.). **CC.** Leaves 3–5-nerved from or above the base; trees, shrubs, or climbers— STRYCHNOS (Tropics and Subtropics).

231. OLEACEAE

Trees, shrubs, or climbers; leaves *opposite* or very rarely alternate, simple or *pinnate*; stipules absent; flowers bisexual or rarely unisexual, actinomorphic;

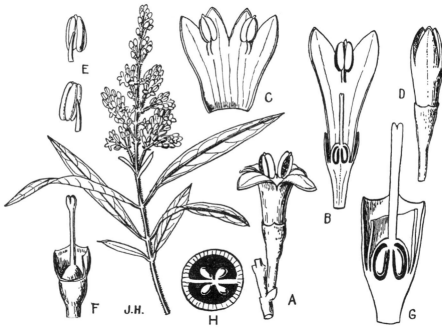

FIG. 231. Ligustrum massalongianum *Vis.* (Oleaceae). A, flower. B, same in vertical section. C, same opened. D, bud. E, stamens. F, ovary. G, same in vertical section. H, same in transverse section. (After De Wild.)

calyx lobed or dentate, rarely absent; petals present or absent, *free or connate*, often 4, imbricate or induplicate-valvate; stamens hypogynous or epipetalous, *usually 2*, rarely 4; anthers apiculate, 2-locular, *loculi back to back*, opening lengthwise; disk absent; ovary superior, *2-locular*; style simple with a capitate or bifid stigma; ovules usually 2 in each loculus, axile, pendulous or ascending, fruit capsular and loculicidally dehiscent, baccate, or drupaceous; seeds usually with endosperm; embryo straight, the radicle sometimes hidden within the base of the cotyledons. B.H. **2**, 672; E.P. **4**, 2, 1. Temperate and

Tropical Regions.—JASMINUM, SCHREBERA, FORSYTHIA, SYRINGA, FRAXINUS, PHILLYREA, OSMANTHUS, CHIONANTHUS, LINOCIERA, NOTELAEA, OLEA, LIGUSTRUM, &c.

USEFUL PRODUCTS: *American Ash* (Fraxinus americana *L.*); *Manna Ash* (F. ornus *L.*), S. Eur.; *Common Ash* (F. excelsior *L.*), Eur.; *Iron Wood* (Notelaea ligustrina *Vent.*), Austral., Tasm.; *Black Iron Wood* (Olea laurifolia *Lam.*), S. Afr.; *Olive Tree* (Olea europaea *L.*), SE. Eur., Asia Minor, widely cultivated, yields *Olive Oil*. Several ornamental trees and shrubs: *Lilac* (Syringa); *Privet* (Ligustrum vulgare *L.*).

ORDER 51. APOCYNALES

Woody or herbaceous; leaves opposite, simple, without stipules; petals united; stamens the same number as the corolla-lobes; pollen granular or glutinate; corona often present; carpels 2, often free, or becoming free in fruit; styles united above, with a common stigma, rarely free; seeds usually with endosperm and straight embryo, often winged or appendaged with long silky hairs.—Mainly Tropics.

A. Pollen granular:
 B. Fruits capsular, i.e. composed of 2 united carpels and dehiscing along both sides; ovules 4, parietal in pairs, the lower 2 erect, the upper 2 pendulous; seeds with a tuft of hairs at the apex; style twice lobed in the upper part   *Plocospermaceae*
 BB. Fruits follicular, dehiscing ventrally by one side only, or fruits indehiscent; ovules not arranged as above; styles united and thickened at the top, often free below:
  C. Stamens without a coronal appendage; pollen granular and transported freely; fruits follicular or indehiscent   *Apocynaceae*
  CC. Stamens with a coronal appendage; pollen transported by spathulate carriers; fruits follicular, dehiscing ventrally   *Periplocaceae*
AA. Pollen in waxy subpellucid masses (pollinia); filaments connate into a tube; fruits follicular, dehiscing ventrally   *Asclepiadaceae*

232. PLOCOSPERMACEAE

Shrubs or trees; leaves opposite or approximately verticillate, small, oblong or ovate, shining; *stipules absent*; flowers axillary, 1–4 together, pedicellate; calyx 6–5-partite, segments lanceolate; corolla funnel-campanulate-shaped, tube short, throat broad, lobes 6–5, broad, *imbricate*; stamens 6 or 5, inserted in the corolla-tube; anthers ovate, *cordate at the base*, loculi parallel; *pollen granular*; ovary 1-locular, contracted into a stipe at the base; style *twice lobed* in the upper part; ovules 4, *parietal in pairs*, the lower 2 *erect*, the upper 2 *pendulous*; capsule elongated, subterete, many-ribbed and sulcate, 2-valved from the apex; seed mostly solitary, long-linear, subterete, *with a dense tuft of hairs at the apex*; endosperm thin and fleshy, embryo linear, straight.— Central America.—PLOCOSPERMA (Fig. 232.).

FIG. 232. Plocosperma buxifolium *Benth.* (Plocospermaceae). A, corolla, laid open, and gynoecium. B, vertical section of ovary. C, fruit. D, seed. (Orig.)

233. APOCYNACEAE

Trees, shrubs, or climbers, rarely perennial herbs; leaves *opposite* or *verticillate*, rarely alternate, simple, entire; *stipules absent*; flowers ☿, actinomorphic; calyx often *glandular inside*; lobes 5 or rarely 4, *imbricate*; corolla tubular, variously shaped lobes, *contorted*-imbricate, very rarely valvate;

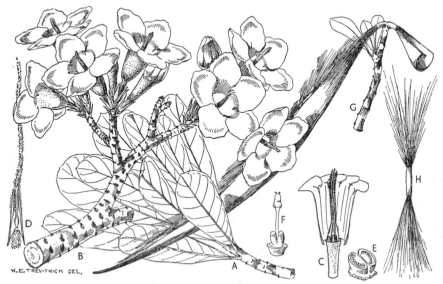

FIG. 233. Adenium honghel *A.DC.* (Apocynaceae). A, leafy shoot. B, flowering shoot. C, flower opened with calyx removed. D, anther. E, cross-section of ovary. F, ovary and style. G, fruiting carpel. H, seed. (Orig.)

stamens 5 or rarely 4, inserted in the tube; filaments free or rarely united, without a coronal appendage; anthers often *sagittate*, free or connivent around the stigma, rarely adherent to the latter, 2-locular, opening lengthwise, connective often *produced at the apex*; pollen *granular* and transported freely; disk usually present, annular, cupular, or of separate glands; ovary superior, 1-locular with 2 *parietal* placentas or 2-locular with the placentas adnate to the septa, or carpels 2 and free or connate only at the base with ventral placentas in each carpel; style 1, split at the base or entire, thickened and stigmatose below the apex; ovules 2 or more in each carpel; fruit entire and indehiscent or of 2 separate carpels, baccate, drupaceous, or follicular; seeds mostly with endosperm and large straight embryo, often winged or appendaged with long silky hairs. B.H. **2**, 681; E.P. **4**, 2, 109. Mainly Tropics and Subtropics.—ALLAMANDA, LANDOLPHIA, MELODINUS, CARISSA, ACOKANTHERA, RAUWOLFIA, ALYXIA, CERBERA, ASPIDOSPERMA, VINCA, PLUMERIA, ALSTONIA, TABERNAEMONTANA, PRESTONIA, FORSTERONIA, PARSONSIA, ADENIUM, NERIUM, STROPHANTHUS, APOCYNUM, BAISSEA, FUNTUMIA, ECHITES, DIPLADENIA, MANDEVILLA, HAPLOPHYTON, &c.

USEFUL PRODUCTS: *Landolphia Rubbers* (Landolphia heudeloti *A.DC.* and L. owariensis *P. Beauv.*, W. Afr.; L. kirkii *Dyer*), E. Afr.; *Karaunda fruits* (Carissa carandas *L.*), India; *Arrow poisons* from Acokanthera schimperi *Schweinf.*, E. Trop. Afr., and A. venenata *G. Don*, S. Afr.; *Paddle wood* (Aspidosperma excelsum *Bth.*), Guiana; *Kombe seeds* (Strophanthus kombe *Oliv.*), Trop. E. Afr.; *Silk Rubber Tree* (Funtumia elastica *Stapf.*), Trop. Afr.

234. PERIPLOCACEAE

Climbing, twining, or erect shrubs or shrublets, rarely trees or herbs; rootstock sometimes tuber-like; leaves opposite, linear to obovate, entire, pinnately nerved; *stipules absent*; flowers bisexual, actinomorphic, usually small, rarely large and showy; inflorescence cymose; bracts usually very small; calyx-tube very short, segments 5, imbricate or valvate; corolla sympetalous, 5-lobed or -fid, tube short, rarely rather long and slender, lobes *contorted or rarely valvate*; corona absent or present, simple and of various forms, sometimes of linear or filiform scales; stamens 5, inserted at or near the base of the corolla-tube; filaments free at the apex or from the base; anthers 2-locular, introrse, basifixed, connivent at the apex above the stigma, acute, acuminate, or produced into dilated subrecurved-spreading appendages; *pollen granular*, often cohering into masses in each loculus but easily separated; *disk absent*; ovary of 2 *separate carpels*; styles 2, free up to the stigma; stigma 1, peltately dilated and disk-like, convex, conical, or beaked; ovules numerous in each carpel, several-seriate on a single adaxial placenta; fruit of 2 follicles, these parallel or divergent, sometimes only 1 by abortion, sessile, elongated to ovoid or ellipsoidal, smooth, warted or winged, dehiscing lengthwise on the adaxial side; seeds compressed and often margined, *mostly crowned with a coma of long silky hairs*; endosperm present; embryo straight, nearly as long as the seed; cotyledons flat. Confined to the Temperate and Tropical Regions of the Old World.—GYMNOLAEMA, GONGYLOSPERMA, PHYLLANTHERA, PENTANURA, FINLAYSONIA, GONOCRYPTA (*Kompitsia*), ATHEROSTEMON,

HARPANEMA, SCHLECHTERELLA (*Pleurostelma*), UTLERIA, GYMNANTHERA, BRACHYLEPIS, DECALEPIS, ATHERANDRA, ATHEROLEPIS, STREPTOCAULON, MYRIOPTERON, CAMPTOCARPUS, SYMPHYTONEMA, TANULEPIS, CHLOROCODON, TACAZZEA, CHLOROCYATHUS, BATESANTHUS, PERIPLOCA, PARQUETINA, ECTADIUM, CRYPTOSTEGIA, HEMIDESMUS, BASEONEMA, CRYPTOLEPIS (*Curroria*), STOMATOSTEMMA, TELECTADIUM, ECTADIOPSIS, PENTOPETIA, AECHMOLEPIS, MITOLEPIS, RAPHIONACME, STELMATOCRYPTON, ZYGOSTELMA, COCHLANTHUS,

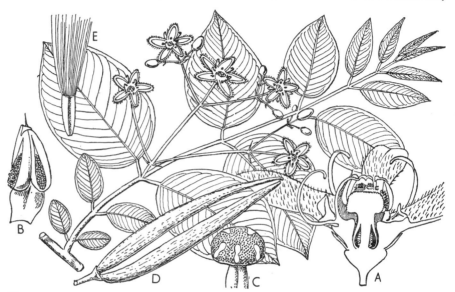

FIG. 234. Periploca graeca *L.* (Periplocaceae). A, vertical section of flower. B, stamen. C, stigma. D, fruit. E, seed. (Dissections partly after Baillon.)

OMPHALOGONUS, STREPTOMANES, MACROPELMA, MENABAEA, PENTAPETIOPSIS, MAFEKINGIA, BARONIELLA, ZACZATEA, ISCHNOLEPIS.

USEFUL PRODUCTS: *Indian Sarsaparilla* (Hemidesmus indicus *R. Br.*).

In addition to the late Dr. N. E. Brown of Kew, Rudolph Schlechter, a German botanist, studied the *Asclepiadaceae* intensively. It seems worth while to reproduce his remarks (*Notizbl. Bot. Gart. Berlin* 9, 23 (1924) when he proposed the separation of the *Periplocaceae* as a separate family:

'Schon wiederholt habe ich Gelegenheit genommen, darauf hinzuweisen, daß ich die *Periplocaceae* als eigene Familie betrachte. Die freien Staubfäden, die Form der Antheren, die eigentümlichen löffel-oder tütenförmigen Staubträger, die die zu Tetraden vereinigten Pollenkörner führen, und der Narbenkopf sind so verschieden von denen der übrigen *Asclepiadaceen*, daß ich eine Trennung der beiden Familien nicht nur für berechtigt, sondern für notwendig halte.

'Tatsächlich stehen die *Periplocaceen* im ganzen Bau ihrer Blüten meiner Ansicht nach den *Apocynaceen* näher als den *Asclepiadaceen*. Daß wir es hier mit einer sehr scharf umgrenzten Gattungsgemeinschaft zu tun haben, geht schon daraus hervor, daß alle Genera altweltlich sind, kein einziges also in Amerika auftritt.

'Grade bei den *Gamopetalen* sind viele Familien erheblich schlechter umgrenzt als die *Periplocaceen*. Ich erinnere nur an die *Symplocaceen* und *Styraceen*, die *Loganiaceen*, die *Caprifoliaceen* und andere mehr.

'Es scheint mir unter diesen Umständen geboten, hier und in Zukunft bei weiteren Arbeiten die Familie stets als selbständig gegenüber den *Asclepiadaceen* zu behandeln.'

235. Asclepiadaceae

Climbing, twining, or erect shrubs or shrublets, herbs, or rarely trees; leaves opposite or verticillate, linear to orbicular-obovate, entire, pinnately nerved; *stipules absent*; flowers bisexual, actinomorphic; inflorescence mostly cymose; bracts usually small; calyx-tube short, segments 5, imbricate or valvate; corolla sympetalous, 5-lobed or -fid, tube mostly short, lobes contorted or

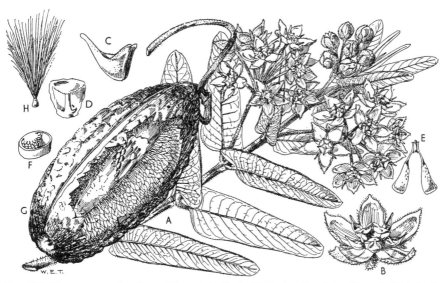

Fig. 235. Pachycarpus lineolatus (*Decne.*) *Bullock* (Asclepias lineolata (*Decne.*) *Schlechter*) (Asclepiadaceae). A, flowering shoot. B, open flower. C, outer corona-lobe. D, inner corona-lobe. E, pollinia. F, cross-section of carpel. G, fruit. H, seed.

valvate, sometimes connivent at the apex; corona present or absent, simple or of separate scales; stamens 5, inserted at or near the base of the corolla-tube; filaments connate into a tube shorter (rarely longer) than the anthers; anthers 2-locular, introrse, basifixed, connivent at the apex above the stigma, acute, acuminate, or produced into dilated subrecurved-spreading appendages; *pollen in waxy or subpellucid masses* (*pollinia*) and *solitary* or rarely in pairs in each loculus; disk absent; ovary of 2 *separate carpels*; styles 2, free up to the stigma; stigma 1, *peltately dilated and disk-like*, convex, conical, or beaked; ovules numerous, several-seriate on a single adaxial placenta in each carpel; fruit of 2 *follicles*, these parallel or divergent, sometimes only 1 by abortion, sessile, elongated to ovoid or ellipsoidal, smooth, warted or winged, dehiscing lengthwise on the adaxial side; seeds compressed and often margined, *mostly crowned with a coma of long silky hairs*; endosperm present; embryo straight, nearly as long as the seed; cotyledons flat. B.H. **2**, 728 (partly); E.P. **4**, 2, 189 (partly). Mainly Warmer Regions, very numerous in S. Africa, rare in cool countries.—Calotropis, Secamone, Philibertia, Oxypetalum, Xysmalobium, Schizoglossum, Gomphocarpus, Asclepias, Metastelma, Ditassa, Vincetoxicum, Cynanchum, Daemia, Gonolobus, Gymnema,

TYLOPHORA, MARSDENIA, STEPHANOTIS, SARCOSTEMMA, HOYA, DISCHIDIA, CEROPEGIA, BRACHYSTELMA, HOODIA, STAPELIA, &c.

USEFUL PRODUCTS: *Yercum* or *Madar fibre* (Calotropis gigantea *R. Br.*), India; *Condurango bark* (Marsdenia cundurango *Nichols.*), S. Amer.; *Rajmahal hemp* (Marsdenia tenacissima *W. & A.*), India.

ORDER 52. RUBIALES

Trees, shrubs, or herbs; leaves opposite, stipulate, mostly entire; stipules inter- or intra-petiolar; petals united (very rarely free); stamens epipetalous (very rarely epigynous), alternate with the corolla-lobes; ovary inferior, syncarpous; placentation axile, very rarely parietal; style 1; ovules numerous to one; seeds mostly with endosperm.—Mainly Tropics.

A. Stamens 25–16, in 2 whorls, epigynous and free from the corolla; filaments connate at the base into a ring; petals free, 4 in 2 whorls; seeds numerous and pointed at each end *Dialypetalanthaceae*

AA. Stamens as many as corolla-lobes, epipetalous; filaments free from one another; petals united into a tube, very rarely free from the base
Rubiaceae

236. DIALYPETALANTHACEAE

Trees; young branches densely white-tomentose; leaves opposite, stipulate, broadly elliptic, entire, pinnately nerved, acuminate; *stipules intrapetiolar*, large, *connate in pairs*, persistent for some time; inflorescence terminal, paniculate, bracteate, many-flowered; bracts resembling but smaller than the stipules; flowers bisexual, showy, actinomorphic, 2-bracteolate at the base, white and scented like *Jasminum*; calyx *adnate to the ovary*, 4-lobed, lobes imbricate, rounded-ovate, with very broad glabrous margins; petals 4, free, imbricate, *in 2 whorls*, with markedly glabrous margins; *stamens 25–16*, often about 18, *in 2 whorls, epigynous and free from the corolla*, all fertile and equal; filaments *connate at the base* into a short tube, anthers partly exserted, erect in bud, 2-locular, introrse, the two loculi long and narrow, quite separate on the broad connective, opening lengthwise; disk short, divided into short thread-like lobes; ovary inferior, 2-locular; style terminal, simple, with a very short bifid stigma; ovules numerous on axile placentas, imbricate in several series, anatropous; fruit a *loculicidal capsule* crowned by the calyx and at length *partly produced above the latter*, 2-locular, many-seeded; seeds numerous, very narrow and *pointed at each end*; testa membranous; endosperm present, thin, oily; embryo straight, terete; radicle small, thick; cotyledons short. Brazil.—DIALYPETALANTHUS.

Only a single species (*D. fuscescens* Kuhlmann) of this interesting genus is known, which on discovery was described by Kuhlmann[1] and placed in the tribe *Cinchonieae* of the family *Rubiaceae*. Although it bears a great superficial resemblance to some members of that tribe, it possesses characters which exclude it from the *Rubiaceae*, as pointed out by Rizzini and Occhioni, who have made it the type of a separate family. These are the *free petals* and

[1] Kuhlmann, *Archiv. Jard. Bot. Rio Janeiro*, **4**, 363, t. 33 (1925), and *Rodriguesia*, 1942, no. 15, 25.

FIG. 236. Dialypetalanthus fuscescens *Kuhlm.* (Dialypetalanthaceae). A, partly opened corolla and calyx. B, part of the two whorls of stamens. C, one stamen showing the broad connective and two separate anther-loculi. D, disk and style. E, transverse section of ovary. F, fruit. G, seed. (Orig.)

C C

the numerous *epigynous stamens*, a combination of characters unknown in the *Rubiaceae*, in which the stamens are always inserted on the corolla-tube. In itself the character of the free petals, though relatively important, would not exclude it from the *Rubiaceae*, for the corolla is divided to the base in at least three genera, *Molopanthera*, *Synaptanthera*, and *Aulacodiscus*; but all these are clearly related to other genera of *Rubiaceae* with sympetalous corollas and epipetalous stamens. And there are twice the number of stamens as corolla-lobes in at least one genus, *Praravinia*, but they are inserted in the throat of the sympetalous corolla. I cannot agree with the authors of the family, however, who consider it to be related to *Myrtaceae*, *Rhizophoraceae*, and *Melastomaceae*, for I can find no relationship with any of the tribes or genera of those families. On the contrary I consider it to be a primitive type near to *Rubiaceae* and closely linked with *Loganiaceae*.

237. RUBIACEAE

Trees, shrubs, or more rarely herbs; leaves *opposite* or *verticillate*, *entire* or rarely toothed, simple; stipules often *inter-* or *intra-petiolar*, free or connate,

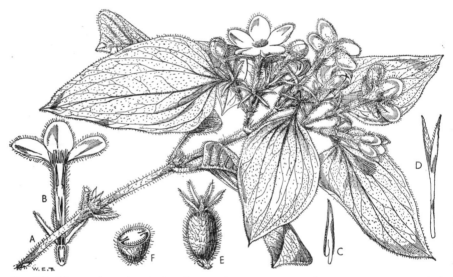

FIG. 237. Mussaenda erythrophylla *Schum. & Thonn.* (Rubiaceae). A, flowering shoot. B, vertical section of flower. C, anther. D, style. E, ovary and calyx. F, transverse section of ovary. (From Hutch. and Dalz., *Fl. W. Trop. Afr.*)

sometimes *leafy* and indistinguishable from the leaves; flowers mostly ☿, very rarely slightly zygomorphic, solitary to capitate; calyx adnate to the ovary; corolla epigynous, more or less tubular; lobes 4–10, contorted, imbricate, or valvate; stamens as many as corolla-lobes and *alternate with them*, inserted in the tube or at its mouth; anthers mostly free, 2-locular, opening lengthwise; *ovary inferior*, 2- or more-locular with axile, apical, or basal placentation, rarely 1-locular with parietal placentas; style often slender, variously lobed; ovules 1 to many; fruit a capsule, berry, or drupe; seeds rarely winged, mostly with endosperm; embryo straight or curved. B.H. **2**, 7; E.P. **4**, 4, 1. Generally distributed, but mostly Tropical.—NAUCLEA, UNCARIA, CINCHONA, CASCARILLA, BOUVARDIA, MANETTIA, EXOSTEMMA, LUCULIA, BIKKIA, RONDELETIA, WENDLANDIA, ARGOSTEMMA, PENTAS, HEDYOTIS, OLDENLANDIA, HOUSTONIA,

OPHIORRHIZA, MUSSAENDA, UROPHYLLUM, SABICEA, BERTIERA, ALIBERTIA, MASTIXIODENDRON (*Dorisia*), POSOQUERIA, BURCHELLIA, WEBERA, RANDIA, GARDENIA, OXYANTHUS, GUETTARDA, CANTHIUM (*Plectronia*), VANGUERIA, IXORA, PAVETTA, COFFEA, MORINDA, FARAMEA, PSYCHOTRIA, GAERTNERA, PALICOUREA, CEPHAELIS, LASIANTHUS, LEPTODERMIS, PLOCAMA, NERTERA, COPROSMA, PHYLLIS, SPERMACOCE, RUBIA, GALIUM, ASPERULA, &c.

USEFUL PRODUCTS: *Quinine* (Cinchona spp.), S. Amer., much cultivated in E. Tropics; *Coffee* (mainly Coffea arabica *L.*), E. Trop. Afr., Arabia; *Ipecacuanha root* (Cephaelis ipecacuanha (*Brot.*) *A. Rich.*), Trop. S. Amer.; *Gambier* (Uncaria gambier (*Hunt*) *Roxb.*), Malaya.

ORDER 53. BIGNONIALES

Trees, shrubs, climbers, or herbs, sometimes with tendrils; leaves alternate or opposite, mostly compound; stipules mostly absent; flowers bisexual, calyx-lobes or segments imbricate or valvate; corolla sympetalous, mostly zygomorphic, lobes imbricate, rarely contorted; stamens 5, 4, or 2, inserted on the corolla-tube; staminodes often present; disk present; ovary superior, 4–1-locular, with axile or parietal placentas; style terminal; fruit capsular or indehiscent; seeds without or with very scanty endosperm.—Tropics and Subtropics.

A. Leaves stipulate, alternate, pinnately compound, the end pair tendriliform; corolla actinomorphic, lobes contorted; stamens 5, all fertile, anther-loculi parallel, not separated; ovary 3-locular   *Cobaeaceae*
AA. Leaves without real stipules, mostly opposite; stamens 4 or 2, often with a staminode; ovary 4–2–1-locular:
  B. Trees, shrubs, or climbers, very rarely herbs; leaves mostly compound, digitate or pinnate, sometimes the terminal leaflet tendriliform
                                              Bignoniaceae
  BB. Perennial or annual herbs, rarely shrubby, never climbing; leaves simple, no tendrils; flowers mostly with characteristic glands (metamorphosed flowers) at the base of the stalks; ovary superior or inferior
                                            Pedaliaceae
  BBB. Perennial or annual herbs, never climbing; leaves simple, no tendrils; flowers without glands as described above   *Martyniaceae*

238. COBAEACEAE

Climbing shrubs; leaves alternate, *pinnately compound*; leaflets mostly 3 pairs, opposite, the end pair *completely modified into slender tendrils*; stipules *large and foliaceous*, often resembling a lower pair of leaflets but in *Cobaea stipularis* quite distinct from them; flowers axillary, showy, solitary or 2–3 together on a long peduncle, pendulous; calyx-tube very short, 5-ribbed or 5-winged; lobes or segments 5, sometimes foliaceous; corolla campanulate, much longer than the calyx, lobes ovate to linear and then much elongated; stamens 5, inserted *near the base of the corolla*, filaments bearded in the lower part, anthers exserted, versatile, 2-locular; disk large and fleshy, deeply lobed;

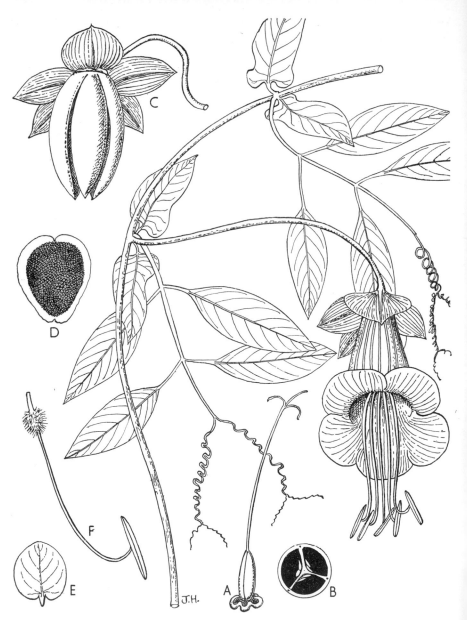

FIG. 238. Cobaea scandens *Cav.* (Cobaeaceae), a long-time favourite of British greenhouses. A, disk, ovary and style. B, transverse section of ovary. C, fruit and persistent calyx. D, seed. E, embryo. F, stamen. (Orig.)

ovary superior, *3-locular*; style exserted, 3-lobed; ovules 2 or more in each loculus on axile placentas; capsule coriaceous, *septicidally 3-valved* to the base; seeds ascending, *medifixed*, compressed, imbricate in 2 series, *broadly winged*; embryo white, cotyledons large, filling the seed-body, cordate, fleshy; *endosperm absent*. Central America, south to Chile.—COBAEA.

A generically monotypic family of 9 species referred by its original author to *Bignoniaceae*, but by later botanists to *Polemoniaceae*. D. Don, however, regarded it as of family rank and, I think, with some justification. It differs from *Bignoniaceae* by the actinomorphic contorted corolla, by the long undivided anthers, 3 stigmas, its 3-locular ovary, and septicidally 3-valved capsule. From all other *Polemoniaceae* it differs by the woody climbing habit, pinnate *stipulate* leaves with the end pair modified into tendrils, and by the *septicidal* capsule. In *Cobaea scandens* Cav. the seeds are densely covered with peltate scales, but whether all the species are alike in this respect I cannot say, not having seen the seeds.

239. BIGNONIACEAE

Trees or shrubs, sometimes scandent, very rarely herbs; leaves *opposite*, rarely alternate, mostly *compound*, digitate or pinnate, sometimes the terminal leaflet tendril-like; stipules absent; flowers often showy, ⚥, more or less *zygomorphic*; calyx campanulate, closed or open in bud, truncate or 5-toothed; corolla with 5 imbricate lobes sometimes forming 2 lips, the upper of 2, the lower of 3 lobes; stamens alternate with the corolla-lobes, only 4 or 2 perfect; anthers *connivent in pairs* or rarely free, 2-locular, opening lengthwise; staminode representing the fifth stamen often short, sometimes absent, often 3 present when only 2 stamens; disk usually present; ovary superior, 2-locular with 2 placentas in each loculus or 1-locular with 2 *parietal* bifid placentas; style terminal, 2-lipped; ovules *numerous*; fruit capsular or fleshy and indehiscent; seeds often *winged*, without endosperm; embryo straight. B.H. **2**, 1026; E.P. **4**, 3*b*, 189. Tropics and Subtropics.—BIGNONIA, MACFADYENA, ADENOCALYMNA, ANEMOPAEGMA, PITHECOCTENIUM, CATALPA (Fig. 239), TABEBUIA, TECOMA, NEWBOULDIA, SPATHODEA, DOLICHANDRONE, STEREOSPERMUM, INCARVILLEA, ECCREMOCARPUS, JACARANDA, CRESCENTIA, KIGELIA, &c.

USEFUL PRODUCTS: Ornamental trees, climbers, and herbs (*Catalpa, Jacaranda, Tecomaria*, &c.).

240. PEDALIACEAE

Annual or perennial herbs, rarely shrubs; leaves opposite, or the upper alternate, simple; *stipules absent*; flowers bisexual, *zygomorphic*, axillary, mostly with *characteristic glands* (metamorphosed flowers) at the base of the stalks; sepals 5, more or less united; corolla sympetalous, limb often oblique; lobes imbricate; stamens 4, *didynamous*, with a small subulate *staminode* in place of the fifth, or (in *Trapella*) 2 fertile and 2 with reduced infertile anthers; anthers often *connivent or contiguous* in pairs, 2-locular, loculi more or less *parallel*, opening lengthwise; disk hypogynous, fleshy; ovary superior or rarely inferior, 4–2-locular or rarely 1-locular, sometimes the loculi again divided by spurious septa; style terminal; ovules several to one on each

W.E.T.

FIG. 239. Catalpa speciosa *Warder* ex *Engelm*. (Bignoniaceae). A, ovary. B, stamens and staminodes. C, fruit. D, seed. (Partly orig.)

placenta; fruit a capsule or subdrupaceous; endocarp hardened and often horned or prickly; seeds without or with very little endosperm and straight embryo. B.H. **2**, 1054 (excl. Tribe *Martynieae*); E.P. **4**, 3*b*, 253, figs 97–101 (1895). Including *Trapellaceae* Li (1954). Old World Tropics and Subtropics, rare in Temperate Regions.

USEFUL PRODUCTS: *Grapple plant* (Harpagophytum procumbens *DC.*), S. Afr.; *Oil of Sesamum* (from Sesamum indicum *L.*), cultivated.

A. Ovary superior; land plants: B. Herbs; flowers in the axils of the leaves, solitary or fasciculate, with glands at the base of the pedicels: C. Ovary 2-

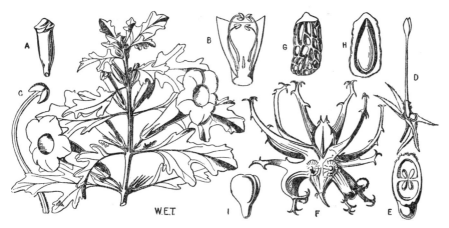

FIG. 240. Harpagophytum procumbens *DC.* (Pedaliaceae). A, bud. B, stamens and staminode. C, stamen. D, style. E, transverse section of ovary. F, fruit. G, seed. H, vertical section of same. I, embryo. (Partly orig.)

locular, loculi not again divided: **D.** Ovules numerous in each loculus (8 or more): **E.** Corolla not pouched at the base—HARPAGOPHYTUM (S. Afr.). **EE.** Corolla deeply and broadly pouched at the base—HOLUBIA (S. Afr.). **DD.** Ovules 2 in each loculus: **F.** Fruits armed, but not winged—PEDALIUM (India, Socotra, Afr., Madag.). **FF.** Fruits unarmed, winged—PTERODISCUS (Trop. and S. Afr.). **CC.** Ovary 4–2-locular, the loculi again spuriously divided: **G.** Fruit a capsule: **H.** Loculi of the capsule very unlike each other, the larger loculus at length dehiscent—ROGERIA (Trop. Afr.). **HH.** Loculi of the capsule equal: **J.** Upper angle of capsule rounded—SESAMUM (Old World Tropics). **JJ.** Upper angle of capsule armed with sharp prickles—CERATOTHECA (Trop. and S. Afr.). **GG.** Fruit a nut: **K.** Fruit discoid with 2 erect spines near the middle—DICEROCARYUM (*Pretrea*) (Trop. and S. Afr.). **KK.** Fruit globose or ellipsoidal, with numerous short thorns—JOSEPHINA (*Preterothamnus*) (N. Austral.). **BB.** Shrubs; flowers in the axils of very reduced bracts, few or many in terminal inflorescences, with or without glands at the stalks: **L.** Corolla-tube long and cylindrical, spurred or not at the base; leaves small, on short branches—SESAMOTHAMNUS (Trop. and S. Afr.). **LL.** Corolla-tube broadened upwards; leaves relatively large on long stalks—UNCARINA (Madag.). **AA.** Ovary inferior; aquatic plants—TRAPELLA (E. Asia).

241. MARTYNIACEAE

Perennial or annual herbs, *glutinous-villous*; leaves alternate or opposite; *stipules absent*; flowers bisexual, *zygomorphic*, in terminal racemes; sepals 5, nearly free or partly united, *sometimes spathaceous*; corolla sympetalous, 5-lobed, tube expanded from the base, or long and narrow, lobes imbricate;

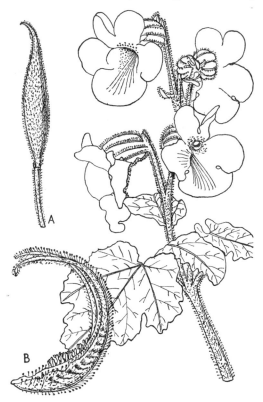

FIG. 241. Proboscidea fragrans (*Lindl.*) *Decne.* (Martyniaceae). A, young fruit. B, mature fruit. (After *Bot. Mag.*)

fertile stamens 4 or 2, the fifth reduced to a staminode; anther-loculi *divaricate*; disk glandular, symmetrical; ovary superior, of 2 united carpels, *1-locular with 2 parietal placentas* divided into 2 divaricate lobes; style long, with 2 stigmas; ovules numerous; fruit a more or less long-horned capsule with soft deciduous pericarp, loculicidally dehiscent, more or less *4-locellate* by the intrusive placentas; seeds many or few, rarely 1 in each locellus, pendulous; endosperm thin, embryo straight. B.H. **2,** 1055 (in *Pedaliaceae*); Stapf, E.P. **4,** 3*b.* 265, fig. 102 (1895). America.

A. Fertile stamens 4: **B.** Corolla-tube broadened from the base—PROBO-SCIDEA (*Ibicella*) (S. Amer.). **BB.** Corolla-tube very long, cylindrical, narrow, campanulate at the upper end—CRANIOLARIA (S. Amer.). **AA.** Fertile stamens 2; corolla-tube broadened from the base—MARTYNIA (Mexico).

ORDER 54. VERBENALES

Trees, shrubs, or rarely herbs, branches often quadrangular; leaves alternate, *opposite or whorled*; stipules *absent*; flowers bisexual; calyx persistent; corolla actinomorphic or zygomorphic, 4–5-lobed, lobes imbricate; stamens as many as corolla-lobes or one fewer, often 4, rarely 5 or 2, inserted in corolla-tube, anthers 2-locular; ovary superior, 9–1-locular; style *terminal*, simple; ovules 1 or 2 in each loculus, erect, axile, or rarely pendulous; fruit a *drupe or berry*; seeds with scanty or no endosperm.

A. Leaves alternate; stamens as many as corolla-lobes; corolla actinomorphic   *Ehretiaceae*

AA. Leaves opposite or verticillate; stamens usually one less than the corolla-lobes; corolla mostly more or less zygomorphic:

  B. Calyx actinomorphic (not bilabiate); ovary 9–2-locular; ovules 2 or 1, anatropous:

    C. Seeds without endosperm   *Verbenaceae*

    CC. Seeds with endosperm:

      D. Ovules 1 in each loculus, erect; indumentum when present not stellate; leaves verticillate; flowers in dense terminal spikes; South African shrubs   *Stilbeaceae*

      DD. Ovules usually 2 in each loculus, laterally inserted on the central axis; indumentum often dense and consisting of stellate or dendriform hairs, rarely lepidote; inflorescence often capitate or corymbose-paniculate, or flowers axillary; Australia and Pacific Is.
                                                       Chloanthaceae

  BB. Calyx bilabiate; ovary 1-locular; ovule 1, orthotropous, erect from near the base of the loculus; no stellate hairs; flowers in slender axillary and terminal spikes, strongly reflexed in fruit and appressed to the axis
                                                        Phrymaceae

242. EHRETIACEAE

Trees or shrubs, sometimes spiny, very rarely subshrubs, or rarely scabrid or woolly herbs; leaves *alternate* or rarely subopposite, entire or toothed; *stipules absent*; flowers in cymes, cylindrical spikes, or in heads, or rarely all axillary or leaf-opposed; calyx tubular or campanulate, dentate or variously divided, sometimes membranous, enlarged and inflated in fruit and enclosing it; corolla tubular, lobes 5, rarely 4 or 6 or more, plicate, *imbricate or subcontorted*, very rarely valvate; stamens *as many as and alternate with the corolla-lobes*, equally or unequally inserted in the tube, exserted or included; anthers 2-locular, ovate or oblong to rounded; style *terminal* on the ovary, simple and 2–4-fid or lobed, or styles 2, stigmas clavate or capitate; ovary superior, 4–2-locular, loculi sometimes 2-locellate; ovules *paired*, erect, basally or laterally attached to the axis, or rarely pendulous; fruit drupaceous, often enclosed by the persistent sometimes enlarged calyx, hard and dry or baccate; seeds with or without endosperm; cotyledons flat or plicate. B.H. **2**, 838; E.P. **4**, 3*a*, 80 (in *Boraginaceae*). Including *Duckeodendraceae* Kuhlm. (1950). Tropics and Subtropics, especially Central and S. America.

A. Style absent; stigma sessile, bilobed; leaves lepidote—LEPIDOCORDIA (Brazil). **AA.** Style or styles present: **B.** Style twice divided, i.e. the style arms 2-lobed: **C.** Calyx not or only slightly enlarged in fruit—CORDIA (Tropics and Subtropics). **CC.** Calyx much enlarged in fruit: **D.** Calyx in fruit with 5 broadly linear segments spreading stellately below the fruit like a small Dipterocarp—PATAGONULA (S. Amer.). **DD.** Calyx in fruit erect and inflated, hiding the fruit and forming 5 reticulate wings, cordate at the base—AUXEMMA

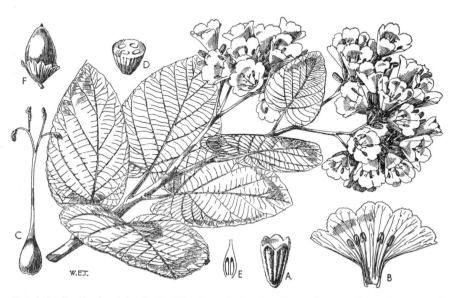

FIG. 242. Cordia abyssinica *R. Br.* (Ehretiaceae). A, calyx. B, corolla opened out. C, ovary and style. D, cross-section of fruit. E, vertical section of ovary. F, fruit with persistent calyx. (From Hutch. and Dalz., *Fl. W. Trop. Afr.*)

(Brazil). **BB.** Style undivided or at most 2-lobed, or styles 2, free: **E.** Anthers free from each other: **F.** Styles 2, free from each other: **G.** Fruits not compressed: **H.** Fruits fleshy, with 4 drupes; spiny shrubs; leaves not woolly—ROCHEFORTIA (West Indies, Trop. Amer.). **HH.** Fruits slightly fleshy, separating into 4 nuts; shrublets or rarely herbs with setose or woolly leaves—COLDENIA (Tropics and Subtropics). **GG.** Fruits compressed, with broad reticulate margins—PTELEOCARPA (Malacca). **FF.** Style 1, entire or divided up to about the middle: **J.** Anthers oblong or ovoid; *Lycium*-like shrubs—ROTULA (*Rhabdia*) (Tropics). **JJ.** Anthers almost globose; shrubs with obovate leaves and panicles of dense spikes of flowers—POSKEA (NE. Trop. Afr.). **K.** Calyx not enlarged in fruit: **L.** Calyx closed in bud, at length 2–5-partite—BOURRERIA (Florida, Trop. Amer.). **LL.** Calyx 5-lobed—EHRETIA (Tropics and Subtropics). **LLL.** Calyx 10–15-toothed; leaves shortly trilobed—CORTESIA (Argentine). **KK.** Calyx enlarged, inflated and enclosing the fruit, oblong-elliptic, 5-toothed and almost closed at the top—SACCELLIUM (S. Amer.). **EE.** Anthers united into a cone around the style—HALGANIA (Austral.). Of uncertain position DUCKEODENDRON (Trop. Amer.).

243. VERBENACEAE

Woody or herbaceous, often with *quadrangular* branchlets; leaves usually *opposite* or whorled, simple or compound; stipules absent; flowers ⚥, more or less zygomorphic; calyx 4–5-lobed or toothed, persistent; corolla sympetalous, tubular, 4–5-lobed, lobes imbricate; stamens on the corolla-tube, 4 or rarely 2, rarely 5; anthers 2-locular, loculi often divergent, opening lengthwise; ovary superior, 9–2-locular, often 4-locular; *style terminal*; ovules solitary or paired, erect or rarely pendulous, anatropous; fruit a drupe or

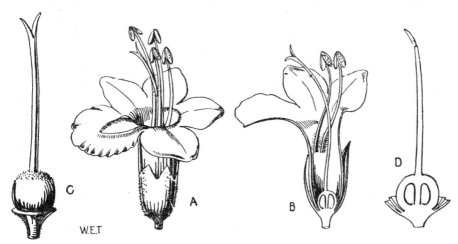

FIG. 243. Vitex agnus-castus *L.* (Verbenaceae). A, flower. B, vertical section of same. C, ovary. D, vertical section of same. (After Baill.)

berry; seeds with straight embryo and very scanty or no endosperm; B.H. **2**, 1131; E.P. **4**, 3*a*, 132. Mostly Tropics and S. Temperate.—LANTANA, LIPPIA, BOUCHEA, CHASCANUM, STACHYTARPHETA, VERBENA, PETRAEA, CITHAREXYLUM, DURANTA, CALLICARPA, AEGIPHILA, TECTONA, PREMNA, VITEX, CLERODENDRUM (*Clerodendron*), HOLMSKIOLDIA, AVICENNIA, &c.

USEFUL PRODUCTS: *Fiddle wood* (Petitia domingensis *Jacq.*), West Indies; *Teak wood* (Tectona grandis *L.*), India to Malaya. Some beautiful garden plants.

244. STILBEACEAE

Erect shrubs or shrublets; branchlets densely leafy; leaves *verticillate, linear or acicular*, thick, with recurved margins; *no stipules*; flowers in dense terminal *spikes*, these oblong-cylindric to subglobose; bracts leaf-like; calyx tubular and 5-lobed or bilabiate or deeply 5-partite, segments slightly imbricate or valvate; corolla sympetalous, actinomorphic or zygomorphic, lobes 5 or 4, *imbricate*; stamens 4, inserted towards the top of the corolla-tube or between the lobes; filaments free, filiform; anthers 2-locular, dehiscing lengthwise, loculi parallel or divergent from the apex; *no disk*; ovary superior, 2-locular, loculi with 1 *erect anatropous ovule*; style slender, entire; fruit a capsule or

indehiscent; seeds often reticulate, with endosperm and straight embryo.—
S. Africa.

A. Anther-loculi parallel: **B.** Calyx not 2-lipped: **C.** Calyx deeply 5-partite;
corolla 4-lobed; fruit a 4-valved capsule—CAMPYLOSTACHYS. **CC.** Calyx
5-toothed or 5-fid; corolla 5-lobed; fruit indehiscent—STILBE. **BB.** Calyx
2-lipped; corolla 2-lipped; fruit not known—XEROPLANA. **AA.** Anther-
loculi divergent from the apex, at length confluent into one: **D.** Calyx 5-

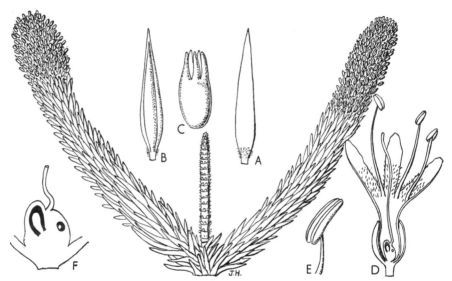

FIG. 244. Stilbe vestita Berg. (Stilbeaceae). A, leaf showing upper surface. B, leaf, lower surface.
C, calyx. D, vertical section of flower. E, anther. F, vertical section of ovary. (Orig.)

toothed; corolla-limb 2-lipped—EURYLOBIUM. **DD.** Two posticous calyx-
segments free, 3 anticous connate into one and 3-toothed; corolla-limb equally
5-lobed—EUTHYSTACHYS.

245. CHLOANTHACEAE[1]

Shrubs or shrublets, tomentose, woolly or clothed with *much-branched or
dendriform hairs,* rarely lepidote, glabrous, or scabrid; leaves *opposite or
verticillate,* rarely scattered, sessile or subsessile, ovate to linear, mostly
densely clothed with *stellate hairs,* very rarely lepidote, sometimes linear and

[1] **Chloanthaceae** Hutch., fam. nov. Frutices vel suffrutices, tomentosi, lanati, vel pilis
multiramosis vel stellatis induti, rare lepidoti, glabri vel scabridi; folia opposita vel verticillata, rare sparsa, sessilia vel subsessilia, ovata ad linearia, plerumque pilis stellatis induta,
interdum linearia et grosse bullata; inflorescentia terminalis, spicata, capitata vel corym-
boso-paniculata, vel flores axillares; bracteae parvae; calyx 8-4-lobatus, rare fructu auctus
et membranaceus; corolla sympetala, actinomorpha vel zygomorpha, 8-4-lobata vel rare
truncata, lobis imbricatis; stamina tot quot corollae lobis vel uno minus, in tubo vel ad
marginem corollae tubi inserta; antherae 2-loculares, loculis saepe basi muticis; discus
nullus; ovarium superum, 2-loculare; ovula pro loculo 2, axilia; stylus gracilis, bifidus vel
2-lobatus; fructus indehiscens, plerumque 1-spermus; semina endospermio et embryo recto.
Genus typicum CHLOANTHES.

very strongly bullate, often with recurved margins; inflorescence terminal, spicate, capitate, or corymbose-paniculate, or flowers axillary; bracts small; calyx 8–4-lobed, unchanged in fruit or rarely at length enlarged and membranous; corolla sympetalous, actinomorphic or zygomorphic, truncate to 8–4-lobed, lobes *imbricate*; stamens as many as corolla-lobes or one fewer, inserted in the tube or on the rim of the corolla; anthers 2-locular, dehiscing lengthwise, the loculi often muticous at the base; *disk absent*; ovary superior,

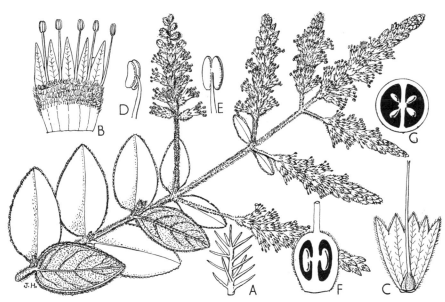

Fig. 245. Newcastlia spodotricha *F. Muell.* (Chloanthaceae). A, branched hair from the branchlet. B, corolla opened out, with stamens. C, calyx opened out, with ovary and style. D and E, anthers. F, vertical section of ovary. G, transverse section of ovary. (Orig.)

2-locular; *ovules 2 in each loculus*, axile; style slender, bifid to 2-lobed; fruit *indehiscent*, often 1-seeded; seeds with endosperm and straight embryo. Benth., *Fl. Austral.* **5**, 37 (1870); B.H. **2**, 1132 (as tribe *Chloantheae* of *Verbenaceae*).—Australia.

A. Corolla actinomorphic; lobes 8–4, subequal; stamens as many as lobes; anthers not muticous at the base: **B.** Corolla distinctly lobed: **C.** Style bifid or very shortly 2-lobed: **D.** Flowers spicate: **E.** Flowers 6–5-merous—New-castlia. **EE.** Flowers 4-merous—Physopsis. **DD.** Flowers capitate, heads solitary or corymbose; flowers 4-merous—Mallophora. **CC.** Style deeply 2-lobed; flowers in heads, cymes, or panicles—Dicrastyles. **BB.** Corolla truncate or very shortly 8–5-lobed; stamens on the rim of the corolla; plants densely woolly with much-branched or dendriform hairs—Lachnostachys. **AA.** Corolla zygomorphic, 2-lipped or lobes 5 and unequal; stamens 4; anthers often muticous at the base: **F.** Leaves decurrent, usually linear and very strongly bullate; corolla-tube elongated; anthers not appendaged at the base—Chloanthes. **FF.** Leaves not decurrent and not bullate; corolla-tube usually broad and short: **G.** Calyx not enlarged or only slightly so after flowering; flowers axillary: **H.** Aromatic shrubs not broom-like; leaves in whorls of 3, or scattered; anther-loculi not muticous at the base—DENISONIA. **HH.** Leafy shrubs or shrublets more or less covered with cottony wool; anthers usually muticous at the base—PITYRODIA. **HHH.** Broom-like plants and appearing almost leafless; anther-loculi with minute tips at the base— SPARTOTHAMNUS. **GG.** Calyx much expanded after flowering, opening out flat and becoming membranous, reticulate; peduncles axillary, 1–3-flowered, the flowers forming a loose terminal panicle—CYANOSTEGIA.

246. PHRYMACEAE

Erect perennial herbs with divaricate *quadrangular* branches; leaves opposite, simple, ovate, petiolate, coarsely dentate, thin, pinnately nerved; *stipules*

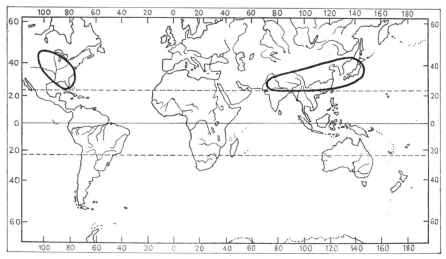

A genus of herbs, such as Phryma, has usually not such a strikingly discontinuous distribution as shown on the map, though this is more common in woody plants such as some Magnoliaceae and Hamamelidaceae, &c.

absent; flowers bisexual, in slender axillary and terminal *spikes*, erect in bud, soon spreading, *strongly reflexed in fruit* and appressed to the axis, purplish or blue; bracts subulate, small; calyx tubular, prominently 5-ribbed, *bilabiate*, posterior 3 lobes subulate and *hooked at the apex*, anterior 2 short and muticous; corolla sympetalous, tube cylindrical, a little longer than the calyx-tube, limb *bilabiate*, posterior lip erect, shortly 2-lobed, anterior longer, spreading, broadly 3-fid; stamens 4, didynamous, inserted above the middle of the corolla-tube, shortly exserted; filaments slender; anthers subreniform; ovary superior, ovoid, *1-locular*; style terminal, shortly 2-fid at the apex; ovule 1, *erect from almost the base*, orthotropous; fruit enclosed by the persistent, narrow, reflexed, ribbed calyx with its hooked 3 lobes, laterally mucronate near the apex; pericarp membranous; seed basal, testa membranous, loose, closely applied to the pericarp; embryo oblong, cotyledons broad

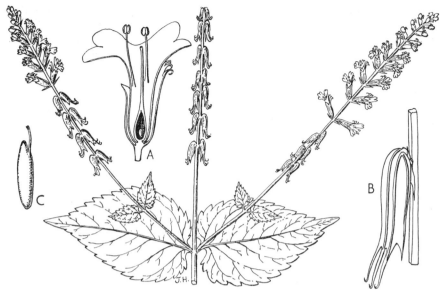

Fig. 246. Phryma leptostachya *L*. (Phrymaceae). A, vertical section of flower. B, calyx in fruit. C, fruit. (Orig.)

and folded; endosperm absent. B.H. **3,** 1137 (in *Verbenaceae*); E.P. **4,** 3*b*, 362; Engl. and Diels, *Syllabus*, edn. 11, 357. E. Asia, Atlantic N. America.— PHRYMA.

DIVISION II. HERBACEAE
ORDER 55. RANALES

Herbaceous, often with scattered vascular bundles in the stem, or softly woody with broad medullary rays; flowers hypogynous to rarely perigynous, ♂, hemicyclic to rarely completely cyclic; petals mostly present; stamens ∞, free; apocarpous, or rarely 1 carpel; seeds with copious uniform endosperm and minute embryo. Leaves alternate or rarely opposite, very rarely stipulate, simple or much divided.—Cosmopolitan, but rare in the Tropics.

A. Disk present; stamens centrifugal, numerous; seeds arillate   *Paeoniaceae*

AA. Disk absent but torus sometimes much enlarged with sunken carpels; stamens centripetal or few; seeds not arillate:

  B. Ovules basal or axile and inserted on the adaxial suture of the carpels; anthers introrse:

    C. Ovary of more than 1 carpel:

      D. Carpels with more than 1 ovule; fruits follicular, rarely baccate or connate and dehiscing at the apex   *Helleboraceae*

      DD. Carpels with 1 erect or pendulous ovule; fruit a bunch of free dry (indehiscent) achenes, rarely berry-like   *Ranunculaceae*

      DDD. Carpels united into a many-locular ovary or sunk in the enlarged torus; aquatics   *Nymphaeaceae*

    CC. Ovary of 1 carpel; stamens as many or twice as many as the petals   *Podophyllaceae*

BB. Ovule pendulous from the apex of the carpels; seeds without endosperm; aquatic herbs without petals   *Ceratophyllaceae*

BBB. Ovules parietal, spread over the abaxial wall of the carpels, not confined to the suture; sepals and petals 3 each; anthers extrorse
Cabombaceae

247. PAEONIACEAE

Herbs or rarely undershrubs; root perennial, a thick subhorizontal stock,
sometimes the roots thickened into ovate or cylindrical tubers; stem-base

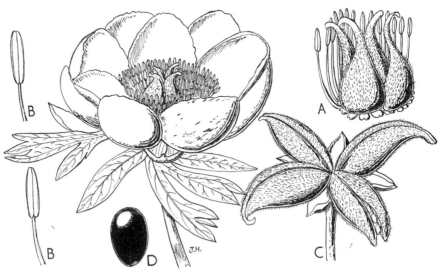

FIG. 247. Paeonia peregrina *Mill.* (Paeoniaceae). A, carpels and some stamens. B, stamens.
C, fruiting carpels. D, seed. (Orig.)

covered with scale-like sheaths; leaves alternate, petiolate, *twice ternate*,
segments pinnately nerved; flowers bisexual, large and showy, of various
colours, often much doubled in cultivation; sepals 5, free, subfoliaceous,
unequal, more or less rounded, *persistent*, imbricate; petals usually 5 or sometimes 6–10, orbicular, subequal, not clawed, imbricate; stamens numerous,
centrifugal, free, *spirally arranged*; anthers 2-locular, *extrorse*, opening by
slits lengthwise; *disk around the carpels fleshy*, sometimes at length nearly
covering the carpels and resembling a fig (*Ficus*) with an apical ostiole; carpels
5–2, *free*, large and fleshy, *arcuate-divergent*; stigma sessile, thick, falcate,
2-lipped; fruiting follicles 5–2, divergent, dehiscing by the adaxial (upper)
suture; seeds globose, *arillate*, shining, with a rather prominent umbilicus;
endosperm copious, embryo small. S. and Central Europe from Spain and
N. Africa to Siberia, and in NW. America.—PAEONIA.

Corner[1] considers the order of development of stamens—centrifugal or centripetal—to
be of phylogenetic importance, and gives a list of the families known to him having either
type. Largely because of this character he considers *Paeonia*, with centrifugal stamens, to
be misplaced in the *Ranunculaceae*, which otherwise have centripetal stamens, and would

[1] E. J. H. Corner, 'Centrifugal Stamens', *J. Arnold Arbor.* **27**, 423 (1946).

put *Paeonia*, because of this, near the *Dilleniaceae*. I am not at all convinced that this character alone is sufficient to support this treatment, for in sorting a pile of specimens of various families I should never place *Paeonia* anywhere near *Dilleniaceae*.

I consider *Paeonia* to be something of a link between the *Magnoliaceae* and *Helleboraceae*, but much more closely related to the latter. The recognition of *Paeonia* as a separate family was advocated on anatomical evidence by Worsdell[1] in 1908.

248. HELLEBORACEAE

Perennial herbs with underground rhizomes or tubers, very rarely annuals; leaves sometimes all or mostly radical, alternate, *palmately or pedately nerved*,

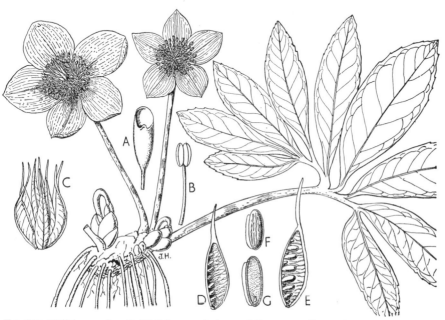

FIG. 248. Helleborus niger *L.* (Helleboraceae). A, petal. B, stamen. C, carpels. D, vertical section of carpel. E, same in fruit. F, seed. G, vertical section of seed. (Orig.)

lobed or dissected, rarely peltate, sometimes the upper leaves resembling an *involucre*, very rarely pinnately divided; petioles sometimes dilated into *stipule-like auricles at the base*; venation reticulate; flowers bisexual, *actinomorphic or zygomorphic*, solitary or few together, more rarely racemose or paniculate, sometimes precocious, yellow, white, green, lilac, rose, or blue; sepals 5 or more, rarely 3 or 4, free, green or petaloid, rarely spurred at the base, imbricate; petals 8–5, rarely up to 12 or more, sometimes *reduced and nectary-like*, when absent the *sepals often petaloid*, often with a nectariferous pit at the base; stamens hypogynous, filaments free; anthers 2-locular, opening by slits lengthwise; *no disk*; carpels numerous to 5, very rarely 2 or 1, *free* or rarely partially connate; style simple; ovules many to several, in 3–1 series on the adaxial suture, rarely only 2 ovules near the middle of the carpel; fruit

[1] W. C. Worsdell, 'The Affinities of Paeonia', *J. Bot.* **46**, 114 (1908); *Ann. Bot.* **22**, 663 (1908).

follicular, free and dehiscing by the adaxial suture, rarely carpels united and dehiscing at the apex, rarely baccate; seeds angular, sometimes *keeled, winged, or ridged*, with copious endosperm and small straight embryo with 2 cotyledons. Mostly N. Temperate Regions, rarer in the S. Hemisphere.—Tribes *Helleboreae* and *Delphineae* of B.H. **1,** 1.—TROLLIUS, ASTEROPYRUM, HELLEBORUS, ERANTHIS, CALTHA, CALATHODES, GLAUCIDIUM, HYDRASTIS, ANEMONOPSIS, PARAQUILEGIA, PAROPYRUM, NEOLEPTOPYRUM, COPTIS, ISOPYRUM, ENEMION, SEMIAQUILEGIA, AQUILEGIA, NIGELLA, KOMAROFFIA, GARIDELLA, BEESIA, SOULIEA, CIMICIFUGA, ACTAEA, XANTHORHIZA, DELPHINIUM, ACONITUM.

USEFUL PRODUCTS: *Stavesacre seeds* (Delphinium staphisagria *L.*), SE. Eur.; *Aconite root* (Aconitum napellus *L.*), Eur.; *Black Cohosh* or *Black Snake root* (Cimicifuga racemosa *Nutt.*), N. Amer.; *Hydrastis rhizome* (Hydrastis canadensis *L.*), N. Amer. Many beautiful garden plants.

249. RANUNCULACEAE

FIG. 249. Ranunculus cortusifolius *Willd.* (Ranunculaceae). A, carpels. B, one carpel. (Orig.)

Perennial and annual herbs with *radical and alternate* leaves, or shrubs or climbers with *opposite often compound* leaves, but with *soft wood* and *broad medullary rays*; stipules *absent* or represented by stipule-like petiolar basal sheaths; flowers bisexual or rarely dioecious, actinomorphic (*never zygomorphic*), solitary to paniculate, yellow to white, blue, or pink, rarely purple or scarlet, sometimes subtended by an *involucre of leaves or one leaf*; sepals 5–8, rarely more or reduced to 3 or 4, imbricate, to semi-valvate or valvate, mostly deciduous, sometimes *petaloid*, rarely spurred at the base; petals many to few, often 5, free, mainly with a nectariferous claw, showy or much reduced or absent and then the *sepals often petaloid*; stamens numerous; filaments free, usually in several series, rarely the outer staminodal and petaloid; anthers short, dehiscing by slits lengthwise; *no disk*; carpels usually many, rarely only 1 or few, *free*, inserted on a short globular to elongated axis; style slightly bifid or stigma sessile; *ovule 1, erect or pendulous*; fruit a bunch of *dry achenes*, sometimes with long feathery tails, rarely berry-like, seeds with very small straight embryo (rarely with only 1 cotyledon) in copious endosperm. B.H. **1**, 1 (partly); E.P. **3**, 2, 43 (partly). Mostly in N. Temperate Regions, fewer in the Tropics and in the S. Hemisphere. Composed of tribes *Ranunculeae, Anemoneae,* and *Clematideae* of B.H. **1**, 1.—MYOSURUS, OXYGRAPHIS, CALLIANTHEMUM, RANUNCULUS, LACCOPETALUM (*Cryptochaete*), ADONIS, KNOWLTONIA, GAMPSOCERAS, PAROXYGRAPHIS, HAMADRYAS, TRAUTVETTERIA, SCHLAGINTWEITIELLA, THALICTRUM (*Piuttia*), KINGDONIA, OREITHALES, ANEMONELLA, ANEMONE, HEPATICA, BARNEAUDIA, CLEMATOPSIS, CLEMATIS, NARAVELIA.[1]

USEFUL PRODUCTS: Some beautiful garden plants.

250. NYMPHAEACEAE

Aquatic herbs with peltate or cordate often floating leaves on long petioles; flowers ⚥, solitary, large and showy, often sweet-scented; sepals 4–6, free or adnate to the torus; petals numerous, hypogynous or perigynous, imbricate, sometimes gradually passing into the stamens, the latter numerous, with introrse anthers opening longitudinally; carpels 8 or more, united into a many-locular ovary (*Nuphar*) or sunk in the enlarged torus (*Nelumbo*); ovules 1 to many, on the walls or from the apex of the carpel; endosperm usually present; embryo straight. B.H. **1**, 45 (partly); E.P. **3**, 2, 1. Widely dispersed in ponds, streams, and lakes. Tropics and N. Temperate Zone. Including *Euryalaceae, Barclayaceae,* Li (1955).

Several beautiful hardy NYMPHAEA spp. suitable for water gardening. *Victoria Water Lily* (Victoria amazonica (*Poeppig*) *Sowerby*), Guiana and Brazil; *Egyptian Lotus* (Nelumbo nucifera (*Gaertn.*) *Willd.*).

A. Ovules numerous in each loculus or carpel: **B.** Carpels or ovary inserted above the torus; sepals, petals, and stamens hypogynous; leaves with a basal sinus—NUPHAR (N. Hemisph.). **BB.** Carpels or ovary more or less immersed in the torus; sepals, petals, or stamens epigynous: **C.** Sepals all hypogynous; petals and stamens epigynous; leaves with a basal sinus—BARCLAYA (Indo-Malaya). **CC.** Sepals or some of them more or less epigynous: **D.** Outer sepals and petals subhypogynous; leaves with a basal sinus—NYMPHAEA (Cosmopol.). **DD.** All sepals and petals epigynous; plants armed with prickles:

[1] Only such synonyms of these genera as are additional to Dalla Torre and Harms, *Genera Siphonogam.*, are included.

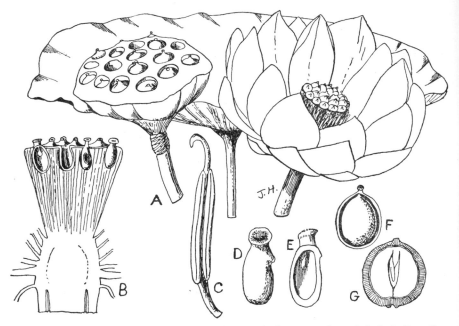

FIG. 250. Nelumbo lutea (*Willd.*) *Pers.* (Nymphaeaceae). A, torus and carpels in fruit. B, section of torus. C, anther. D, carpel. E, section of carpel. F, section of fruit. G, section of seed. (After Le Maout & Decne.)

E. Stamens all fertile—EURYALE (E. Asia). **EE.** Inner stamens sterile—VICTO-RIA (E. Tropics, S. Amer.). **AA.** Ovule solitary from the apex of the loculus; carpels sunk in the enlarged torus—NELUMBO (*Nelumbium*) (Tropics of Amer., Asia, and Austral.).

251. PODOPHYLLACEAE

Perennial herbs with more or less *fleshy rootstock* and often thick roots; leaves mostly all *radical*, peltate, palmi-nerved or lobed or 2–3-foliolate; *stipules absent*; flowers bisexual, solitary or cymose and subumbellate, terminal, rarely spicate; sepals 6–4, *petaloid or green*, imbricate, rarely absent; petals 9–6, larger than the sepals, imbricate, rarely absent; stamens *as many as the petals or twice as many*, free; anthers opening by *slits lengthwise* or by *valves* from the base upwards; *no disk*; ovary superior, composed of *1 carpel*, 1-locular; ovules numerous on the adaxial side or reduced to 1; fruit a berry or a follicle opening transversely or obliquely; seeds with copious endosperm and small embryo.—N. Hemisphere, mainly in Temperate Regions.

USEFUL PRODUCT: *May Apple* or *Podophyllum roots* (Podophyllum peltatum *L.*) N. Amer.

A. Ovules 2- or more-seriate on the adaxial suture of the ovary: **B.** Leaves palmi-nerved or -lobed or bipartite: **C.** Anthers opening by slits lengthwise; flowers solitary or subumbellate; fruit a berry—PODOPHYLLUM (E. Asia and

Eastern N. Amer.). **CC.** Anthers opening by 1 or 2 valves from the base upwards: **D.** Sepals and petals present: **E.** Sepals 6; petals 6, flat; stamens 6; fruit a berry: **F.** Flowers cymose; leaves deeply lobed and lobulate—DIPHYL-LEIA (NE. Asia, Atlantic N. Amer.). **FF.** Flowers single; leaves 3-foliolate—RANZANIA (Japan). **EE.** Sepals 4; fruit dehiscent: **G.** Leaves bilobed to the apex of the petiole; fruit transversely dehiscent—JEFFERSONIA (Atlantic N. Amer.). **GG.** Leaves only slightly bilobed at the top; fruit obliquely dehiscent—PLAGIORHEGMA (NE. Asia). **DD.** Sepals and petals absent; stamens up

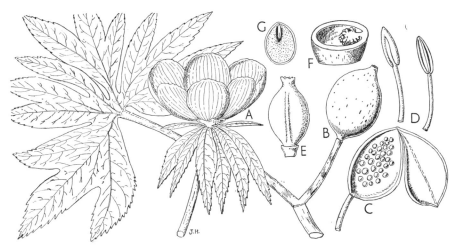

FIG. 251. Podophyllum hexandrum *Royle* (Podophyllaceae). A, flower and whorl of leaves. B, fruit. C, fruit opened out. D, stamens. E, ovary. F, cross-section of ovary. G, vertical section of seed. (Adapted from *Bot. Mag.*)

to 9; anthers 1-valved; ovule 1; fruit dorsally dehiscent—ACHLYS (Pacific N. Amer.). **BB.** Leaves pinnately 1–3-ternate: **H.** Sepals 15–12; petals smaller and nectary-like, 6; stamens 6—VANCOUVERIA (Pacific N. Amer.). **HH.** Sepals 8–7; petals 4; stamens 4: **J.** Leaves pinnately 2–3-sect—EPIMEDIUM (SE. Eur. to Japan, N. Afr.). **JJ.** Leaves 2-foliolate—ACERANTHUS (Japan). **AA.** Ovules few, erect from the base of the loculus; leaves pinnately nerved or pinnatisect, or pinnately 2–3-ternate or decompound: **K.** Petals scarcely smaller than the sepals, flat; stamens 6; fruit bladdery, indehiscent, the pericarp persistent and enclosing the seeds—BONGARDIA (E. Mediterr. to India). **KK.** Petals small and nectary-like: **L.** Fruit bladdery, indehiscent, pericarp persistent and enclosing the seeds—LEONTICE (E. Mediterr. to NE. Asia). **LL.** Fruit dehiscent, the pericarp falling away very early and exposing the drupe-like seeds—CAULOPHYLLUM (E. Asia, Atlantic N. Amer.).

252. CERATOPHYLLACEAE

Aquatic *submerged herbs*, with leafy floating branches; leaves *verticillate*, variously divided with thread-like or linear segments; flowers *monoecious*, solitary in the whorls, the males and females at separate nodes, sessile; calyx thinly herbaceous, many-parted into narrow subvalvate segments often dentate or lacerate at the apex. Male flowers: stamens 10–20, crowded on a flat torus; anthers almost sessile, erect, linear-oblong, 2-locular, loculi parallel, opening lengthwise, with the connective produced beyond the loculi, thick and often coloured. Female flowers: staminodes 0; ovary sessile, ovoid, 1-locular; style continuous with the ovary; ovule 1, pendulous, anatropous; fruit a nut, ovoid or ellipsoidal; seed pendulous; endosperm 0; embryo straight; cotyledons oblong, equal; radicle very short; the plumule already well developed and showing several leaves in the seed. B.H. **3**, 415; E.P. **3**, 2, 10. Cosmopolitan.— CERATOPHYLLUM.

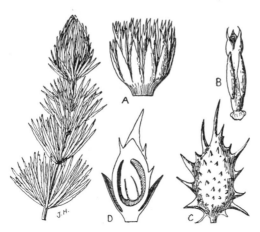

FIG. 252. Ceratophyllum demersum *L.* var. (Ceratophyllaceae). A, flower. B, stamen. C, fruit. D, vertical section of same. (After Martius.)

253. CABOMBACEAE

Aquatic herbs with perennial rhizomes; stems coated with mucilage; leaves alternate, the *submerged ones finely dissected*, the floating *peltate*; flowers axillary, solitary, *hypogynous*, actinomorphic; sepals 3, petaloid; petals 3; stamens 3–18; anthers extrorse, opening lengthwise; carpels 2–18, free,

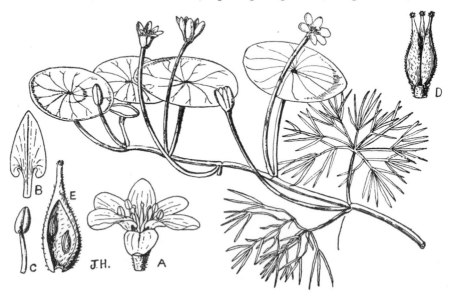

FIG. 253. Cabomba aquatica *Aubl.* (Cabombaceae). A, flower. B, petal. C, stamen. D, carpels. E, same open. (After *Bot. Mag.*)

1-locular, stigma subsessile, entire; ovules 2–3, parietal, orthotropous; fruits indehiscent; seeds 1–3 on the dorsal suture; embryo at the base of fleshy endosperm; cotyledons fleshy. B.H. **1**, 46 (under *Nymphaeaceae*). America, India, Australia, and Tropical Africa.

A small family formerly included in the *Nymphaeaceae*, but more closely allied to the preceding.

A. Stamens 18–12; carpels numerous to 6; leaves all peltate—BRASENIA (N. Amer. south to Cuba and Guatemala), E. Asia, Austral., Trop. Afr.). AA. Stamens 6; carpels usually 3; submerged leaves much divided—CABOMBA (E. Amer. from southern States to Argentine).

ORDER 56. BERBERIDALES

Herbaceous to shrubby or climbing; stem often with broad medullary rays; flowers hypogynous; ♀ to ♂♀, cyclic; petals present, small or rarely absent; stamens mostly definite in number, free, opposite the petals; carpels usually 1–3, free, rarely numerous; seeds with copious endosperm and small to large embryo. Leaves alternate, simple or compound, exstipulate.—Mainly N. Temperate Zone.

A. Carpels 3 or more, free, very rarely 1; flowers unisexual; shrubs or climbers, the wood with broad primary medullary rays:
  B. Leaves compound; endosperm not ruminate:
    C. Carpels numerous, spirally arranged   *Sargentodoxaceae*
    CC. Carpels few (up to 9) in whorls   *Lardizabalaceae*
  BB. Leaves simple; fruit drupaceous; endosperm sometimes ruminate
                                  Menispermaceae
AA. Carpel 1; flowers bisexual; shrubs or very rarely herbs:
  D. Anthers opening by slits lengthwise; ovules pendulous:
    E. Shrub with 2–3 times pinnately compound leaves and long panicles of small flowers; sepals numerous, spirally arranged; stamens 6
                                    Nandinaceae
    EE. Annual herb with a rosette of spinulose dentate leaves; stamens 2; flower solitary, axillary; sepals 2, valvate   *Circaeasteraceae*
  DD. Anthers opening by valves from the base upwards; ovules ascending; stamens 6, opposite the petals; petals with 2 nectariferous glands on the inner side; small trees or shrubs with pinnate or unifoliolate leaves
                                    Berberidaceae

254. SARGENTODOXACEAE[1]

Climbers; leaves alternate, trifoliolate; stipules absent; flowers unisexual; inflorescences from axillary perulate buds; racemose; male flowers: sepals 6, free, conspicuous in bud, biseriately imbricate; petals 6, very small and scale-like; stamens 6, opposite the petals; anthers extrorse, 2-locular, connective

[1] This family in many ways combines in its two sexes the characters of the *Lardizabalaceae* and *Schisandraceae*, with the male flowers similar to the former, and the gynoecium of the latter.

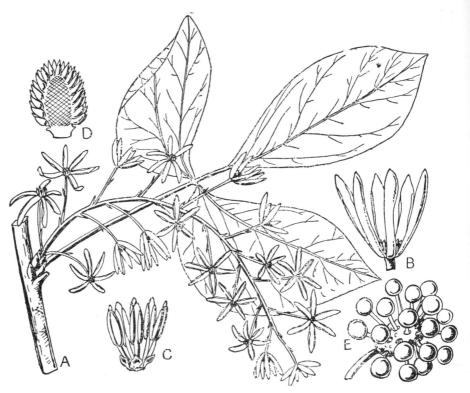

FIG. 254. Sargentodoxa cuneata (*Oliv*.) *Rehd. & Wils.* (Sargentodoxaceae). A, male shoot. B, male flower. C, petals and stamens. D, section of female without sepals and petals. E, fruit. (Partly original.)

shortly produced at the apex; female flowers: sepals and petals as in the male; staminodes 6; carpels numerous, spirally arranged, free; ovule 1, pendulous; fruit baccate; seeds with copious smooth endosperm and minute embryo. W. China.—SARGENTODOXA.

255. LARDIZABALACEAE

Twining or rarely erect shrubs; wood with *broad primary medullary rays*; leaves alternate, *digitately compound* or rarely pinnate; petiolules swollen at the base; hairs simple; flowers racemose, arising with the leaves from *perulate buds*, ♂♀, actinomorphic; sepals 3 or 6, imbricate, or the outer valvate, often petaloid; petals 6, smaller than the sepals or absent; stamens 6, free or connate; anthers free, opening lengthwise; connective often produced; staminodes 6 or absent from the ♀ flowers; carpels 3 (or more), soon divergent; stigma oblique, subsessile; ovules numerous or solitary; mature carpels fleshy, coloured, indehiscent or opening by the adaxial suture; seeds ovoid or sub-reniform, with fleshy copious endosperm; embryo small. B.H. **1,** 40 (under *Berberidaceae*); E.P. **3,** 2, 67. Temperate S. America, E. Asia.

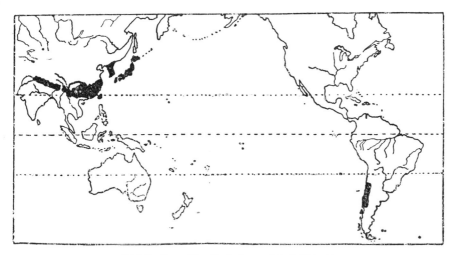

Distribution of Lardizabalaceae (shaded black).

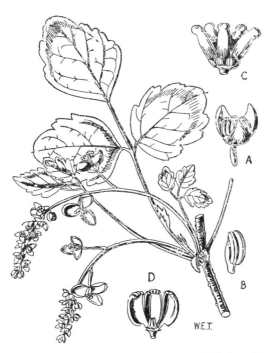

FIG. 255. Akebia lobata *Decne.* (Lardizabalaceae).
A, male flower. B, anther. C, female flower. D, fruit.
(After *Bot. Mag.*)

A. Leaves pinnate with several pairs of opposite leaflets; stem erect— DECAISNEA (India, China). **AA.** Leaves digitate, pinnately 3-foliolate or 2–3-ternate; stems climbing: **B.** Leaves once pinnately or digitately foliolate: **C.** Pedicels without bracts; flowers monoecious—SINOFRANCHETIA (China). **CC.** Pedicels with a bract at the base, this sometimes deciduous: **D.** Stamens free: **E.** Sepals 6; petals 6, minute; leaves evergreen—HOLBOELLIA (E. Asia). **EE.** Sepals 3; petals absent; leaves deciduous—AKEBIA (E. Asia). **DD.** Stamens united into a tube or column: **F.** Flowers monoecious; anthers long-apiculate; leaves pinnately trifoliolate—PARVATIA (E. Himal.). **FF.** Flowers dioecious: **G.** Petals 6; ovules few; leaves pinnately 3-foliolate—BOQUILA (Chile). **GG.** Petals absent; ovules numerous; leaves digitately 3- or more-foliolate— STAUNTONIA (E. Asia). **BB.** Leaves 2–3-ternate; pedicels bracteate—LARDI-ZABALA (Chile).

256. MENISPERMACEAE

Twining or rarely erect shrubs or small trees, with the wood in cross-section showing *broad medullary rays*; root bitter; leaves petiolate, alternate, *exstipu-*

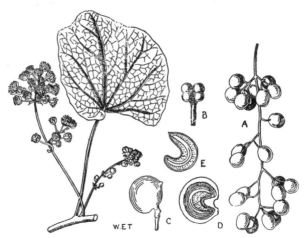

FIG. 256. Menispermum canadense *L.* (Menispermaceae). A, fruits. B, anther. C, fruit. D, section of same. E, section of seed. (After Le Maout & Decne.)

late, usually simple, rarely trifoliolate or palmately lobed and nerved; inflorescence cymose, paniculate, fasciculate, or rarely the flowers solitary, axillary, or borne on the older wood; flowers small, inconspicuously coloured, *unisexual*, dioecious, actinomorphic, rarely slightly zygomorphic. Male flowers: sepals in 2–4 series, imbricate, the outer smaller; petals usually smaller than the sepals, minute or absent, free or rarely united; stamens usually 6 or 3, or indefinite, when few *opposite to the petals*, free or variously united; anthers short. Female flowers: staminodes present or absent; *carpels 3 or 6*, rarely 1 or several, *free*, sessile or stipitate; stigma terminal, entire or lobed; ovules 2, soon reduced to 1 by abortion, attached to the ventral suture; carpels drupaceous, with the scar of the style subterminal or near the base by *excentric growth*, sessile or stipitate; exocarp membranous or subcoriaceous, mesocarp more or less pulpy, endocarp often bony and rugose, tuberculate or ribbed; seed often curved in the form of a horseshoe, with uniform or ruminate endosperm or without endosperm; embryo often curved, with a small radicle and flat or semi-terete cotyledons. B.H. **1**, 30; E.P. **3**, 2, 78. Mainly Tropics and Subtropics.—TINOSPORA, COCCULUS, MENISPERMUM, STEPHANIA, CISSAMPELOS, &c.

USEFUL PRODUCT: *Levant berries* (Anamirta paniculata *Coleb.*), E. Asia.

257. NANDINACEAE

Erect shrub; leaves alternate, *2–3 times pinnately compound*, leaflets entire, acuminate, pinnately nerved, nerves looped; joints swollen and rimmed when

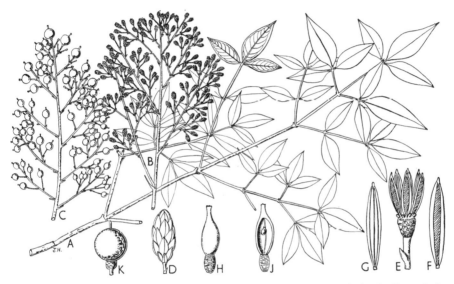

FIG. 257. Nandina domestica (Nandinaceae). A, leaf. B, inflorescence. C, fruits. D, flower-bud. E, stamens. F, and G, stamens. H, ovary. J, vertical section of ovary. K, fruit. (Orig.)

dry; stipules absent; flowers small, white, bisexual, numerous in *terminal panicles*; bracts subulate, persistent; bracteoles few, small; *sepals numerous, spirally arranged*, gradually larger from the outer to the innermost; petals 6, a little larger than the inner sepals; *no nectaries*; stamens 6, in a single whorl, *opposite the petals*; anthers subsessile, adaxially dehiscent by slits lengthwise, linear, with a broad abaxial connective shortly produced at the apex; *carpel 1*, 1-locular, slightly obliquely ellipsoidal, gradually narrowed into a short style and subentire terminal stigma; ovule 1, pendent from above the middle of the wall of the loculus; fruit a globose *berry* tipped by the persistent style; seed with a very small embryo in copious endosperm. Sect. *Nandineae* of *Ranunculaceae*. Bernhardi, *Linnaea*, **8**, 452 (1833). China and Japan.—NANDINA.

258. CIRCAEASTERACEAE

Small *annual herb* with a rosette of obovate spinulose-dentate leaves; flowers solitary in the upper leaf-axils, shortly pedicellate, ♀, actinomorphic; sepals 2, membranous, valvate, persistent; *petals absent*; stamens 2, free, alternate with the sepals, erect in bud, rarely reduced to one and the other sepaloid;

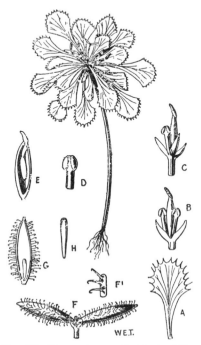

FIG. 258. Circaeaster agrestis *Maxim.* (Circaeasteraceae). A, leaf. B and C, flowers. D, anther. E, section of ovary. F, fruit. F¹, prickles from fruit. G, section of fruit. H, embryo. (After Hook. *Ic. Pl.*)

anthers 2-locular, introrse, loculi divergent from the apex, opening lengthwise; ovary superior, linear, 1-locular, stigma sessile; ovule 1, *pendulous* from the apex of the loculus; fruit indehiscent; seed with copious endosperm; embryo terete, straight, with short cotyledons. NW. Himalaya.—CIRCAEASTER.

Diels (*Beih. bot. Centralb.* **49**, Ergänz. 55, fig. 1, 2 (1932)) considered *Circaeaster* to be related to *Kingdonia* in *Ranunculaceae*, and suggested that it should be included in that family. I cannot see any affinity between these two genera, and I regard it (rightly or wrongly) as a very reduced relative of the *Podophyllaceae* or *Berberidaceae*.

259. BERBERIDACEAE (*sensu strictissimo*)

Undershrubs or shrubs; leaves alternate, simple or compound, *exstipulate*; flowers ♀, solitary to paniculate; *sepals and petals similar*, in 2 to several series, free, hypogynous, imbricate or outer valvate, caducous; stamens 6, *opposite the petals*, hypogynous, free; anthers 2-locular, opening by *valves*; *carpel 1*; style short; ovules few, ascending, anatropous; fruit a berry; seeds with copious endosperm, and small or long embryo; cotyledons short. B.H.

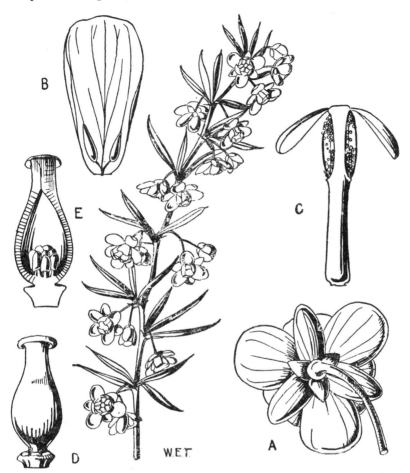

Fig. 259. Berberis stenophylla *Hance* (Berberidaceae). A, flower from below. B, petal. C, stamen. D, ovary. E, section of ovary. (Orig.)

1, 40 (partly); E.P. **3,** 2, 70 (partly). Mainly N. Temperate Zone and mountains of S. America.

USEFUL PRODUCTS: Many beautiful garden shrubs.

A. Leaves of long shoots compound, trifoliolate to imparipinnate, evergreen; inflorescence arising from the axils of scales of winter buds which terminate long shoots—MAHONIA (N. Temp. Zone, south to Siam and Philipp. Is., Pacific N. Amer. to Cent. Amer. and Cuba). **AA.** Leaves of long shoots transformed into thorns, those of the short shoots simple, often deciduous; inflorescence terminating short shoots arising in the axils of leaf-thorns—BERBERIS (N. Temp. Zone, mountains of E. Trop. Afr. and S. Amer.).

ORDER 57. ARISTOLOCHIALES

Softly woody with broad medullary rays, or parasitic or epiphytic herbs, flowers hypogynous to epigynous, ♀ to ♂♀; no petals; stamens ∞ to few; parietal or axile placentation; endosperm present or absent, with small to large embryo. Leaves (when present) alternate, simple, exstipulate.—Mostly Tropics.

A. Flowers bisexual; ovary inferior or rarely semi-superior:
  B. Climbing shrubs with broad medullary rays, or rarely herbs, not parasitic; leaves well-developed; calyx often enlarged and petaloid, sometimes unilateral and highly coloured   *Aristolochiaceae*
  BB. Parasitic herbs on the roots of trees and shrubs; no leaves; calyx very thick, valvately 3–4-lobed   *Hydnoraceae*
AA. Flowers unisexual:
  C. Ovary inferior or semi-inferior with parietal or apical placentas; parasites with scale-like leaves; anthers sessile in 1–3 series around a fleshy column; fruit fleshy, indehiscent or opening irregularly   *Cytinaceae*
  CC. Ovary superior, with axile placentas; leaves divided when adult into petiole, blade, tendril, pitcher, and operculum; filaments crowded into a column; fruit a loculicidal capsule   *Nepenthaceae*

260. ARISTOLOCHIACEAE

Climbing shrubs or rarely dwarf and erect; stems of the woody species in cross-section showing *broad medullary rays*; roots often medicinal; leaves

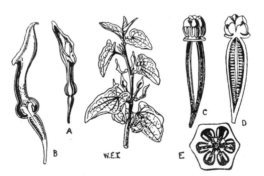

Fig. 260. Aristolochia clematitis *L.* (Aristolochiaceae). A, flower. B, section of same. C, fruit. D, vertical section of fruit. E, cross-section of same.

petiolate, alternate, simple, mostly entire, *without stipules*; flowers solitary or racemose, axillary, terminal or in clusters on the older wood, bisexual, zygomorphic, or rarely actinomorphic; calyx often enlarged and petaloid, variously produced above the ovary, often tubular, the limb either symmetrically 3-lobed, or unilateral and entire or lobed, usually highly coloured and foetid; stamens 6-∞, in 1–2-series *around the apex of the ovary or stylar column*; filaments short, thick, free or scarcely distinguishable from the column; anthers free or adnate, with 2 parallel loculi, extrorse, opening longitudinally; ovary *inferior* or rarely semi-superior, 4-6-locular or imperfectly locular; styles thick, short, united into a column, divided into 3-∞ stigmatic lobes; ovules numerous in each cell; fruit capsular or rarely indehiscent, sometimes dehiscing from the base upwards and hanging like an inverted parachute; seeds numerous, often immersed in the pulpy endocarp, 3-sided or flattened, raphe sometimes thickened or winged; endosperm copious, fleshy; embryo small. B.H. **3,** 121; E.P. **3,** 1, 264. Tropics and Temperate.

USEFUL PRODUCTS: Several used as cures for snake bites; *Alpam Root* (Bragantia wallichii *R. Br.*), India; *Virginian Snake Root* (Aristolochia serpentaria *L.*). U.S.A.

A. Calyx actinomorphic (regular), equally 3-lobed: **B.** Petals present, broad and very conspicuous—SARUMA (China). **BB.** Petals absent or very minute: **C.** Stamens in 2 series: **D.** Stamens 12; ovary subglobose; herbs with creeping rhizomes; flowers terminal, solitary—ASARUM (Mainly N. Temp. Reg.). **DD.** Stamens numerous; ovary linear; erect or sarmentose shrubs; flowers cymose or racemose—THOTTEA (Malaya). **CC.** Stamens in 1 series: **E.** Stamens free from the style or only adnate to the base; fruit capsular, long and linear, 4-angled, 4-valved: **F.** Stems short from a rhizome, bearing very few cordate or elliptic often tomentose leaves; racemes borne towards the base of the stems; stamens 6; styles 3, free—CYCLODISCUS (Indo-Malaya). **FF.** Shrubs or small trees; inflorescences axillary or terminal: **G.** Inflorescence axillary; stamens 9; styles 6–9, free—APAMA (Indo-Malaya). **GG.** Inflorescence terminal, cymose; stamens 6–12; styles united into a many-rayed disk—ASIPHONIA (Indo-Malaya). **EE.** Stamens wholly adnate to the stylar column: **H.** Fruit a capsule—ISOTREMA (E. Asia, N. Amer.). **HH.** Fruit much elongated, ribbed, hard and indehiscent—PARARISTOLOCHIA (Trop. Afr.). **AA.** Calyx zygomorphic, usually oblique or unilateral; anthers 6 or more, 1-seriate, adnate to the stylar column: **J.** Calyx more or less constricted above the genitalia—ARISTOLOCHIA (Mostly Tropics, rare in Temp. Reg.). **JJ.** Calyx not constricted above the genitalia—HOLOSTYLIS (Brazil).

261. HYDNORACEAE

Parasitic herbs on the roots of various trees and shrubs; scale-leaves 0; flowers ☿, solitary, subsessile, rather large; calyx very thick, valvately 3–4-lobed; anthers numerous, sessile in a single or double series on the tube of the calyx, the loculi densely crowded, linear, opening lengthwise; ovary inferior, 1-locular, crowned by the sessile stigma; ovules very numerous from *apical or parietal placentas* often nearly meeting in the middle; fruit baccate; seeds numerous, small or minute, in copious endosperm. B.H. **3,** 120 (under *Cytinaceae*); E.P. **3,** 1, 282. Tropics and Temperate.

A. Placentas parietal, intruding nearly to the middle of the ovary—PROSOPANCHE (Argentine). **AA.** Placentas pendulous from the top of the ovary—HYDNORA (Fig. 261) (Trop. and S. Afr., Madag.).

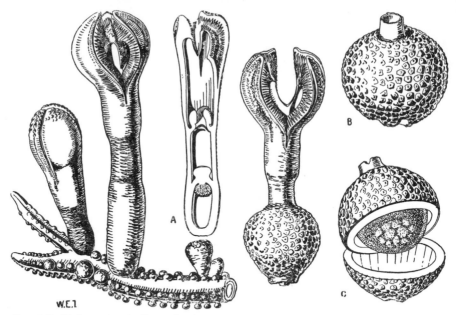

W.C.1

FIG. 261. Hydnora longicollis *Welw.* (Hydnoraceae). A, vertical section of flower. B, fruit. C, fruit in section. (After Welw.)

262. CYTINACEAE

(Rafflesiaceae)

Fleshy *parasites* with *scale-like leaves*, on the roots, stems, and branches of various trees and shrubs; flowers often large, solitary, rarely spicate, diclinous by abortion, rarely polygamous or ♀; calyx more or less epigynous with 4–10 imbricate or very rarely valvate segments; anthers sessile, arranged in 1–3 series around a fleshy column, 2-locular, opening lengthwise by slits or by terminal pores; pollen often viscous; ovary inferior or subinferior, 1-locular or the placentas reaching nearly into the middle; stigma undivided, discoid or lobate or the stigmas numerous on the top of the ovary; ovules very numerous on *parietal placentas* or from the apex of the loculi, with a single integument; fruit fleshy, indehiscent or opening irregularly; seeds minute, very numerous; endosperm cellular; embryo minute. B.H. **3**, 116; E.P. **3**, 1, 274 (as *Rafflesiaceae*). Tropics and Temperate.

The flower of *Rafflesia arnoldii* R. Br. is the largest in the vegetable kingdom.

A. Flowers numerous, spicate; stem developed; scales scattered: **B.** Calyx of both sexes tubular with a plate-like limb; flowers with 2 lateral bracts— CYTINUS (Mediterr. Reg. and Cape Reg. of S. Afr.). **BB.** Calyx flat and spreading, rotate; bracts absent—BDALLOPHYTON (Cent. Amer.). **AA.** Flowers solitary and sessile on the rhizome: **C.** Bracts imbricate, crowded, adnate at the base to the ovary and subsimilar to the calyx-segments—APODANTHES (*Pilostyles*) (Persia Trop. Afr., Trop. Amer.). **CC.** Bracts imbricate, adnate to the base of the ovary, very dissimilar to the calyx-segments: **D.** Calyx-segments imbricate: **E.** Calyx-lobes 5; stigmas numerous on a flat column, conical—RAFFLESIA

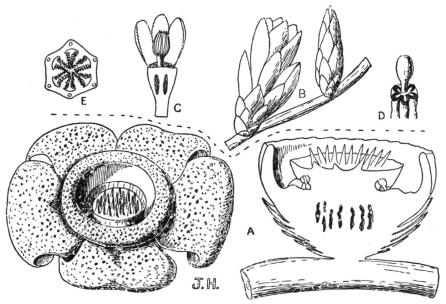

FIG. 262. A, Rafflesia patma *Bl.* (Cytinaceae). B, Cytinus. C, vertical section of flower. D, stigma. E, transverse section of ovary.

(Malay Archip., Philipp. Is.). **EE.** Calyx-lobes 10, in 2 series; stigma solitary in the middle of a columnar disk—SAPRIA (E. India). **DD.** Calyx-segments induplicate-valvate, 2–3-fid; stigma undivided—BRUGMANSIA (Malay Archip.).

263. NEPENTHACEAE

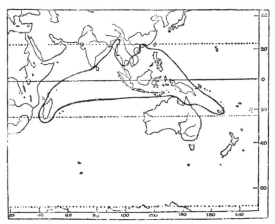

The distribution of the remarkable and distinct genus Nepenthes emphasizes the close relationship between the island of Madagascar and Indo-Malaya.

Shrubs or undershrubs, prostrate, erect, or scandent; leaves alternate, sessile or petiolate, divided when adult into petiole, blade, *tendril, ascidium* (pitcher),

W.E.T.

FIG. 263. **Nepenthes rafflesiana** *Jack* (Nepenthaceae). A, male flower. B, fruit. (After Hook.)

and *operculum*; flowers *dioecious*, small, actinomorphic; sepals 4–3, separate or rarely connate at the base, imbricate, glandular and nectariferous inside; stamens 4–24; *filaments connate into a column*; anthers crowded into a mass, 2-locular, opening lengthwise; ovary of 4-carpels very rarely 3, opposite the sepals, 3–4-locular; style absent or very short; stigma discoid; ovules numerous in many series on the central placentas; fruit a capsule, sessile or shortly stipitate, loculicidally dehiscent; seeds numerous, imbricate; ascending, filiform; endosperm fleshy with straight cylindrical embryo in the middle. B.H. **3**, 115; E.P. **3**, 2, 253. Malaya to Madagascar.—NEPENTHES (*Anurosperma*). Well-known 'Pitcher-Plants'.

ORDER 58. PIPERALES

Herbs, shrubs, or trees; herbaceous stems often with scattered bundles as in *Monocotyledons*; flowers hypogynous to epigynous; usually no calyx; petals absent; ovary superior to rarely inferior; carpels rarely free; placentation parietal to subaxile; seeds with copious endosperm and minute embryo. Leaves alternate or opposite, usually stipulate.—Mostly Tropics.

A. Leaves alternate, or rarely opposite or whorled; stipules more or less adnate to the petiole or absent:
  B. Ovule 1, erect; ovary superior; bracts not petaloid   *Piperaceae*
  BB. Ovules 2 or more in each carpel or placenta; ovary superior or inferior; bracts or sometimes the upper leaves petaloid and very conspicuous
                                                                     Saururaceae
AA. Leaves opposite; petioles more or less connected at the base, with very small free stipules; ovule 1, pendulous; ovary inferior; bracts small and inconspicuous   *Chloranthaceae*

264. PIPERACEAE

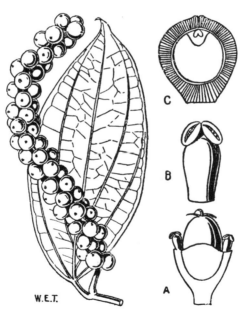

FIG. 264. Piper nigrum *L.* (Piperaceae). A, flower. B, stamen. C, section of fruit. (After Le Maout & Decne.)

Herbs or shrubs, erect or scandent; vascular bundles more or less scattered as in *Monocotyledones*; leaves usually alternate, entire, rarely opposite or whorled, petiolate; stipules *adnate to the petiole* or absent; flowers minute, bisexual or unisexual, usually densely spicate or spikes umbellate; calyx absent; stamens 2–6, hypogynous; filaments usually free; anthers 2-locular, distinct or confluent; ovary superior, 1-locular, 1-ovuled; stigmas 1–5, short; ovule erect; fruit baccate, small, with a succulent, thin or dry pericarp; seeds small, with small endosperm and copious mealy perisperm; embryo very small. B.H. **3**, 125; E.P. **3**, 1, 3. Mainly Tropics.—PIPER, PEPEROMIA, &c.

USEFUL PRODUCTS: *Pepper* (Piper nigrum *L.*), Tropics; *Cubebs* (P. cubeba *L.*), Malay Archip.

A family of rather doubtful origin, but probably an extreme reduction from the *Ranales*, becoming more or less woody.

265. SAURURACEAE

FIG. 265. Anemopsis californica (*Nutt.*) *Hk. f.* (Saururaceae). A, flower showing ovary in vertical section. B, ovary, cross-section. (After *Bot. Mag.*)

Perennial herbs; leaves alternate, simple; *stipules adnate to the petiole*; flowers ⚥, in dense spikes or racemes; bracts or upper leaves conspicuous; perianth absent; stamens 3, 6, or 8, rarely fewer by abortion, free or adnate to the

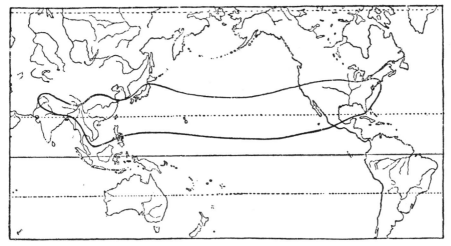

Range of Saururaceae. A distinct family common to E. Asia and N. America.

ovary at the base or quite epigynous; anthers 2-locular, opening lengthwise; ovary composed of 3 or 4 *free* or *connate carpels*, in the latter case the ovary 1-locular with *parietal placentas*; styles free; ovules in each free carpel 2–4, on each placenta 6–8; fruit of separate dehiscent cocci or opening at the top; seeds with little endosperm, copious mealy perisperm and small embryo. B.H. **3,** 127 (under *Piperaceae*); E.P. **3,** 1, 1. N. Temperate and Subtropical; Indo-Malaya.

A. Upper leaves sometimes coloured but not forming an involucre below the inflorescence; leaves cordate: **B.** Carpels free—SAURURUS (Eastern U.S.A). **BB.** Carpels united—GYMNOTHECA (China). **AA.** Upper leaves forming an involucre of bracts; carpels united: **C.** Stamens 8–5; leaves oblong-elliptic, rounded or slightly cordate at the base—ANEMOPSIS (*Anemiopsis*) (N. Amer.). **CC.** Stamens 3; leaves ovate-cordate—HOUTTUYNIA (E. Asia).

266. CHLORANTHACEAE

Herbs, shrubs, or trees, mostly aromatic; leaves opposite, simple; *petioles more or less connate at the base*; stipules small; flowers spicate, paniculate, or capitate; calyx absent from the male flowers; stamens 1–3, connate into a mass; anthers 1–2-locular, opening lengthwise; female calyx adnate to the ovary, often minutely 3-dentate at the apex; ovary inferior, 1-locular; stigma sessile or on a short style; ovule solitary, orthotropous, pendulous; drupe small, ovoid or globose, exocarp more or less succulent, endocarp hardened; seed with copious fleshy endosperm and minute embryo. B.H. **3,** 133; E.P. **3,** 1, 12. Tropics and S. Temperate.

A. Flowers pseudo-bisexual, the males laterally adnate to the females, spicate; males with 1–3 stamens adnate to the base of the ovary; leaves often crowded into pseudo-whorls of 4—CHLORANTHUS (E. Asia). **AA.** Flowers unisexual; stamen 1; leaves opposite: **B.** Male and female flowers spicate; ovary

FIG. 266. Ascarina lanceolata *Hk. f.* (Chloranthaceae). A, male flower. B, stamen. C, fruit. D,
vertical section of ovary. (After Seemann.)

nude—ASCARINA (Polynesia, New Zeal.). **BB.** Male flowers spicate, female
flowers paniculate or capitate; ovary crowned by the minute 3-dentate calyx
—HEDYOSMUM (Trop. Amer.).

ORDER 59. RHOEADALES

Herbaceous to subwoody; flowers hypogynous to rarely subperigynous,
♀, actinomorphic to zygomorphic; petals present; stamens ∞ to few, free
or united in two bundles; syncarpous, with parietal placentation; seeds
with copious endosperm and minute embryo. Leaves alternate or rarely
subopposite, simple or much divided, exstipulate. Mainly N. Temperate
Regions.

A. Stamens numerous, free; flowers actinomorphic; petals free, neither
saccate nor spurred; fruit a capsule   *Papaveraceae*
AA. Stamens 4 or 6, sometimes united into bundles; flowers often zygomorphic; petals more or less connivent, the outer 2 often saccate or
spurred at the base; fruit a capsule or nut   *Fumariaceae*

267. PAPAVERACEAE

Annual to perennial herbs with coloured juice, rarely shrubs (*Dendromecon*)
or small trees (*Bocconia*); leaves alternate or the floral ones opposite or
whorled (*Platystemoneae*), often much divided; stipules 0; indumentum of
simple or barbellate hairs; flowers mostly solitary, showy, actinomorphic, ♀,
visited by insects for pollen; sepals 2–3, caducous or calyptrate; petals 4–6 or

8–12, free, biseriate, imbricate, often crumpled; nectaries 0; stamens numerous, free; anthers 2-locular, opening lengthwise; ovary superior, composed of 2 or more united carpels, 1-locular with parietal placentas, or several-locular by the intrusive placentas reaching the middle, rarely 2-locular by a spurious wall; carpels rarely loosely united and becoming free in fruit (*Platystemon*); stigmas opposite to or alternate with the placentas; ovules numerous,

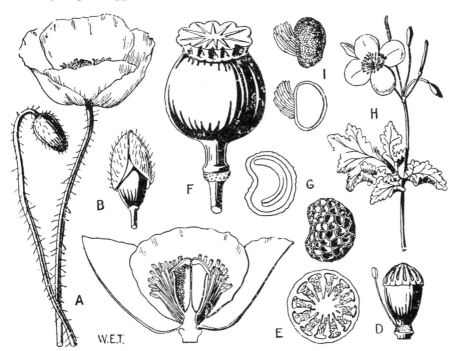

FIG. 267. Papaver rhoeas *L.* (Papaveraccae). A, flower. B, flower-bud showing caducous sepals. D, ovary with one stamen. E, ovary, cross-section. F, capsule. G, seed. H, Chelidonium majus *L.* I, seed of same. (After Le Maout & Decne.)

anatropous; fruit capsular, opening by valves or pores; seeds small, with a crested or smooth raphe or arillate; embryo minute in copious fleshy or oily endosperm. B.H. **1**, 49, partly; E.P. **3**, 2, 130. Mainly N. Temperate and Subtropics.—PLATYSTEMON, PAPAVER, ROMNEYA, ARGEMONE, MECONOPSIS, BOCCONIA, MACLEAYA, CHELIDONIUM, ESCHSCHOLTZIA, SANGUINARIA, &c.

USEFUL PRODUCTS: *Opium Poppy* (Papaver somniferum *L.*), Eastern countries; *Blood Root* or *Puccoon* (Sanguinaria canadensis *L.*), N. Amer. Many ornamental plants.

268. FUMARIACEAE

Herbaceous, with brittle stems and watery juice, sometimes scandent; leaves radical, alternate or rarely subopposite, usually much divided; flowers ☿, often *zygomorphic*; sepals 2, small, deciduous; petals 4, imbricate, more or less *connivent*, the two outer often saccate or spurred at the base, the two inner narrower and sometimes coherent to the apex; stamens 4, *free and opposite the petals*, or 6 and *united into two bundles*; ovary superior, 1-locular with two parietal placentas; style slender; ovules 1 to many, anatropous; fruit cap-

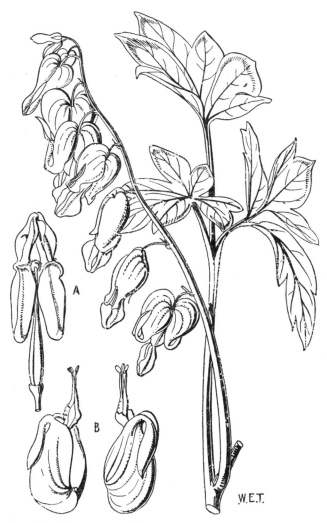

FIG. 268. Dicentra spectabilis (*L.*) *Lem.* (Fumariaceae). A, inner petals with ovary and style. B, outer petals with stamens in bundles of 3. (After *Bot. Mag.*)

sular or a nut, capsule sometimes transversely septate and breaking into 1-seeded indehiscent segments or dehiscing by valves; seeds shining, crested or nude; endosperm fleshy with minute embryo. B.H. **1,** 54; E.P. **3,** 2, 137 (under *Papaveraceae*). Mainly N. Temperate Zone.—FUMARIA, CORYDALIS, DICENTRA, HYPECOUM, &c.

USEFUL PRODUCTS: Several handsome garden plants.

Order 60. CRUCIALES

Herbs, rarely somewhat woody, with watery juice; sepals 4; petals 4; stamens 6, tetradynamous (4 longer and 2 shorter); ovary of 2 united carpels with 2 parietal placentas, often divided by a false septum; seeds without endosperm. Leaves mostly alternate; stipules absent.—Cosmopolitan, rarer in the Tropics.

269. Cruciferae

Annual or perennial herbs, rarely somewhat shrubby, with watery juice; indumentum of simple, *medifixed*, or *stellate hairs*, rarely glandular; leaves

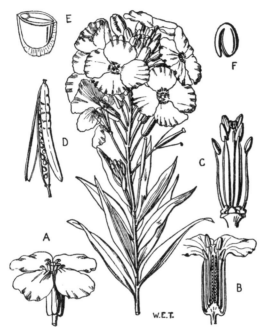

FIG. 269. Cheiranthus cheiri *L.* (Cruciferae). A, flower. B, flower cut vertically. C, stamens and ovary. D, fruit splitting from below. E, section of seed. F, embryo. (After Baill.)

alternate or rarely opposite; *stipules absent*; flowers ☿, mostly actinomorphic, usually racemose, rarely bracteate; sepals 4, free, imbricate in 2 series, rarely valvate; petals 4, rarely 0, mostly equal, often long-clawed, imbricate or contorted; glands mostly present on the torus, often opposite the sepals; stamens 6, *tetradynamous*, very rarely numerous or fewer, free or connate in pairs; anthers 2- (rarely 1-) locular, opening lengthwise; ovary sessile or rarely stipitate, usually of 2 united carpels, 1-locular with 1–2 *parietal placentas* and divided by a *spurious membranous septum*, or sometimes transversely several- or many-locular; stigmas 2 or connate; ovules usually many; fruit elongated (siliqua) or short (silicule), bivalved or indehiscent, rarely transversely jointed; seed without endosperm (very rarely a little endosperm present), *usually folded*; cotyledons accumbent, incumbent, or folded. B.H. **1,** 57; E.P. **3,** 2, 145. Cosmopolitan.—BRASSICA, CHEIRANTHUS, NASTURTIUM, BARBAREA, ARABIS, CARDAMINE, ANASTATICA, LUNARIA, AUBRIETA, ALYSSUM, DRABA, COCHLEARIA, SISYMBRIUM, DIPLOTAXIS, CAPSELLA, LEPIDIUM, AETHIONEMA, ISATIS, CRAMBE, CAKILE, RAPHANUS, &c.

USEFUL PRODUCTS: *Cabbage* (Brassica oleracea *L.*); *Common Turnip* (Brassica rapa *L.*); *Mustard* (Brassica alba *Boiss.*, and B. nigra *Koch*); *Horse Radish* (Armoracia lapathifolia *Gilibert*); *Radish* (Raphanus sativus *L.*); *Watercress* (Nasturtium officinale *Br.* and N. microphyllum *Reichb.*).—Many beautiful plants for the garden and rockery, including the *Wallflower* (Cheiranthus cheiri *L.*).); *Honesty* (Lunaria rediviva *L.*).

ORDER 61. RESEDALES

Characters of the single family below.

270. RESEDACEAE

Annual or perennial herbs with watery juice, rarely woody; leaves alternate. simple or pinnately divided; stipules small, *gland-like*; flowers mostly *zygo-*

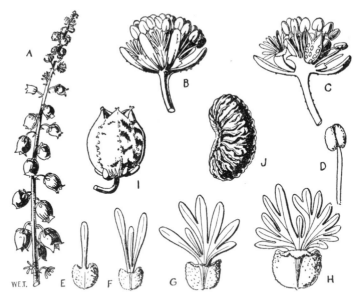

FIG. 270. Reseda arabica *Boiss.* (Resedaceae). A, inflorescence. B, flower. C, flower cut vertically. D, stamen. E, F, G, H, petals. I, capsule open at the apex. J, seed. (After Cosson.)

morphic, ♀, rarely ♂ ♀, racemose or spicate; calyx persistent, mostly zygomorphic, 4–7-lobed, imbricate; petals small and inconspicuous or 0, *valvate,* free or slightly coherent, *often laciniate*, sometimes with a scale at the base; disk present, often dilated on the adaxial side; stamens 3–40, perigynous or on the disk, not covered by the petals in bud; filaments free or united at base; anthers 2-locular, introrse; ovary of 2–6 free or connate carpels, closed or *gaping at the top*, each carpel with a *separate stigma*; ovules numerous on parietal placentas or at the base of the ovary; fruit a *gaping capsule* or baccate; seeds numerous, kidney-shaped or horse-shoe-shaped; no endosperm; embryo curved or folded; cotyledons incumbent. B.H. **1**, 110; E.P. **3**, 2. 237. Mainly Mediterranean.—RESEDA, OLIGOMERIS, &c.

USEFUL PRODUCTS: Fragrant garden plants; *Mignonette* (Reseda odorata *L.*).

ORDER 62. CARYOPHYLLALES

Herbaceous, becoming fleshy; flowers hypogynous to perigynous, ☿, actinomorphic; petals usually present; stamens mostly definite; syncarpous; axile to free-central placentation; seeds with copious endosperm and curved (rarely straight) embryo. Leaves mostly opposite or verticillate, stipulate or not.— Mainly Temperate Regions.

A. Sepals 3 or more; stamens if the same number opposite to the sepals, often twice as many:
  B. Stamens hypogynous:
    C. Placentation of ovules axile, the ovary completely 5–3-locular; superior:
      D. Capsule septicidally dehiscent; seeds without endosperm
           Elatinaceae
      DD. Capsule loculicidally dehiscent or by a transverse slit, rarely fruit indehiscent; seeds with endosperm   *Molluginaceae*
    CC. Placentation of ovules free-central, the ovary 1-locular or imperfectly more-locular, superior   *Caryophyllaceae*
  BB. Stamens perigynous; petals numerous or absent; ovary superior to inferior, 1–several-locular   *Ficoidaceae*
AA. Sepals 2; stamens as many as and opposite the petals, or more numerous; ovary superior to half-inferior, 1-locular with a free basal placenta falling short of the top of the ovary   *Portulacaceae*

271. ELATINACEAE

Herbs or low shrubs; leaves *opposite or verticillate*, simple; stipules present, paired; flowers small, actinomorphic, bisexual, axillary, solitary or cymose; sepals 3–5, free, imbricate; petals as many, hypogynous, imbricate, persistent; stamens from as many to twice as many as the petals, free, hypogynous; anthers 2-locular, opening by longitudinal slits; ovary superior, 3–5-locular; placentation axile; styles 3–5, free; ovules numerous; fruit a septicidal capsule; seeds without endosperm; embryo straight or curved, with short cotyledons. B.H. **1**, 162, E.P. **3**, 6, 277.—Cosmopolitan.

  A. Sepals free from each other or nearly so, with thickened midrib and thin margins; herbs or shrublets; capsule crustaceous; ovary ovoid, gradually

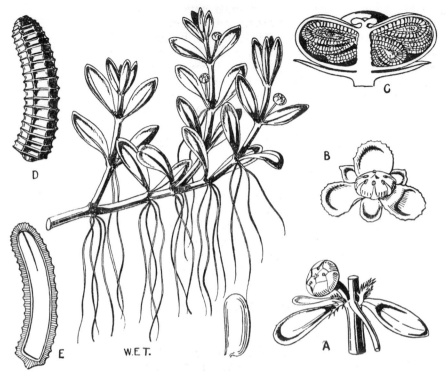

FIG. 271. Elatine hexandra (*Lapierre*) *DC*. (Elatinaceae). A, portion of stem with flower. B, flower opened. C, ovary (of E. hydropiper *L*.) in vertical section. D, seed (of E. triandra *Schkuhr*). E, seed cut lengthwise. (After Le Maout & Decne.)

narrowed into the styles—BERGIA (Tropics and Subtropics). **AA.** Sepals connate for $\frac{1}{4}$ to $\frac{1}{2}$ their length, membranous-herbaceous, without a midrib; aquatic or creeping herbs; capsule membranous; ovary depressed-globose, very abruptly narrowed into the styles—ELATINE (Tropics, Subtropics, and Temp. Reg.).

272. MOLLUGINACEAE

Herbs, sometimes with fleshy leaves; leaves opposite, subopposite, alternate, or subverticillate; stipules none or small and fugacious; flowers actinomorphic, bisexual, solitary or cymose, usually small and inconspicuous; sepals free or united at the base, imbricate, persistent; petals small or absent; stamens hypogynous or slightly perigynous, definite or indefinite; filaments free or variously connate at the base; anthers 2-locular, opening by longitudinal slits; disk absent or annular; ovary syncarpous (except *Gisekia*), usually several-locular; style or stigmas as many as the loculi; ovules curved or inverted; fruit dry, dehiscing loculicidally or by a transverse slit, rarely indehiscent, usually surrounded by the persistent calyx; seeds with endosperm, the embryo curved or around the periphery. B.H. **1,** 856 (under *Ficoidaceae*); E.P. **3,** 1*b*, 33

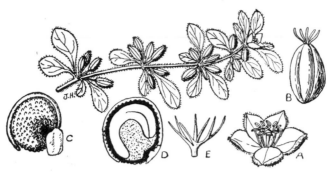

FIG. 272. Glinus lotoides *Loefl.* (Molluginaceae). A, flower. B, ovary.
C, seed. D, seed cut vertically. E, hair. (Partly original.)

(under *Aizoaceae*). Mainly Tropics and Subtropics.—MOLLUGO, PHARNA-
CEUM, ADENOGRAMMA, GISEKIA, LIMEUM, &c. Mostly weedy plants of dry
places.

273. CARYOPHYLLACEAE

Herbs, annual or perennial; leaves *opposite*, simple, *entire*, often connected
at the base by a *transverse line*;
stipules absent or if present
often scarious; flowers actinomorphic, mostly bisexual, solitary or in cymes; sepals free
or united into a tube, imbricate,
often with membranous margins; petals as many as the
sepals, often small or absent;
stamens up to 10, free from
one another; anthers 2-locular,
dehiscing longitudinally; ovary
superior, sessile or shortly stipitate, 1-locular or imperfectly
divided at the base, with *free-
central placentation*; styles free
or variously connate; ovules
mostly numerous; fruit a dry
capsule, usually opening by
valves or apical teeth; seeds
with endosperm and a more or
less *curved peripheral or excentric embryo*; funicle sometimes
conspicuous. B.H. **1**, 141; E.P. **3**,
1*b*, 61. Mainly N. Temperate and
Cold Regions.—DIANTHUS, TU-
NICA, GYPSOPHILA, SAPONARIA,

FIG. 273. Dianthus seguieri *Vill.* (Caryophyllaceae).
A, petal. B, ovary with styles. C, cross-section of ovary.
D, fruit dehisced.

SILENE, LYCHNIS, CERASTIUM, STELLARIA, ARENARIA, SAGINA, DRYMARIA, POLYCARPAEA, &c.

USEFUL PRODUCTS: Many beautiful garden plants, *Pinks*, *Sweet William* (Dianthus barbatus *L.*); *Gypsophila* (G. elegans *Bieb.*), Asia Minor, &c.

274. FICOIDACEAE

(Aizoaceae)

Herbs or low shrubs, erect or prostrate, often *fleshy*; leaves alternate or opposite, sometimes minute, stipulate or not; flowers usually bisexual, actino-

FIG. 274. Gasoul crystallinum (*L.*) *Rothm.* (Ficoidaceae). A, fruit.

morphic; calyx-tube free or adnate to the ovary; lobes 5–8, imbricate, or rarely valvate, herbaceous; petals numerous or absent, 1- or more-seriate, inserted in the calyx-tube, linear; stamens perigynous, many in several series or few, rarely 1, free or united at the base into bundles; anthers 2-locular, small, opening lengthwise; ovary superior or inferior, 1-several-locular; ovules solitary to many, basal, apical or axile; fruit a capsule or nut-like and drupaceous, often clasped by the persistent calyx. B.H. **1,** 851, partly; E.P. **3,** 1*b*, 33 (as *Aizoaceae*). Mainly S. African and Mediterranean; a few in Australia, West Indies, and S. America; often on sandy seashores or desert places.—MESEMBRYANTHEMUM, TETRAGONIA, AIZOON, GALENIA, GUNNIA, SESUVIUM, TRIANTHEMA, CYPSELEA, &c.

USEFUL PRODUCTS: Numerous species of *Mesembryanthemum* and many genera now separated from it are suitable for cool greenhouses; a few naturalized on the southwest coast of Britain.

275. PORTULACACEAE

Herbs or undershrubs, often succulent; leaves alternate or opposite, with scarious or setose stipular appendages; flowers actinomorphic, bisexual, solitary or variously cymose or racemose; sepals 2, imbricate, free or united at the base; petals 4–6, imbricate, free or connate at the base, soon falling; stamens as many as and opposite the petals or more numerous, free; anthers 2-locular; ovary superior or half inferior, 1-locular with basal placenta; ovules 1 to many; style usually variously divided; fruit a capsule dehiscing

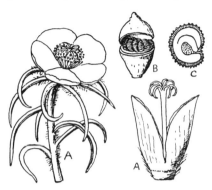

FIG. 275. A, Portulaca grandiflora *L.* B, C,
Portulaca oleracea *L.* (Portulacaceae). (Orig.)

by valves or by a transverse split (circumscissile), rarely a nut and indehiscent; seeds globose-reniform; embryo surrounding the copious mealy endosperm. B.H. **1**, 155; E.P. 3, 1*b*, 51. Mainly America.—PORTULACA, ANACAMPSEROS, PORTULACARIA, CERARIA, TALINUM, CALYPTROTHECA, CALANDRINIA, CLAYTONIA, LEWISIA, &c. Some ornamental garden plants.

ORDER 63. POLYGONALES

Herbaccous, &c., as in *Caryophyllales*, but without petals; ovary 1-locular, 1–2-ovuled; seeds with straight or curved embryo in copious endosperm. Leaves alternate or opposite; stipules mostly present, often intrapetiolar or sheathing and membranous or scarious.

A. Stipules forming a tube (ochrea) around the stem; fruit a trigonous or 2-sided nut; leaves alternate or very rarely opposite *Polygonaceae*
AA. Stipules not forming a tube around the stem, often scarious and bilobed or more divided; leaves opposite *Illecebraceae*

276. POLYGONACEAE

Herbs, shrubs, or climbers, rarely trees; leaves alternate or rarely opposite, the base of the petiole often dilated into a *membranous sheath* (ochrea); flowers ☿ or ♂ ♀, actinomorphic, small; sepals 3–6, imbricate, often enlarged and becoming membranous in fruit; petals absent; stamens usually 6–9, rarely more; filaments free or united at the base; anthers 2-locular, opening lengthwise; disk annular or central; ovary superior, sessile, 1-locular; styles 2–4, usually free; ovule *solitary, basal,* sessile or stalked; fruit a trigonous

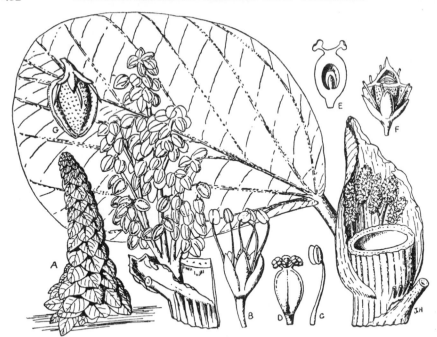

Fig. 276. Rheum nobile *Hk. f.* (Polygonaceae). A, plant showing habit. B, flower. C, stamen. D, ovary. E, ovary cut vertically. F, cross-section of fruit. G, fruit. (After Hook.)

or 2-sided nut; seeds with abundant mealy endosperm and often excentric embryo. B.H. **3,** 88; E.P. **3,** 1*a*, 1. Cosmopolitan.—ERIOGONUM, CHORIZANTHE, CALLIGONUM, ATRAPHAXIS, OXYGONUM, POLYGONUM, RHEUM, RUMEX, MUEHLENBECKIA, COCCOLOBA, TRIPLARIS, RUPRECHTIA, HARPAGOCARPUS, &c.

USEFUL PRODUCTS: *Rhubarb* (Rheum rhaponticum *L.*); *Buckwheat* (Fagopyrum sagittatum *Gilibert*).

277. ILLECEBRACEAE

Herbs, rarely subshrubs; leaves mostly *opposite*, small, simple, often connate at the base, mostly entire; *stipules scarious*, simple or connate, rarely 0; flowers small, green or white, often with *scarious bracts*, mostly ⚲, actinomorphic; calyx herbaceous or leathery, persistent, 4–5-lobed or parted, lobes imbricate; petals 0 or sometimes replaced by small staminodes; stamens the same number as and opposite the calyx-lobes, rarely fewer or more, mostly perigynous; filaments free or connate at the base into a ring; anthers 2-locular, opening lengthwise; ovary free, sessile, 1-locular; style 1, terminal, or styles 2–3; ovule 1, rarely 2, erect or pendulous from a basal funicle; fruit a utricle or nut, mostly indehiscent, 1-seeded, enclosed by the calyx; seed with copious or scanty endosperm; embryo annular to straight. B.H. **3,** 12; E.P. **3,** 1*b*, 91 (under *Caryophyllaceae*). Dry arid regions mainly.—ILLECEBRUM, PARONYCHIA, HERNIARIA, SCLERANTHUS, &c.

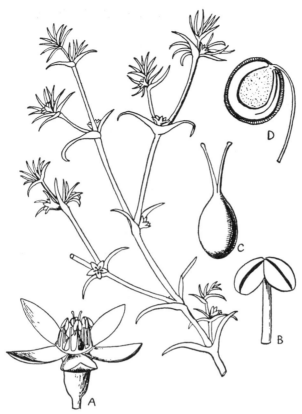

FIG. 277. Scleranthus annuus *L.* (Illecebraceae). A, flower.
B, stamen. C, ovary. D, seed cut lengthwise. (Orig.)

USEFUL PRODUCTS: *Thé Arabe* or *Algerian tea* (flowers of Paronychia
argentea *Lam.* and P. capitata *Lam.*); *Sergena root* (Corrigiola littoralis *L.*).

ORDER 64. CHENOPODIALES

More or less as in *Polygonales* but stipules absent or very small; carpels
numerous to solitary, free or connate; seeds with curved embryo around the
endosperm, rarely the embryo straight. Leaves alternate or opposite. Mostly
dry regions.

A. Anthers opening by slits lengthwise:
 B. Fruits free from each other and not united together into a fleshy mass;
    petals absent:
   C. Ovary 2- or more-locular:
    D. Ovary superior:
     E. Ovary-carpels not connate around a central column:
      F. Fruit a capsule   *Barbeuiaceae*
      FF. Fruit indehiscent, fleshy or drupe-like   *Phytolaccaceae*

EE. Ovary-carpels connate around a central column often dilated into a flat disk-like top; fruit dehiscent   *Gyrostemonaceae*

DD. Ovary half-inferior; fruit indehiscent, winged by the persistent dry calyx-segments   *Agdestidaceae*

CC. Ovary 1-locular:

  G. Calyx 3–5-lobed or partite:

    H. Stipules often present though sometimes modified; stamens if the same number as the segments then alternate with them   *Petiveriaceae*

    HH. Stipules absent; stamens usually the same number as the calyx-segments and opposite to them:

      J. Filaments usually free and staminodes very rare   *Chenopodiaceae*

      JJ. Filaments united at the base and often with staminodes between   *Amaranthaceae*

  GG. Male calyx 2-partite; segments valvate; stamens up to 20, no staminodes; style becoming basal   *Cynocrambaceae*

BB. Fruits united together into a fleshy mass; petals present, clawed, claws united at the base; seed with straight embryo and no endosperm   *Batidaceae*

AA. Anthers opening by terminal pores or short pore-like slits; endosperm copious, surrounded by the spirally twisted embryo   *Basellaceae*

278. Barbeuiaceae

Trees; leaves alternate, petiolate, ovate, entire, petiole *articulated at the base*; *stipules absent*; flowers bisexual, in short rigid axillary racemes; bracts subulate; pedicels long and slender, thickened below the calyx; sepals 5, orbicular,

Fig. 278. Barbeuia madagascariensis *Baill.* (Barbeuiaceae). A, flower. B, side view of ovary showing insertion of one ovule and stamen. C, vertical section of ovary. D, cross-section of ovary. E, fruit. F, vertical section of seed. (Partly after Baill.)

concave, spreading in fruit but not enlarged; *petals absent*; stamens *numerous, in several series*, inserted on an *annular disk*; filaments short; anthers linear, *sagittate*, introrsely dehiscent; ovary superior, depressed-globose, 2-locular; stigmas 2, linear-oblong, thick, erect-spreading, very shortly connate at the base; ovule solitary in each loculus, basal, campylotropous; fruit capsular, 2-locular, 2-seeded; seeds partially enclosed by a *fleshy aril*, reniform; testa smooth; embryo *annular*, surrounding the mealy endosperm; cotyledons oblong, unequal. B.H. **3**, 85 (in *Phytolaccaceae*); Walter, Engl. *Pflanzenr. Phytolaccac.* 63, fig. 19. Madagascar.—BARBEUIA.

279. PHYTOLACCACEAE

Herbs, shrubs, or rarely trees, erect or scandent; leaves alternate, entire, pinnately nerved; *stipules absent*; flowers small, bisexual or rarely dioecious, in

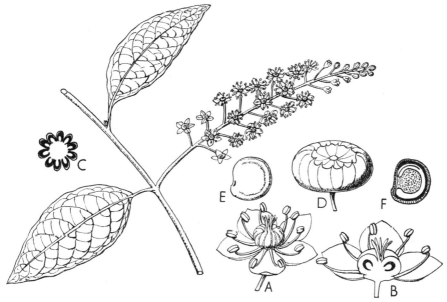

FIG. 279. Phytolacca americana *L.* (Phytolaccaceae). A, flower. B, vertical section of flower. C, transverse section of ovary. D, fruit. E, seed. F, vertical section of seed. (Partly after Baill.)

terminal, *leaf-opposed*, or *axillary* spikes or racemes; bracts and bracteoles present, small; calyx green or somewhat coloured, 10–4-partite, segments equal or unequal; *petals absent*; stamens 30–5, inserted on a *fleshy disk*; filaments free or connate at the base; anthers 2-locular, *introrse*, dorsifixed, opening lengthwise; ovary globose, composed of 12–4 *free or more or less connate carpels*; stigmas as many as carpels, free or connate at the base; ovule 1 in each carpel, *basal*, campylotropous; fruit of as many carpels, free or connate, *fleshy* or *drupe-like*; seed more or less reniform, without an arillus; embryo *annular*, surrounding the copious mealy endosperm; cotyledons half-terete or narrow and flat. B.H. **3**, 78 (in part); E.P. **3**, 1*b*, 1 (in part). Tropics and Subtropics, mainly S. America.

A. Inflorescence terminal, racemose or spicate; herbs with turnip-like rootstocks, or shrublets; calyx-segments unequal—ANISOMERIA (Chile). **AA.** Inflorescence axillary, shortly spicate; shrubs; calyx-segments equal—ERCILLA (Chile, Peru). **AAA.** Inflorescence leaf-opposed or rarely also subterminal, racemose; herbs, shrubs, or rarely trees, sometimes scandent; calyx-segments equal—PHYTOLACCA (Tropics and Subtropics).

280. GYROSTEMONACEAE

Trees, shrubs, or undershrubs; leaves alternate, undivided, entire, more or less succulent; stipules very small or absent; flowers small, *unisexual*, dioecious

FIG. 280. Codonocarpus cotinifolius (*Desf.*) *F. Muell.* (Gyrostemonaceae). A, male flowering shoot. B, male flower from above. C, the same from below. D, female flowering shoot. E, female flower from above. F, fruit. G, fruiting carpel. H, seed. J, section of seed. (Orig.)

or monoecious, axillary and solitary or racemose or spicate; bracteoles present; calyx more or less lobed or truncate, persistent in fruit; *petals absent*; stamens 6 or more, in one or more series around or on a *flat central disk-like axis*; anthers oblong, nearly sessile, 2-locular, opening by slits lengthwise; ovary superior, of 2 or more carpels connate around a *central column often dilated into a flat disk at the top*; styles *free* or nearly so around the top of the column; ovules solitary in each carpel, attached to the inner angle; fruiting carpels dry, dehiscent, usually becoming free and separating from the axis, or rarely completely syncarpous and indehiscent; seeds with a crustaceous testa and a small *membranous basal aril*; embryo curved *around the central fleshy endosperm*. B.H. **3**, 86 (in *Phytolaccaceae*); E.P. edn. 2, **16c**, 165.—Australia and Tasmania.

A small but very distinct, highly advanced family formerly included in the *Phytolaccaceae*; confined to Australia and Tasmania. The flowers are unisexual and mostly dioecious, the males of most of the genera being scarcely distinguishable from each other except by slight differences in the inflorescence. A very distinctive feature is the large flat disk-like top of the floral axis surrounded by the often numerous, whorled, subsessile anthers and carpels.

A. Calyx sinuately toothed or truncate; carpels more than 2: **B.** Flowers axillary; carpels separating when mature and opening by the outer edge or both outer and inner edges—GYROSTEMON (Austral.). **BB.** Flowers in spikes or racemes; carpels separating when mature and opening by the inner edge only—CODONOCARPUS (Austral.). **BBB.** Flowers in spikes or the females solitary and axillary; carpels connate into a globular almost woody indehiscent fruit—TERSONIA (W. Austral.). **AA.** Calyx more or less deeply 4–2-lobed; flowers axillary; carpels 2–1: **C.** Ovary of 2 carpels; fruit dehiscent— DIDYMOTHECA (Austral., Tasm.). **CC.** Ovary of 1 carpel; fruit indehiscent —CYPSELOCARPUS (SW. Austral.).

281. AGDESTIDACEAE

Twining herb with large *turnip-like rootstock*; leaves alternate, rounded-cordate, apiculate, entire; petioles twisted near the base; *stipules absent*;

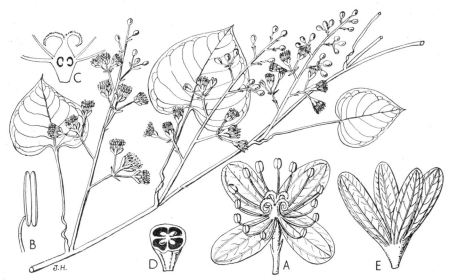

FIG. 281. Agdestis clematidea *Moc. & Sesse* (Agdestidaceae). A, flower. B, anther. C, vertical section of ovary. D, cross-section of ovary. E, calyx in fruit. (Orig.)

flowers bisexual, in loose axillary panicles of cymules; pedicels bracteate and bracteolate; calyx *half-superior*, 5–4-partite, segments oblong, spreading stellately and reticulate-veiny in fruit; *petals absent*; stamens 20–15, inserted in more than one series on a thin perigynous disk at the base of the segments; filaments filiform; anthers dorsifixed, oblong, 2-fid at each end, opening at the sides by slits lengthwise; ovary *half-inferior*, turbinate, 4–3-locular; style short and conical, with 4–3 recurved stigmas; ovules solitary in each loculus, basal-axile, half anatropous; fruit inferior, turbinate, *winged by the persistent dry reticulate calyx-segments,* by abortion 1-locular and 1-seeded, the coriaceous pericarp adherent to the seed; seed globose; no aril; embryo *annular around thin mealy endosperm*; cotyledons broadly oblong. Central America and Tropical S. America.—AGDESTIS.

Originally placed by De Candolle in the *Menispermaceae* and later assigned to *Phytolaccaceae*; considered here to be more closely related to *Basellaceae*.

282. PETIVERIACEAE

Shrubs, often climbing, or herbs, sometimes annuals; leaves alternate, entire or rarely obscurely crenate; stipules small or absent, rarely tuberculate or represented by *decurved prickles*; flowers bisexual or rarely unisexual, in racemes, panicles, or spikes, usually small; bracts and bracteoles present; calyx 5–4-partite, segments sometimes enlarged in fruit or *petaloid*; *petals absent*; stamens 25–4, when the same number as the calyx-segments then *alternate with them*; filaments free or slightly connate at the base; anthers dorsifixed, 2-locular, often deeply bifid at one or each end, opening lengthwise by slits; hypogynous disk present or absent; ovary superior, *1-locular with 1 basal ovule*; stigmas 5–1, often subsessile, sometimes *plumose* or *papillous*; fruit *indehiscent*, often *samaroid*, pericarp mostly adherent to the seed; seed 1, erect; embryo *annular, surrounding the usually copious endosperm*, or straight; cotyledons equal or one larger and folded over the other. Mostly S. Hemisphere.

A. Fruits not winged (sometimes bristly); stamens few or rarely numerous: B. Flowers bisexual: C. Calyx-segments all free, not oblique: D. Fruit dry: E. Stamens 12 or more; fruit ovoid or globose: F. Stamens irregularly placed —SCHINDLERIA (S. Amer.). FF. Stamens 8, 4 opposite the calyx-segments— LEDENBERGIA (Trop. S. Amer.). EE. Stamens 8–4; fruit elongated, hooked at the apex—PETIVERIA (Fig. 282) (Trop. Amer.). EEE. Stamens 9–4; fruit not elongated, more or less ribbed or glochidiate: G. Anthers didymous, broader than long; fruits tuberculate or shortly glochidiate—MICROTEA (Trop. Amer.). GG. Anthers oblong, longer than broad; fruits smooth or ribbed—LOPHIOCARPUS (S. Afr.). DD. Fruit succulent and berry-like: H. Stamens 8 or more— TRICHOSTIGMA (Trop. Amer.). HH. Stamens 4—RIVINA (Trop. and Subtrop. Amer.). CC. Calyx-segments oblique, the posticous free, the other 3 partly connate—HILLERIA (S. Amer.). BB. Flowers unisexual, in very slender spike-like racemes; fruits covered with hooked prickles, indehiscent—MONOCOCCUS (E. Austral., New Caled.). AA. Fruits winged (like those of *Acer* and *Securidaca*); stamens numerous; flowers bisexual, paniculate: J. Calyx 4-partite, segments erect in fruit and becoming ribbed—GALLESIA (S. Amer.). JJ. Calyx 5-partite, segments reflexed in fruit, more or less membranous— SEGUIERIA (Trop. Amer., West Indies).

283. CHENOPODIACEAE

Annual or perennial herbs or shrubs, often glaucous; stems sometimes jointed; *leaves alternate* or rarely opposite, simple; stipules absent; flowers small or minute, often green, ♀ or ♂♀, mostly actinomorphic, often bracteate; calyx 3–5-lobed, rarely absent (in the ♀ flowers), often accrescent in fruit; lobes imbricate or subvalvate; petals absent; stamens often the same number

Fig. 282. Petiveria alliacea *L.* (Petiveriaceae). A, flower-bud with bract and bracteole. B, section of same. C, bract and bracteole. D, calyx-lobe. E, stamens,
F, cross-section of ovary. G, fruit. (Orig.)

as the calyx-lobes and opposite to them, hypogynous or inserted on a disk or on the calyx; staminodes rare; filaments usually free; anthers 2-locular, incurved in bud, opening lengthwise; disk present or absent; ovary superior or immersed in the base of the calyx, 1-locular; style terminal, solitary or 2–3; *ovule solitary*, erect or suspended from a basal funicle; fruit a nut, indehiscent, rarely circumscissile; seed often erect; endosperm present or absent; *embryo peripheral, surrounding the endosperm.* B.H. **3**, 43; E.P. **3**, 1*a*, 36. Cosmopolitan.—RHAGODIA, CHENOPODIUM, BETA, ATRIPLEX, CORISPERMUM, CHENO-

FIG. 283. Chenopodium rubrum *L.* (Chenopodiaceae). A, male flower. B, stamen. C, bisexual flower. D, flower showing ovary. E, section of seed. (Orig.)

LEA, KOCHIA, ARTHROCNEMUM, SALICORNIA, SUAEDA, CORNULACA, SALSOLA, ANABASIS, HALOPHYTUM, DYSPHANIA, &c.

USEFUL PRODUCTS: *Spinach* (Spinacia oleracea *L.*); *Beet-root* (Beta vulgaris *L.*).

284. AMARANTHACEAE

Annual or perennial herbs, rarely undershrubs or climbers; leaves alternate or opposite, simple, *exstipulate*; flowers actinomorphic, usually bisexual, small, in spikes, heads, or racemes with often *scarious* bracts and bracteoles, the latter sometimes hooked; sepals 3–5, free or nearly so, imbricate, more or less *dry* and membranous; petals absent; stamens mostly 5, *opposite the sepals*, hypogynous; filaments united at the base *into a short tube*, often with staminodes between; anthers 1- or 2-locular, opening by longitudinal slits; ovary superior, 1-locular; style short or long; stigma capitate or 2–3-fid; ovules solitary or rarely several, on a basal funicle; fruit dehiscing by a lid, or indehiscent; seeds globose, compressed or ellipsoidal, smooth; embryo annular, surrounding the copious endosperm. B.H. **3**, 20; E.P. **3**, 1*a*, 91. Widely dispersed.—CELOSIA, AMARANTHUS, SERICOCOMA, CYATHULA, PUPALIA,

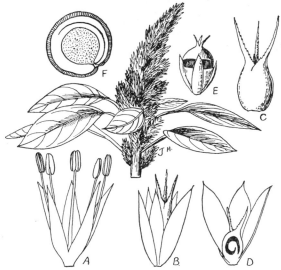

FIG. 284. Amaranthus retroflexus *L.* (Amaranthaceae). A,
male flower. B, female flower. C, ovary. D, vertical section
of female flower. E, fruit. F, section of seed. (Orig.)

PTILOTUS, TRICHINIUM, AERVA, ACHYRANTHES, PFAFFIA, TELANTHERA, ALTER-
NANTHERA, GOMPHRENA, HEBANTHE, IRESINE, &c.

SOME ORNAMENTAL PLANTS: *Cockscomb* (Celosia cristata *L.*), Asia.

285. CYNOCRAMBACEAE

Fleshy annual herb; lower leaves opposite, upper alternate, succulent; *stipules
uniting the base of the petioles*; flowers *monoecious*, in small sessile cymes

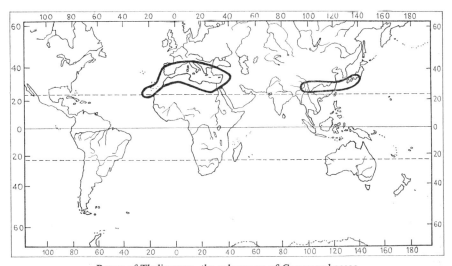

Range of Theligonum, the sole genus of Cynocrambaceae.

opposite the upper leaves, abortive in the lower opposite leaves; petals absent; male flowers 2–3 together, subsessile, female 1–3 from the same or different nodes, shortly pedicellate; male calyx closed in bud, at length valvate, 2-partite, segments spreading, 5-nerved; stamens up to about 20 in the centre; filaments

FIG. 285. Theligonum prostratum *Gaertn.* (Cynocrambaceae). A, male flower. B, female flower. C, fruit. D, vertical section of fruit. E, section of seed. (Orig.)

free, slender; anthers erect in bud, linear, opening lengthwise; female flower with a very oblique tubular calyx enclosing the ovary at the base and becoming lateral by the enlargement of the latter, slightly 3-lobulate; style simple, *becoming basal* by the lateral enlargement of the ovary; ovule solitary, erect from the base; fruit a subglobose nut included in the thin membranous calyx; seed sessile, erect; endosperm fleshy. B.H. **3**, 395 (under *Urticaceae*); E.P. **3**, 1*a*, 121. Atlantic Islands, Mediterranean, China, and Japan.—THELIGONUM (*Cynocrambe*).

286. BATIDACEAE

Littoral straggling plants; leaves *opposite*, simple, fleshy; stipules 0; flowers dioecious, densely spicate; spikes bracteate and cone-like; ♂ flowers subtended by closely imbricate bracts; calyx membranous, campanulate, *2-lipped*; petals 4, clawed, claws united at the base; stamens 4, alternate with the petals; filaments free; anthers 2-locular, opening lengthwise; ovary rudimentary or 0; female flowers united into a fleshy spike; bracts smaller than

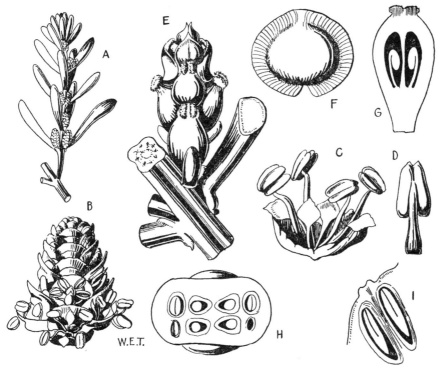

FIG. 286. Batis maritima *L*. (Batidaceae). A, male branch. B, male inflorescence. C, male flower. D, stamen. E, female inflorescence. F, seed. G, vertical section of ovary. H, cross-section of same. I, section of fruit. (After Martius.)

in the male; calyx and petals absent; ovaries 8–12, coherent, 4-locular; stigma capitate, sessile; ovules solitary, erect, anatropous; fruits united and forming a fleshy ovoid mass; seed oblong, straight, without endosperm; embryo straight. B.H. **3**, 88; E.P. **3**, 1*a*, 118. Tropical America and Pacific islands.—BATIS.

287. BASELLACEAE

Twiners with slender stems and rather fleshy, alternate, entire, petiolate leaves; stipules absent; flowers bisexual, actinomorphic, in spikes, racemes, or panicles; bracts small; bracteoles 2, often united to the base of the calyx, sometimes wing-like; sepals 5, often coloured, almost free or united into a 5-lobed tube, imbricate, persistent in fruit; petals absent; stamens 5, inserted opposite to and at the base of the sepals; filaments free, short; anthers versatile and reversed in bud with 2 parallel loculi opening by apical pores or pore-like slits or lengthwise; ovary superior, 1-locular, with a solitary basal shortly stalked campylotropous ovule; style terminal, often deeply divided into 3 stigmas; fruit indehiscent, surrounded by the *persistent, often fleshy, calyx* or winged bracteoles; seed solitary, almost spherical, with a membranous testa; endosperm usually copious, surrounded by the *spirally twisted or semi-annular embryo*. B.H. **3**, 76 (under *Chenopodiaceae*); E.P. **3**, 1*a*, 124. Tropics.

A. Filaments straight in bud; embryo spiral; endosperm absent or very thin: **B.** Flowers sessile on the axis of the inflorescence; sepals erect, obtuse; stigmas 3—BASELLA (Trop. Asia). **BB.** Flowers pedicellate on the axis; sepals spreading: **C.** Stigmas 3; sepals obtuse—TOURNONIA (Trop. S. Amer.). **CC.** Style short, with a single undivided stigma; sepals caudate-acuminate—

FIG. 287. Ullucus tuberosus *Caldas* (Basellaceae). A, flowers. B, anthers showing dehiscence. C, ovary. D, fruit. (After *Bot. Mag.*)

ULLUCUS (S. Amer.). **AA.** Filaments recurved in bud; embryo semi-annular; endosperm mealy: **D.** Floral bracteoles oblong, obtuse, shorter than the perianth—BOUSSINGAULTIA (Trop. Amer.). **DD.** Floral bracteoles boat-shaped, broadly winged—ANREDERA (Texas to Peru).

ORDER 65. LYTHRALES

Herbaceous to woody, reduced forms often aquatic; flowers perigynous to epigynous, ⚥, actinomorphic; calyx tubular, lobes valvate, rarely calyx absent; petals usually present, often clawed; stamens as many or twice as many as the petals, sometimes in two distinct whorls; placentation axile; seeds usually with no endosperm. Leaves simple, usually opposite and without stipules.

A. Calyx (sometimes much reduced) and petals present, rarely the latter absent:

  B. Ovary superior; leaves opposite or verticillate, very rarely alternate; sepals united into a tube, often with appendages between the lobes; petals when present often crumpled in bud; filaments usually inflexed in bud   *Lythraceae*

  BB. Ovary inferior to semi-inferior; leaves alternate or opposite; calyx-lobes 4–5, valvate; petals contorted or imbricate, rarely absent; style 1; ovules usually numerous, axile:

  C. Cotyledons equal   *Onagraceae*

  CC. Cotyledons very unequal   *Trapaceae*

  BBB. Ovary inferior; styles 1–4; ovules as many as styles, pendulous; leaves alternate or verticillate, sometimes huge, submerged ones often much divided   *Halorrhagaceae*

AA. Calyx and petals absent; flowers minute, unisexual, male with 1 stamen subtended by 2 bracts, female composed of a 4-lobed 4-locular ovary with 2 elongated free styles; ovule 1, pendulous in each loculus

                                                                 Callitrichaceae

288. LYTHRACEAE

FIG. 288. Nesaea erecta *Guill. & Perr.* (Lythraceae). A, flower. B, calyx cut open. C, stamen. D, seed. E, ovary. (After Guill. & Perr.)

Herbs or rarely shrubby; leaves *opposite or verticillate*, rarely alternate; stipules *absent* or very small; flowers usually actinomorphic, ☿, solitary to paniculate; sepals *united into a tube*, *valvate*, often with *appendages* between the lobes; petals present or absent, inserted towards the top of the calyx-tube, *crumpled* in bud; stamens usually 4 or 8, rarely more, inserted below the petals; filaments *variable in length,* usually *inflexed* in bud; anthers 2-locular, opening lengthwise; ovary superior, sessile or shortly stipitate, completely or incompletely 2–6-locular (rarely 1-locular); style simple, variable in length; ovules numerous on an axile placenta sometimes not reaching the top of the ovary; fruit usually capsular, opening by a transverse slit, by valves, or irregularly; seeds numerous, without endosperm; embryo straight. B.H. **1**, 773; E.P. **3**, 7, 1. Widely spread. AMMANNIA, PEPLIS, CUPHEA, LYTHRUM, NESAEA, &c.

289. ONAGRACEAE

(Oenotheraceae)

Herbs or rarely shrubs, often aquatic; leaves simple, opposite or alternate; stipules mostly absent or deciduous; flowers ⚥, actinomorphic, often solitary;

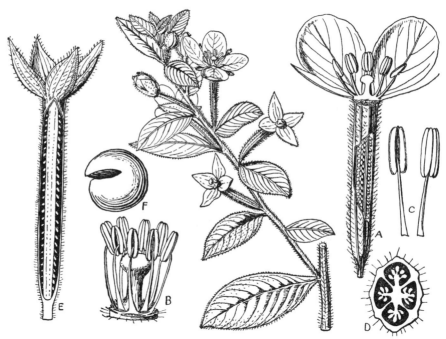

FIG. 289. Jussiaea suffruticosa *L.* (Onagraceae). A, flower dissected to show parts. B, stamens and ovary. C, stamens. D, cross-section of ovary. E, fruit. F, seed. (After Baill.)

calyx adnate to the ovary; lobes 4–5, *valvate*; petals 4–5, free, contorted or imbricate, rarely absent; stamens as many or twice as many as the calyx-lobes; anthers 2-locular, opening lengthwise; ovary inferior or rarely semi-superior, 2–6-locular, rarely incompletely locular; ovules 1 to many, on axile placentas; style simple; fruit a capsule, berry, or nut; seeds numerous or rarely solitary, without endosperm; embryo straight or nearly so. B.H. **1**, 785; E.P. **3**, 7, 199. Temperate and Subtropics.—EPILOBIUM, JUSSIAEA, LUDWIGIA, CLARKIA, OENOTHERA, FUCHSIA, LOPEZIA, GAURA, CIRCAEA, &c.

USEFUL PRODUCTS: Ornamental plants, 'Clarkias', 'Fuchsias'. *Evening Primrose* (Oenothera), &c.

290. TRAPACEAE

(Hydrocaryaceae)

Floating herbs; *leaves of two kinds*, the submerged opposite, pinnatisect, resembling roots, the emerged in a rosette, petiolate, rhomboid, dentate, with a spongy inflated petiole; no stipules; flowers axillary, *solitary*, shortly stalked;

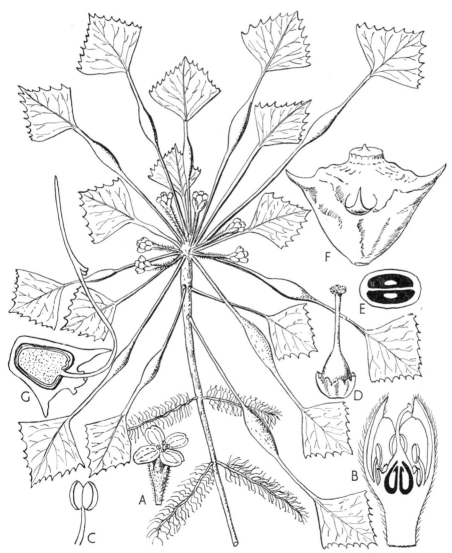

FIG. 290. Trapa bispinosa *Roxb.* (Trapaceae). A, flower. B, vertical section of flower. C, stamen. D, disk and pistil. E, transverse section of ovary. F, fruit. G, vertical section of germinating seed. (Orig.)

calyx-tube short, surrounding the base of the ovary and *semi-superior*; limb 4-partite, segments *valvate*, persistent, sometimes spinescent; petals 4, inserted at the base of an undulate *epigynous disk*, free, sessile; stamens 4, inserted with the petals; filaments subulate; anthers oblong, 2-locular, dehiscing lengthwise; ovary *semi-inferior*, 2-locular, conical above the calyx; style subulate-filiform, persistent, stigma capitate; ovule 1 in each loculus, pendulous from the septum; fruit turbinate, coriaceous or somewhat bony, surrounded by the tumid calyx-limb or with *2–4 spines*, becoming 1-locular, 1-seeded; seed without endosperm but with very *unequal cotyledons*, one large, the other scale-like; embryo with the radicle on germination *perforating the top of the fruit*. Central and S. Europe, Tropical and Subtropical Africa and Asia.— TRAPA.

USEFUL PRODUCT: *Singhara flour* (fruits of Trapa bispinosa *Roxb.*) a valuable food in NW. India.

291. HALORRHAGACEAE

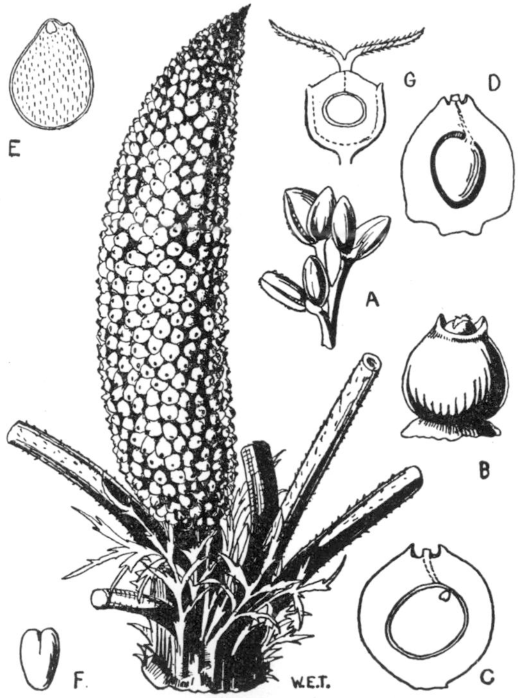

FIG. 291. Gunnera tinctoria (*Molina*) *Mirb.* (Halorrhagaceae). A, male flowers. B, single female flower. C, section of fruit. D, section of ovary. E, section of seed. F, embryo. G, section of ovary. (After Le Maout & Decne.)

Herbs or undershrubs, often aquatic; leaves alternate, opposite, or verticillate, sometimes very large, the submersed ones often much divided; *stipules absent*; flowers ♀ or ♂♀, solitary to paniculate or corymbose, often very small; calyx-tube *adnate* to the ovary; lobes 2–4 or absent; petals 2–4 or absent, *valvate* or slightly imbricate; stamens 2–8, rarely 1, large; anthers basifixed, 2-locular, opening lengthwise; ovary *inferior*, 1–4-locular; styles 1–4; ovules as many as the styles, pendulous from the apex of the loculi; fruit small, a nut or drupe, sometimes winged, indehiscent or rarely breaking up into cocci; seeds pendulous, with copious endosperm and straight fairly large (rarely small)

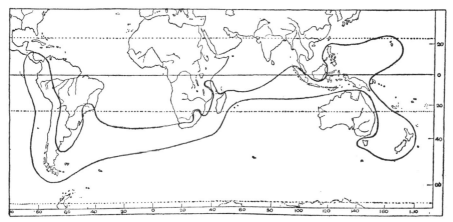

Range of Gunnera (Halorrhagaceae), a distinctly austral genus.

embryo. B.H. **1,** 673; E.P. **3,** 7, 226. Mostly *aquatic* and scattered throughout the world.—Halorrhagis, Hippuris, Gunnera, Myriophyllum, &c.

Useful Products: *Gunnera* spp., with large handsome foliage, often planted near lakes and ponds.

292. Callitrichaceae

Annual herbs, terrestrial or aquatic, with slender stems; leaves *opposite,* linear, entire; stipules absent; flowers minute, *unisexual,* axillary, solitary or rarely the male and female in the same axil; calyx and corolla absent; *stamen* 1, subtended by 2 bracts; filament slender; anther 2-locular, opening lengthwise at the side, the slit becoming confluent at the top; ovary subsessile, 4-lobed, 4-locular; styles 2, elongated, *free,* papillose; ovules solitary and pendulous from the apex of each loculus; fruit 4-lobed, lobes margined or winged; seeds with a membranous testa, fleshy endosperm, and terete straight embryo. B.H. **1,** 676 (under *Halorrhagaceae*); E.P. **3,** 5, 120. Cosmopolitan.—Calli-triche.

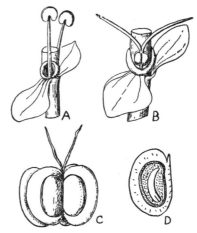

Fig. 292. Callitriche verna *L.* (Callitrichaceae). A, male flowers. B, female flower. C, fruit. D, section of same to show seed. (Orig.)

ORDER 66. GENTIANALES

Herbs with opposite, rarely alternate, leaves; corolla actinomorphic; stamens **epipetalous**, the same number as and alternate with the corolla-lobes; disk **often** present; ovary superior, 1-locular with parietal placentation; ovules numerous; seeds with copious endosperm and small embryo.—Temperate Regions and Subtropics mainly.

A. Leaves opposite, often connate at the base by a transverse line, never peltate; corolla-lobes contorted or rarely imbricate   *Gentianaceae*

AA. Leaves alternate, entire or 3-foliolate, sometimes peltate, petiole sheathing at the base; corolla-lobes valvate or induplicate-valvate
Menyanthaceae

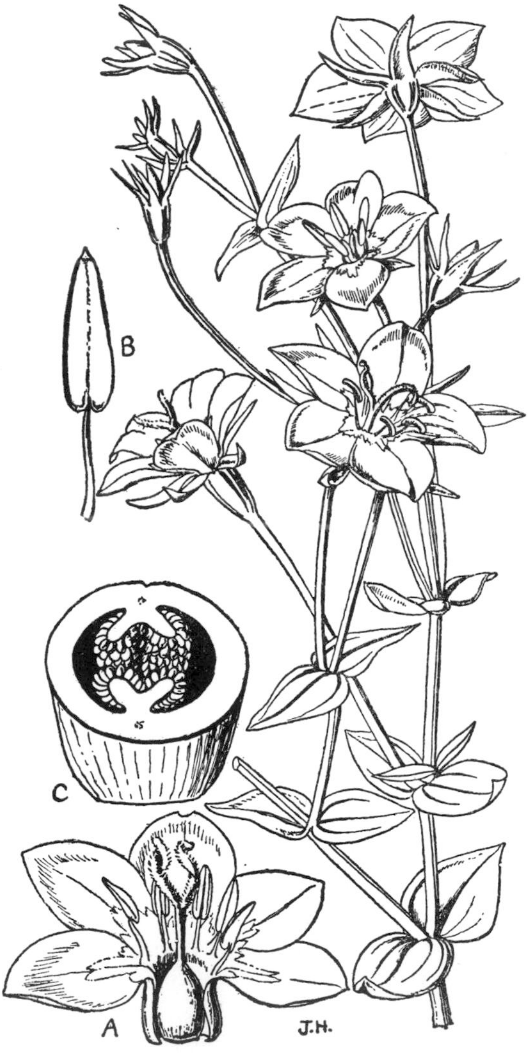

293. GENTIANACEAE

Annual or perennial herbs, very rarely woody; leaves *opposite*, entire, often *connate at the base* or connected by a transverse line; *stipules absent*; flowers ☿, rarely polygamous, actinomorphic, mostly showy and bright-coloured; calyx tubular or of separate sepals, imbricate; corolla sympetalous, lobes 4–12, *contorted* or very rarely imbricate; stamens the same number as the corolla-lobes and *alternate with them*, inserted on the corolla; anthers 2-locular, opening lengthwise; disk absent or annular or of 5 glands below the ovary;

FIG. 293. Sabbatia campestris *Nutt.* (Gentianaceae). A, flower opened. B, stamen. C, transverse section of ovary. (After *Bot. Mag.*) Note the close resemblance to some *Caryophyllaceae.*

ovary superior, mostly 1-locular with *2 parietal placentas*, sometimes 2-locular with the placentas adnate to the septa; *style simple*; ovules often numerous; fruit often capsular; seeds with copious endosperm and small subterete or conical embryo. B.H. **2,** 799; E.P. **4,** 2, 50. Mainly Temperate and Subtropical Regions.—EXACUM, SEBAEA, CHIRONIA, VOYRIA, LEIANTHUS, BLACKSTONIA (CHLORA), CENTAURIUM (ERYTHRAEA), SABBATIA, CANSCORA, SCHULTESIA, EUSTOMA, LISIANTHUS, GENTIANA, SWERTIA, HALENIA, &c.

USEFUL PRODUCTS: Bitter properties. *Gentian Root* (Gentiana lutea *L.*), S. Eur., &c.; *Chiretta* (Swertia chirata *Hamilt.*), N. India. Many beautiful plants suitable for rock gardening.

294. MENYANTHACEAE

Aquatic or marsh herbs; leaves *alternate*, entire or *3-foliolate*, sometimes orbicular and *peltate*; petiole sheathing at the base; flowers bisexual, race-

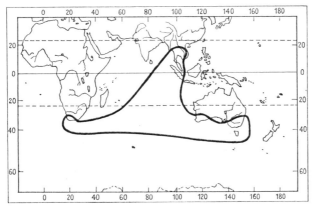

Villarsia, an austral genus of Menyanthaceae, shows a remarkable discontinuous distribution.

mose, solitary, paired, or fasciculate, or in many-flowered cymes, panicles, or involucrate heads; calyx 5-lobed or -partite; corolla sympetalous, 5-lobed, lobes *valvate or induplicate-valvate*, margins or inside sometimes *fimbriate or crested*; stamens 5, inserted towards the base of the tube or between the corolla-lobes; anthers 2-locular, sagittate and versatile; hypogynous nectaries usually present; ovary superior, *1-locular, with 2 parietal placentas*; style 1, bifid at the apex; fruit a capsule, 4- or 2-valved, rarely fruit fleshy or pulpy and indehiscent; seeds numerous to few, winged or not, with copious endosperm and small embryo.—*Gentianaceae* tribe *Menyantheae*, B.H. **2,** 819 (1876); subfam. *Menyanthoideae* Gilg, E.P. **4,** 2, 62 (1895). Temperate Regions of both Hemispheres.

A. Corolla-lobes keeled in the middle on the upper surface; leaves reniform, coarsely toothed—FAURIA (*Nephrophyllum*) (E. Asia, N. Amer.). AA. Corolla-lobes not keeled on the upper surface, often provided with fimbriae; leaves or leaflets entire or slightly emarginate: B. Fruits dehiscent: C. Leaves undivided; capsule 4-valved at the apex—VILLARSIA (Austral., Malaya, S. Afr.). CC. Leaves trifoliolate; capsule splitting irregularly at the apex—MENYANTHES (Temp. N. Hemisph.). BB. Fruits indehiscent: D. Aquatic plants with

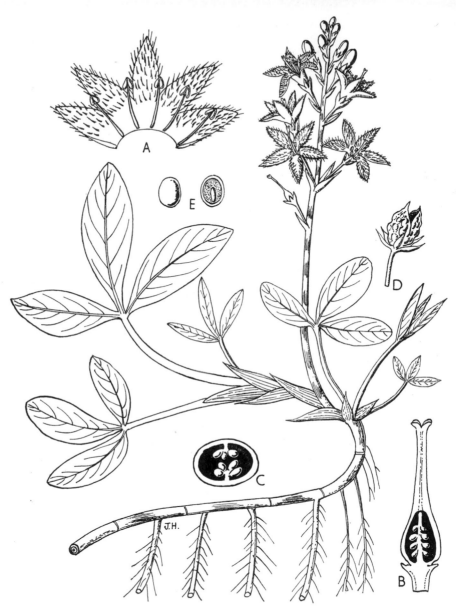

Fig. 294. Menyanthes trifoliata *L*. (Menyanthaceae). A, corolla laid open showing the fimbriate lobes and the stamens. B, vertical section of ovary. C, cross-section of ovary. D, fruit. E, seed. (Orig.)

cordate floating leaves; flowers mostly fasciculate—NYMPHOIDES (*Limnan-themum*) (widely distrib.). **DD.** Small creeping plants with linear entire somewhat fleshy leaves; flowers solitary—LIPAROPHYLLUM (Tasm., New Zeal., Stewart Is.).

ORDER 67. PRIMULALES

Herbs or rarely climbers; no stipules; flowers often subumbellate; petals united, imbricate, rarely absent; stamens epipetalous, the same number as and opposite the corolla-lobes; ovary superior, 1-locular, with free-basal placenta and numerous to solitary ovules; seeds with or without endosperm. —Mainly mountains of N. Hemisphere and maritime shores.

A. Ovules numerous on a free basal placenta; style undivided; seeds usually numerous; calyx often herbaceous; mostly herbs   *Primulaceae*
AA. Ovule 1, pendulous from a basal funicle; styles 5, free or variously connate; seed solitary; calyx membranous between the lobes or teeth; herbs to climbers, mostly maritime   *Plumbaginaceae*

295. PRIMULACEAE

Perennial or annual herbs, rarely undershrubs; leaves all basal or sometimes cauline, alternate, opposite, or verticillate, simple or variously lobate; flowers from solitary to paniculate or umbellate, bracteate, actinomorphic, very rarely zygomorphic, ⚥, often heterostyled; calyx persistent, often rather foliaceous; corolla tubular, sometimes split nearly to the base, lobes usually 5, imbricate, rarely absent; stamens inserted *opposite the petals*, rarely with alternating staminodes; ovary superior, rarely semi-superior, 1-locular, with a *free-basal* sessile or stipitate placenta; style simple; ovules numerous, with 2 integuments; fruit a capsule, variously dehiscent, usually many-seeded; seeds angular, with small straight embryo immersed in copious endosperm. B.H. **2**, 628; E.P. **4**, 1, 98. Mostly mountain regions of the N. Temperate Zone, rare in the Tropics and S. Hemisphere.—HOTTONIA, PRIMULA (Fig. 295), ANDROSACE, CORTUSA, SOLDANELLA, DODECATHEON, CYCLAMEN, LYSIMACHIA, TRIENTALIS, GLAUX, ANAGALLIS, CORIS, SAMOLUS, etc.
    USEFUL PRODUCTS: Value mainly horticultural.

296. PLUMBAGINACEAE

Herbs, undershrubs, or climbers; stipules absent; flowers ⚥, actinomorphic, often in unilateral inflorescences or subumbellate; bracts often sheathing, dry and membranous; calyx inferior, gamosepalous, often conspicuously *ribbed*, often *membranous between the lobes* or teeth; corolla mostly sympetalous, imbricate, often persistent; stamens 5, *opposite* to the petals or corolla-lobes and more or less adnate to the tube; anthers 2-locular, opening lengthwise; disk absent; ovary superior, mostly sessile, *1-locular*; styles 5, free or variously connate; ovule 1, pendulous from a *basal funicle*; fruit indehiscent or at length calyptrately dehiscent, rarely valvate from the base

Fig. 295. Primula calciphila *Hutch*. (Primulaceae). A, vertical section of thrum-eyed flower. B, same of pin-eyed flower. C, vertical section of ovary. (Orig.)

upwards; seed with or without endosperm, and straight fairly large embryo. B.H. **2,** 623; E.P. **4,** 1, 116. Mainly maritime shores and mountains; numerous

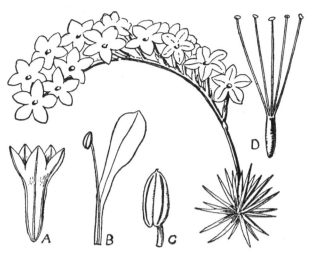

FIG. 296. Acantholimon venustum *Boiss.* (Plumbaginaceae). A, calyx. B, stamen and petal. C, anther. D, ovary and styles.

around the Mediterranean.—ACANTHOLIMON, LIMONIUM (*Statice*), ARMERIA, PLUMBAGO, CERATOSTIGMA, &c.

USEFUL PRODUCTS: Some of medicinal use, but chiefly of horticultural value.

ORDER 68. PLANTAGINALES

Characters of the family, below.

297. PLANTAGINACEAE

Herbs; leaves all radical, alternate or opposite, simple, sometimes reduced, often *sheathing at the base;* flowers usually ⚥ and spicate, actinomorphic; calyx herbaceous, *4-lobed* or parted, sometimes the abaxial sepals more or less united; corolla sympetalous, scarious, 3–4-lobed, lobes imbricate; stamens 4 (rarely 1–2), inserted on the corolla-tube and alternate with the lobes or hypogynous; anthers 2-locular, opening lengthwise; ovary superior, 1–4-locular; style simple; ovules 1 or more in each loculus, axile or basal; fruit a circumscissile capsule or a bony nut; seeds peltately attached; embryo straight, in the middle of fleshy endosperm, rarely curved. B.H. **2,** 1223; E.P. **4,** 3*b,* 363. Widely dispersed.

USEFUL PRODUCTS: *Ispaghul* or *Spogel seeds* (Plantago ovata *Forssk.*), NW. India; *Psyllium seeds* (Plantago psyllium *L.*).

A. Fruits dehiscing by a transverse circular slit (circumscissile); flowers in spikes or heads, mostly or all bisexual; ovules 1 or more in each loculus; stamens 4—PLANTAGO (widely distrib.). **AA.** Fruits indehiscent: **B.** Flowers

FIG. 297. Plantago lagopus *L.* (Plantaginaceae). A, flower. (Orig.)

spicate-capitate, a few at the top bisexual, the others female; ovary 1-locular, 1-ovulate; stamens 2–1—BOUGUERIA (S. Amer.). **BB.** Male flowers on a long peduncle, females sessile around the base of the peduncle; ovary 1-locular, 1-ovulate; stamens 4—LITTORELLA (Eur.).

ORDER 69. SAXIFRAGALES

Herbaceous; flowers actinomorphic, more or less perigynous or rarely epigynous; petals present; stamens definite, free; apocarpous to syncarpous with axile placentation; seeds with copious endosperm and small straight embryo. Leaves radical, alternate or opposite, sometimes much modified, exstipulate.—Cosmopolitan.

A. Carpels free or united only at the base:
  B. Leaves of one kind, not modified into pitchers, often thick and fleshy; calyx rarely coloured; petals present; hypogynous scales within the stamens   *Crassulaceae*

BB. Leaves of two kinds, some modified into lidded pitchers like those of *Nepenthes*; calyx coloured; petals absent; a setose-glandular disk within the 12 stamens   *Cephalotaceae*

AA. Carpels united into a superior to inferior ovary:
  C. Petals free from each other or petals absent; anthers 2-locular:
    D. Fruit a capsule; staminodes absent; styles usually free or absent; flowers rarely solitary:
      E. Stigmas dorsal to the carpels (not commissural):
        F. Leaves alternate or all radical; placentas axile or axile-basal:
          G. Ovules more than 1 in each loculus, axile   *Saxifragaceae*
          GG. Ovule 1 in each loculus, erect from the base of the axis
                                                Eremosynaceae
        FF. Leaves opposite; placentas hanging from the top of the ovary
                                               Vahliaceae
      EE. Stigmas lateral to the carpels (commisural); flowers in lax elongated racemes; stamens 8 or 4, rarely 5; no staminodes   *Francoaceae*
    DD. Fruit indehiscent; staminodes absent; styles free; flowers solitary
                                               Donatiaceae
    DDD. Fruit a capsule; staminodes alternate with the stamens, clavate, cuneate, or multifid and gland-tipped; ovary 1-locular with parietal placentas; flowers solitary   *Parnassiaceae*
  CC. Petals united into a broad short tube; anthers 1-locular; ovary sub-inferior; ovules solitary in each loculus; flowers capitate   *Adoxaceae*

298. CRASSULACEAE

Herbs or undershrubs, usually succulent; leaves opposite or alternate, *without stipules*; flowers actinomorphic, bisexual, usually cymose; sepals free or united

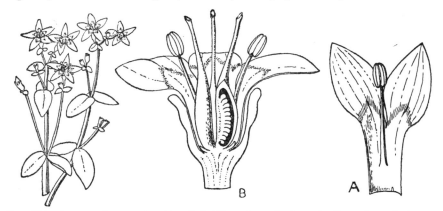

Fig. 298. Grammanthes gentianoides *DC.* (Crassulaceae). A, part of corolla and stamen. B, flower cut vertically. (After *Bot. Mag.*)

into a tube, often 4 or 5; petals the same number as the sepals, free or variously connate, hypogynous; stamens as many or twice as many as the petals, if few then alternate with the petals, slightly perigynous; filaments free; anthers 2-locular, introrse, dehiscing longitudinally; hypogynous scales present within the stamens; carpels superior, *the same number as the petals, free or united at the base*, 1-locular; ovules many or rarely few, inserted on the adaxial suture; style short or elongated; fruit follicular, membranous or leathery, often sur-

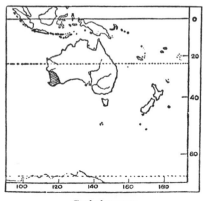

Cephalotaceae.

rounded by the persistent membranous corolla, opening on the adaxial side; seeds minute, usually with fleshy endosperm; embryo straight. B.H. **1**, 656; E.P. **3**, 2*a*, 23. Mainly warm dry regions. —CRASSULA, ROCHEA, BRYOPHYLLUM, KALANCHOE, COTYLEDON, SEDUM, SEMPERVIVUM, MONANTHES, &c.

USEFUL PRODUCTS: Many curious and beautiful garden and greenhouse plants.

299. CEPHALOTACEAE

Perennial herbs with short underground rhizomes; leaves of two kinds, some flat, elliptic, entire, nerveless, others (ascidia) *composed of a petiole dilated at the top into a lidded pitcher like* NEPENTHES; flowers borne on a leafless

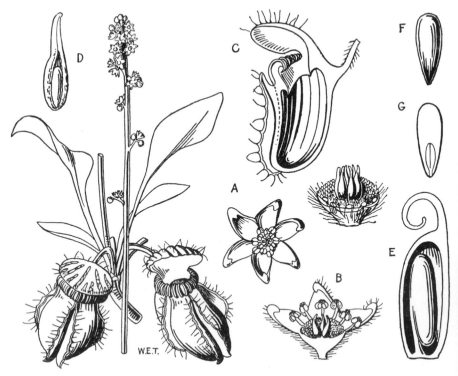

FIG. 299. Cephalotus follicularis *Labill.* (Cephalotaceae). A, flower. B, section of same. C, section of ascidium. D, carpel. E, same in section. F, G, seeds. (After Le Maout & Decne.)

narrow raceme of cymules bracteate at the base; calyx coloured, 6-lobed; lobes *valvate*, hooded; petals *absent*; stamens 12, perigynous, inserted at the top of the calyx-tube on the outer margin of a setose glandular disk, six longer than the others; filaments free; anthers 2-locular, opening lengthwise, connective swollen at the top and glandular; carpels 6, free, in a single whorl, 1-locular and usually with 1 (rarely 2) *basal erect ovules* in each; follicles surrounded by the accrescent calyx, shortly stipitate, thickly hairy outside, 1-seeded; seeds with fleshy endosperm and rather small, straight embryo. B.H. **1,** 655 (under *Saxifragaceae*); E.P. **3,** 2a, 39. Australia.—CEPHALOTUS.

300. SAXIFRAGACEAE

Herbs, not or slightly succulent; leaves alternate, *not stipulate*; flowers actinomorphic, bisexual, rarely solitary; sepals usually 5, imbricate or valvate;

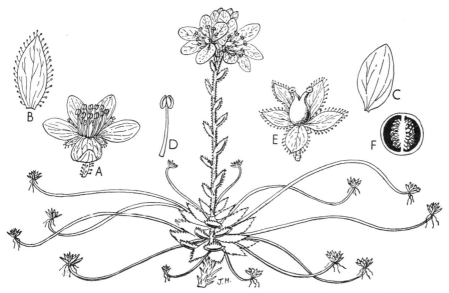

FIG. 300. Saxifraga flagellaris *Willd. & Sternb.* (Saxifragaceae). A, flower. B, sepal. C, petal. D, stamen. E, calyx and ovary. F, cross-section of ovary. (Orig.)

petals alternate with the sepals or absent, often clawed, *perigynous or rarely epigynous*; stamens inserted with the petals, 5–10; filaments free, anthers 2–locular, dehiscing longitudinally; ovary 1–3-locular, free or adnate to the tubular receptacle; styles usually free, dorsal to the carpels; ovules numerous, on axile placentas; fruit a capsule; seeds numerous, small, with endosperm; embryo minute, straight. B.H. **1,** 629; E.P. **3,** 2a, 41 (partly). Mainly Cold and Temperate Regions.—SAXIFRAGA, ASTILBE, ROGERSIA, BERGENIA, HEUCHERA, CHRYSOSPLENIUM, &c.

USEFUL PRODUCTS: Many plants for the herbaceous border, rock garden, and greenhouse.

301. EREMOSYNACEAE[1]

Small annual herb, much branched from the base, thinly pilose all over; radical leaves spathulate-oblanceolate, entire to pinnately lobed; cauline leaves alternate, sessile, gradually reduced to bracts, pinnately lobed; *stipules absent*; flowers very small, in terminal dichotomous cymules; calyx-tube very short, *adnate to the lowermost third of the ovary*; lobes 5, *valvate*, narrow;

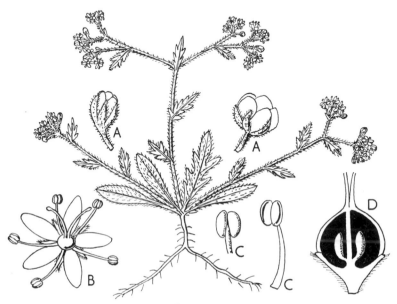

FIG. 301. Eremosyne pectinata *Endl.* (Eremosynaceae). A, flower-buds. B, open flower. C, stamens back and front. D, vertical section of ovary.

petals 5, free, narrowly elliptic, spreading; stamens 5, alternate with the petals, free; filaments subulate; anthers rounded-ellipsoidal, dehiscing longitudinally; ovary about ¾ *superior*, 2-locular; styles 2, divergent, *dorsal to the carpels*, stigmas capitellate; ovule 1 in each loculus, axile near the base of the septum, ascending; capsule about ½ *superior*, thin, subdidymous, 2-locular, loculicidally 2-valved; seeds erect, with copious endosperm. *Saxifragaceae* tribe *Eremosyneae* Engl., E.P. **3**, 2*a*, 65 (1890); B.H. **1**, 634. SW. Australia.—EREMOSYNE.

[1] **Eremosynaceae** Dandy, fam. nov.; herba parva, annua, e basi multi ramosa, ubique tenuiter pilosa; folia radicalia spatulato-oblanceolata, integra ad pinnatim lobata; caulina alterna, sessilia, ad bracteas gradatim reducta, pinnatim lobata; stipulae nullae; flores minimi, in cymulis dichotomis terminalibus dispositi; calycis tubus brevissimus, ad partem inferiorem ovarii adnatus, lobis 5 valvatis angustis; petala 5, libera, anguste elliptica, patula; stamina 5, petalis alterna, libera; filamenta subulata; antherae rotundato-ellipsoideae, longitudinaliter dehiscentes; ovarium circiter ¾ superius, 2-loculare; styli 2, divergentes, dorsales, stigmatibus capitellatis; ovulum in loculo unicum, prope basin septi adscendens; capsula circiter 1 superior, tenuis, subdidyma, 2-locularis, loculicide 2-valvis; semina erecta, endospermio copioso. Genus typicum EREMOSYNE.

302. VAHLIACEAE[1]

Annual herbs, erect, dichotomously branched, glabrous, pubescent or glandular-pilose; leaves *opposite*, ovate to linear, entire; *stipules absent*;

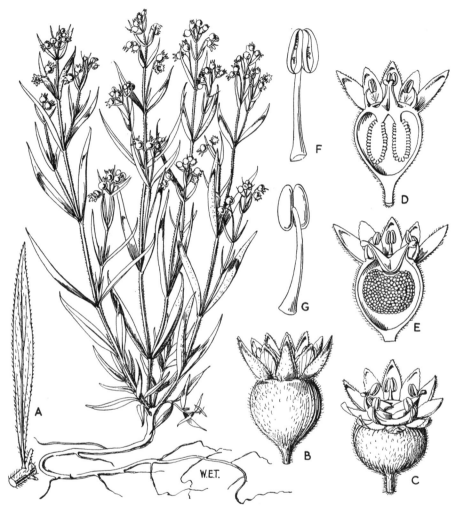

FIG. 302. Vahlia dichotoma (*Murr.*) *O. Ktze.* (Vahliaceae). A, leaf. B, flower. C, the same open. D, vertical section of flower showing the pendulous placentas. E, the same showing one placenta. F, G, stamens. (After Hutch. and Dalz., *Fl. W. Trop. Afr.* **1**, 106.)

[1] **Vahliaceae** Dandy, fam. nov. Herbae annuae, pubescentes vel glandulosae, rare glabrae, erectae, subdichotome ramosae; folia opposita, ovata ad linearia, integra; stipulae nullae; flores axillares, geminati, albidi; calycis tubus hemisphaericus, ovario adnatus; lobi 5, ovati vel lanceolati, valvati; petala 5, calycis lobis breviora, obovato-spatulata; stamina 5, margine disci epigyni inserta, filamentis subulatis liberis; ovarium inferum, 1-loculare; styli 2 vel 3, breves vel elongati, stigmatibus capitellatis; ovula numerosissima, placentis ab apice loculi pendulis affixa; capsula subglobosa vel obovoidea, apice 2–3-valvis, 2-lamellosa, lamellis membranaceis, polysperma; semina minuta, oblonga. Genus typicum VAHLIA.

flowers axillary, paired, subsessile or pedicellate, white or yellow; calyx-tube hemispherical, *adnate to the ovary*, lobes 5, *valvate*; petals 5, free, shorter than the calyx-lobes, obovate-spathulate; stamens 5, inserted on the margin of the epigynous disk; filaments free, subulate; ovary *inferior*, 1-locular; styles 2 or 3, short or elongated, 1 dorsal to the carpels, stigmas capitellate; ovules very numerous, attached to two large placentas *hanging from the apex of the loculus*; capsule subglobose or obovoid, 2–3-valved at the top; seeds many, minute. oblong. B.H. **1**, 637; E.P. **3**, 2*a*, 65 (in *Saxifragaceae*). Tropical and S. Africa and Madagascar, through Upper Egypt and Iraq to India.—VAHLIA.

A genus of about 8 species bearing a remarkable resemblance to certain species of *Oldenlandia* in the *Rubiaceae*, but recognized at once by the absence of stipules, the free petals, and the numerous ovules from the top of the unilocular ovary.

303. FRANCOACEAE

Perennial scapigerous herbs, glandular-pilose or tomentose; rhizome thick or slender; leaves crowded or subradical, lyrate-pinnatifid or subpinnate, or rounded-cordate and palmately nerved; *stipules absent*; flowers in lax elongated racemes, bracteate; calyx 5–4-partite, persistent, segments *valvate*; petals 4 (rarely 5) inserted at the base of the calyx, imbricate or contorted, venose, equal or unequal with 2 much smaller or deficient, clawed or subsessile; stamens 8 or 4, rarely 5, alternating with as many *disk-glands*; filaments free; anthers subcordate-oblong or didymous; ovary superior, 4-sided, 4-lobed at the apex, *4-locular*, with 4 sessile *commissural* stigmas; ovules numerous, axile; capsule elongated or oblong, 4-lobed, 4-locular, septicidally or loculicidally 4-valved; seeds striolate; embryo minute, in the middle of fleshy endosperm.—Chile.

A. Leaves lyrate-pinnatifid or pinnate, pinnately nerved; petals clawed, equal; stamens 4 (5)—FRANCOA (Fig. 303). **AA.** Leaves rounded-cordate, palmately nerved; petals unequal, 2 much smaller or deficient; stamens 8— TETILLA.

304. DONATIACEAE[1]

Low pulvinate-caespitose herbs with fleshy stilt-like roots; leaves linear, coriaceous, pustulate, very densely and *spirally arranged*, densely pilose in the axils; stipules absent; flowers terminal, solitary, sessile; calyx-tube *adnate to the ovary*, obconical, lobes 7–5, equal or unequal, lanceolate; petals 10–5, free, oblong-linear or ovate; stamens 3–2, inserted within the *epigynous disk*; filaments free, short or filiform; anthers 2-locular, extrorse, broadly ellip-

---

[1] **Donatiaceae** Hutch., fam. nov.; herbae nanae, pulvinato-caespitosae, radicibus rigidis carnosis; folia linearia, coriacea, pustulata, dense spiraliter disposita, in axillis dense pilosa; stipulae nullae; flores terminales, solitarii, sessiles; calycis tubus ad ovarium adnatus, obconicus, lobis 5–7 lanceolatis aequalibus vel inaequalibus; petala 10–5, libera, oblongolinearia vel ovata; stamina 3–2, intra discum epigynum inserta; filamenta libera; antherae 2-loculares, extrorsae, late ellipsoideae; ovarium inferum, 3–2-loculare; styli 3–2, liberi, subulati, recurvi, stigmate terminali globoso; ovula ad placentas prope apicem ovarii numerosa; fructus turbinatus, indehiscens; semina pauca, oblique ovoidea; embryo minuta, endospermio carnoso circumdata. Genus typicum DONATIA.

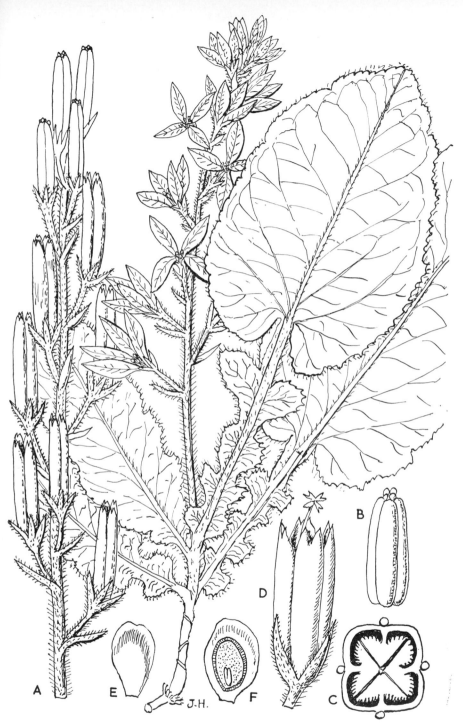

FIG. 303. Francoa sonchifolia *Cav.* (Francoaceae). A, infructescence. B, ovary. C, cross-section of ovary. D, fruit. E, seed. F, vertical section of seed. (Orig.)

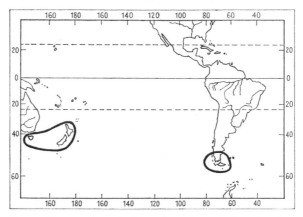

The small genus Donatia (Donatiaceae) emphasizes the close affinity of the floras of New Zealand and subantarctic S. America.

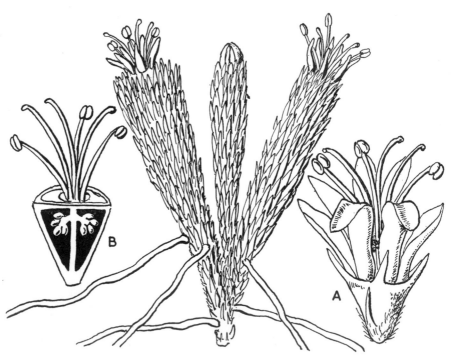

FIG. 304. Donatia fascicularis *Forst*. (Donatiaceae). A, flower. B, vertical section of ovary with calyx and petals removed; neither belonging to Saxifragaceae (according to Hooker) nor to Stylidiaceae (according to Mildbraed), but worthy of separate status as a family near Saxifragaceae. (Orig.)

soidal; ovary *inferior*, 3–2-locular; styles 3–2, free, subulate, recurved, with terminal globose stigma; ovules numerous on placentas *near the top of the axis*; fruit turbinate, *indehiscent*; seeds few, obliquely ovoid, testa membranous; embryo minute, enclosed by the fleshy endosperm. B.H. **1**, 634 (in *Saxifragaceae*); *Saxifragaceae* tribe *Donatieae* Engl., E.P. **3**, 2*a*, 67 (1890); Mildbr., Engl. *Pflanzenr.*, *Stylidiac.* 19, fig. 7 (in *Stylidiaceae*) (1908). Subantarctic S. America, New Zealand, Tasmania.—DONATIA.

An interesting genus with two species, one, the original, *D. fascicularis* Forst., in Antarctic S. America, and the other, *D. novae-zelandiae* Hook. f., in New Zealand and Tasmania. Hooker referred the genus to the *Saxifragaceae*, with which family I consider it to be most closely related, and not to *Stylidiaceae*, in spite of the presence of *inulin*. The occurrence of this may be foreign to the *Saxifragaceae*, but it is no proof that it is related to *Stylidiaceae*, from which it differs by several important characters, particularly the 2–3 completely free stamens inserted within an epigynous disk, extrorse anthers, and the two free or nearly free styles, besides the entirely free petals. In *Stylidiaceae* (*sensu stricto*) the stamens are completely united around the single style, and the petals are united into a sympetalous often strongly zygomorphic corolla.

See especially B. Chandler, *Edinb. Notes* 5: 43 (1911).

305. PARNASSIACEAE

Perennial herbs; radical leaves petiolate, ovate to oblong, often cordate; petioles dilated at the base; flowering stems often with a single leaf about the

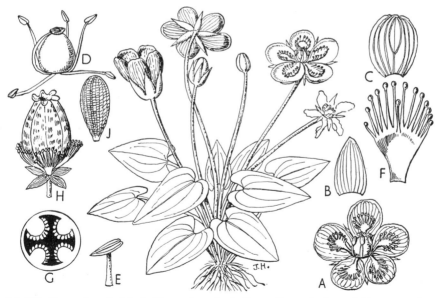

FIG. 305. Parnassia palustris *L.* (Parnassiaceae). A, flower. B, sepal. C, petal. D, stamens (one anther adpressed to the stigma) and ovary. E, anther. F, staminode. G, cross-section of ovary. H, fruit. J, seed.(Orig.)

middle, 1-flowered; calyx-tube short, free from or slightly adnate to the base of the ovary; lobes spreading, broad, imbricate; petals 5, spreading, *marcescent*, entire or fimbriate; stamens 5, hypogynous or perigynous, alternating with the same number of clavate, cuneate, or *multifid gland-tipped staminodes*; anthers ovate-cordate; ovary *superior* or nearly so, 1-locular, ovoid; style 1, very short, thick, with 3–4 *commissural stigmas*; ovules numerous, on *parietal or sub-basal placentas alternating with the stigmas*; capsule superior to half superior, thin, 1-locular, 3–4-valved; seeds numerous, *testa winged*; endosperm thin; embryo cylindrical. B.H. **1,** 639 (in *Saxifragaceae*); E.P. **3,** 2a, 66; Drude, *Linnaea,* **39,** 239 (1875). Arctic and N. Temperate Regions, south to India.—PARNASSIA.

306. ADOXACEAE

Small herbs from a perennial rhizome; stem-leaves 2, opposite, 3-foliolate; radical leaves variously divided; flowers small, green, capitate, about 5 in

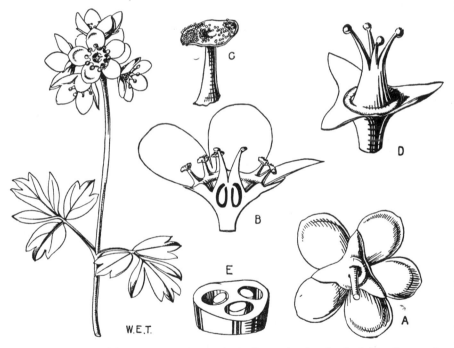

FIG. 306. Adoxa moschatellina *L.* (Adoxaceae). A, flower showing 3 calyx-lobes. B, same in vertical section. C, stamen. D, ovary. E, transverse section of ovary. (Orig.)

each head, the terminal one often 4-merous, the other 5–6-merous; calyx 2–3-lobed; corolla rotate, 4–6-lobed; disk none; stamens on the corolla, 4, 5, or 6 (apparently double these numbers owing to the splitting of the filaments); anthers 1-locular; ovary subinferior, 3–5-locular; style 3–5-lobed; ovules solitary in each loculus, pendulous; fruit a drupe of 1–5 pyrenes; seeds with endosperm and minute embryo. B.H. **2,** 2 (under *Caprifoliaceae*); E.P. **4,** 4, 170. Temperate and Cold Regions of N. Hemisphere.—ADOXA.

ORDER 70. SARRACENIALES

Characters more or less as in *Saxifragales*, but adapted for entrapping insects; leaves tubular or covered with viscid glands, usually radical; stamens numerous to few; syncarpous with parietal or axile placentation.—Cosmopolitan.

A. Ovary 1-locular, with parietal or subbasal placentas; stamens 20–4; anthers extrorse; styles mostly free; leaves usually covered with sticky stipitate glands   *Droseraceae*

AA. Ovary 5–3-locular, with axile placentas; stamens numerous; style simple, mostly peltately expanded at the apex; leaves tubular with a small lamina like those of *Nepenthes*   *Sarraceniaceae*

307. DROSERACEAE

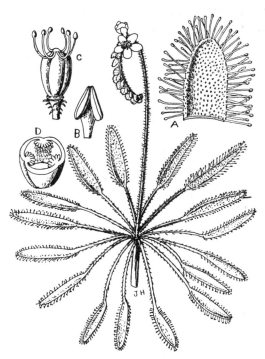

FIG. 307. Drosera capensis *Harv.* (Droseraceae). A, portion of leaf with gland-tipped tentacles. B, stamen. C, ovary with styles. D, ovary in cross-section.

Herbs, often stemless, with rosettes of leaves, the latter often circinate in bud and usually covered with sticky stipitate glands or marginal bristles which entrap insects; flowers bisexual, in usually simple circinate cyme; sepals 5–4, mores or less connate at the base, imbricate, persistent; petals 5, hypogynous, very rarely perigynous, nervose; stamens 4–20, often 5, hypogynous, free or rarely united at the base; anthers 2-locular, extrorse, opening by longitudinal slits; ovary free, 1-*locular*, with *parietal* or *subbasal* placentas; ovules many or rarely few; styles 3–5, mostly free; fruit a loculicidal capsule; seeds with fleshy endosperm; embryo straight; cotyledons short. B.H. **1**, 661; E.P. **3**, 2, 261. Cosmopolitan in sandy and boggy places.

A. Stamens 2–4 times as many as the petals; placenta basal: **B.** Styles free—DROSOPHYLLUM (Spain, Portugal, Morocco). **BB.** Styles connate nearly to the apex—DIONAEA (N. Amer.). **AA.** Stamens the same number as the petals; placentas parietal: **C.** Aquatic plants with jointed leaves, these verticillate; carpels 5—ALDROVANDRA (Eur. to Austral.). **CC.** Terrestrial plants, leaves scattered or rarely verticillate, not jointed—DROSERA (widely distrib.).

308. SARRACENIACEAE

Herbs with radical tubular leaves with small lamina; flowers scapose, solitary or few in racemes, nodding, ♀; sepals 4–5, free, hypogynous, imbricate, *often*

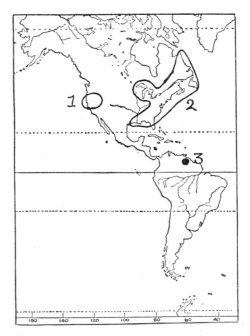

Distribution of Sarraceniaceae. 1, Darlingtonia;
2, Sarracenia; 3, Heliamphora.

coloured, persistent; petals 5, free, imbricate, or absent; *stamens numerous*, hypogynous, free; anthers 2-locular, opening lengthwise; ovary free, 3–5-locular, with axile placentas and numerous anatropous ovules; style simple, often *peltately dilated* at the apex; fruit a capsule, *loculicidally* 3–5-valved; seeds numerous, small, with fleshy endosperm and small embryo. B.H. **1**, 48; E.P. **3**, 2, 244.—America.

A. Petals 5; ovary 5-locular: **B.** Style 5-rayed—DARLINGTONIA (Western

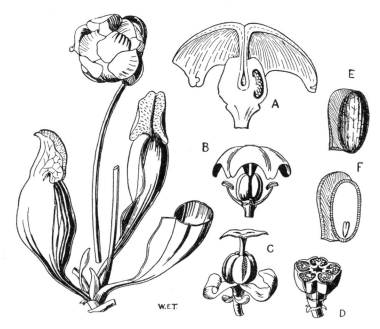

FIG. 308. Sarracenia purpurea *L.* (Sarraceniaceae). A, section of flower. B, stamens and pistil. C, fruit. D, section of fruit. E, F, seed. (After Le Maout & Decne.)

U.S.A.). **BB.** Style broadly expanded and umbrella-like—SARRACENIA (Atlantic N. Amer.). **AA.** Petals absent; ovary 3-locular; style entire, truncate at the apex—HELIAMPHORA (Guianas).

ORDER 71. PODOSTEMALES

Submerged freshwater herbs like mosses, hepatics, or algae; petals absent; stamens 1–4, free or partly connate; syncarpous with parietal or central placentation; seeds minute, without endosperm.—Tropics and Subtropics.

A. Flowers bisexual, solitary or cymose, often enclosed when young in a spathe composed of partially connate bracts; calyx present; ovary with a central placenta   *Podostemaceae*

AA. Flowers unisexual, dioecious, densely spicate, solitary and sessile in the axil of each bract; calyx absent; stamen 1; ovary with parietal placentas
                                                    Hydrostachyaceae

309. PODOSTEMACEAE

Submerged fresh-water herbs often greatly resembling mosses, hepatics, and algae; flowers ☿, small, solitary or cymose, actinomorphic, often enclosed when young in a spathe composed of partially connate bracts; sepals 2–3, usually small, connate in the lower part; petals absent; stamens 1–4, hypogynous; filaments free or partially connate; anthers 2-locular, small, opening

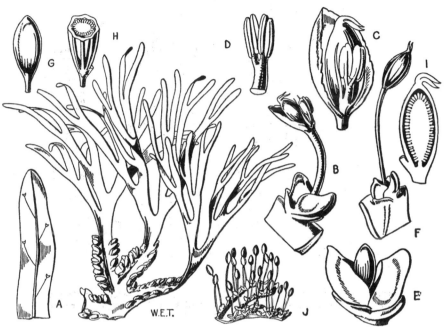

FIG. 309. Dicraea algiformis *Bedd.* (Podostemaceae). A, portion of frond enlarged. B, expanded flower with involucre. C, flower itself magnified. D, stamen. E, bud in involucre. F, fruit. G, bud enclosed in involucre. H, fruit in cross-section. I, ovary in vertical section. J, portion of fruiting frond. (After Fitch.)

lengthwise; ovary sessile or shortly stipitate, superior, 1–3-locular with a *central placenta*; styles 2–3, slender; ovules numerous; fruit a septicidal capsule; seeds minute, without endosperm. B.H. **3,** 105; E.P. **3,** 2*a*, 1. Mainly Tropics.—TRISTICHA, TERNIOLA, MARATHRUM, RHYNCHOLACIS, LIGEA, APINAGIA, PODOSTEMUM, DICRAEA, &c.

310. HYDROSTACHYACEAE

Submerged fresh-water herbs; stems thick, *tuber-like*; leaves simple to 2 or 3 times pinnatisect, dilated and ligulate at the base; *flowers dioecious*, densely spicate, solitary and sessile in the axil of each bract; *calyx and petals absent*; stamen 1; anthers 2-locular, opening lengthwise; ovary 1–locular, with 2 *parietal placentas*; styles 2, divergent; fruit a small capsule; ovules numerous; seeds numerous, without endosperm. B.H. **3,** 115 (under *Podostemaceae*). E.P. **3,** 2*a*, 1. Madagascar and S. Africa.—HYDROSTACHYS.

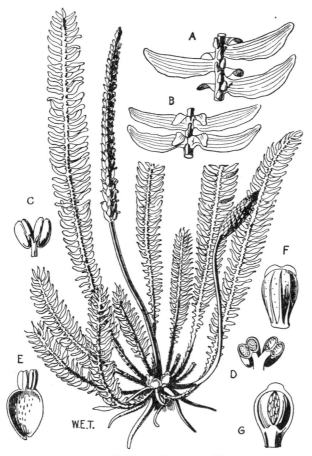

FIG. 310. Hydrostachys distichophylla *A. Juss.* (Hydrostachyaceae).
A and B, parts of leaf. C, stamen. D, section of anther. E, stamen.
F, fruit. G, section of fruit. (After Deless.)

ORDER 72. UMBELLALES

Herbs, rarely somewhat woody, with furrowed hollow stems or with wide
soft pith; leaves alternate, usually much divided, sheathing at the base; no
stipules; flowers in simple or compound umbels, rarely in heads; ovary
inferior, 2-locular; fruit dividing into 2 mericarps; carpels mostly ribbed and
often with parallel resin canals (vittae).

311. UMBELLIFERAE

Herbaceous, very rarely somewhat woody, with *furrowed stems* and wide
soft pith; leaves alternate, mostly *much divided, sheathing* at the base; flowers
☿, rarely unisexual, in simple or compound *umbels* or rarely capitate; calyx
adnate to the ovary, 5-lobed; petals 5, *valvate* or slightly imbricate, epigynous,
free, soon falling off, mostly inflexed in bud; stamens 5, alternate with the

petals; filaments *inflexed* in bud; anthers 2-locular, opening lengthwise; ovary inferior, 2-locular; styles 2, thickened at the base and capping the ovary; ovules solitary in each loculus, pendulous; fruit inferior, dry, 2-locular, dividing into 2 mericarps, these often remaining suspended at the top by the divided thread-like central axis (carpophore); carpels mostly *prominently ribbed* and often with parallel *resinous canals* (vittae); seeds with copious endosperm and minute embryo. B.H. **1**, 859; E.P. **3**, 8, 63. Temperate Regions mainly, in the Tropics mostly on the mountains.—HYDROCOTYLE, AZORELLA, ERYNGIUM, ALEPIDEA,

FIG. 311. Foeniculum vulgare *Mill.* (Umbelliferae). A, flower. B, schizocarps. C, section of same showing vittae. (Orig.)

ASTRANTIA, SANICULA, SMYRNIUM, BUPLEURUM, APIUM, AMMI, CARUM, PIMPINELLA, CONOPODIUM, CHAEROPHYLLUM, SCANDIX, ANTHRISCUS, SESELI, OENANTHE, LIGUSTICUM, ACIPHYLLA, SELINUM, PLEUROSPERMUM, ANGELICA, FERULA, PEUCEDANUM, HERACLEUM, DAUCUS, LASERPITIUM, &c.

USEFUL PRODUCTS: *Celery* (Apium graveolens *L.*); *Carrots* (Daucus carota *L.*), Eur. to India; *Parsnips* (Peucedanum sativum *Bth. & Hk. f.*); *Caraway seeds* (Carum carvi *L.*), Eur. to Himal.; *Gum Ammoniacum* (Dorema ammoniacum *Don*), Orient; *Anise* (Pimpinella anisum *L.*), SE. Eur.; *Dill seed* (Peucedanum graveolens *Bth. & Hk. f.*), S. Eur. to Abyss.; *Coriander seeds* (Coriandrum sativum *L.*), Mediterr.; *Fennel* (Foeniculum vulgare *Mill*), S. Eur.; *Common Hemlock* (Conium maculatum *L.*), Eur. &c.; and many minor products.

ORDER 73. VALERIANALES

Perennial or annual herbs; leaves radical, alternate or opposite; stipules absent; flowers usually zygomorphic, sometimes unisexual, cymose to capitate or verticillate, sometimes with an involucre of bracts; calyx and sympetalous corolla epigynous; stamens usually 4, alternate with the corolla-lobes; ovary inferior, 3–1-locular, only 1 loculus fertile; ovule 1, pendulous; fruit indehiscent.

A. Ovary 3-locular, but only 1 loculus fertile; corolla-lobes imbricate; leaves opposite or all radical; flowers mostly in cymes   *Valerianaceae*

AA. Ovary 1-locular:

  B. Corolla-lobes imbricate; leaves opposite or verticillate; flowers often capitate, with an involucel below the real calyx   *Dipsacaceae*

  BB. Corolla-lobes valvate; leaves alternate or radical; flowers in heads surrounded by an involucre of 1–2 series of bracts, without an involucel below the real calyx   *Calyceraceae*

312. VALERIANACEAE

Herbs, often with strong-smelling rhizomes, rarely shrubs; leaves *opposite* or radical, often much divided; *stipules absent*; flowers ⚥ or ♂ ♀, mostly cymose, often somewhat zygo-morphic; calyx epigynous, various, sometimes the lobes plumose; corolla sympetalous, tubular; tube often saccate or spurred at the base; lobes imbricate; stamens on the corolla-tube, alternate with the corolla-lobes, 4–1; anthers 2-locular, opening lengthwise; ovary inferior, 3-locular, *only 1 loculus fertile*; style simple, slender; ovule solitary, *pendulous* from the top; fruit dry and indehiscent, 1-seeded; embryo straight; endosperm absent. B.H. **2**, 151; E.P. **4**, 4, 172. Generally distributed, but very rare in Africa and absent from Australasia.

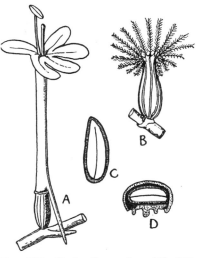

FIG. 312. Centranthus ruber (*L.*) *DC.* (Valerianaceae). A, flower. B, achene. C, longitudinal section of same. D, transverse section of same.

USEFUL PRODUCTS: *Spikenard* (Nardostachys jatamansi *DC.*), Himal.; *Valerian Root* (Valeriana officinalis *L.*), Eur. to Japan.

A. Stamens 4; corolla-tube at most only shortly gibbous at the base, not spurred: **B.** Corolla yellow; calyx-limb obscure, not enlarged in fruit—PATRINIA (*Clarkeifedia*). (Cent. and E. Asia, Himal.). **BB.** Corolla pinkish-red or purple; calyx-limb membranous, 5-lobed, slightly enlarged in fruit—NARDOSTACHYS (Himal.). **AA.** Stamens 3–1; corolla-tube spurred or not at the base: **C.** Corolla-tube not spurred at the base or at most slightly pouched: **D.** Calyx-limb not modified in fruit and not pappus-like: **E.** Peduncle much elongated and thick—ASTREPHIA (Peru and Chile). **EE.** Peduncle absent or very short: **F.** Perennial herbs or shrubs: **G.** Corolla-tube thick and wide—PHYLLACTIS (Amer.). **GG.** Corolla-tube very long and narrow—BELONANTHUS (Boliv., Peru). **FF.** Annuals—VALERIANELLA (Temp. and Subtrop. N. Hemisph.). **DD.** Calyx-limb pappus-like in fruit; bracts small; stamens mostly 3: **H.** Anthers with distinct filaments, rounded to ovoid: **J.** Flowers bisexual—VALERIANA (Cosmopol.). **JJ.** Flowers dioecious—PHUODENDRON (Brazil).—**HH.** Anthers sessile, linear —STANGEA (Peru). **CC.** Corolla-tube spurred at the base: **K.** Calyx-limb pappus-like in fruit; stamen 1 or rarely 2—CENTRANTHUS (Mediterr. Reg., Cent. Eur.). **KK.** Calyx-limb not pappus-like in fruit: **L.** Stamens 2; corolla-limb 2-lipped—FEDIA (Mediterr. Reg.). **LL.** Stamens 3; corolla-limb subequally lobed—PLECTRITIS (*Aligera*) (Western N. Amer., Chile).

313. DIPSACACEAE

Perennial or annual herbs; leaves opposite or verticillate; *stipules absent*; flowers ⚥, zygomorphic, often capitate, with a single or double involucel

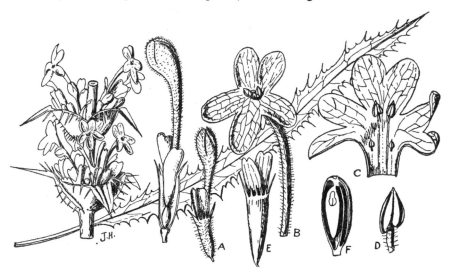

FIG. 313. Morina longifolia *Wall.* (Dipsacaceae). A, flower. B, corolla. C, corolla opened to show insertion of stamens. D, stamen. E, achene. F, same in vertical section. (After De Wild.)

below the calyx; calyx epigynous, cupular or tubular or divided into *pappus-like segments*; corolla epigynous, sympetalous; lobes imbricate; stamens *usually 4*, rarely 2–3, alternate with the corolla-lobes and inserted towards the *top of the tube*; filaments free or *united in pairs*; anthers 2-locular, opening lengthwise; ovary inferior, *1-locular*, mostly adnate to the receptacle; style slender; ovule solitary, *pendulous* from the top; fruit indehiscent; embryo large, straight in scanty endosperm. B.H. **2**, 157; E.P. **4**, 4, 182. Old World; absent from Australasia, Polynesia, and America except as introductions.

USEFUL PRODUCT: *Fuller's Teasel* (Dipsacus fullonum *L.*), Europe.

A. Flowers with a single involucel below the calyx: **B.** Flowers arranged in verticillasters (as in many *Labiatae*); bracts and leaves with very prickly margins—MORINA (Balkans, Cent. Asia, India). **BB.** Flowers arranged in heads: **C.** Involucral bracts in several series, usually rigid, mostly smaller than the paleae of the receptacle—CEPHALARIA (S. Eur., Mediterr. Reg., N. Afr.). **CC.** Involucral bracts mostly 1–2-seriate, rarely rigid, then always 1-seriate and larger than the paleae of the receptacle: **D.** Paleae of the receptacle and mostly the involucral bracts rigid, sharply acuminate—DIPSACUS (Eur. to E. Asia, N. and E. Afr.). **DD.** Paleae of the receptacle herbaceous or represented by hairs: **E.** Involucral bracts not united: **F.** Paleae almost equal in size to the flowers—SUCCISA (Eur. to N. Afr.). **FF.** Paleae smaller than the flowers or absent: **G.** Outer calyx without distinct grooves, ribs at most slightly prominent; limb at most shortly toothed—KNAUTIA (Eur., Mediterr. Reg.). **GG.** Outer calyx distinctly 8-grooved or 8-ribbed, the limb spreading out saucer-like: **H.** Calyx 10- or more rayed, often caducous: **J.** Outer calyx 8-grooved the whole length—PTEROCEPHALUS (Mediterr. Reg. to Trop. Afr. and India). **JJ.** Outer calyx 8-grooved only in the upper part—CALLISTEMMA (E. Mediterr. Reg.). **HH.** Calyx 5-rayed, persistent—SCABIOSA (*Spongostemma*). **EE.** Involucral bracts united at the base or up to the middle into a lobed cup—PYCNOCOMON (W. Mediterr. Reg.). **AA.** Flowers with a double involucel below the real calyx; herb glandular in the upper part, especially the outer involucel—TRIPLOSTEGIA (*Hoeckia*) (Himal., China, Malay Archip., New Guin.).

314. CALYCERACEAE

Annual or perennial herbs; leaves radical or alternate, entire or pinnately lobed; stipules absent; flowers *capitate* on a common receptacle surrounded

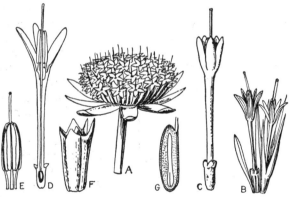

FIG. 314. Calycera balsamitifolia *Rich.* (Calyceraceae). A, capitulum. B, flowers showing relation to bracts. C, flower. D, vertical section of same. E, stamens and pistil. F, calyx. G, vertical section of seed showing embryo. (After Le Maout & Decne.)

by 1–2 series of *bracts*, ⚥ or rarely unisexual, actinomorphic; calyx-tube adnate to the ovary, angled and dentate; corolla tubular, with 4–6 valvate lobes; stamens the same number as and alternate with the corolla-lobes, inserted towards the *top of the tube*; filaments more or less *connate*; anthers more or less *connate around the style*, 2-locular, opening lengthwise; ovary inferior, 1-locular; style undivided, slender; ovule solitary, pendulous; fruits (achenes) sometimes becoming connate; seed solitary, pendulous, with thin or copious endosperm; embryo straight. B.H. **2**, 161; E.P. **4**, 5, 84. Temperate and subtropical S. America.

A. Fruits free from one another: **B.** Fruits of one kind, with unchanged calyx in fruit—BOOPIS. **BB.** Fruits of two kinds, some with hardened calyx, some unchanged—CALYCERA. **AA.** Fruits of the outer flowers united with one another—ACICARPHA.

ORDER 74. CAMPANALES

Herbaceous to somewhat woody; corolla actinomorphic to zygomorphic, epigynous; stamens free from or inserted low down on the corolla; anthers free to connivent; ovary inferior or rarely superior; ovules usually numerous, axile.—Mainly Temperate Regions.

A. Anthers free from each other; corolla actinomorphic   *Campanulaceae*
AA. Anthers cohering into a tube around the style, very rarely free; corolla zygomorphic   *Lobeliaceae*

315. CAMPANULACEAE

Herbs, rarely small shrubs to small trees, nearly always with *milky juice*; leaves alternate, rarely opposite, simple; *stipules absent*; flowers often showy, ☿, actinomorphic; calyx-tube usually adnate to the ovary, 3–10-lobed, lobes imbricate or valvate; corolla sympetalous, tubular or campanulate, lobes *valvate*; stamens as many as the corolla-lobes and alternate with them, inserted near the *base* of the corolla or on the disk; filaments usually free from each other; anthers free, 2-locular, opening lengthwise; ovary *inferior* or rarely superior, 2–10-locular, with *axile placentas*, rarely the placentas basal or apical; ovules mostly numerous; fruit capsular and variously dehiscent, or baccate, often crowned by the persistent calyx-lobes. B.H. **2**, 541; E.P. **4**, 5, 40. Widely distributed.—JASIONE, LIGHTFOOTIA, WAHLENBERGIA,

FIG. 315. Campanula allionii *Vill.* (Campanulaceae). A, vertical section of flower. B, ovary. C, transverse section of same. D, stamen. (After *Bot. Mag.*)

PLATYCODON, CODONOPSIS, CYANANTHUS, CANARINA, ROELLA, PRISMATO-CARPUS, PHYTEUMA, CAMPANULA, LEGOUSIA (*Specularia*), ADENOPHORA, TRACHELIUM, PENTAPHRAGMA, SPHENOCLEA, &c. Value mainly horticultural.

As in Bentham and Hooker's *Genera Plantarum* and Engler and Prantl's *Natürl. Pflanzen-familien*, I prefer to retain the genus *Sphenoclea* in *Campanulaceae*, where its position has not been questioned except by Airy Shaw.[1] Shaw says 'there is no evidence of affinity with *Campanulaceae*, with which it has hitherto been associated'. He does not qualify this negative statement but considers it to be related to *Phytolaccaceae*. In my opinion, however, the resemblance to *Phytolacca* is entirely superficial and due to parallel evolution of the inflorescence. There are numerous similar inflorescences among flowering plants, and even that of *Michauxia*, in *Campanulaceae*, approaches it quite closely.

In **Phytolaccaceae** (*sensu stricto*) there are *no petals*,	In **Sphenoclea**, on the contrary, the corolla is *sympetalous*,
the stamens, when definite in number, are *alternate* with the *sepals* (if petals were present they would therefore be opposite to them), a condition unknown in *Campanulaceae*),	the stamens are *alternate* with the *corolla-lobes*,
the ovary is *superior* and the ovule is solitary in each carpel,	the ovary is *semi-inferior*, 2-locular, and with large multi-ovulate pendulous placentas,
the carpels in *Phytolacca* itself in fruit are free or connate and indehiscent.	the fruit is a capsule dehiscing by a *transverse slit* (circumscissile).

From a comparison of the embryological and anatomical features of *Sphenoclea* with those of *Phytolaccaceae*, K. Subramanyam has come to a similar conclusion to mine (see *Proc. Indian Acad. Sci.* **31**, 60 (1950); also Maheshwari, 'The Embryology of Angiosperms, A Retrospect and Prospect', *Curr. Sci.* **25**, 106–10 (1956). I also consider *Pentaphragma* (*Pentaphragmataceae* of Airy Shaw) to be equally correctly placed in *Campanulaceae*.

316. LOBELIACEAE

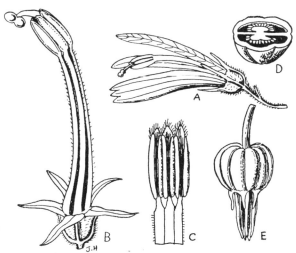

FIG. 316. Pratia physaloides *Hemsl.* (Lobeliaceae). A, flower. B, same with perianth removed. C, stamens. D, transverse section of ovary. E, fruit.

Herbaceous, sometimes woody below, rarely entirely woody; juice often *milky*; leaves alternate, simple; stipules absent; flowers ☿, rarely ♂ ♀, calyx adnate to the ovary, 5-lobed; corolla *zygomorphic*, epigynous, sympetalous, 1–2-lipped, the lips reversed (resupinate) by a twisting of the

[1] Airy Shaw, *Flora Malesiana*, **4**, 1, 27 (1948).

pedicel, lobes *valvate*; stamens 5, alternate with the corolla-lobes, epipetalous or free; filaments free from each other at the base; anthers *cohering into a tube* around the style; ovary more or less inferior, 2–3-locular (rarely sub-1-locular); style simple, or 2-lobed and girt with a ring of hairs; ovules numerous, axile; fruit fleshy or capsular and variously dehiscent; seeds numerous, small, with small straight embryo in copious endosperm. B.H. **2**, 545; E.P. **4**, 5, 40 (under *Campanulaceae*). Mainly Tropics and Subtropics.—CENTRO-POGON, SIPHOCAMPYLUS, ISOTOMA, LAURENTIA, PRATIA, LOBELIA, CYPHIA, &c. Value mainly horticultural. *Indian Tobacco* (Lobelia inflata *L.*), N. Amer.

ORDER 75. GOODENIALES

Herbs or undershrubs; leaves alternate or rarely opposite, simple, or all radical; stipules absent or scale-like; flowers bisexual, actinomorphic to zygomorphic; calyx-tube adnate to the ovary, rarely free; corolla sympetalous, 2–1-lipped, lobes imbricate or valvate; stamens 5, alternate with the lobes, or 2; filaments free or connate around the style; anthers opening lengthwise; ovary mostly inferior, 1–4-locular; stigma indusiate.

A. Stamens 5; anthers free from the style; ovary mostly inferior   *Goodeniaceae*
AA. Stamens 5; anthers connate into a tube around the style; ovary superior
                                                                        Brunoniaceae
AAA. Stamens 2; filaments and style connate into a column; ovary inferior
                                                                        Stylidiaceae

317. GOODENIACEAE

Herbs or undershrubs, rarely spinescent; leaves alternate or rarely opposite, sometimes all radical; stipules absent; flowers from solitary to paniculate, ☿,

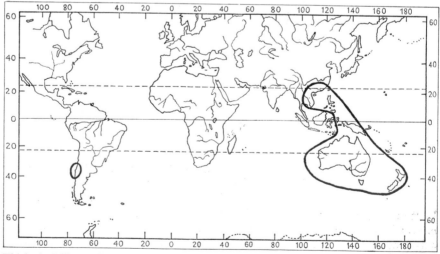

The herb, Selliera radicans *Cav.* (Goodeniaceae), has a remarkable discontinuous distribution on both sides of the Pacific Ocean.

zygomorphic; calyx tubular, adnate to the ovary, rarely free; lobes mostly 5; corolla sympetalous, 5-merous, *bilabiate* or rarely *1-lipped*, lobes *valvate*, often induplicate; stamens 5, alternate with the corolla-lobes, free or rarely shortly adnate to the corolla-tube; anthers free or connivent around the style, 2-locular, opening lengthwise; ovary mostly inferior, 1–2- (rarely 4-) locular; style simple or fid; *stigma indusiate* at the apex; ovules 1 or more in each loculus, mostly erect or ascending; fruit drupaceous or nut-like, or capsular; seeds small, flat, with straight embryo in the middle of copious endosperm. B.H. **2**, 536; E.P. **4**, 5, 70. Mainly Australian; a few in New

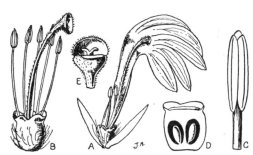

FIG. 317. Scaevola gracilis *Hook. f.* (Goodeniaceae). A, flower. B, same with corolla removed. C, stamen. D, vertical section of ovary. E, stigma. (Orig.)

Zealand, S. Africa, Antarctic S. America, and Tropical Asia.—LESCHENAULTIA, VELLEIA, GOODENIA, SELLIERA, SCAEVOLA, DAMPIERA, &c.

USEFUL PRODUCT: *Taccada Pith* (Scaevola koenigii *Vahl*), E. Tropics.

318. BRUNONIACEAE

Perennial herb; leaves all radical, entire; stipules absent; flowers bisexual, actinomorphic, densely *capitate* on a common peduncle; bracts present;

FIG. 318. Brunonia australis *R.Br.* (Brunoniaceae). A, flower. B, calyx. C, vertical section of flower. D, stigma. E, vertical section of fruit. (Partly after Baill.)

calyx-tube free from the ovary, lobes 5, persistent in fruit; corolla blue, sympetalous, inserted at the base of the calyx-tube; lobes 5, spreading, *valvate*; stamens 5, inserted near the base of the corolla-tube; anthers *connate around the style*, 2-locular, introrse, opening by slits lengthwise; ovary superior, enclosed by the calyx-tube, *1-locular*; style simple, stigma small, surrounded by a *cupular indusium*; ovule 1, *erect*; fruit dry and indehiscent, enclosed by the persistent calyx-tube; seed 1, erect, *without endosperm*; embryo straight, cotyledons ovate. B.H. **2**, 541; E.P. **4**, 5, 79; Krause, Engl. *Pflanzenr. Brunoniaceae*, 1–6, fig. 1 (1912). Australia.— BRUNONIA.

319. STYLIDIACEAE

Herbs or rarely undershrubs; leaves radical or fasciculate on the stems, simple; stipules absent or rarely scaly; flowers ☿ or ♂ ♀, mostly zygomorphic,

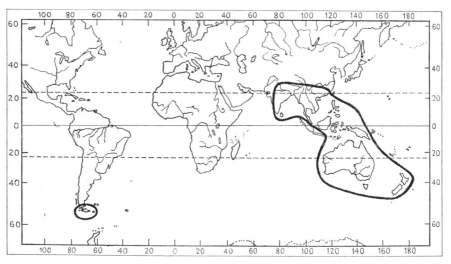

The family Stylidiaceae is confined to Eastern Asia, Malaya, and Australasia, except for one genus, Phyllachne, in Subantarctic S. America.

in racemes or corymbs; calyx-tube adnate to the ovary; lobes 5–7, free or connate and 2-lipped; corolla sympetalous, 5-lobed, lobes imbricate, mostly unequal, the lowermost forming a lip; *stamens 2*; filaments *connate into a column around the style* but free from the corolla; disk present or absent, sometimes glandular; ovary inferior, 2-locular, or 1-locular at the base; style divided at the apex of the staminal column; ovules numerous in each loculus, axile; capsule 2-locular or 1-locular by the disappearance of the septum, rarely fruit indehiscent; seeds small, with fleshy endosperm and minute embryo. B.H. **2**, 534; E.P. **4**, 5, 79 (as *Candolleaceae*). Mildbraed, Engl. *Pflanzenr. Stylidiaceae* (1908) (excl. *Donatia*). Australia, Tropical Asia, New Zealand, Subantarctic S. America.

   A. Corolla actinomorphic or nearly so: **B.** Flowers subsessile; anthers 2-locular—OREOSTYLIDIUM (New Zeal.). **BB.** Flowers on long peduncles;

anthers monothecous—FORSTERA (New Zeal., Tasm.). **BBB.** Flowers sessile among the leaves; anthers monothecous—PHYLLACHNE (Subantarct. S. Amer., New Zeal.). **AA.** Corolla zygomorphic, the fifth lobe very different from the others: **C.** Labellum small or more or less reduced; staminal column curved

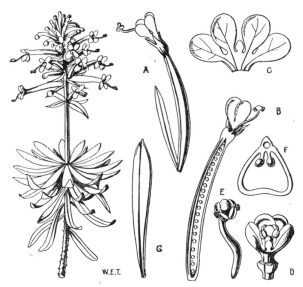

FIG. 319. Stylidium adnatum, var. abbreviatum *De Wild.* (Stylidiaceae). A, flower. B, same in vertical section. C, corolla. D, flower with calyx removed. E, style and stamens. F, transverse section of fruit. G, bract. (After De Wild.)

or geniculate, irritable—STYLIDIUM (Austral.). **CC.** Labellum large, hooded, more or less long-stipitate; staminal column erect, not mobile—LEVENHOOKIA (Austral.).

ORDER 76. ASTERALES

Herbaceous to woody, rarely trees; leaves alternate, opposite, or all radical; no stipules; flowers collected into heads surrounded by an involucre of bracts, rarely heads compound; outer flowers either ligulate and female (rarely sterile), the inner flowers tubular and bisexual, or all the flowers ligulate and bisexual; anthers united into a tube; filaments free, inserted on the corolla-tube; ovary inferior, 1-locular; style mostly 2-lobed; ovule 1, erect; fruit an achene, usually crowned by a pappus (modified calyx).—World-wide distribution.

320. COMPOSITAE

Herbs, shrubs, or rarely trees or climbers; leaves alternate or opposite, simple or variously divided; *stipules absent*; flowers *crowded into heads* (capitula) surrounded by an *involucre* of one or more series of free or connate bracts; sometimes the head compound and the partial heads reduced to a single flower; receptacle bracteate amongst the flowers, honeycombed or nude, usually convex, rarely elongated or hollowed out; flowers ⚥ or ♂ ♀, rarely dioecious, the outer ones often *ligulate* (rayed), the inner ones *tubular*, or all ligulate; calyx much modified and thread-like (*pappus*), rarely dry and chaffy, epigynous; corolla sympetalous, 4–5-fid, *valvate*, actinomorphic or zygomorphic, rarely bilabiate; stamens 5 or rarely 4, epipetalous, mostly included in the corolla-tube; filaments free from each other; anthers

FIG. 320*a*. Helichrysum leucopsideum *DC*. (Compositae). A, disk flower. B, same opened to show stamens. C, involucral bract. D, stamen. E, pappus-bristle. F, style. (After Hook.)

connate (syngenesious) into a tube, very rarely free, 2-locular, opening length-wise; ovary *inferior*, 1-locular, 1-ovuled; style of the ⚥ flowers mostly 2-fid or 2-lobed with various forms of collecting hairs which serve to brush out the pollen; ovule erect from the base; fruit (achene) sessile, sometimes beaked; seed without endosperm; embryo straight with plano-convex cotyledons. B.H. **2**, 163; E.P. **4**, 5, 87. Distribution world-wide.—Sparganophorus, Erlangea, Vernonia, Stokesia, Elephantopus, Ageratum, Stevia, Eupatorium, Mikania, Solidago, Pteronia, Bellis, Aster, Olearia, Celmisia, Erigeron, Baccharis, Tarchonanthus, Sphaeranthus, Antennaria, Leontopodium, Anaphalis, Gnaphalium, Raoulia, Helichrysum, Humea, Inula, Pulicaria, Buphthalmum, Zinnia, Xanthium, Montanoa, Rudbeckia, Coreopsis, Bidens, Dahlia, Cosmos, Tagetes, Achillea, Santolina, Anthemis, Chrysanthemum, Matricaria, Artemisia, Tussilago, Senecio, Othonna, Calendula, Ursinia, Arctotis, Echinops, Carduus, Serratula, Centaurea, Barnadesia, Mutisia, Gerbera, Cichorium, Crepis, Hieracium, Sonchus, Lactuca, &c.

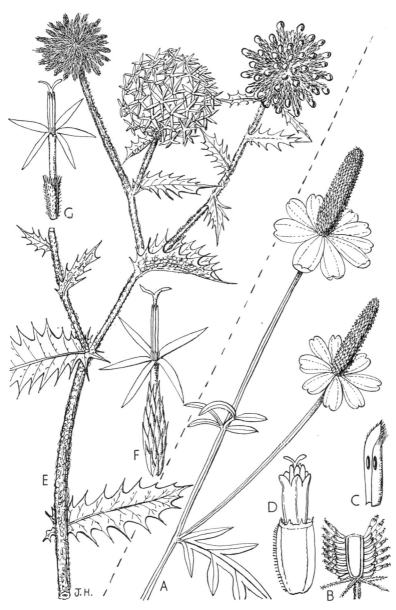

Fig. 320b. Two examples of Compositae: A, a primitive member, Ratibida columnifera (*Nutt.*) *Woot. & Standl.*; B, part of inflorescence showing the primitive bract below each flower; C, bract; D, flower. E, a very highly evolved and reduced member, Echinops sphaerocephalus *L.*; the heads are compound, each partial head being reduced to a single flower; F, G, single flower.

USEFUL PRODUCTS: *Jerusalem Artichoke* (Helianthus tuberosus *L.*), U.S.A.; *Globe Artichoke* (Cynara scolymus *L.*); *Santonin* (Artemisia cina *Berg.*), Turkestan; *Chicory* (Cichorium intybus *L.*); *Lettuce* (Lactuca scariola *L.*), and numerous minor medicinal products and dyes, besides a great number of ornamental garden plants.

ORDER 77. SOLANALES

Mostly herbs or twiners; leaves alternate; no stipules; corolla actinomorphic; stamens the same number as and alternate with the corolla-lobes; ovary superior, 1–4-locular, often 2-locular, or of almost free carpels, ovules numerous to solitary, axile; seeds with some endosperm and often curved embryo.—General distribution.

A. Ovules numerous in each loculus, axile; embryo cyclic, spiral, or straight
   in fleshy endosperm; ovary 2-locular (except in *Nicandra* and *Jaborosa*)

   Solanaceae

AA. Ovules 1–4 in each loculus, erect from the base of the loculi; embryo
    variously folded or much incurved with very scanty or no endosperm:
B. Ovary usually of 2 carpels   *Convolvulaceae*
BB. Ovary of 5 carpels   *Nolanaceae*

321. SOLANACEAE

Herbaceous or woody; leaves *alternate*, simple; *stipules absent*; flowers ⚥, mostly *actinomorphic*; calyx 4–6-lobed, persistent; corolla sympetalous, usually 5-lobed, lobes folded, contorted or valvate; stamens inserted on the corolla-tube and alternate with its lobes; anthers 2-locular, loculi parallel, opening lengthwise or by apical pores; *ovary 2-locular*, the loculi sometimes again divided by a false septum; style terminal; ovules very *numerous*, axile; fruit a capsule or berry; seeds with copious endosperm and curved or annular embryo. B.H. **2**, 882; E.P. **4**, 3*b*, 4. Generally distributed in Temperate and Tropical Regions.—SOLANUM, PHYSALIS, CAPSICUM, WITHANIA, LYCIUM, ATROPA, DATURA, HYOSCYAMUS, JUANULLOA, CESTRUM, NICOTIANA (Fig. 321), PETUNIA, SCHIZANTHUS, SALPIGLOSSIS, BRUNFELSIA, SCHWENKIA, &c.

USEFUL PRODUCTS: *Potato* (Solanum tuberosum *L.*), Chile; *Tomato* (Lycopersicum esculentum *Mill.*), S. Amer.; *Capsicums* or *Chillies* (Capsicum annuum *L.* and C. frutescens *L.*); *Cayenne Pepper* from same source; *Deadly Nightshade* (Atropa belladonna *L.*), Eur.; *Henbane* (Hyoscyamus niger *L.*) Eur.; *Tobacco* (Nicotiana tabacum *L.*), Amer.

322. CONVOLVULACEAE

Herbaceous or woody, often climbing, juice usually milky; leaves *alternate*, simple; *stipules absent*; flowers ⚥, actinomorphic; bracts often forming an *involucre*; sepals usually free, imbricate, persistent; corolla sympetalous, lobes 5, plicate-*contorted* or rarely imbricate; stamens 5, inserted towards the *base* of the corolla-tube and alternate with the lobes; anthers 2-locular, opening lengthwise; ovary often surrounded by a *disk*, 1–4-locular; ovules *solitary* or *paired* erect; style terminal; fruit a capsule or fleshy and indehis-

A

W.E.T.

B

FIG. 321. Nicotiana fragrans *Hook*. (Solanaceae). A, ovary. B, transverse section of same. (After *Bot. Mag.*)

cent; seeds sometimes hairy, with rather scanty endosperm and more or less
curved embryo; cotyledons *folded* or *crumpled*; B.H. **2**, 865; E.P. **4**, 3*a*, 1.
Generally distributed. (Incl. *Humbertiaceae*.)—IPOMOEA, HUMBERTIA, HEWIT-
TIA, CALYSTEGIA, JACQUEMONTIA, CONVOLVULUS, EVOLVULUS, &c.

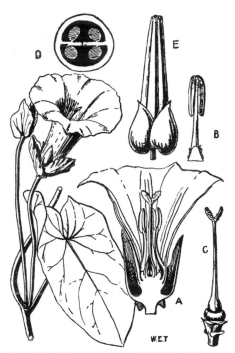

FIG. 322. Calystegia sepium (*L.*) *R. Br.* (Convolvulaceae). A, vertical section of flower. B, stamen.
C, ovary. D, transverse section of same. E, bud.

USEFUL PRODUCTS: *Jalap* (Exogonium purga (*Wendl.*) *Benth.*), Mexico;
Sweet Potato (Ipomoea batatas *Poir.*), Tropics; *Scammony* (Convolvulus
scammonia *L.*), Asia Minor.

323. NOLANACEAE

Herbs or shrublets, sometimes diffuse or prostrate; leaves alternate, sometimes paired, sessile or petiolate, flat or terete, sometimes fleshy; *no stipules*;
flowers axillary, subsessile or pedicellate; calyx tubular-campanulate, more or
less 5-lobed, lobes slightly imbricate; corolla sympetalous, actinomorphic,
campanulate or funnel-shaped, lobes 5, *plicate*; stamens *unequal* (3 long and
2 short), included or slightly exserted, inserted towards the base of the
corolla; anthers ovoid or oblong; disk *annular or cushion-like*, crenate or
lobulate; ovary superior, entire or 5–10-lobed, 5-locular, loculi 4–1-ovulate;
ovules attached at the base; style terminal or between the lobes, with a *peltate
stigma*; fruit a schizocarp or divided into nutlets; seeds with endosperm and
a terete curved or spiral embryo. B.H. **2,** 879 (in *Convolvulaceae*). E.P. **4,** 3*b*, 1.

I. M. Johnston, 'A Study of Nolanaceae', *Proc. Amer. Acad.* **71,** 1–87 (1936).—
Western S. America.

A. Carpels united together and to the axis of the fruit; shrubs—ALONA
(*Osteocarpus*). **AA.** Carpels attached only to the receptacle and free or nearly so
from one another, nut-like; herbs or shrubs—NOLANA (*Dolia, Bargemontia*).

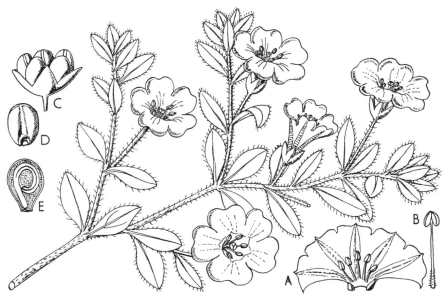

FIG. 323. Nolana paradoxa *Lindl.* (Nolanaceae). A, corolla opened out. B, stamen. C, fruit.
D, seed. E, vertical section of seed. (Orig.)

In the first edition of this book, following Bentham and Hooker, the two genera composing
this family were included in *Convolvulaceae*. Since then I. M. Johnston (see ref. above) has
made a careful study of the group and gives some very cogent reasons for retaining it as a
separate family, which he considers to be more closely related to *Solanaceae* than *Convolvulaceae*. They form a very natural group of more or less succulent herbs and small shrubs
characteristic of the coastal districts of northern Chile and southern Peru. They differ from
the *Solanaceae* in the nature and structure of their remarkable fruit, which is bony, basically
pentamerous, schizocarpic (*Aloma*), or consisting of 3 to numerous 8–1-seeded nutlets, the
seeds uniseriate or pluriseriate in superimposed series. In *Solanaceae*, with a single exception
(*Nicandra*), the ovary is 2-merous and the placentation of the ovules is axile. In *Convolvulaceae*
the ovary is usually 2-merous and the ovules are attached at the base, as they are in
Nolanaceae.

ORDER 78. PERSONALES

More or less as in preceding; leaves alternate to opposite; corolla always
more or less zygomorphic; stamens fewer than the corolla-lobes, often 4 or 2;
placentation usually axile but sometimes parietal; ovules numerous.—General
distribution.

A. Ovary superior:
  B. Ovary completely 2-locular; loculi antero-posterior in relation to the
    floral axis;

C. Leaves alternate or opposite; placentas of fruit not elastic; seeds mostly with endosperm   *Scrophulariaceae*

CC. Leaves opposite from tumid nodes; placentas of fruit usually elastic; seeds mostly without endosperm   *Acanthaceae*

  BB. Ovary 1-locular:

  D. Placentas parietal:

   E. Not parasitic; leafy plants with green colouring; carpels to right and left of floral axis, seeds with scanty or no endosperm   *Gesneriaceae*

   EE. Parasitic leafless plants devoid of green colouring; carpels antero-posterior   *Orobanchaceae*

  DD. Placentas basal, globose; seeds without endosperm; stamens 2, with 1-locular anthers; aquatic or swamp plants   *Lentibulariaceae*

AA. Ovary inferior; carpels to right and left of floral axis:

  F. Trees or shrubs; stamens 2, anthers large, undulate-plicate; leaves opposite   *Columelliaceae*

  FF. Herbs; stamens 4 or 2; anthers often connivent in pairs, not plicate   *Gesneriaceae*

324. SCROPHULARIACEAE

Herbs or shrubs, rarely small trees; leaves alternate, opposite, or verticillate; *stipules absent*; flowers ⚥, mostly *zygomorphic*; calyx imbricate or valvate;

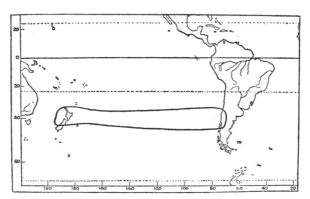

The range of Jovellana (Scrophulariaceae), formerly included in Calceolaria, points to the probability of a former land connexion between these now widely separated regions.

corolla sympetalous; limb 4–5-, rarely 6–8-lobed, often more or less *2-lipped*, lobes *imbricate*; stamens *often 4*, didynamous, or 2, inserted on the corolla-tube and alternate with the lobes, the fifth (adaxial) stamen represented by a *staminode* or absent, rarely perfect; filaments free from each other; anthers 2-locular, opening lengthwise or the loculi confluent at the apex and opening by one continuous slit, sometimes the anthers connivent in pairs; ovary superior, sessile, entire, usually perfectly *2-locular*; style *terminal*; ovules axile, *numerous*, rarely few; fruit a capsule, rarely a berry; seeds numerous, with fleshy endosperm and straight or slightly curved embryo. B.H. **2**, 913;

E.P. **4,** 3*b*, 39. Generally distributed.—Verbascum, Calceolaria, Nemesia, Linaria, Antirrhinum, Scrophularia, Paulownia, Pentstemon, Sutera, Mimulus, Torenia, Sibthorpia, Scoparia, Rehmannia, Digitalis, Erinus,

Fig. 324. Torenia fournieri *Linden ex Four.* (Scrophulariaceae).
A, flower opened to show insertion of stamens. B and C, stamen.
D, ovary. (After *Bot. Mag.*)

Veronica, Hebe, Striga, Sopubia, Castilleja, Euphrasia, Bartsia, Pedicularis, Rhinanthus, Melampyrum, &c.

Useful Products: Mostly of horticultural value. *Foxglove* (Digitalis purpurea *L.*), Eur., &c.

325. Acanthaceae

Herbaceous or climbing, rarely somewhat shrubby; leaves opposite, often with distinct *cystoliths*; stipules absent; flowers ♀, *zygomorphic*, often with conspicuous bracts; calyx-segments or lobes 4 or 5, imbricate or valvate, rarely the calyx reduced to a ring; corolla sympetalous, *2-lipped* or sometimes 1-lipped, lobes imbricate or contorted; *stamens 4*, didynamous, or 2, inserted on the corolla-tube and alternate with its lobes; filaments free amongst themselves, or partially connate in pairs; anthers 2-locular or 1-locular by reduction, loculi confluent or separated, sometimes one *much smaller* than the

FIG. 325. Acanthus montanus (*Nees*) *T. Anders*. (Acanthaceae). A, bracts and pistil, and ovary. C, fruit. D, one valve of fruit. (Orig.)

other, opening lengthwise; disk present; ovary superior, sessile on the disk, 2-locular; style simple; ovules axile, 2 or more in each loculus; fruit a capsule, often club-shaped, mostly elastically dehiscent from the apex downwards, the valves recurved and leaving the central axis; seeds mostly with *indurated funicle*; endosperm rarely present; embryo large. B.H. **2**, 1060; E.P. **4**, 3*b*, 274. Warm Regions.—THUNBERGIA, RUELLIA, STROBILANTHES, BLEPHARIS, ACANTHUS, BARLERIA, ASYSTASIA, ERANTHEMUM, LEPIDAGATHIS, APHELANDRA, JUSTICIA, BELOPERONE, DIANTHERA, JACOBINIA, THYRSACANTHUS, DICLIPTERA, HYPOESTES, &c. Mainly of horticultural value.

326. GESNERIACEAE

Herbs, shrubs, or rarely trees; leaves radical or opposite, equal or alternately large and small, sometimes the smaller one like a stipule, or the alternate one

FIG. 326. Aeschynanthus peelii *Hk. f. & Thoms.* (Gesneriaceae). A, flower opened to show insertion of stamens. B, ovary. C, transverse section of same. D, fruits. E, seeds. (After Hook. f.)

altogether reduced; flowers ⚥, usually zygomorphic, often large and showy; calyx usually tubular, free to completely adnate to the ovary; lobes *valvate* or rarely imbricate; corolla sympetalous with an *oblique limb*, often more or less 2-lipped, lobes imbricate, the adaxial pair usually interior; stamens 4 or 2, often with an additional staminode; anthers *connate* or *connivent* in pairs, rarely free, 2-locular, opening lengthwise; disk annular or 1-sided or of separate glands or scales; ovary superior to inferior, 1-locular, with 2 *parietal* or *intrusive* placentas; ovules numerous; fruit a capsule or rarely a berry; seeds numerous, small, with or without endosperm; embryo straight. B.H. **2**, 990; E.P. **4**, 3*b*, 133. Mainly Tropics and Subtropics.—GLOXINIA, ACHIMENES, ISOLOMA, GESNERIA, PENTARHAPHIA, EPISCIA, ALLOPLECTUS, COLUMNEA, CYRTANDRA, AESCHYNANTHUS, BESLERIA, DIDYMOCARPUS, CHIRITA, STREPTOCARPUS, RAMONDIA, HABERLEA, SINNINGIA, &c.

USEFUL PRODUCTS: Mainly of horticultural value; many beautiful greenhouse plants.

327. OROBANCHACEAE

Herbs *parasitic* on roots, often covered with scales at the base, *never green*; stems with alternate, often crowded, scales; flowers solitary in the axils of bracts, often crowded, ♀, *zygomorphic*; calyx 4–5-toothed or lobed or variously split, lobes open or *valvate*; corolla sympetalous, often curved; limb

FIG. 327. Cistanche laxiflora *Aitch. & Hemsl.* (Orobanchaceae).
A, ovary. B, same in transverse section. C, corolla. D, stamen.
(After Hemsl.)

oblique or 2-lipped, lobes 5, imbricate, the adaxial 2 interior; *stamens 4*, didynamous, inserted below the middle of the corolla-tube, alternate with the lobes, the fifth (adaxial) one reduced to a *staminode* or absent; anthers often connivent in pairs, opening lengthwise; ovary superior, 1-locular, with 4 *parietal* placentas; style terminal; ovules numerous; capsule often enveloped by the calyx, opening by 2 valves; seeds very numerous, small, with fleshy endosperm and minute embryo. B.H. **2**, 980; E.P. **4**, 3*b*, 123. Rather scattered distribution.—AEGINETIA, CHRISTISONIA, PHELIPAEA, CISTANCHE, OROBANCHE, LATHRAEA, &c.

328. LENTIBULARIACEAE

Herbs of wet or damp places, sometimes submerged or epiphytic; leaves in rosettes or alternate and reduced; flowers scapose, ♀, *zygomorphic*; calyx 2–5-parted, lobes open or slightly imbricate; corolla sympetalous, *spurred* at the back; limb 2-lipped, lobes 5, imbricate; *stamens 2*, inserted at the base of the corolla, with 2 *rudimentary* stamens; anthers 1–2-locular, opening lengthwise; disk absent; ovary superior, 1-locular; stigma often sessile; ovules numerous on *basal* globose or ovoid placenta, rarely 2; fruit a capsule opening irregularly or by 2 or 4 valves; seeds numerous, rarely 1, without endosperm. B.H. **2**, 986; E.P. **4**, 3b, 108. Temperate and Tropical Regions.

A. Ovules numerous; corolla mostly with a distinct spur at the base: **B.** Calyx 5–4-merous: **C.** Calyx-segments 5–4, 1-seriate: **D.** Posticous corolla-lip

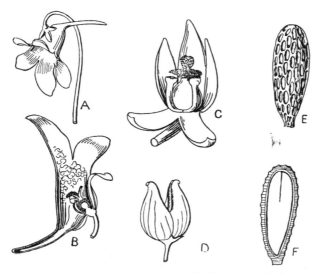

FIG. 328. Pinguicula vulgaris *L.* (Lentibulariaceae). A, flower. B, vertical section of same. C, same with corolla removed. D, fruit. E, seed. F, vertical section of same. (After Baill.)

erect; anthers parallel, with confluent loculi—GENLISEA (Trop. Amer., Trop. Afr.). **DD.** Posticous corolla-lip spreading; anthers terminal, subtransverse, 1-locular—PINGUICULA (Amer., Eur., Asia). **CC.** Calyx-segments 4, in 2 series; anthers dorsifixed, parallel, confluent, and 1-locular—POLYPOMPHOLYX (Austral., S. Amer.). **BB.** Calyx 2-merous, 2-partite, or lobed; anthers dorsifixed, parallel, loculi divaricate or confluent into one—UTRICULARIA (widely distrib.). **AA.** Ovules 2; corolla at most saccate at the base—BIOVULARIA (Trop. Afr., India).

329. COLUMELLIACEAE

Trees or shrubs; leaves *opposite*, simple; stipules absent; flowers in terminal cymes, ☿, slightly zygomorphic; calyx-tube *adnate to the ovary*; lobes 5, scarcely imbricate; corolla sympetalous; tube very short, subcampanulate; lobes usually 5, imbricate; *stamens 2*, inserted near the base of the corolla, alternate with the adaxial and lateral lobes; anther-loculi undulately *plicate* and *twisted*; disk absent; ovary almost quite *inferior*, imperfectly 2-locular; style terminal; ovules numerous on 2 *parietal* placentas which are subcon-

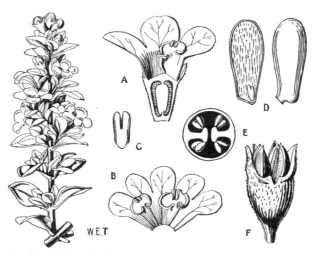

Fig. 329. Columellia obovata *R. & P.* (Columelliaceae). A, vertical section of flower. B, flower opened. C, embryo. D, seed. E, transverse section of ovary. F, capsule.

tiguous in the middle of the ovary; fruit a capsule; seeds numerous, with fleshy endosperm and minute straight embryo. B.H. **2**, 989; E.P. **4**, 3*b*, 186. Andes of S. America.—Columellia.

Order 79. GERANIALES

Herbs or undershrubs, very rarely arborescent; flowers hypogynous, ☿, actinomorphic to zygomorphic; sepals imbricate or rarely valvate; petals present and often clawed, usually free; stamens as many to twice as many as the petals; disk-glands often present; syncarpous with axile placentation; ovules solitary to few; seeds mostly without endosperm, embryo straight. Leaves alternate or radical, rarely opposite, simple to much-divided or pinnate; stipules present or absent.—General distribution.

A. Stipules present; dorsal sepal not spurred or if so then the spur adnate to the pedicel (revealed by a cross section); seeds with little or no endosperm; ovules 1–2 in each loculus, rarely more; ovary more or less 3–5-lobed, lobes in fruit often beaked   *Geraniaceae*

AA. Stipules absent:

　B. Petals contorted; flowers actinomorphic; dorsal sepal not spurred:

　　C. Sepals valvate; seed without endosperm; carpels free or nearly so
　　　　　　　　　　　　　　　　　　　　　　　　Limnanthaceae

　　CC. Sepals imbricate; seed with copious endosperm; carpels united
　　　　　　　　　　　　　　　　　　　　　　　　Oxalidaceae

　BB. Petals imbricate; flowers zygomorphic; dorsal sepal produced into a free spur:

　　D. Leaves peltate, digitately nerved; upper 2 petals exterior; ovule 1 in each loculus   *Tropaeolaceae*

DD. Leaves not peltate, pinnately nerved; 1 upper petal exterior, the lateral petals more or less united; ovules several in each loculus

Balsaminaceae

330. GERANIACEAE

Annual herbs or undershrubs, rarely arborescent; leaves alternate or opposite, mostly lobate, dissected or compound; stipules often paired; flowers often

FIG. 330. Erodium macradenium *L'Hérit*. (Geraniaceae). A, flower with petals removed. B, calyx and ovary.

handsome, ♀, actinomorphic or slightly zygomorphic, axillary, solitary to subumbellate; sepals persistent, 4–5, free or connate to the middle, *imbricate* or rarely valvate, the dorsal one *sometimes spurred*; petals 5, rarely 4, very rarely absent, hypogynous or subperigynous, *imbricate*, rarely contorted; stamens 2–3 times the number of the sepals, sometimes a few without anthers, filaments mostly more or less *connate at the base*; anthers 2-locular, opening lengthwise; *ovary* 3–5-lobed; ovules 1–2 in each loculus, superposed, pendulous, rarely more than 2; fruit lobed, lobes 1-seeded, rarely more-seeded, *often beaked*; seeds pendulous, with thin or no (rarely copious) endosperm and mostly curved embryo. B.H. **1**, 269; E.P. **3**, 4, 1. Mainly N. Temperate Zone; great concentration in S. Africa.

USEFUL PRODUCTS: Chiefly cultivated for their handsome flowers and scented leaves. The so-called bedding and greenhouse 'Geranium' is a Pelargonium; *Geranium Oil* (Pelargonium spp.).

A. Calyx without a spur; disk-glands alternate with the petals; corolla actinomorphic: **B.** Stamens 15, all with fertile anthers: **C.** Filaments more or less free from one another; stems fleshy; petioles becoming spiny—SARCO-CAULON (S. Afr.). **CC.** Filaments united into 5 bundles; stems not fleshy; petioles not spiny—MONSONIA (Afr., W. Asia, India). **BB.** Stamens 10: **D.** Stamens mostly all bearing anthers; beaks of the carpels spirally revolute in fruit—GERANIUM (*Neurophyllodes*) (widely distrib.). **DD.** Stamens with 5 fertile anthers, the other 5 scale-like; beaks of the carpels coiled in fruit— ERODIUM (widely distrib.). **AA.** Calyx with a spur adnate to the pedicel, disk-glands absent from between the petals; corolla zygomorphic; beaks of the carpels coiled-revolute in fruit—PELARGONIUM (Mostly S. Afr., few in Austral., Asia Minor, Trop. Afr.).

331. LIMNANTHACEAE

Annual succulent marsh herbs; leaves alternate, much-divided; *stipules absent*; flowers ⚥, actinomorphic, solitary on long stalks, axillary; sepals 3–5, *valvate*

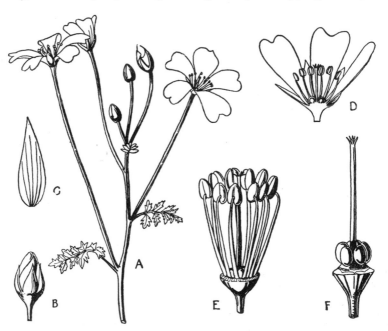

FIG. 331. Limnanthes douglasii *R. Br.* (Limnanthaceae). A, branch with flowers. B, flower-bud. C, sepal. D, vertical section of flower. E, stamens. F, ovary. (After Le Maout & Decne.)

or slightly imbricate; petals 3–5, free, *contorted*, slightly perigynous; stamens 6 or 10, subperigynous, free, some with a gland at the base; anthers 2-locular, opening lengthwise; carpels 5 or 3, *free* or nearly so, but connected by a *common gynobasic style* with 3–5 short lobes; ovule solitary in each carpel, *ascending*; *ripe carpels free*, indehiscent; seed erect, without endosperm;

embryo straight, with large cotyledons and small radicle. B.H. **1**, 274 (under *Geraniaceae*). E.P. **3**, 5, 136. N. America.

A. Flowers 5-merous; stamens 10; ovary 5-locular—LIMNANTHES. **AA.** Flowers 3-merous; stamens 6; ovary 3-locular—FLOERKEA.

332. OXALIDACEAE

Herbaceous or suffrutescent; leaves alternate or radical, digitately or pinnately compound, sometimes simple by suppression of the leaflets; leaflets

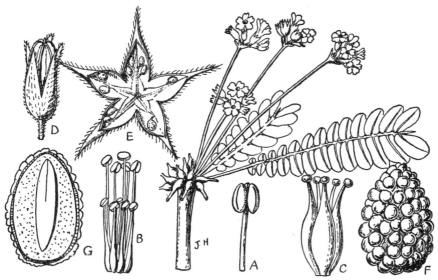

FIG. 332. Biophytum sensitivum (*L.*) *DC.* (Oxalidaceae). A, stamen. B, stamens. C, ovary. D, flower in bud. E, fruit. F, seeds. G, section of seed. (Orig.)

spirally coiled when young, usually folded at night; *stipules absent*; flowers ♀, actinomorphic, sometimes of *two kinds*, some perfect and others minute and apetalous; flowers solitary or subumbellate, rarely racemose or cymose; calyx 5-fid or partite, *imbricate*; petals 5, shortly clawed, free or shortly connate at the base, *contorted*; stamens 10, hypogynous, connate at the base, sometimes five *without anthers*; anthers 2-locular, opening lengthwise; ovary 5-locular, superior; styles 5, *free*, persistent; stigmas capitate or shortly divided; ovules 1 or more, axile; fruit a capsule; seeds often with an elastic testa; endosperm fleshy, copious; embryo straight. B.H. **1**, 276 (under *Geraniaceae*); E.P. **3**, 4, 15. Tropics and Subtropics; large number in S. Africa and S. Amer.

USEFUL PRODUCT: *Arracacha* (Oxalis crenata *Jacq.*, edible tubers, Peru).

A. Stamens 15, in 3 series; styles united—HYPSEOCHARIS (S. Amer.). **AA.** Stamens 10, in 2 series: **B.** Leaves pinnate: **C.** Leaves with a terminal leaflet; mature carpels slightly united at the base—EICHLERIA (S. Amer.). **CC.** Leaves with a bristle representing the end-leaflet; carpels at length free—BIOPHYTUM (Asia, Afr., Trop. Amer.). **BB.** Leaves 1–3-foliolate; mature carpels united—OXALIS.

333. TROPAEOLACEAE

Succulent prostrate or twining herbs with watery juice; root often tuberous; leaves alternate or the lower opposite, simple, *peltate*, sometimes dotted;

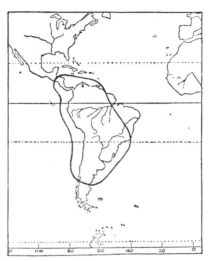

Range of Tropaeolum (Tropaeolaceae).

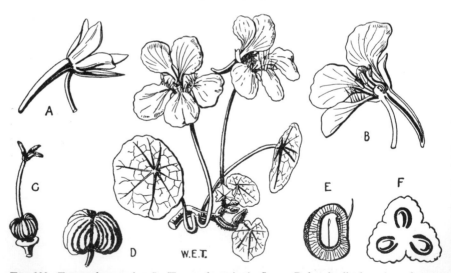

FIG. 333. Tropaeolum majus *L.* (Tropaeolaceae). A, flower. B, longitudinal section of same. C, ovary. D, fruit. E, section of same. F, cross-section of ovary. (After Le Maout & Decne.)

stipules absent; flowers ☿, *zygomorphic*, solitary, axillary; calyx coloured, 2-*lipped*; sepals imbricate or valvate, the lateral often broader, the dorsal *produced into a spur* (sometimes regarded as a part of the axis); petals 5 or rarely fewer by abortion, slightly perigynous, imbricate, the upper two exterior and often more or less different from the others; *stamens* 8, free, declinate; anthers 2-locular, opening lengthwise laterally; ovary superior, sessile, 3-locular, loculi 1-ovulate; ovule pendulous; style one, apical, with 3 stigmas; carpels separating from the short central axis, indehiscent, hardening, rugose; seeds without endosperm; embryo straight, with thick fleshy cotyledons. B.H. **1,** 274 (under *Geraniaceae*); E.P. **3,** 4. 23. Central and S. America.—TROPAEOLUM.

USEFUL PRODUCTS: Several commonly cultivated. *Canary Creeper* (Tropaeolum peregrinum *L.*), Peru, and other species used as bedding plants.

334. BALSAMINACEAE

Succulent herbs, rarely shrubby; leaves alternate or opposite; *stipules absent*; flowers zygomorphic, ♀, brightly coloured, solitary to subumbellate;

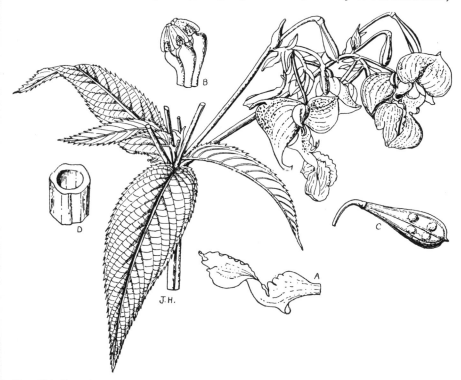

FIG. 334. Impatiens glandulifera *Royle* (I. roylei *Hk. f.*) (Balsaminaceae). A, lateral petals. B, stamens. C, fruit. D, section of stem. (After *Bot. Mag.*)

sepals 3, rarely 5, often coloured, imbricate, unequal, the lowermost elongated into a *tubular spur*; petals 5, the upper one exterior, usually erect, concave, the lateral ones united; stamens 5; filaments short and broad, connate towards the top; anthers 2-locular, *connate around the ovary*; ovary superior, 5-locular, with axile placentas; stigmas 1–5, more or less sessile; ovules numerous; fruit a succulent capsule *opening elastically* into 5 *twisted* valves, rarely a berry;

seeds without endosperm and with straight embryo. B.H. **1**, 277 (under *Geraniaceae*); E.P. **3**, 5, 383. Mainly Tropical Asia and Africa, a few species in cooler regions.

USEFUL PRODUCTS: Several cultivated *Impatiens* with very attractive flowers.

A. Petals all free; drupe berry-like—HYDROCERA (Trop. E. Asia, Malay Archip.). **AA.** Lateral petals connate in pairs; fruit an elastically dehiscent capsule—IMPATIENS (*Petalonema, Impatientella*) (widely distrib.).

ORDER 80. POLEMONIALES

Herbs or rarely shrubs or twiners; corolla sympetalous, actinomorphic; stamens epipetalous, alternate with the corolla-lobes; ovary superior, entire, with numerous or few ovules on parietal or axile placentas.—Mostly American.

A. Corolla-lobes contorted; style 1, filiform; ovary mostly 3-locular, with axile placentas   *Polemoniaceae*

AA. Corolla-lobes imbricate or rarely contorted; styles often 2 and mostly separate:

B. Annual or perennial herbs or subshrubs with green leaves; stamens without scales between the filaments   *Hydrophyllaceae*

BB. Leafless and rootless parasitic herbs without green colouring; stems thread-like and often intertwined or massed on other plants; stamens with lobed or fimbriate scales between the filaments   *Cuscutaceae*

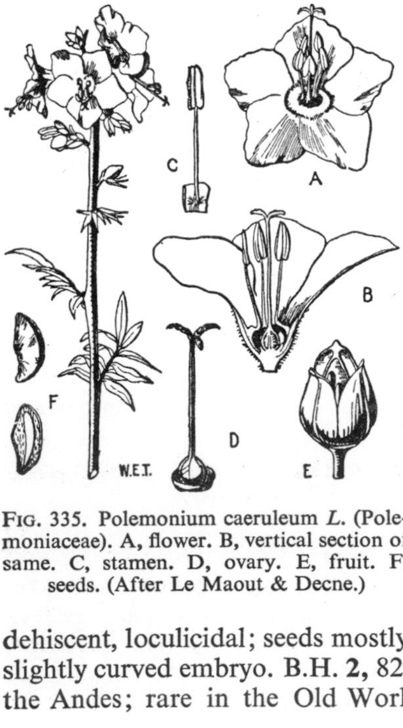

FIG. 335. Polemonium caeruleum *L.* (Polemoniaceae). A, flower. B, vertical section of same. C, stamen. D, ovary. E, fruit. F, seeds. (After Le Maout & Decne.)

335. POLEMONIACEAE

Annual to perennial herbs or rarely shrubs; leaves alternate or opposite, entire or palmately or pinnately partite; flowers ⚥, actinomorphic, rarely subbilabiate, terminal, rarely axillary, often crowded into corymbs or heads; sepals 5, ± connate; corolla of 5 united petals, tubular, lobes contorted; stamens 5, inserted on the corolla and alternate with the lobes, free from one another, included or exserted; anthers 2-locular, opening lengthwise; ovary superior, *inserted on a disk*, 3- (rarely 2-) locular, sessile; ovules 1 or more in each loculus, inserted on the inner angle of the loculi; style 1, filiform; stigmas 3 or rarely 2; fruit a capsule or rarely indehiscent, loculicidal; seeds mostly with copious endosperm and straight or slightly curved embryo. B.H. **2**, 820; E.P. **4**, 3a, 40. Mostly N. America and the Andes; rare in the Old World.—PHLOX, COLLOMIA, GILIA, IPOMOPSIS,

Leptodactylon, Linanthus, Dactylophyllum, Huthia, Elaphocera, Leptosiphon, Navarretia, Eriastrum (*Huegelia*), Gymnosteris, Microsteris, Langloisia, Polemonium, Polemoniella, Loeselia, Bonplandia, Cantua. Value mainly horticultural.

336. Hydrophyllaceae

Annual or perennial herbs, rarely subshrubby, often hairy or scabrid, sometimes spiny; leaves radical or alternate, rarely opposite, entire to pinnately or palmately lobed; flowers often cymose, ♀, actinomorphic; calyx-segments

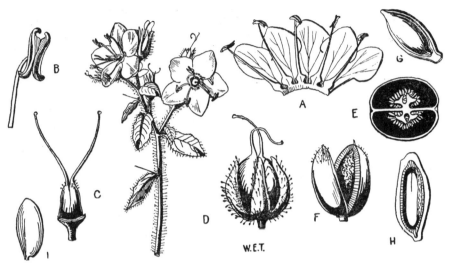

Fig. 336. Hydrolea spinosa *L.* (Hydrophyllaceae). A, flower opened. B, stamen. C, ovary. D, fruit. E, transverse section of same. F, capsule. G, seed. H, vertical section of same. I, ovule. (After Le Maout & Decne.)

mostly 5, imbricate, often with *appendages* between; corolla sympetalous, mostly 5-lobed, lobes imbricate or rarely contorted; stamens the same number as the corolla-lobes and alternate with them, often inserted towards the base of the tube; anthers 2-locular, opening lengthwise; disk hypogynous or absent; ovary superior, 1-locular with *2 parietal placentas* or spuriously or completely 2-locular with the placentas adnate to the septa; styles 1 or 2; ovules often numerous; fruit a loculicidal capsule, rarely septicidal; seeds with fleshy endosperm and small straight embryo. B.H. **2**, 825; E.P. **4**, 3*a*, 54; Brand, Engl. *Pflanzenr. Hydrophyllaceae* (1913). Mainly N. America.— Hydrophyllum, Nemophila, Phacelia, Codon, Wigandia, Hydrolea, &c. Some useful garden annuals.

337. Cuscutaceae

Leafless and rootless *parasitic herbs* without green colouring; stems *thread-like* and often forming a mass on other plants; flowers small, white or pink, stalked or subsessile in clusters, without bracts; sepals 5–4, free or more or less united; corolla sympetalous, short, ovoid or globose, 5–4-lobed, lobes *imbricate*; stamens inserted in the throat of the corolla and alternate with the lobes; anthers short, obtuse; *scales between the stamens lobed or fimbriate*; ovary superior, completely or incompletely 2-locular, 4-ovulate; styles 2, separate or more or less connate; fruit a globose or ovoid capsule, dry or

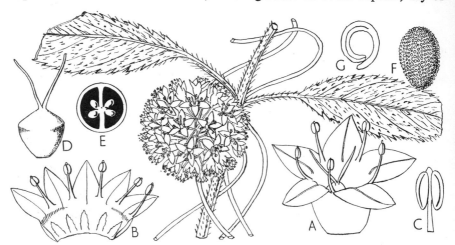

Fig. 337. Cuscuta europaea *L.* (Cuscutaceae). A, flower. B, corolla laid open. C, anther. D, pistil. E, cross-section of ovary. F, seed. G, embryo. (Orig.)

fleshy, opening by a *transverse slit or irregularly splitting*; seeds with the *embryo surrounding the endosperm*, embryo linear, terete, curved or spirally twisted. B.H. **2,** 881 (in *Co*ı*ıvolvulaceae*); E.P. **4,** 3*a*, 38. Generally distributed.—Cuscuta.

Order 81. BORAGINALES

More or less as in *Polemoniales*; ovary often deeply lobed with gynobasic style, bicarpellate with paired ascending ovules.

338. Boraginaceae[1]

Herbs, glabrous or often scabrid or hispid; leaves *alternate* or very rarely opposite, simple; *stipules absent*; flowers often in *scorpioid cymes*, actinomorphic or rarely oblique, mostly ⚥; calyx-lobes imbricate or rarely valvate; corolla sympetalous with contorted or imbricate lobes; stamens the same number as the corolla-lobes and alternate with them, inserted on the corolla; anthers 2-locular, opening lengthwise; disk present or obsolete; ovary superior, 2-locular or 4-locular by spurious septa, entire or *deeply 4-lobed*; style from the middle of the lobes (*gynobasic*); ovules paired, *erect* or spreading from the central axis; fruit of *4 nutlets*; seeds with or without endosperm, and straight or curved embryo. B.H. **2,** 832, partly; E.P. **4,** 3*a*, 71, partly. Widely dispersed, numerous in the Mediterranean region.—Coldenia,

[1] For the fundamentally woody genera formerly included in this family see *Ehretiaceae* (p. 393).

TOURNEFORTIA, HELIOTROPIUM, TRICHODESMA, OMPHALODES, CYNOGLOSSUM, RINDERA, ECHINOSPERMUM, ERITRICHIUM, AMSINCKIA, SYMPHYTUM, BORAGO, ANCHUSA, NONNEA, PULMONARIA, ALKANNA, MERTENSIA, MYOSOTIS, LITHOSPERMUM, LOBOSTEMON, ECHIUM, ONOSMA, CERINTHE, TETRACHONDRA, &c.

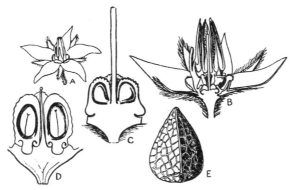

FIG. 338. Borago officinalis *L.* (Boraginaceae). A, flower. B, vertical section of same. C, vertical section of ovary. D, vertical section of fruit. E, seed. (Orig.)

USEFUL PRODUCTS: *Alkanet Root* (Alkanna tinctoria *Tausch.*), Mediterr.; *Thé de Montagne* (Lithospermum officinale *L.*), Pyrenees. Some beautiful garden plants.

ORDER 82. LAMIALES

As in preceding groups but leaves mostly opposite or whorled, rarely alternate; ovary often deeply lobed with gynobasic style; ovules mostly paired; corolla often bilabiate; stamens 4 or 2.—General distribution.

A. Leaves alternate, rarely subopposite; ovary entire or only slightly lobed; style terminal:
B. Trees or shrubs with axillary flowers; leaves usually studded with resinous glands; ovules 2 or more in each loculus; anthers 2-locular *Myoporaceae*
BB. Shrublets or perennial herbs; flowers in terminal spikes, corymbs, or heads; ovule solitary in each loculus:
C. Inflorescence without a common involucre; anthers 1-locular; ovary 2-locular *Selaginaceae*
CC. Inflorescence capitate, girt by a common involucre of numerous bracts; anthers at first 2-locular, becoming 1-locular with a continuous slit; ovary 1-locular *Globulariaceae*
AA. Leaves opposite or verticillate; flowers axillary or whorled; ovary deeply vertically 4-lobed with a gynobasic style *Labiatae*

339. MYOPORACEAE

Shrubs or rarely trees; indumentum sometimes *lepidote* or *plumose*; leaves *alternate* or rarely opposite, simple; stipules absent; flowers axillary, solitary or fasciculate, ♀, usually *zygomorphic*; calyx 5-lobed or 5-fid, imbricate or open; corolla sympetalous, usually 5-lobed, lobes imbricate; stamens 4 or rarely the same number as the corolla-lobes, inserted on the corolla-tube and alternate with the lobes; anthers 2-locular, but the loculi often *divergent* and

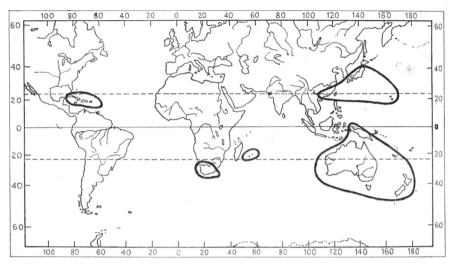

Myoporaceae, a small and homogeneous family, is found mainly in Australasia, with outliers in the West Indies, S. Africa, the Mascarenes, and extreme E. Asia.

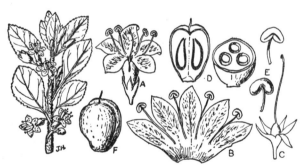

Fig. 339. Myoporum viscosum *R. Br.* (Myoporaceae). A, flower. B, same opened. C, ovary. D, sections of fruit. E, stamens. F, fruit. (Orig.)

confluent at the apex, opening lengthwise; ovary superior, normally 2-locular, loculi 2-ovuled and ovules collateral, or 4–8-ovuled and ovules superposed in pairs, rarely with numerous loculi; style simple; ovules pendulous from near the top of the central axis; fruit drupaceous; seeds with thin or scarcely any endosperm and straight or slightly curved embryo. B.H. **2**, 1123; E.P. **4**, 3*b*, 354. S. Africa and Mascarene Islands to Australia, New Zealand, and Japan, West Indies.

    A. Corolla actinomorphic or very slightly zygomorphic, mostly white: **B.** Corolla-tube mostly shorter than the lobes—Myoporum (E. Asia, Austral.,

New Zeal., Polynesia, Mauritius). **BB.** Corolla-tube longer than the lobes—
OFTIA (S. Afr.). **AA.** Corolla zygomorphic, more or less 2-lipped, mostly
coloured: **C.** Corolla deeply 2-lipped, posticous lip erect and bifid, lower lip
recurved and 3-fid—BONTIA (West Indies). **CC.** Corolla not deeply 2-lipped,
lips spreading and only slightly unequal—PHOLIDA (*Eremophila*) (Austral.).

340. SELAGINACEAE

Herbs or undershrubs; leaves *alternate* or subopposite, simple, *mostly ericoid*;
stipules absent; flowers ☿, zygomorphic, often spicate; calyx persistent, 3–5-

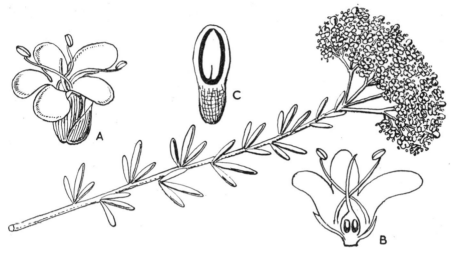

FIG. 340. Selago corymbosa *L.* (Selaginaceae). A, flower. B, vertical section of flower. C, vertical
section of fruit.

toothed or lobed, rarely of 2 free sepals; corolla sympetalous; tube sometimes
split; limb 4–5-lobed, lobes imbricate; stamens on the corolla-tube, alternate
with the lobes, 2, 4, or 5; *anthers 1-locular*, opening lengthwise; ovary superior,
2-locular; style terminal, simple; ovules *solitary* from the top of each loculus;
fruit of two *unequal carpels* separating when ripe, one often *sterile* or obsolete;
seeds with straight large embryo in the middle of fleshy endosperm. B.H. **2**,
1126; E.P. **4**, 3*b*, 80 (under *Scrophulariaceae*). S. Africa, Mascarene Is., E.
Tropical Africa.—HEBENSTREITIA, SELAGO, MICRODON, CROMIDON, GOSELA,
AGATHELPIS, WALAFRIDA, DISCHISMA, GLOBULARIOPSIS, &c.

341. GLOBULARIACEAE

Shrubs or undershrubs; leaves *alternate*, simple; stipules absent; flowers
capitate, ☿, zygomorphic, arranged on a scaly receptacle and surrounded by an
involucre of numerous bracts; calyx 5-lobed, actinomorphic or rarely 2-lipped;
corolla sympetalous; limb 1–2-lipped, lobes imbricate; stamens 4, inserted
at the top of the corolla-tube, and alternate with the lobes; anthers *reniform*,
at first 2-locular, at length the loculi confluent and opening by a *single slit*;

ovary superior, *1-locular*, inserted on a short disk or the latter gland-like or absent; style 1; ovule solitary, *pendulous*; fruit enveloped by the persistent calyx, mucronate; seeds with straight embryo in the middle of fleshy endosperm. B.H. **2**, 1130 (under *Selaginaceae*); E.P. **4**, 3*b*, 270. N. Temperate Old World.

A. Inflorescence spicate; lobes of the upper lip of the corolla similar to those of the lower lip and scarcely shorter—COCKBURNIA (Socotra). **AA.** Inflorescence capitate; lobes of the upper lip of the corolla distinct from and shorter

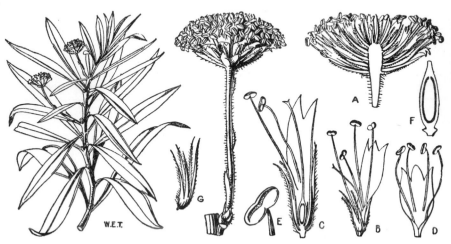

FIG. 341. Globularia salicina *Lam.* (Globulariaceae). A, capitulum. B, flower. C, vertical section of same. D, stamens showing insertion. E, stamen. F, vertical section of ovary. G, calyx. (Orig.)

than those of the lower lip: **B.** Inflorescence terminating the main shoots—GLOBULARIA (S. Eur. and Mediterr. to Baltic). **BB.** Inflorescence terminating the lateral axillary shoots—LYTANTHUS (Atlantic Islands).

342. LABIATAE

Herbaceous or rarely woody, often odoriferous; stems usually *quadrangular*; leaves *opposite* or whorled, simple; stipules absent; flowers ⚥, zygomorphic, rarely almost actinomorphic, *axillary or whorled*; calyx persistent, of 5 variously united sepals, often 2-lipped; corolla sympetalous, hypogynous, tubular; lobes 4–5, imbricate, often forming 2 lips or rarely 1 lip; stamens on the corolla-tube, 4 or 2; anthers 2–1-locular, loculi often *divergent*, opening lengthwise; ovary superior, of *2 deeply lobed carpels*, the style (*gynobasic*) rising from the inner base of the lobes; stigma mostly bifid; ovules 4 in each ovary, *erect*; fruit of 4 achene-like *nutlets*, free or cohering in pairs; seeds with usually straight embryo, without endosperm, or the latter very scanty. B.H. **2**, 1160; E.P. **4**, 3*a*, 183. Widely distributed.—OCIMUM, ACROCEPHALUS, MOSCHOSMA, HOSLUNDIA, PLECTRANTHUS, COLEUS, HYPTIS, LAVANDULA, POGOSTEMON, ELSHOLTZIA, MENTHA, ORIGANUM, THYMUS, MICROMERIA, CALAMINTHA, SALVIA, ROSMARINUS, NEPETA, DRACOCEPHALUM, SCUTELLARIA, PRUNELLA,

FIG. 342. Leonotis africana *Briq.* (Labiatae). A, flower. B, anther. C, ovary and base of style,
(After Hutch. and Dalz., *Fl. W. Trop. Afr.*)

SIDERITIS, MARRUBIUM, STACHYS, LEONURUS, LEONOTIS, LAMIUM, BALLOTA, LEUCAS, PHLOMIS, PROSTANTHERA, TEUCRIUM, AJUGA, &c.

USEFUL PRODUCTS: *Mint* (Mentha viridis *L.*); *Lavender Oil* (Lavandula vera *DC.*), S. Eur.; *Patchouli* (Pogostemon heyneanus *Bth.*), India; *Peppermint* (Mentha piperita *L.*). Culinary herbs are: *Marjoram* (Origanum marjorana *L.*), *Thyme* (Thymus vulgaris *L.*), and *Sage* (Salvia officinalis *L.*); *Rosemary* (Rosmarinus officinalis *L.*); *Chinese Artichoke* (Stachys sieboldii *Miq.*), China. Many beautiful garden plants, and some (Coleus spp.) with edible tubers.

GLOSSARY

abaxial, away from the axis.

abortion, suppression of parts usually present.

accumbent, lying against.

achene, small dry indehiscent fruit containing a single seed.

actinomorphic (regular), capable of vertical division into equal halves through two or more planes.

acyclic, floral parts not in whorls.

adaxial, next the axis.

adnate, united to a member of another series.

aestivation, arrangement of sepals or petals in bud.

amentiferous, bearing catkins.

anemophilous, wind-pollinated.

apocarpous, of separate carpels.

aril, appendage arising from the funicle and often covering the seed.

articulate, jointed.

axile, attached to the central axis.

baccate, berry-like.

bilabiate, 2-lipped.

bisexual, with two sexes in the same flower or inflorescence.

bullate, blistered or puckered.

calyx, outer envelope of a flower of the *Dicotyledons*, often green or scarious.

capitate, head-like.

capsule, dry fruit (composed of more than one carpel) which opens.

carpel, a separate or united unit of an ovary.

caruncle, a wart or protuberance near the hilum of a seed as in many *Euphorbiaceae*.

catkin, a close bracteate, often pendulous spike.

circinate, inwardly coiled upon itself, like a watch-spring.

circumscissile, opening transversely all around.

cirrhose, with tendrils.

cleistogamous, fertilization within the unopened flower.

compound, composed of several similar parts, as a leaf of several leaflets.

conduplicate, folded together lengthwise.

connate, when similar parts are united.

contorted, twisted in bud, such as sepals or petals which overlap on one side only.

corolla, the inner envelope of the flower.

corona, a ring of appendages (sometimes united) on the inside of the petals or corolla.

corymb, a flat-topped inflorescence.

cotyledon, seed leaf.

cyclic, with floral parts in whorls.

cyme, a broad divaricate inflorescence.

deciduous, not evergreen.

dehiscent, opening spontaneously.

diadelphous, in two bundles (as in *Papilionaceae*, often with one stamen separate from the other nine).

didymous, in pairs, as the separate lobes of anthers or fruits.

digitate, diverging from the same point like the fingers of a hand.

dimorphic, of two forms.

dioecious, with male flowers on one individual, females on another.

discoid, like a disk; applied to *Compositae* without ray flowers.

disk, an enlargement of the receptacle within the calyx, petals, or stamens.

dissepiments, partitions of an ovary or fruit.

embryo, the rudimentary plant still enclosed in a seed.

endosperm, the nutritive food material within the seed.

entomophilous, insect-pollinated.

epigynous, above the pistil or gynoecium.

epipetalous, on the petals, or corolla.

epiphyte, plant growing or supported on another.

exstipulate, without stipules.

extrorse, facing outwards.

follicle, a several-seeded fruit, resulting from a separate carpel opening by one suture.

free basal placentation, ovules arranged on a basal placenta in a 1-locular ovary.

free central placentation, ovules on a central placenta reaching from the bottom to the top of a 1-locular ovary.

funicle, cord or thread connecting ovule or seed to placenta.

gamopetalous (= sympetalous, monopetalous), a corolla with the petals partially or wholly united.

gamosepalous, sepals more or less united.

glandular, clothed with glands.

glochidiate, furnished with barbed bristles.

gynoecium (pistil), the female part of the flower (in the middle), consisting of free or united carpels, with style or stigma.

gynobasic, a style which arises from near the base of the carpels or ovary lobes.

gynophore, a stalk supporting the ovary.

herb, plant not woody.

hilum, scar of attachment on a seed.

hypogynous, with its parts inserted below the gynoecium or pistil.

imbricate, overlapping; applied to sepals or petals with one or more wholly outside or inside and some half out and half in.

incumbent, lying on.

indehiscent, not opening.

indumentum, the hairy covering.

induplicate, folded inwards.

indusiate, like a small cup.

inferior, below, as the ovary below the other parts of the flower.

interpetiolar, between the petioles.

intrapetiolar, within the petiole.

introrse, facing inwards.

irregular, see *zygomorphic*.

legume, pod opening by one or two sutures (cf. *Papilionaceae*).

lepidote, clothed with scales.

locellate, subdivided into smaller loculi.

locular, chambered ('celled').

loculi, chambers ('cells') of an ovary or anther.

loculicidal, opening into the loculi.

monadelphous, in one bundle.

monochlamydeous, a flower with only one whorl of the perianth.

monocotyledon, a plant with only one seed-leaf.

monoecious, unisexual flowers on the same plant.

monopetalous, petals more or less united or one petal.

muticous, pointless.

ochreate, sheathing, as the stipules in *Polygonaceae*.

opposite, inserted at the same level.

ovary, the lower part of the pistil containing the ovules.

ovule, the potential seed.

panicle, a branched raceme.

papillous, with short protuberances.

parietal placentation, ovules attached to the walls of a 1-locular syncarpous ovary.

pellucid, translucent.

pendulous, hanging down.

perennial, lasting for more than two seasons.

perianth, the floral envelope or envelopes.

perigynous, placed around the ovary but free from it.

phalange, a bundle of stamens.

pistil, see *gynoecium*.

placenta, the part of the ovary to which the ovules are attached.

plicate, folded like a fan.

pollen, the powdery contents of an anther.

polygamous, flowers male, female, and bisexual on the same plants.

polypetalous, petals free from each other.

protandrous, anthers ripening before the stigmas.

protogynous, stigmas receptive before the anthers open.

punctate, dotted.

racemose, inflorescence with stalked flowers on a single axis.

radical, leaves from the base of the plant.

radicle, embryonic root.

receptacle, the part of the floral axis bearing the sepals, petals, stamens, and carpels.

regular, see *actinomorphic*.

ruminate, endosperm into which the inner layer of the testa protrudes.

septate, divided by partitions.

septicidal, a fruit which opens between the loculi.

simple, the opposite of compound.

spike, inflorescence with sessile flowers on a single elongated axis.

spur, a hollow horn-like extension of a part of the flower.

staminode, an abortive, sometimes much modified or reduced, stamen.

stellate, star-like.

stigma, the receptive part of the style.

stipe, the stalk of a carpel or pistil.

stipitate, furnished with a stipe.

stipules, basal appendages to the leaf or petiole.

stoma (pl. *stomata*), the breathing apparatus in the epidermis of leaves.

style, the narrow part of the pistil bearing the stigma.

superior, above, as an ovary above the other parts of the flower.

superposed, placed one above another.

sympetalous, a corolla with the petals partially or wholly united.

syncarpous, composed of united carpels.

testa, seed coat.

tetradynamous, four long and two short.

torus, see *receptacle*.

umbel, an inflorescence the branches of which spring from the same point.

unisexual, of one sex.

valvate, margins of sepals or petals not overlapping.

valves, of anthers which open by flaps.

vernation, folding of leaves in bud.

zygomorphic (*irregular*), flowers which may be divided into equal halves in only one plane.

PRINTED IN GREAT BRITAIN
AT THE UNIVERSITY PRESS, OXFORD
BY VIVIAN RIDLER
PRINTER TO THE UNIVERSITY